FINITE ELEMENT ANALYSIS

With Numeric and Symbolic Matlab

FINITE ELEMENT ANALYSIS

With Numeric and Symbolic Matlab

JOHN E AKIN

Rice University, USA

World Scientific

NEW JERSEY • LONDON • SINGAPORE • BEIJING • SHANGHAI • HONG KONG • TAIPEI • CHENNAI • TOKYO

Published by

World Scientific Publishing Co. Pte. Ltd.

5 Toh Tuck Link, Singapore 596224

USA office: 27 Warren Street, Suite 401-402, Hackensack, NJ 07601

UK office: 57 Shelton Street, Covent Garden, London WC2H 9HE

Library of Congress Cataloging-in-Publication Data
Names: Akin, J. E., author.
Title: Finite element analysis : with numeric and symbolic Matlab /
John E. Akin, Rice University, USA.
Description: New Jersey : World Scientific, [2023] | Includes index.
Identifiers: LCCN 2022015205 | ISBN 9789811250613 (hardcover) |
ISBN 9789811251900 (paperback) | ISBN 9789811250620 (ebook for institutions) |
ISBN 9789811250637 (ebook for individuals)
Subjects: LCSH: MATLAB. | Finite element method.
Classification: LCC TA347.F5 A356 2023 | DDC 518/.25--dc23/eng/20220527
LC record available at https://lccn.loc.gov/2022015205

British Library Cataloguing-in-Publication Data
A catalogue record for this book is available from the British Library.

For any available supplementary material, please visit
https://www.worldscientific.com/worldscibooks/10.1142/12677#t=suppl

Desk Editors: Jayanthi Muthuswamy/Steven Patt

Typeset by Stallion Press
Email: enquiries@stallionpress.com

Preface

This book covers parametric finite element analysis (FEA), which has been in wide use since the early 1960s, in combination with symbolic Matlab analysis for solving algebra and calculus problems. Parametric FEA employs a non-dimensional polynomial as a piecewise approximation of the spatial solution of some differential equation that governs an engineering application. Parametric FEA also uses the same or a similar polynomial and geometric control points on a geometric region to define the shape of the region. The essential boundary conditions (EBCs) are applied at points on the geometric region (and interpolated on its boundary).

This contrasts to the newer isogeometric FEA where the shape of a geometric region is first exactly modeled using Non-Uniform Rational B-Splines (NURBS). An isogeometric FEA assumes that the spatial solution is approximated by the same NURBS using solution values at the NURBS control points. For detailed information about that newer approach, the reader should see *Isogeometric Analysis: Toward Integration of CAD and FEA* by J.A. Cottrell, T.J.R. Hughes, Y. Bazilevs, John Wiley, 2009.

In teaching the classic parametric FEA for more than four decades, I have observed that most of the difficulties and mistakes arise because students have forgotten some aspects of calculus, matrix algebra, and differential equation terminology that they typically studied in their first 2 years in college. Therefore, this presentation will begin with a review of those concepts. Many students also have difficulty in understanding how the parametric polynomials are derived and how their various combinations are integrated in integrals with physical interpretations. Symbolic software has been around for about 50 years. However, such tools have not been user-friendly until recently when it was included as a tool in the Matlab environment. Now Matlab can and will herein be utilized to execute both symbolic and numerical solutions formulated as finite element simulations.

The classic linear FEA theory and common applications are covered in detail, including their implementation with Matlab.

While the FEA can yield exact or approximate analytic solutions, it usually requires an implementation on a digital computer for application to practical problems. Therefore, the reader should understand various programming approaches required by numerical FEA. Unfortunately, most undergraduates today do not have training in efficient engineering programming. However, students do often have experience with the Matlab numerical environment, its matrix operations, and graphical outputs. Thus, the FEA algorithms necessary to solve several classes of engineering applications will be presented using the Matlab environment included in each application. In addition, a large library of heavily commented Matlab scripts for processing typical FEA applications is made available at the Supplemental Material section of the publisher's web page.

About the Author

John E Akin is a professor in the Department of Mechanical Engineering, and a professor in the Department of Computational and Applied Mathematics at Rice University, USA. He received his B.S. from Tennessee Polytechnic Institute, his M.S. from Tennessee Technological University, and his Ph.D. from Virginia Polytechnic Institute. Dr. Akin is a fellow of the American Society of Mechanical Engineers (ASME). He is a member of the American Society of Civil Engineers, the Society of Petroleum Engineers, and the U.S. Academy for Computation Mechanics. He serves on the editorial board of the journal *Multiscale and Multidisciplinary Modeling, Experiments and Design*. His areas of interest are self-adaptive finite element analysis and the applications of computational mechanics in engineering. He currently works with a team at Rice to rapidly develop practical custom implants for individuals who have lost part of their pelvis due to cancer.

Contents

List of Examples

List of Matlab Scripts

List of Useful Tables

Chapter 1

Overview

1.1 Introduction

This book covers the review of mathematical topics and programming skills that are required in understanding, applying, and implementing many finite element simulations. The main concepts are presented through discussions, examples, scripts, and figures. The computer implementation is demonstrated using the symbolic and numeric Matlab environment to develop a complete set of software with examples that are available from the associated website.

Chapters 2–7 are intended for readers who are not familiar with all of their topics and need a detailed review of some of the prerequisite material. The sections in each chapter begin with the mathematical considerations, and most are followed by detailed examples, including sample Matlab scripts. Each chapter ends with a summary that can serve to guide the reader in selecting review topics. Topics that can be delayed until later have an asterisk appended to that section heading. Occasionally, symbolic Matlab scripts are included to illustrate how the computer can provide the exact answers to messy algebra and calculus problems that otherwise would have to be worked out by hand. Practical application of a finite element simulation generally requires numerical evaluation of arrays and their matrix products. Matlab scripts for numerical calculations are included to gradually build up a complete library of functions that at the end will provide the reader with a complete finite element simulation system that can be applied to any linear elliptical differential equation in one-, two-, or three-dimensions. That is, for example, stress analysis, thermal analysis, and vibrations.

A physical problem to be solved for a variable $u(x, y, z)$ is formulated initially in a physical region with spatial coordinates (x, y, z). The physical problem is typically originally stated as a partial differential equation (PDE), involving u and its derivatives with respect to x, y, and z, on the interior of a physical region in space. That differential equation has essential and non-essential boundary conditions applied in non-overlapping portions of the boundary of the region. Mathematicians refer to the essential boundary conditions (EBCs) as Dirichlet conditions, and the non-essential or secondary boundary conditions (NBCs) as Neumann conditions.

In a finite element analysis (FEA), an equivalent integral form is always used that is capable of yielding a solution that is exactly the same as the one that would be obtained from the differential equation. The equivalent integral form must be subject to the same essential (Dirichlet) boundary conditions and secondary boundary conditions included by being integrated over their physical region. Both types of boundary conditions must be satisfied for an exact solution. In an approximate solution, the EBCs are satisfied exactly, but the secondary boundary conditions might be satisfied only weakly.

A typical sketch of a two-dimensional mesh is shown in Fig. 1.1-1. It shows that the primary unknowns are located at node points.

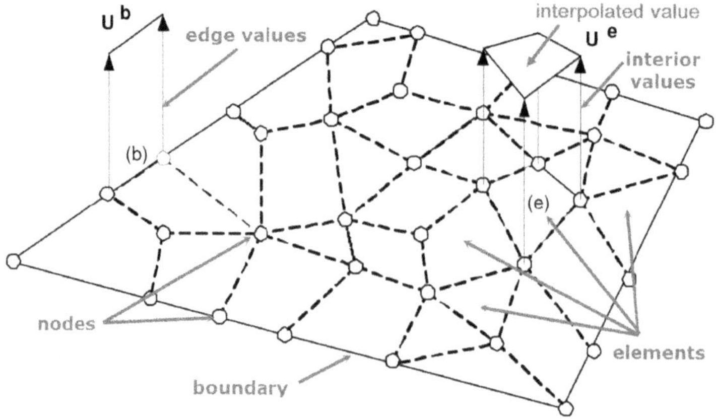

Fig. 1.1-1: A mesh of a two-dimensional domain.

Each node is connected to one or more elements. The list of nodes on each element governs the assembly of the element's contributions into the governing matrix system. The elements occupy portions of the solution domain. Within each element, the spatial distribution of the solution is approximated by interpolating between the solution's values at the nodes connected to the element. Some elements lie adjacent to the boundary. Those element interpolations at the boundary degenerate to a one-degree lower spatial dimension and just interpolate the solution using only the nodes on that boundary segment.

1.2 Finite Element Data

The major power of finite element methods, and the relative disadvantage compared to finite difference methods, is the mesh and its powerful data sets. The shape of the mesh is completely arbitrary and that lets it accurately model real shapes with curved surfaces encountered in engineering. The coordinates of each and every node point must be supplied. In addition, any node having an EBC must be connected to the EBC values. Here, those coordinate data are stored in a sequential text file (*msh_bc_xyz.txt*) that has the coordinates of every node and a flag code number to identify if it is connected to an EBC. The actual EBC data are stored in a text file (*msh_ebc.txt*) that has three items for each EBC: the node number, the degree of freedom number being set, and the value assigned to that freedom number.

Every volume element and/or surface element, like a conduction region (say of type 1) or a convection region (say of type 2), is defined by an element Type integer code and the list of nodes to which it is connected. Those data are stored in the text file *msh_typ_nodes.txt*. A mesh can contain functionally different element classes like conducting solid elements and convecting face and/or edge elements (say of type 3). Usually, each Type of element in an application has a different number of nodes in its connection list. The element Type identifies which class of element is being input and which matrix constructions are needed to build it.

The material properties of every element must be supplied. The number of properties is dependent on the application being solved and the Type of element. For example, a conducting solid element has fewer properties than a convecting face or edge element. The mesh property data are stored in a text file, *msh_properties.txt*. It contains either the properties for every element, or for every element Type (which is usually a smaller list). Each line begins with the element Type number and is followed by the properties required by the application. Many applications have materials that are directionally dependent. In that case, the element data need to contain the direction angles to the principal material axes in the element.

Likewise, the mesh has associated boundary conditions. The non-essential (secondary or weak) boundary conditions (NBCs) occur on a surface (or edge or point) of the mesh. There are typically three classes for such surface element conditions: a "natural Neumann boundary condition" (NatBC) of zero normal flux at the surface element, or a specified non-zero normal flux Neumann condition, or a normal flux coupled to the unknown surface solution which is known as a mixed condition (convection condition in heat transfer). The NatBC is the default for all surfaces and does not require any input in finite element solutions. Here, the Neumann and mixed NBC data are contained in the properties text file that begins with the element Type number and is followed by one or more surface data terms required by the application.

All of these data give the user a significant engineering analysis capability. However, the data preparation can be a burden in two- or three-dimensions. All commercial FEA systems provide automatic mesh generators that create these data sets and hide them from the user. Here, the learner must provide the required data in text files. Several public domain two- and three-dimensional mesh (and data) generators are available. Their output files are usually easily re-formatted to build the text files needed by the provided analysis codes.

1.3 Matrix Notation* (an optional section)

Most finite element literature employs matrix notation and matrix operations; so a brief review of matrices follows. Here **bold letters** will denote matrices in the text. Usually (and in Matlab), a matrix is a doubly subscripted array of coefficients or functions having n rows and m columns:

$$\boldsymbol{A} = \begin{bmatrix} a_{11} & a_{12} & \cdots & a_{1m} \\ a_{21} & a_{22} & \cdots & a_{2m} \\ \cdots & \cdots & \cdots & \cdots \\ a_{n1} & a_{n2} & \cdots & a_{nm} \end{bmatrix} \Longleftrightarrow a_{ij} = A(i,j). \tag{1.3-1}$$

The derivative of a matrix is the matrix formed by taking the derivative of every coefficient. Likewise, the integral of a matrix is the matrix formed by taking the integral of every coefficient:

$$d\boldsymbol{A} = \begin{bmatrix} da_{11} & da_{12} & \cdots & da_{1m} \\ da_{21} & da_{22} & \cdots & da_{2m} \\ \cdots & \cdots & \cdots & \cdots \\ da_{n1} & ad_{n2} & \cdots & d_{nm} \end{bmatrix} \Longleftrightarrow da_{ij}, \tag{1.3-2}$$

$$\int \boldsymbol{A}\, dx = \begin{bmatrix} \int a_{11}\, dx & \int a_{12}\, dx & \cdots & \int a_{1m}\, dx \\ \int a_{21}\, dx & \int a_{22}\, dx & \cdots & \int a_{2m}\, dx \\ \cdots & \cdots & \cdots & \cdots \\ \int a_{n1}\, dx & \int a_{n2}\, dx & \cdots & \int a_{nm}\, dx \end{bmatrix} \Longleftrightarrow \int a_{ij}\, dx. \tag{1.3-3}$$

If the number of rows and columns are different, then the array is a rectangular matrix, say $\boldsymbol{R}$. A common case is where the number of rows and columns are equal and that defines a square matrix, say $\boldsymbol{S}$. A square matrix is said to be symmetric if $a_{ij} = a_{ji}$. If all of the coefficients on one side of the diagonal of a square matrix are zero, the matrix is called a triangular matrix. There are two types of triangular matrices used here: an upper triangular matrix, $\boldsymbol{U}$, whose elements below the diagonal are zero, and a lower triangular matrix, $\boldsymbol{L}$, where all of the coefficients above the diagonal are zero. A diagonal matrix is zero everywhere except for its diagonal ($a_{ij} = 0, i \neq j$). An identity matrix, $\boldsymbol{I}$, is a diagonal matrix that has unity terms on the diagonal and zeros elsewhere.

When there is only one column ($m = 1$), then the array is called a column vector, say $\boldsymbol{a}$:

$$\boldsymbol{a} \equiv \begin{Bmatrix} a_1 \\ a_2 \\ \cdots \\ a_n \end{Bmatrix} \Longleftrightarrow a_i.$$

When there is only one row ($n = 1$), then the array is called a row matrix, say $\boldsymbol{r}$:

$$\boldsymbol{r} = \begin{bmatrix} r_1 & r_2 & \cdots & r_m \end{bmatrix} \Longleftrightarrow r_j.$$

Note: when allocating memory for row or column arrays in Matlab, you need to include the number one as the first or second subscript, respectively.

The transpose, $\boldsymbol{A}^{\mathrm{T}}$, of a matrix $\boldsymbol{A}$ is formed by interchanging all rows for the corresponding columns. This means that the transpose of a column matrix is a row matrix and vice versa. A transpose is denoted by the superscript T. In Matlab, the single quote is appended to a matrix name to denote its transpose, $\boldsymbol{A}^{\mathrm{T}} \leftrightarrow \boldsymbol{A}'$. The transpose of the product of a set of size conformable matrices is the product of the transpose of the matrices take n in the reverse order:

$$(\boldsymbol{ABC})^{\mathrm{T}} = \boldsymbol{C}^{\mathrm{T}}\boldsymbol{B}^{\boldsymbol{T}}\boldsymbol{A}^{\mathrm{T}}. \tag{1.3-4}$$

Two matrices can be multiplied to form a third matrix if they are conformable. That is, if the number of columns in the first matrix equals the number of rows in the second matrix.

$$\boldsymbol{C} = \boldsymbol{AB} \neq \boldsymbol{BA}, \quad C_{ij} \equiv \sum_k A_{ik}B_{kj}. \tag{1.3-5}$$

That means that in (1.3-5) the number of columns, k, in the first matrix, $\boldsymbol{A}$, must equal the number of rows in the second matrix, $\boldsymbol{B}$, in order to multiply them together. This size constraint on the two matrices is illustrated in Fig. 1.3-1.

Size compatibility must also be satisfied in matrix addition or subtraction. Two matrices must have the same number of rows and

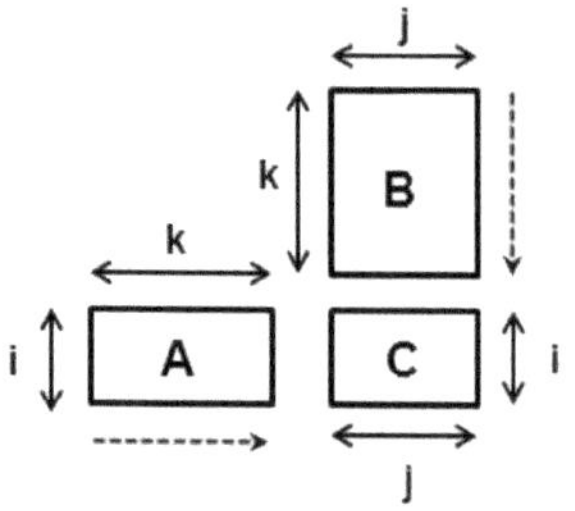

Fig. 1.3-1: Matrix multiplication $\boldsymbol{AB} = \boldsymbol{C}$, $\sum_{\mathbf{k}} A_{ik}B_{kj} = C_{ij}$.

columns before they can be added or subtracted. The resulting third matrix is the same size and its components are simply the sum of the corresponding coefficients in the original matrices:

$$\boldsymbol{A} \pm \boldsymbol{B} = \boldsymbol{C}, \quad \boldsymbol{C}_{ij} = \boldsymbol{A}_{ij} \pm \boldsymbol{B}_{ij}.$$

In FEA, the element square matrix, $\boldsymbol{S^e}$, is much smaller than the system square matrix, $\boldsymbol{S^e} \ll \boldsymbol{S}$ (except for single element models). A similar size difference exists between the element and system column vectors, $\boldsymbol{c^e} \ll \boldsymbol{c}$.

Using the connectivity of the element, it will be shown later that there are theoretically valid ways to change the size of the small element arrays so that they can properly be added to the larger corresponding system arrays. In other words, given additional information on the target rows where a small element column $\boldsymbol{c^e}$ is to be added into a larger number of available rows in the system column $\boldsymbol{c}$ a third matrix could be built that expands $\boldsymbol{c^e}$ by inserting null rows to expand it to the proper size for valid matrix addition, say $\underline{\boldsymbol{c^e}}$ (as shown in Example 1.3-1). However, adding zeros is not efficient, so an equivalent "direct assembly" method is used.

A square matrix, **S**, has an inverse matrix, $\boldsymbol{S}^{-1}$, if their product forms an identity matrix:

$$\boldsymbol{S}^{-1}\boldsymbol{S} = \boldsymbol{I} = \boldsymbol{S}\,\boldsymbol{S}^{-1}. \tag{1.3-6}$$

The inverse of a diagonal matrix is simply the diagonal matrix formed by dividing each original coefficient into one. In theory, the inverse of a matrix is important in the solution of a system of linear equations. For example, if the system of equations has a known square matrix, **S**, a known source vector, **c**, and an unknown vector, **x**, they are often related by the linear matrix system $\boldsymbol{Sx} = \boldsymbol{c}$. Once the inverse of **S** is known, multiplying both sides by that inverse gives the values of the vector **x**:

$$\boldsymbol{S}^{-1}\boldsymbol{Sx} = \boldsymbol{Ix} = \boldsymbol{x} = \boldsymbol{S}^{-1}\boldsymbol{c}. \tag{1.3-7}$$

The Matlab command for calculating the inverse of a square matrix $\boldsymbol{S}$ is "inv($\boldsymbol{S}$)". Since the inverse matrix is usually multiplied by another matrix, there is a shorthand *backslash* command "$\boldsymbol{S}\backslash\boldsymbol{c}$" that is used instead of writing the product "**inv (S) * c**". For large matrices the

Matlab *backslash* command uses much more efficient operations such as matrix factorization for a solution.

Calculating the analytic inverse of a matrix is only practical for relatively small matrices. A commonly encountered matrix in this book is the small 2×2 square matrix which has a simple analytic inverse matrix:

$$\mathbf{M} = \begin{bmatrix} m_{11} & m_{12} \\ m_{21} & m_{22} \end{bmatrix}, \quad \mathbf{M}^{-1} = \frac{1}{\mathrm{d}} \begin{bmatrix} m_{22} & -m_{12} \\ -m_{21} & m_{11} \end{bmatrix},$$
$$d = m_{11}m_{22} - m_{12}m_{21}. \tag{1.3-8}$$

The determinant of a square matrix, $\boldsymbol{A}$, is a precisely computable scalar denoted as $|\boldsymbol{A}|$, and in Matlab it is obtained with the command "det $(\boldsymbol{A})$".

Example 1.3-1* Given: At a point in the element assembly loop the 5×1 system vector has the values $\boldsymbol{c^T} = [1.1 \quad 0.0 \quad 1.3 \quad 2.5]$ and the next 3×1 element column vector has the values $\boldsymbol{c^{e^T}} = \begin{bmatrix} 1.4 & 4.0 & 2.2 \end{bmatrix}$. If the element connection list is 5, 3, and 2, assemble (scatter) the element column vector into the system one. **Solution:** The two matrices cannot be added because they are not the same size. The extra information provided by the connection list means that the first row of $\boldsymbol{c^e}$ is to be added to the fifth row of $\boldsymbol{c}$; the second row of $\boldsymbol{c^e}$ is to be added to the third row of $\boldsymbol{c}$, etc. That extra information can be utilized to expand $\boldsymbol{c^e}$ to the larger array, say $\underline{\boldsymbol{c^e}}$, which is the same size as $\boldsymbol{c}$. The expansion occurs by selectively inserting additional rows containing a zero for any node not in the connection list. To do that by using valid matrix algebra it is necessary to first have a new rectangular matrix having rows equal in number to those in $\boldsymbol{c^e}$ and columns equal in number to those in $\boldsymbol{c}$. The trick is simple. Build the rectangular matrix so that it is full of zeros, except for one unity term per row. For each row in the rectangular matrix, corresponding to a row in $\boldsymbol{c^e}$, place the single unity term in the column number that equals the target row of $\boldsymbol{c}$. Specifically, use the above given additional information that the current element is connected to system equation numbers

(5, 3, 2) to build the 3×5 rectangle as

$$\boldsymbol{\beta}^e \equiv \begin{bmatrix} 0 & 0 & 0 & 0 & 1 \\ 0 & 0 & 1 & 0 & 0 \\ 0 & 1 & 0 & 0 & 0 \end{bmatrix}, (n_i \times n_d)$$

Next, use matrix multiplication to first expand the element vector to form $\underline{\boldsymbol{c}^e} = \boldsymbol{\beta}^{e^T} \boldsymbol{c}^e$, which is

$$\underline{\boldsymbol{c}^e} = \begin{bmatrix} 0 & 0 & 0 \\ 0 & 0 & 1 \\ 0 & 1 & 0 \\ 0 & 0 & 0 \\ 1 & 0 & 0 \end{bmatrix} \begin{Bmatrix} 1.4 \\ 4.0 \\ 2.2 \end{Bmatrix} = \begin{Bmatrix} 0 \\ 2.2 \\ 4.0 \\ 0 \\ 1.4 \end{Bmatrix}$$

$$(n_d \times n_i)\,(n_i \times 1) = (n_d \times 1)$$

and then add: $c \rightarrow c + \underline{c^e} = \begin{Bmatrix} 1.1 \\ 0 \\ 3.4 \\ 1.3 \\ 2.5 \end{Bmatrix} + \begin{Bmatrix} 0 \\ 2.2 \\ 4.0 \\ 0 \\ 1.4 \end{Bmatrix} = \begin{Bmatrix} 1.1 \\ 2.2 \\ 7.4 \\ 1.3 \\ 3.9 \end{Bmatrix}.$

Any rectangular matrix containing zeros except for one unity term per row is called a Boolean matrix. The theoretical use of a Boolean matrix, representing extra information about an element, satisfies the laws of matrix algebra, but it is not a numerically efficient process and a much better way to do such additions will be developed later.

Example 1.3-2 Given: A matrix system with two unknowns $\boldsymbol{Sx} = \boldsymbol{c}$ has the form

$$\begin{bmatrix} 16 & -8 \\ -8 & 7 \end{bmatrix} \begin{Bmatrix} x_1 \\ x_2 \end{Bmatrix} = \begin{Bmatrix} 4 \\ 3 \end{Bmatrix}.$$

Determine the unknown values $\boldsymbol{x}$.

Solution: The determinant of the square matrix is

$$|\boldsymbol{S}| = d = 16\,(7) - (-8) = 48$$

and the inverse of $\boldsymbol{S}$ is the matrix $\boldsymbol{S}^{-1} = \frac{1}{48}\begin{bmatrix} 7 & 8 \\ 8 & 16 \end{bmatrix}$.
Multiplying both sides of the system by the inverse yields the solution

$$x = \frac{1}{48}\begin{bmatrix} 7 & 8 \\ 8 & 16 \end{bmatrix}\begin{Bmatrix} 4 \\ 3 \end{Bmatrix} = \frac{1}{48}\begin{Bmatrix} 7\,(4) + 8(3) \\ 8\,(4) + 16(3) \end{Bmatrix} = \frac{1}{12}12\begin{Bmatrix} 13 \\ 20 \end{Bmatrix} = \begin{Bmatrix} x_1 \\ x_2 \end{Bmatrix}.$$

Example 1.3-3 Given: Write a Matlab script to numerically evaluate the analytic inverse of a 3 × 3 matrix.

Solution: The known analytic inverse is in the function *invert_3_by_3.m*:

```
function [A_inv, A_det] = invert_3_by_3 (A)
% inverse and determinant of matrix A(3, 3)
% A_det = determinant of matrix A (~= 0)
% A_inv = inverse of matrix A

A_det = det (A) ; % determinant of A

% Analytic inverse of 3 by 3 matrix
A_inv(3,3) =  A(1,1)*A(2,2) - A(2,1)*A(1,2) ;
A_inv(1,1) =  A(2,2)*A(3,3) - A(3,2)*A(2,3) ;
A_inv(2,1) = -A(2,1)*A(3,3) + A(3,1)*A(2,3) ;
A_inv(3,1) =  A(2,1)*A(3,2) - A(3,1)*A(2,2) ;
A_inv(1,2) = -A(1,2)*A(3,3) + A(3,2)*A(1,3) ;
A_inv(2,2) =  A(1,1)*A(3,3) - A(3,1)*A(1,3) ;
A_inv(3,2) = -A(1,1)*A(3,2) + A(3,1)*A(1,2) ;
A_inv(1,3) =  A(1,2)*A(2,3) - A(2,2)*A(1,3) ;
A_inv(2,3) = -A(1,1)*A(2,3) + A(2,1)*A(1,3) ;

if ( A_det ~= 0 ) ; % complete inversion
  A_inv = A_inv / A_det ; % inversion done
else
  error ('Singular matrix in invert_3_by_3')
end ; % if division by zero
% end invert_3_by_3
```

Example 1.3-4 Given: Verify that the product of the above 2 × 2M and $\mathbf{M}^{-1}$ matrices in Eq. (1.3-8) yields an identity matrix.

Solution:

$$\boldsymbol{M}\,\boldsymbol{M}^{-1} = \begin{bmatrix} m_{11} & m_{12} \\ m_{21} & m_{22} \end{bmatrix}\begin{bmatrix} m_{22} & -m_{12} \\ -m_{21} & m_{11} \end{bmatrix}\frac{1}{d},$$

$$M\,M^{-1} = \frac{1}{d}\begin{bmatrix} (m_{11}m_{22} + m_{12}(-m_{21})) & (m_{11}\,(-m_{12}) + m_{12}m_{11}) \\ (m_{21}m_{22} + m_{22}\,(-m_{21})) & (m_{21}\,(-m_{12}) + m_{22}m_{11}) \end{bmatrix},$$

$$M\,M^{-1} = \frac{1}{d}\begin{bmatrix} (m_{11}m_{22} - m_{12}m_{21}) & 0 \\ 0 & (m_{11}m_{22} - m_{12}m_{21}) \end{bmatrix}$$

$$= \begin{bmatrix} 1 & 0 \\ 0 & 1 \end{bmatrix} = I.$$

Since the determinant of the first matrix is $d = (m_{11}m_{22} - m_{12}m_{21})$.

Example 1.3-5 Given: Solve the matrix system

$$\begin{bmatrix} 16 & -8 \\ -8 & 7 \end{bmatrix} \begin{Bmatrix} x_1 \\ x_2 \end{Bmatrix} = \begin{Bmatrix} 4 \\ 3 \end{Bmatrix}$$

using a Matlab script.

Solution: The following Matlab script follows the steps in the above manual solution:

```
% Solve a 2 by 2 matrix system
% S x = c for x
S = [16 -8;
      -8  7] ;    % Given data
c = [4;
      3] ;        % Given data
det_S = det (S) % Matrix determinant
inv_S = inv (S) % Matrix inverse
x = inv_S * c   % Solution
x = S \ c       % Alternate solution

% Running gives:
% det_S = 48
% inv_S = 0.1458    0.1667
%         0.1667    0.3333
% x = 1.0833
%     1.6667
% x = 1.0833
%     1.6667
```

1.4 Matrix Partitions

It is easy to verify that a matrix or a matrix product can be partitioned into a matrix of smaller sub-matrices separated by horizontal and/or vertical lines. For example, a square 3×3 matrix can be partitioned into four sub-matrices as

$$\boldsymbol{A} = \begin{bmatrix} \mathrm{a}_{11} & \mathrm{a}_{12} & \vdots & \mathrm{a}_{13} \\ \mathrm{a}_{21} & \mathrm{a}_{22} & \vdots & \mathrm{a}_{23} \\ \cdots & \cdots & \vdots & \cdots \\ \mathrm{a}_{31} & \mathrm{a}_{32} & \vdots & \mathrm{a}_{33} \end{bmatrix} = \begin{bmatrix} \mathrm{A}_{11} & \mathrm{A}_{12} \\ \mathrm{A}_{21} & \mathrm{A}_{22} \end{bmatrix}, \tag{1.4-1}$$

where $\boldsymbol{A_{11}} = \begin{bmatrix} \mathrm{a}_{11} & \mathrm{a}_{12} \\ \mathrm{a}_{21} & \mathrm{a}_{22} \end{bmatrix}$, $\boldsymbol{A_{22}} = [\mathrm{a}_{33}]$, $\boldsymbol{A_{21}} = \begin{bmatrix} \mathrm{a}_{31} & \mathrm{a}_{32} \end{bmatrix}$, $\boldsymbol{A_{12}} = \begin{Bmatrix} \mathrm{a}_{13} \\ \mathrm{a}_{23} \end{Bmatrix}$. If the given matrix is symmetric, $\mathbf{A} = \boldsymbol{A^T}$, then there are additional relations such that $\boldsymbol{A_{21}} = \boldsymbol{A^T_{12}}$, $\boldsymbol{A_{11}} = \boldsymbol{A^T_{11}}$, and $\boldsymbol{A_{22}} = \boldsymbol{A^T_{22}}$. Note that other partition arrangements are possible for the example matrix.

The process of matrix multiplication can also be extended to partitioned matrices, provided that the individual products of sub-matrices are conformable for multiplication. For example, the matrix system of a set of equations, $\boldsymbol{Sx} = \boldsymbol{c}$, is often partitioned as

$$\begin{bmatrix} \boldsymbol{S_{11}} & \vdots & \boldsymbol{S_{12}} \\ \cdots & \cdots & \cdots \\ \boldsymbol{S_{21}} & \vdots & \boldsymbol{S_{22}} \end{bmatrix} \begin{Bmatrix} \boldsymbol{x_1} \\ \cdots \\ \boldsymbol{x_2} \end{Bmatrix} = \begin{Bmatrix} \boldsymbol{c_1} \\ \cdots \\ \boldsymbol{c_2} \end{Bmatrix}. \tag{1.4-2}$$

The multiplications on the left side expand to

$$\begin{Bmatrix} \boldsymbol{S_{11}x_1} + \boldsymbol{S_{12}x_2} \\ \boldsymbol{S_{21}x_1} + \boldsymbol{S_{22}x_2} \end{Bmatrix} = \begin{Bmatrix} \boldsymbol{c_1} \\ \boldsymbol{c_2} \end{Bmatrix}. \tag{1.4-3}$$

The above-partitioned form of a system of equations will be used in many later examples.

1.5 Special Finite Element Matrix Notations

Herein, the symbol **H** will be reserved for a special row matrix where the coefficients are functions that spatially interpolate a scalar quantity within an element or boundary region. They are used to define a special rectangular matrix $\boldsymbol{N} = \boldsymbol{N}(\boldsymbol{H})$ where the coefficients are functions that spatially interpolate only the scalar components of a vector or tensor quantity. In the finite element literature, it is very common to denote a matrix containing (at least) the physical spatial derivatives of $\mathbf{N}$ by the symbol $\boldsymbol{B}$.

In this text, uppercase **bold** Latin letters will generally denote rectangular matrices, $\boldsymbol{R}$, or square matrices, $\boldsymbol{S}$, while lowercase bold Latin letters, such as $\mathbf{c}$, will denote a column matrix (or column vector). A superscript "e" will denote matrices evaluated in an element, while superscript "b" will denote a matrix evaluated on a boundary. The Greek letter $\boldsymbol{\delta}$ is reserved to denote a special column vector that contains all of the problem unknowns. The Greek letter $\boldsymbol{\beta}$ will be reserved to denote a rectangular Boolean matrix (containing zeros and a few ones) that is a theoretical way (only) to express the mesh connectivity of an element. In matrix algebra, the theoretical equivalence of a connection list for an element is denoted by $\boldsymbol{\beta}^{\mathbf{e}}$ and by $\boldsymbol{\beta}^{\mathbf{b}}$ for boundary region.

1.6 Finite Element Integrals

The first step in an FEA simulation requires that the integral formulation of the application must be known or derived. The common integral form concepts from Euler have been known for more than 200 years. Euler gave the integral equivalent of the most common linear differential equations important to engineering and physics. For a given integral, his theorem yielded the corresponding differential equation, and its Dirichlet and secondary boundary conditions.

Much later (1915), Galerkin gave a procedure for converting any linear or nonlinear differential equation into a corresponding integral form. It can be shown that in certain mathematical norms the Galerkin method gives the best approximation of the solution. The least squares method provides another way to create an equivalent integral form from a differential equation, but it is awkward to implement in two- or three-dimensions.

The difficulty with these original approaches was that they required any approximate solution to begin with a single assumed spatial form, over the entire domain, which satisfied all of the boundary conditions in advance. That was only practical for a few shapes like an ellipse, rectangle, triangle, or other regular polygons, but was very difficult for practical shapes with curved boundary regions.

It took modern computers and the concept of a mesh of finite sub-regions to be able to automate the process. To be able to match curvilinear physical shapes, it is necessary to convert (map) a non-dimensional regular parametric space onto the curved physical space. In other words, a change of variables is required to convert physical quantities in a physical space (or time, or space–time) to an integral of physical quantities in a non-dimensional space. In the vast majority of finite element methods, the change of variables is accomplished by using a polynomial interpolation of the physical geometry. Piecewise polynomial interpolation is also employed to model the spatial distribution of the solution, $u(x, y, z)$, being sought.

The steps for completing an FEA require several prerequisite skills. First, it requires that a mesh with node coordinates and elements with a node connection list must be generated. The node connection list governs the assembly (scattering) of each element's contribution to the final governing system matrices. The problems illustrated here are relatively simple and the data will be manually generated. Two-dimensional meshes illustrated herein were generated with a structured (conformal mapping) mesh generator that creates any of the two-dimensional elements used in the Matlab finite element library provided with this text. Commercial finite element systems use unstructured automatic mesh generators that will not be discussed here.

1.7 Linear Spring Networks (Work–Energy)

Putting off how the integral formulations establish the element matrices in most applications, the majority of the FEA steps can be demonstrated by reviewing the classic linear spring equilibrium and an assembly of a network of such springs. In the case of a linear spring, the governing integral form is based on the Principle of Minimum Total Potential Energy, which can be written from basic physics without resorting to calculus. Basically, it states that the displacement field that satisfies the essential displacement boundary conditions and minimizes the total potential energy is the unique one that corresponds to the state of static equilibrium. This implies that displacements are the primary unknowns. The total potential energy, Π, is the strain energy, U, of the structure minus the mechanical work, W, done by the external forces. From introductory mechanics, the mechanical work, W, done by a force is the scalar dot product of the force vector, F, and the displacement vector, u, at its point of application.

The well-known linear elastic spring will be reviewed to illustrate the concept of obtaining equilibrium equations from an energy formulation. Consider a linear spring, of stiffness k, and length L, that has an applied force, F, at the free (right) end, and is restrained from displacement at the other (left) end, as in Figure 1.7-1.

The free end of the spring undergoes a displacement of Δ. The work done by the single external force is $W = \vec{\Delta}\circ\vec{F} = \Delta_x F_x = uF$. The spring stores potential energy, or strain energy, due to its deformation (change in length). That stored energy is given by $U = \frac{1}{2}k\Delta_x^2$. Therefore, the total potential energy for the loaded spring with one end fixed is

$$\Pi = \frac{1}{2}k\Delta_x^2 - \Delta_x F_x. \tag{1.7-1}$$

The equation of equilibrium is obtained by minimizing this total potential energy with respect to the unknown displacement, Δ_x. That is, the partial derivative of the total potential energy with respect to each displacement is set to zero. That yields one equilibrium equation per unknown displacement.

$$\frac{\partial \Pi}{\partial \Delta_x} = 0 = \frac{2}{2}k\Delta_x - F_x. \tag{1.7-2}$$

This simplifies to the common single scalar equation $k\Delta_x = F$, or

$$\Delta_x = F/k, \tag{1.7-3}$$

which is the well-known equilibrium equation for a linear spring.

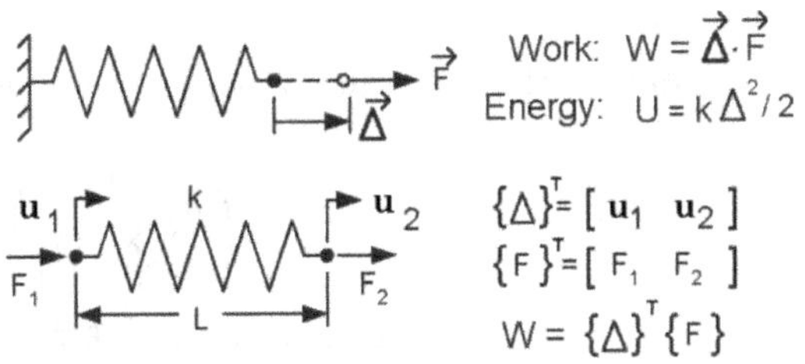

Fig. 1.7-1: Classic (top) and general linear spring element.

In most applications, it is necessary to obtain the gradient of the solution in each element. For the simple linear spring, the displacement gradient is just the change in length divided by the original length: $\varepsilon \equiv \partial\Delta/\partial x = (\Delta_x - 0)/L$.

This example was slightly simplified since we started with the condition that the left end of the spring had no displacement (an essential or Dirichlet boundary condition). Next, we will consider a spring where either end can be fixed or free to move. To obtain the equilibrium condition now, one more step is required. In addition to minimizing the total potential energy, it is also necessary to impose all of the given displacement restraints. Now the spring model has two end displacements, say u_1 and u_2, and two associated axial external forces, say F_1 and F_2. The net deformation of the bar is $\delta = u_2 - u_1$. The total vector of displacement components and the associated vector of external forces are denoted as

$$\vec{\Delta} = \{u\} = \begin{Bmatrix} u_1 \\ u_2 \end{Bmatrix} \quad \text{and} \quad \vec{F} = \{F\} = \begin{Bmatrix} F_1 \\ F_2 \end{Bmatrix}, \tag{1.7-4}$$

respectively. The mechanical work done on the spring is $W = \{\mathrm{u}\}^{\mathrm{T}}\{F\} = u_1\, F_1 + u_2 F_2$. Then the spring's strain energy is now

$$\begin{aligned} \mathrm{U} &= \frac{1}{2}k(u_2 - u_1)^2 = \frac{1}{2}\,(u_2 - u_1)\,k\,(u_2 - u_1) \\ &= \frac{1}{2}k(u_1u_1 - u_1u_2 - u_2u_1 + u_2u_2). \end{aligned}$$

The scalar energy can be written as a triple matrix product

$$\mathrm{U} = \frac{1}{2}\begin{bmatrix} u_1 & u_2 \end{bmatrix}\begin{bmatrix} k & -k \\ -k & k \end{bmatrix}\begin{Bmatrix} u_1 \\ u_2 \end{Bmatrix} = \frac{1}{2}\,\{u\}^{\mathrm{T}}\,[k]\,\{u\}, \tag{1.7-5}$$

where the "spring stiffness matrix" is found to be

$$[k] = k\begin{bmatrix} 1 & -1 \\ -1 & 1 \end{bmatrix}. \tag{1.7-6}$$

The total potential energy, Π, becomes $\Pi = \frac{1}{2}\,\{u\}^{\mathrm{T}}\,[k]\,\{u\} - \{u\}^{\mathrm{T}}\{F\}$ or

$$\Pi = \frac{1}{2}\begin{Bmatrix} u_1 \\ u_2 \end{Bmatrix}^{\mathrm{T}} k\begin{bmatrix} 1 & -1 \\ -1 & 1 \end{bmatrix}\begin{Bmatrix} u_1 \\ u_2 \end{Bmatrix} - \begin{Bmatrix} u_1 \\ u_2 \end{Bmatrix}^{\mathrm{T}}\begin{Bmatrix} F_1 \\ F_2 \end{Bmatrix}. \tag{1.7-7}$$

Note that each term has the units of energy, i.e., force times length. The matrix equations of equilibrium will come from the minimization of the above total potential energy with respect to each and every displacement component, as well as from satisfying all displacement restraints. The minimization requires that the partial derivatives of all the displacements vanish:

$$\frac{\partial \Pi}{\partial \{u\}} = \{0\}, \quad \text{or} \quad \frac{\partial \Pi}{\partial u_j} = 0_j, \ 1 \le j \le n. \tag{1.7-8}$$

That represents only the first stage system of algebraic equations of equilibrium for the elastic system:

$$k\begin{bmatrix} 1 & -1 \\ -1 & 1 \end{bmatrix}\begin{Bmatrix} u_1 \\ u_2 \end{Bmatrix} = \begin{Bmatrix} F_1 \\ F_2 \end{Bmatrix}. \tag{1.7-9}$$

However, the square stiffness matrix has a zero determinant and therefore cannot be inverted. These two symmetric equations do not yet reflect the presence of any EBC on the displacements which are required to define a unique solution and/or to eliminate the axial rigid body motion (RBM). In other words, the full system must be modified to impose the known displacement boundary condition(s) before the unknown displacements can be computed.

In order to enforce the essential displacement boundary conditions (Dirichlet conditions) on this small matrix system, note that the matrix can be partitioned into even smaller matrices associated with the known (k) and unknown (u) displacements as

$$\begin{bmatrix} \boldsymbol{S}_{\mathbf{kk}} & \boldsymbol{S}_{\mathbf{ku}} \\ \boldsymbol{S}_{\mathbf{uk}} & \boldsymbol{S}_{\mathbf{uu}} \end{bmatrix}\begin{Bmatrix} \mathbf{u_k} \\ \mathbf{u_u} \end{Bmatrix} = \begin{Bmatrix} \mathbf{r_k} \\ \boldsymbol{c}_{\mathbf{u}} \end{Bmatrix}, \tag{1.7-10}$$

where $\boldsymbol{S}_{\mathbf{uu}} = [k]$, $\boldsymbol{S}_{\mathbf{kk}} = [k]$, $\boldsymbol{S}_{\mathbf{uk}} = [-k]$, $\boldsymbol{S}_{\mathbf{ku}} = [-k]$, $\mathbf{u_k} = \{u_1\} = \{u_{\text{given}}\}$, $\boldsymbol{c}_{\mathbf{u}} = \{F\}$, and both $\mathbf{u_u} = \{u_2\}$ and $\mathbf{r_k} = \{R\}$ are unknown. Only the lower row(s) are independent equations for the displacements. Once the displacements $\mathbf{u_u}$ are computed, then the top row(s) are the independent equations to compute the reactions at the essential boundary conditions. The displacements, $\mathbf{u_u}$, which satisfy both equilibrium and the imposed displacements, $\mathbf{u_k}$, are

$$\mathbf{u_u} = \boldsymbol{S}_{\mathbf{uu}}^{-1}\,(\boldsymbol{c}_{\mathbf{u}} - \boldsymbol{S}_{\mathbf{uk}}\mathbf{u_k}). \tag{1.7-11}$$

Next, the reactions can be found, if desired as follows:

$$\boldsymbol{S}_{\mathbf{kk}}\mathbf{u_k} + \boldsymbol{S}_{\mathbf{ku}}\mathbf{u_u} = \mathbf{r_k}. \tag{1.7-12}$$

This process works on arrays of any size.

For example, consider the classic spring with which this study began and assume that the left node has a known zero displacement ($u_1 = u_{\text{given}}$) and the right end has the known force, $f_2 = F$. The unknowns are the right displacement, u_2, and the left end reaction force, say $f_1 = R$. The now unique analytic equilibrium relation is partitioned between the known displacements (with unknown reactions) and the independent unknown displacements being subjected to known forces:

$$k \begin{bmatrix} 1 & -1 \\ -1 & 1 \end{bmatrix} \begin{Bmatrix} u_{\text{given}} \\ u_2 \end{Bmatrix} = \begin{Bmatrix} R \\ F \end{Bmatrix}. \tag{1.7-13}$$

There are still two unknowns, R and u_2, related to two known quantities, F and u_{given}. This matrix form has the very desirable property of being symmetric. In theory, the matrices could be rearranged to solve for R and u_2 simultaneously, but that would destroy the important symmetry property. Instead, a two-step process is used: first solve the symmetric subset of equations involving the independent unknown displacements, and then after all displacements are known the equations for the reactions can be solved (but they don't have to be solved).

Here, the independent displacement subset is found from the second row:

$$k\,[1]\,\{u_2\} = \{F\} - k\,[-1]\,\{u_{\text{given}}\},$$

where the known displacement effects have been moved to the right-hand side (RHS). Multiplying both sides by the inverse matrix $[1/k]$ gives the solution

$$\{u_2\} = \{F/k\} + \{u_{\text{given}}\}. \tag{1.7-14}$$

This is the same as the common form when $\{u_{\text{given}}\}$ is zero, namely: $\{u_2\} = \{F/k\}$. Now the system reaction force necessary to maintain $\{u_{\text{given}}\}$ can be obtained from the first row of the matrix system:

$$k \begin{bmatrix} 1 & -1 \end{bmatrix} \begin{Bmatrix} u_1 \\ u_2 \end{Bmatrix} = \{R\}$$

$$k \left[1 * u_{\text{given}} \quad -1 * (u_{\text{given}} + F/k) \right] = \{-F\} = \{R\}. \tag{1.7-15}$$

Thus, the reaction force is equal and opposite to the applied load: $R = -F$, as expected. For this form of the linear spring, the displacement gradient again is just the change in length divided by the original length:

$$\varepsilon \equiv \partial\Delta/\partial x = (u_2 - u_1)/\mathrm{L}.$$

Next, a system, or network, of linear springs, shown in Figure 1.7-2, will be analyzed. Clearly, there are a total of five displacements, or degrees of freedom, of which only three are independent.

The five system displacements and the five external forces are

$$\boldsymbol{\Delta} = [\, u_1 \quad u_2 \quad u_3 \quad u_4 \quad u_5 \,] \quad \text{and} \quad \boldsymbol{F}^{\mathrm{T}} = [\, R_1 \quad R_2 \quad 0 \quad 0 \quad P \,],$$

respectively, where P is a known external load and R_1 and R_2 are unknown external reactions, and nodes 3 and 4 have no external loads. This network of springs is described by a "connection list" which gives the first and second nodes connected to the spring:

Spring	**Stiffness**	**Length**	**Node 1**	**Node 2**
1	k_1	L_1	1	3
2	k_2	L_2	3	4
3	k_3	L_3	3	5
4	k_4	L_4	3	5
5	k_5	L_5	5	4
6	k_6	L_6	4	2

The stiffness matrix of the jth spring is $\begin{bmatrix} k_j & -k_j \\ -k_j & k_j \end{bmatrix}$ and its four components will be directly scattered (added) to the rows and columns to which it is connected. Begin forming the system stiffness matrix $\boldsymbol{K}$ by scattering in the first element having node connections to rows 1 and 3, and to columns 1 and 3:

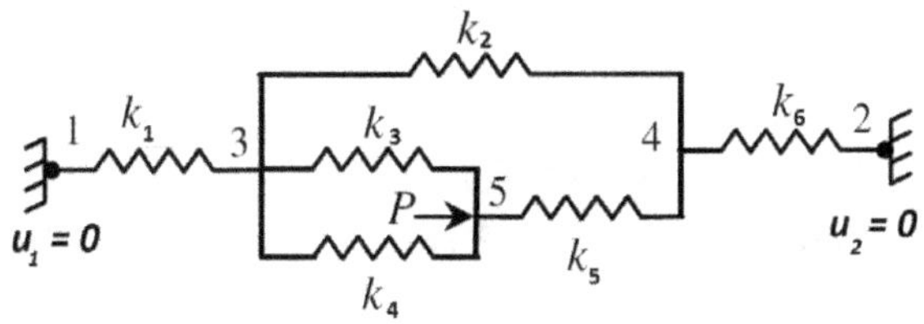

Fig. 1.7-2: A mesh of a six spring network.

$$\boldsymbol{K} = \begin{bmatrix} k_1 & 0 & -k_1 & 0 & 0 \\ 0 & 0 & 0 & 0 & 0 \\ -k_1 & 0 & k_1 & 0 & 0 \\ 0 & 0 & 0 & 0 & 0 \\ 0 & 0 & 0 & 0 & 0 \end{bmatrix}, \text{ add spring 2 at equations 3 and 4:}$$

$$\boldsymbol{K} = \begin{bmatrix} k_1 & 0 & -k_1 & 0 & 0 \\ 0 & 0 & 0 & 0 & 0 \\ -k_1 & 0 & (k_1 + k_2) & -k_2 & 0 \\ 0 & 0 & -k_2 & k_2 & 0 \\ 0 & 0 & 0 & 0 & 0 \end{bmatrix}, \text{ add spring 3 to equations 3}$$

and 5:

$$\boldsymbol{K} = \begin{bmatrix} k_1 & 0 & -k_1 & 0 & 0 \\ 0 & 0 & 0 & 0 & 0 \\ -k_1 & 0 & (k_1 + k_2 + k_3) & -k_2 & -k_3 \\ 0 & 0 & -k_2 & k_2 & 0 \\ 0 & 0 & -k_3 & 0 & k_3 \end{bmatrix}, \text{ add spring 4 to}$$

equations 3 and 4:

$$\boldsymbol{K} = \begin{bmatrix} k_1 & 0 & -k_1 & 0 & 0 \\ 0 & 0 & 0 & 0 & 0 \\ -k_1 & 0 & (k_1 + k_2 + k_3 + k_4) & -k_2 & (-k_3 - k_4) \\ 0 & 0 & -k_2 & k_2 & 0 \\ 0 & 0 & (-k_3 - k_4) & 0 & (k_3 + k_4) \end{bmatrix}, \text{ add spring}$$

5 to equations 5 and 4:

$$\boldsymbol{K} = \begin{bmatrix} k_1 & 0 & -k_1 & 0 & 0 \\ 0 & 0 & 0 & 0 & 0 \\ -k_1 & 0 & (k_1 + k_2 + k_3 + k_4) & -k_2 & (-k_3 - k_4) \\ 0 & 0 & -k_2 & (k_2 + k_5) & -k_5 \\ 0 & 0 & (-k_3 - k_4) & -k_5 & (k_3 + k_4 + k_5) \end{bmatrix},$$

and add spring 6 to equations 4 and node 2 to give the final assembled system stiffness matrix:

$$\boldsymbol{K} = \begin{bmatrix} k_1 & 0 & -k_1 & 0 & 0 \\ 0 & k_6 & 0 & -k_6 & 0 \\ -k_1 & 0 & (k_1 + k_2 + k_3 + k_4) & -k_2 & (-k_3 - k_4) \\ 0 & -k_6 & -k_2 & (k_2 + k_5 + k_6) & -k_5 \\ 0 & 0 & (-k_3 - k_4) & -k_5 & (k_3 + k_4 + k_5) \end{bmatrix}. \tag{1.7-16}$$

Note the general rules that the system stiffness matrix is symmetric and its diagonal element on each row (corresponding to a node) has as many sums as elements connected to that node. Also, the diagonal terms are always positive and the off-diagonal terms are often negative. This means that the assembled system has another important mathematical property: it is "diagonally dominant". The combinations of these matrix properties yield algorithms that can efficiently solve for hundreds of thousands of displacements. The final (singular) system matrix equilibrium equations are as follows:

$$\begin{bmatrix} k_1 & 0 & -k_1 & 0 & 0 \\ 0 & k_6 & 0 & -k_6 & 0 \\ -k_1 & 0 & (k_1 + k_2 + k_3 + k_4) & -k_2 & (-k_3 - k_4) \\ 0 & -k_6 & -k_2 & (k_2 + k_5 + k_6) & -k_5 \\ 0 & 0 & (-k_3 - k_4) & -k_5 & (k_3 + k_4 + k_5) \end{bmatrix} \times \begin{Bmatrix} u_1 \\ u_2 \\ u_3 \\ u_4 \\ u_5 \end{Bmatrix} = \begin{Bmatrix} R_1 \\ R_2 \\ 0 \\ 0 \\ P \end{Bmatrix}. \tag{1.7-17}$$

Here rows 1 and 2 are not independent equations for displacements. They are just optional equations for finding the reaction forces needed to enforce zero displacements at the two ends of the spring assembly. Only the last three rows are independent equations for the system displacements. Also, the first two columns of those rows are stiffnesses multiplied by known displacements, so those products must be carried to the RHS of known values. The system started with five degrees of freedom, but applying two displacement boundary conditions left only three independent degrees of freedom. Applying sufficient boundary conditions always results in a non-singular stiffness matrix partition to find the independent displacements. The active 3×3 independent equations of equilibrium, $\boldsymbol{K}^*\Delta^* = \boldsymbol{F}^*$, are

$$\begin{bmatrix} (k_1+k_2+k_3+k_4) & -k_2 & (-k_3-k_4) \\ -k_2 & (k_2+k_5+k_6) & -k_5 \\ (-k_3-k_4) & -k_5 & (k_3+k_4+k_5) \end{bmatrix} \begin{Bmatrix} u_3 \\ u_4 \\ u_5 \end{Bmatrix}$$
$$= \begin{Bmatrix} 0 \\ 0 \\ P \end{Bmatrix} - u_1 \begin{Bmatrix} -k_1 \\ 0 \\ 0 \end{Bmatrix} - u_2 \begin{Bmatrix} 0 \\ -k_6 \\ 0 \end{Bmatrix}. \tag{1.7-18}$$

Note that this general approach allows for non-zero displacements (unknowns) as the end boundary conditions. Using the vector subscript notations of Matlab and Fortran 90, the above independent equations are

$$\boldsymbol{K}^* = \boldsymbol{K}(3:5, 3:5), \quad \Delta^* = \Delta(3:5), \quad \boldsymbol{F}^* = F(3:5) \text{ or}$$
$$\boldsymbol{K}^* = \boldsymbol{K}(\boldsymbol{free}, \boldsymbol{free}), \quad \Delta^* = \Delta(\boldsymbol{free}), \quad \boldsymbol{F}^* = \boldsymbol{F}(\boldsymbol{free})$$

where the vector subscript array is $\boldsymbol{free} = [3 \quad 4 \quad 5]$. The latter form is used later since it is a more powerful programming approach because it does not require the independent displacement numbers to be sequential.

To simplify this system, assume that all six springs have the same stiffness, k. Then the above system becomes

$$k \begin{bmatrix} (4) & -1 & (-2) \\ -1 & (3) & -1 \\ (-2) & -1 & (3) \end{bmatrix} \begin{Bmatrix} u_3 \\ u_4 \\ u_5 \end{Bmatrix} = \begin{Bmatrix} 0 \\ 0 \\ P \end{Bmatrix} - u_1 \begin{Bmatrix} -k \\ 0 \\ 0 \end{Bmatrix} - u_2 \begin{Bmatrix} 0 \\ -k \\ 0 \end{Bmatrix}. \tag{1.7-19}$$

Now assign numerical values of $k = 120\ kN/m$, $P = 20\ kN$, and $u_1 = u_2 = 0$ m. Then

$$\begin{bmatrix} 480 & -120 & -240 \\ -120 & 360 & -120 \\ -240 & -120 & 360 \end{bmatrix} \begin{Bmatrix} u_3 \\ u_4 \\ u_5 \end{Bmatrix} = \begin{Bmatrix} 0 \\ 0 \\ 20 \end{Bmatrix} - \begin{Bmatrix} 0 \\ 0 \\ 0 \end{Bmatrix} - \begin{Bmatrix} 0 \\ 0 \\ 0 \end{Bmatrix} = \begin{Bmatrix} 0 \\ 0 \\ 20 \end{Bmatrix}$$

and solving for the independent displacements using the Matlab command $\Delta^* = \boldsymbol{K}^* \backslash \boldsymbol{F}^*$ gives

$$\boldsymbol{\Delta}^* = \begin{Bmatrix} u_3 \\ u_4 \\ u_5 \end{Bmatrix} = \begin{Bmatrix} 0.08974 \\ 0.07692 \\ 0.14103 \end{Bmatrix} m. \tag{1.7-20}$$

Now that all of the displacements, Δ, are known, the optional first two rows of the original 5×5 system can be used to recover the two system end reaction forces. For the current numerical values, the reactions are

$$\begin{bmatrix} 120 & 0 & -120 & 0 & 0 \\ 0 & 120 & 0 & -120 & 0 \end{bmatrix} kN/m \begin{Bmatrix} 0 \\ 0 \\ 0.08974 \\ 0.07692 \\ 0.14103 \end{Bmatrix} m$$

$$= \begin{Bmatrix} -10.7692 \\ -9.2307 \end{Bmatrix} kN = \begin{Bmatrix} R_1 \\ R_2 \end{Bmatrix}. \tag{1.7-21}$$

Those two system external reaction forces are shown in Fig. 1.7-3 along with the externally applied force. Checking for equilibrium using Newton's third law shows that the sum of the external axial forces is indeed zero.

At this point, there is usually a post-processing loop over all of the elements where their end displacements are gathered to find the solution gradient and optionally to find the element nodal forces. For each spring the displacement gradient again is just the change in length divided by the original length: $\varepsilon \equiv \partial\Delta/\partial x$. From the element connection list, the first spring is connected to nodes 1 and 3. Those connections can be represented as the entries into a vector subscript

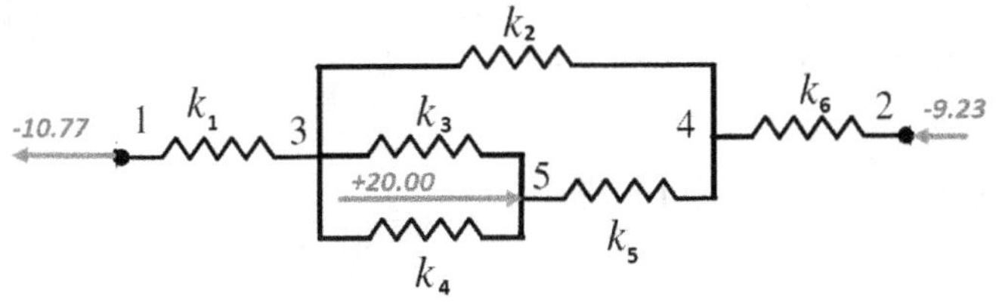

Fig. 1.7-3: System external load and end reaction forces ($\boldsymbol{kN}$).

array $\boldsymbol{list} = [1 \quad 3]$. The spring end displacements are a subset of the system displacements, $\boldsymbol{\delta} \subset \Delta$. Here the two "gathered" spring end displacements on the first spring are

$$\{\boldsymbol{\delta}\} = \{\Delta(\boldsymbol{list})\} = \begin{Bmatrix} \Delta(1) \\ \Delta(3) \end{Bmatrix} = \begin{Bmatrix} 0 \\ 0.08974 \end{Bmatrix} m.$$

From other sources, like Fig. 1.7-7, the length of the first spring is known to be $L_1 = 2m$. Thus, the solution gradient for the first element is

$$\varepsilon \equiv \frac{\partial \Delta}{\partial x} = \frac{\Delta(3)-\Delta(1)}{L_1} = \frac{0.08974\ m - 0\ m}{2\ m} = 0.04487\ m/m.$$

A spring network is one of the rare cases where the solution gradient is not an important item, so the remaining gradients will not be given in detail. In the vast majority of applications, the solution gradient in each element is of vital importance and is always calculated. Conversely, since springs are structural members it is often important to determine the individual spring end forces, typically called the element reactions. Most non-structural applications do not bother to recover the individual element reactions.

From Fig. 1.7-3, the forces in end springs 1 and 6 are obvious from Newton's third law, but the FEA gives them in a systematic way by requiring that each element be in equilibrium: $[\boldsymbol{k}]\{\boldsymbol{\delta}\} = \{\boldsymbol{r}\}$. As shown above, the first spring is connected to nodes 1 and 3 and its end displacements were gathered above. Substituting the data for the first element into the single spring matrix equilibrium equations $[\boldsymbol{k}]_1\{\boldsymbol{\delta}\}_1 = \{\boldsymbol{r}\}_1$ gives the reaction set as

$$120\ kN/m \begin{bmatrix} 1 & -1 \\ -1 & 1 \end{bmatrix} \begin{Bmatrix} 0 \\ 0.08974 \end{Bmatrix} m = \begin{Bmatrix} -10.769 \\ 10.769 \end{Bmatrix} kN = \begin{Bmatrix} r_1 \\ r_2 \end{Bmatrix} \tag{1.7-22}$$

for the first spring. Note that the sign of the second reaction determines if the spring is in tension (+) or in compression (–). For spring 2, the node connections are $\boldsymbol{list} = [3 \quad 4]$ and its reactions are

$$120\ kN/m \begin{bmatrix} 1 & -1 \\ -1 & 1 \end{bmatrix} \begin{Bmatrix} 0.08974 \\ 0.07692 \end{Bmatrix} m = \begin{Bmatrix} 1.5384 \\ -1.5384 \end{Bmatrix} kN = \begin{Bmatrix} r_1 \\ r_2 \end{Bmatrix}$$

and the second node reaction shows that it is compression. Likewise, for springs 3 through 6, their second node reactions are 6.1538,

Fig. 1.7-4: Equilibrium forces (kN) at internal nodes 3 and 5.

6.1538, –7.6923, and –9.2308 kN, respectively. Figure 1.7-4 shows the free-body diagrams of internal nodes 3 and 5 to verify that they are also in equilibrium via Newton's law. The reader should try drawing the equilibrium forces at internal node 4.

The nodes in this network mesh would have assigned coordinates even if they were not required. They could be used to establish the length of each spring for plotting the mesh. In most applications, the length of each element is an important piece of data that appears in the "stiffness".

Example 1.7-1 Given: Let the prior elastic spring mesh represent a DC current electrical network given the interpretations in Table 1.7-1. Assign node 1 to have a Dirichlet boundary condition of 100 Volts and node 2 to be ground at 0 Volts, and let $P = 20$ amp be an external input current source. Let each wire have a resistance of only 1/120 Ohm.

Solution: The matrix system with five equations in 1.7-17 still governs, but is not unique until Dirichlet boundary conditions are applied. Then $k = 120\ 1/\Omega$ and the initial numerical change in the prior equations is the voltage at node 1, $V_1 = 100$. Then (1.7-19) becomes

$$k\begin{bmatrix} (4) & -1 & (-2) \\ -1 & (3) & -1 \\ (-2) & -1 & (3) \end{bmatrix}\begin{Bmatrix} V_3 \\ V_4 \\ V_5 \end{Bmatrix} = \begin{Bmatrix} 0 \\ 0 \\ P \end{Bmatrix} - V_1\begin{Bmatrix} -k \\ 0 \\ 0 \end{Bmatrix} - V_2\begin{Bmatrix} 0 \\ -k \\ 0 \end{Bmatrix}$$

with the new numerical resultant source values of

$$\begin{bmatrix} 480 & -120 & -240 \\ -120 & 360 & -120 \\ -240 & -120 & 360 \end{bmatrix} \begin{Bmatrix} V_3 \\ V_4 \\ V_5 \end{Bmatrix} = \begin{Bmatrix} 0 \\ 0 \\ 20 \end{Bmatrix} - 100 \begin{Bmatrix} -120 \\ 0 \\ 0 \end{Bmatrix} - \begin{Bmatrix} 0 \\ -120 \\ 0 \end{Bmatrix} = \begin{Bmatrix} 1.2e4 \\ 0 \\ 20 \end{Bmatrix} \tag{1.7-23}$$

and solving for the independent voltages using the Matlab command $\Delta^* = \boldsymbol{K}^* \backslash \boldsymbol{F}^*$ gives

$$\boldsymbol{\Delta}^* = \begin{Bmatrix} V_3 \\ V_4 \\ V_5 \end{Bmatrix} = \begin{Bmatrix} 61.6282 \\ 38.5385 \\ 53.9872 \end{Bmatrix} \text{Volts.}$$

Now that all of the voltages, Δ, are known, the optional first two rows of the original 5×5 system can be used to recover the two system end reaction currents. For the present numerical values, the reaction currents are

$$\begin{bmatrix} 120 & 0 & -120 & 0 & 0 \\ 0 & 120 & 0 & -120 & 0 \end{bmatrix} 1/\Omega \begin{Bmatrix} 100 \\ 0 \\ 61.6282 \\ 38.5385 \\ 53.9872 \end{Bmatrix} \text{Volts} = 1e3 \begin{Bmatrix} 4.6046 \\ -4.6046 \end{Bmatrix} \text{Amps} = \begin{Bmatrix} R_1 \\ R_2 \end{Bmatrix}. \tag{1.7-24}$$

looping over all of the wires where their end voltages are gathered to find the element end currents. A current entering the first node of a wire is positive (+). Using the prior connection list, the first wire is connected to nodes 1 and 3. Those connections are represented by the vector subscript array ***list*** $= [1 \quad 3]$. The wire voltages are a subset of the system voltages, $\boldsymbol{\delta} \subset \Delta$. Here the two "gathered" end

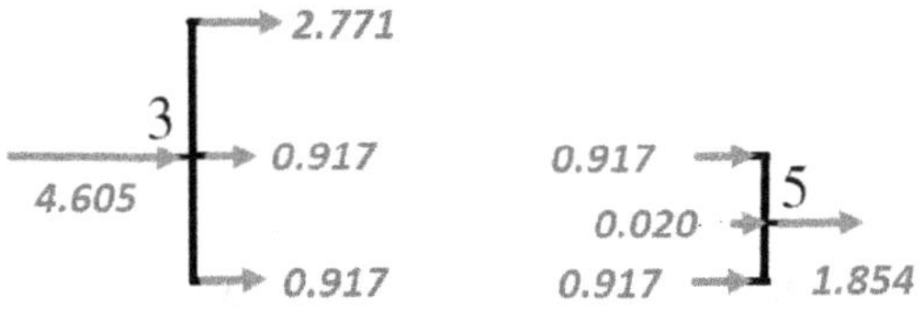

Fig. 1.7-5: Kirchhoff's nodal current law (1e3 Amp) internal nodes 3 and 5.

voltages are

$$\{\boldsymbol{\delta}\} = \{\Delta(\boldsymbol{list})\} = \begin{Bmatrix} \Delta(1) \\ \Delta(3) \end{Bmatrix} = \begin{Bmatrix} 100 \\ 61.6282 \end{Bmatrix} \text{Volts}$$

and the element equilibrium requirement $[\boldsymbol{k}]\{\boldsymbol{\delta}\} = \{\boldsymbol{r}\}$ gives

$$1201/\Omega \begin{bmatrix} 1 & -1 \\ -1 & 1 \end{bmatrix} \begin{Bmatrix} 100 \\ 61.6282 \end{Bmatrix} \text{Volts} = 1e3 \begin{Bmatrix} 4.6046 \\ -4.6046 \end{Bmatrix} \text{Amps} = \begin{Bmatrix} r_1 \\ r_2 \end{Bmatrix}$$

for the first wire. Note that the current enters that wire at the 100 V boundary condition. For wire 2, the node connections are $\boldsymbol{list} = [3 \quad 4]$ and its reactions are

$$120\ 1/\Omega \begin{bmatrix} 1 & -1 \\ -1 & 1 \end{bmatrix} \begin{Bmatrix} 61.6282 \\ 38.5385 \end{Bmatrix} \text{V} = \begin{Bmatrix} 2.7708 \\ -2.7708 \end{Bmatrix} \text{Amps} = \begin{Bmatrix} r_1 \\ r_2 \end{Bmatrix},$$

which shows its current enters at node 3 and exits at node 4. Likewise, for wires 3 through 6, their first node reactions are 916.9231, 916.9231, 1.8538e3, and 4.6246e3 Amp, respectively. Figure 1.7-5 shows Kirchhoff's nodal current law for internal nodes 3 and 5 to verify that they are also in equilibrium. The reader should try drawing Kirchhoff's law at internal node 4.

It so happens that there are several fields of engineering where this same mesh and matrix equations represent other types of equilibrium, and the terms have different units. Such applications include elastic bars, steady DC electrical circuits, heat conduction, torsion of circular shafts, laminar pipe flow through a network, etc. The interpretations of some of these alternate forms, and their units, are listed in Table 1.7-1.

Table 1.7-1: Alternate interpretations of spring networks.

Study	***K*(units)**	***u*(units)**	***F*(units)**	***R* (units)**
Linear Spring	Stiffness per unit length (N/m)	Displacement (m)	External force (N)	Reaction force (N)
Axial Bar	Axial stiffness $k = EA/L$ (N/m)	Displacement (m)	External force (N)	Reaction force (N)
Heat Conduction	Axial conductivity $k = \kappa A/L(W/°C)$	Temperature (°C)	External heat flow (W)	Reaction heat flow (W)
Torsional Shaft	Torsion stiffness $k = GJ/L$ (N-m)	Twist angle (radians)	External torque (N-m)	Reaction torque (N-m)
Electric DC Circuit	Inverse resistance $k = 1/R$ (amp/V)	Voltage (V)	External current source (Amp)	Reaction current (Amp)

1.8 Layout of this Book

In the decades since the introduction of the finite element method, the curriculums of undergraduate engineering programs have reduced the number of required courses needed to obtain a degree. Thus, some subjects that were previously covered in an engineering education are not included in the current educational process. Teaching current students has shown the desirability of reviewing several prerequisite topics that are important to mastering finite element methods. Therefore, the initial chapters in this book contain several optional introductory sections that can be skipped by a reader who has already mastered the topics mentioned in the Summary at the end of each chapter. Those sections are denoted by an asterisk appended to the section heading.

For at least the first seven chapters the reader should first examine the Summary to determine if that chapter contains material which is new to the reader. If the reader has a strong math and engineering background, then he or she can begin with the application chapters, starting with Chapter 8.

The governing differential equation, and its equivalent integral form, always include the derivatives taken with respect to the physical space. At least when the element has curved geometry it is necessary to relate those physical derivatives to the non-dimensional derivatives in the interpolation space. That involves the calculus concept of a change of variables (like going from rectangular coordinates to cylindrical coordinates). It always requires the calculation and inversion of the Jacobian of that coordinate transformation. Those calculations must be done for every element in the mesh. Chapter 2 reviews that important calculus concept (the Jacobian) that is required to complete any element integral. The use of the Galerkin method usually requires the use of integration by parts, and its generalization to three-dimensions (Green's theorem), and that topic is also restated in Chapter 4.

Most finite element studies start with a differential equation and its required boundary conditions to be converted to an equivalent integral formulation. The optional Chapter 3 reviews the three classes of differential equations and the important topic of how to identify the difference between EBCs and NBCs, and their common special case of the Neumann NatBC).

Spatial interpolation inside and on elements is a key feature of the finite element method. To model domains with curvilinear boundaries, it is necessary to do those interpolations in non-dimensional coordinate systems. This book mainly uses unit coordinate systems (varying between zero and one), natural coordinate systems (varying between –1 and 1), and barycentric coordinates (also called area coordinates or volume coordinates) varying between 0 and 1. Chapter 4 will review non-dimensional element interpolation methods using polynomials. Mathematicians use the same approach but use "hat functions" to describe the interpolations at a node in the mesh that is connected to multiple elements. Engineers use element interpolations that cover the entire element volume and are made up from the sum of all of the hat functions portions that fall inside the element.

The finite element method is always based on a governing integral principle. Clearly, that means that each element must be integrated to some extent. It is common to have many thousands of elements. Therefore, those integrals must be done efficiently and automatically. A few special cases of element matrices can be integrated in closed form. But if the element has a curved geometry, and/or variable material properties, that almost always requires numerical integration. Thus, Chapter 5 will illustrate how to numerically integrate non-dimensional and physical interpolations.

A brief summary of the ways that equivalent integral forms are created to be equivalent to a differential equation, and its required boundary conditions, are given in Chapter 6. The most commonly used methods in FEA that begin with a differential equation are the Galerkin method and the next most common approach is the least squares method. Stress analysis applications generally use integral forms of the work–energy principle.

All of the applications covered herein lead to the solution of a system of matrix equations after they have been modified to include EBCs (the secondary boundary conditions are included as known coefficients in the matrices). The matrix algebra procedures for doing that are summarized in Chapter 7. Those topics are usually covered in detail in a course on "Linear Algebra".

Having reviewed the prerequisite subjects, numerous one-dimensional Lagrange interpolation applications of FEA are covered in Chapter 8. The extension of one-dimensional Lagrangian bar elements to model structural trusses is presented in Chapter 9. The application of Hermite interpolation in one-dimension for beams and similar applications is presented in Chapter 10. The extension of one-dimensional Hermite beam elements for structural frames is presented in Chapter 11.

The Lagrange technique is extended to two-dimensional scalar field applications in Chapter 12, with an emphasis on torsion of non-circular bars and heat transfer.

The subject of elastic stress analysis is presented in Chapter 13. Eigenvalue applications are briefly covered in Chapter 14 and time-dependent (transient and dynamic) solution methods are covered in Chapter 15. The advanced topic of error estimation and h-adaptive meshes is presented in Chapter 16, where that material is then applied to illustrate how the accuracy of previous two-dimensional examples is improved to enhance their accuracy.

Most books address only linear or quadratic (first and second degree) two-dimensional elements and there are public domain mesh generators for such elements. This book provides software for first through fourth degree one- and two-dimensional elements. The solid brick element uses the tri-linear interpolation. That is, linear interpolation on each edge, and higher-order interpolation on the faces, and still higher order in the interior.

This book is well suited for use in elementary, intermediate, and advanced courses in FEA and applications. It will also serve as a convenient reference after such courses due to the very heavy subject indexing and due to the detailed summary given at the end of each chapter. For a beginning one-dimensional course with prerequisites of calculus and differential equations, Chapters 4, 6, 8, 9, 10, and 11 could be utilized. For an intermediate level course including two-dimensional analysis, Chapters 4–8, 10, 14, and 14 are suggested. For an advanced level course then all chapters should be covered except for early chapters where their prerequisite knowledge has been required by the instructor.

1.9 Summary and Notation

$n_b \equiv$ Number of boundary segments	$n_d \equiv$ Number of system unknowns
$n_e \equiv$ Number of elements	$n_g \equiv$ Number of unknowns per node
$n_i \equiv$ Number of unknowns per element	$n_m \equiv$ Number of mesh nodes
$n_n \equiv$ Number of nodes per element	$n_p \equiv$ Dimension of parametric space
$n_q \equiv$ Number of total quadrature points	$n_s \equiv$ Dimension of physical space
b = Boundary segment number	e = Element number
$\subset$ = Subset of a larger set	$\cup$ = Union of two sets
Boundary, element, and system unknowns:	$\boldsymbol{\delta}^{\mathbf{b}} \subset_{\mathbf{b}} \boldsymbol{\delta}^{e} \subset_{e} \boldsymbol{\delta}$
Boolean extraction arrays:	$\boldsymbol{\delta}^{\mathbf{b}} \equiv \boldsymbol{\beta}_{\mathbf{b}} \boldsymbol{\delta}, \boldsymbol{\delta}^{e} \equiv \boldsymbol{\beta}_{\mathbf{e}} \boldsymbol{\delta}$
Geometry: $\Omega^e \equiv$ Element domain	$\Omega = \cup_e \Omega^e \equiv$ Solution domain
$\Gamma^b \subset \Omega^e \equiv$ Boundary segment	$\Gamma = \cup_b \Gamma^b \equiv$ Domain boundary

Matrix multiplication: $\boldsymbol{C} = \boldsymbol{AB} \neq \boldsymbol{BA}$, $\boldsymbol{C}_{ij} \equiv \sum_{\mathbf{k}} \boldsymbol{A}_{\mathbf{ik}} \boldsymbol{B}_{\mathbf{kj}}$

Transpose of a product: $(\boldsymbol{A}\ \boldsymbol{B}\ \boldsymbol{C})^{\boldsymbol{T}} = \boldsymbol{C}^{\boldsymbol{T}} \boldsymbol{B}^{\mathbf{T}} \boldsymbol{A}^{\boldsymbol{T}}$

Inverse, 2 ×2 $\mathbf{M} = \begin{bmatrix} m_{11} & m_{12} \\ m_{21} & m_{22} \end{bmatrix}$, $\mathbf{M}^{-1} = \frac{1}{d}\begin{bmatrix} m_{22} & -m_{12} \\ -m_{21} & m_{11} \end{bmatrix}$,

$$d = (m_{11}m_{22} - m_{12}m_{21})$$

Integral form: $I = \sum_e \int_\Omega^e f\, d\Omega + \sum_b \int_\Gamma^b g\, d\Gamma$, plus

EBC: $\begin{cases} = 0, \text{or} \\ \to \text{minimum} \end{cases}$

Interpolation: $u(\vec{\mathbf{x}}) = \boldsymbol{H}(\vec{\mathbf{x}})\,\boldsymbol{\delta}^e = u(\vec{\mathbf{x}})^T = \boldsymbol{\delta}^{e^T}\mathbf{H}(\vec{\mathbf{x}})^T$

Calculus: $\frac{\partial u(\vec{\mathbf{x}})}{\partial \vec{\mathbf{x}}} = \vec{\nabla} u(\vec{\mathbf{x}}) = \frac{\partial \mathbf{H}(\vec{\mathbf{x}})}{\partial \vec{\mathbf{x}}}\delta^e$

Geometry mapping: $\boldsymbol{x}(\vec{\mathbf{r}}) = \boldsymbol{H}(\vec{\mathbf{r}})\,\boldsymbol{x}^e, \partial/\partial \boldsymbol{x} = \partial/\partial \mathbf{r}\,\partial \boldsymbol{x}/\partial \mathbf{r}$

System inversion: $\boldsymbol{S} \cdot \boldsymbol{x} = \boldsymbol{c},\ \boldsymbol{x} = \boldsymbol{S}^{-1}\boldsymbol{c} \equiv S\backslash c$

System factorization: $\boldsymbol{S} \cdot \boldsymbol{x} = \boldsymbol{c},\ \boldsymbol{S} \equiv \boldsymbol{L} \cdot \boldsymbol{U},\ \boldsymbol{U} \cdot \boldsymbol{x} \equiv \boldsymbol{g}$,
so $\boldsymbol{L} \cdot \boldsymbol{g} = \boldsymbol{c}$, forward substitute to get $\boldsymbol{g}$.
Then back substitute into $\boldsymbol{U} \cdot \boldsymbol{x} \equiv \boldsymbol{g}$ for the solution $\boldsymbol{x}$.

Solution integral: $\int_\Omega u(\vec{\mathbf{x}})\, d\Omega = \sum_e \int_{\Omega^e} \mathbf{H}(\vec{\mathbf{x}})\, d\Omega \boldsymbol{\delta}^e$.

Solution energy: $\mathrm{E} = \frac{1}{2}\boldsymbol{\delta}^T \boldsymbol{S} \boldsymbol{\delta}$.

1.10 Review

1. A classic linear spring of stiffness K undergoes a displacement d when subjected to a force F. The potential (strain) energy is _____, and the mechanical work is _____.
2. A particle of mass M moves with a velocity V at a height of h above a reference datum. The kinetic energy of the particle is _____, and its potential energy is _____.
3. Briefly explain the operations of scatter and gather and the type of data upon which they operate.
4. Repeat Example 1.3-2 for a stiffness matrix of $\boldsymbol{S} = \begin{bmatrix} 20 & -8 \\ -8 & 10 \end{bmatrix}$.
5. How is the final assembly of the matrix in (1.3-17) changed if the last spring has its connection list reversed to

Spring	**Stiffness**	**Length**	**Node 1**	**Node 2**
6	k_6	L_6	2	4

Chapter 2

Calculus Review

2.1 Introduction

There are four concepts from calculus that are heavily used in finite element analysis (FEA): (1) The "change of variables" to simplify integrals, (2) The use of the Jacobian to relate differential volumes, (3) Using the inverse Jacobian to relate physical and parametric derivatives, and 4. The use of integration by parts, or Green's Theorem, to reduce the order of the highest derivative that appears in an integral. Those critical topics are reviewed here, and used extensively throughout the text.

The finite element method is always integral-based and thus always requires the integration of matrices over curvilinear shapes. Many beginners in FEA have forgotten the important feature of calculus of using a "change of variables" to simplify integrals. Such a change is particularly helpful when part of the domain is curved, and is always used when a finite element is curved; which is the default in modern modeling techniques.

For example, a commonly required geometry property studied in calculus and applied mechanics is the polar moment of inertia of an area:

$$I_{zz} = \iint_R (x^2 + y^2)dA.$$

For circular areas, that integral is made simpler by using cylindrical (parametric) coordinates r and θ, in Fig. 2.1-1, and re-writing it as

$$f(x,y) = \left(x^2 + y^2\right), \quad I_{zz} = \iint_R f(x,y)dA$$
$$= \iint_G g(r,\theta)(r\,dr\,d\theta) = \iint_G g(r,\theta)\,|\boldsymbol{J}(r,\theta)|\,dG,$$

preceded by defining the physical coordinates in terms of the parametric coordinates as $x = r\cos\theta$, $y = r\sin\theta$. That definition also defines the parametric derivatives of the physical coordinates which, in turn, are the coefficients of the two-dimensional Jacobian matrix:

$$\boldsymbol{J} = \begin{bmatrix} \partial x/\partial r & \partial y/\partial r \\ \partial x/\partial\theta & \partial y/\partial\theta \end{bmatrix} = \begin{bmatrix} \cos\theta & \sin\theta \\ -r\sin\theta & r\cos\theta \end{bmatrix},$$

and its determinant is $|\boldsymbol{J}(r,\theta)| = r\cos^2\theta + r\sin^2\theta = r$. The vast majority of the finite elements considered herein will be defined using parametric coordinates and integrals over those elements will use the Jacobian matrix. Many integrals will be evaluated using numerical integration, described in Chapter 5.

The general three-dimensional form of the Jacobian will be introduced next. The common forms for lines, triangles, quadrilaterals, and tetrahedrons will be presented, and then the inverse Jacobian will be reviewed. In most cases, examples will utilize parametric functions that are derived in Chapter 4.

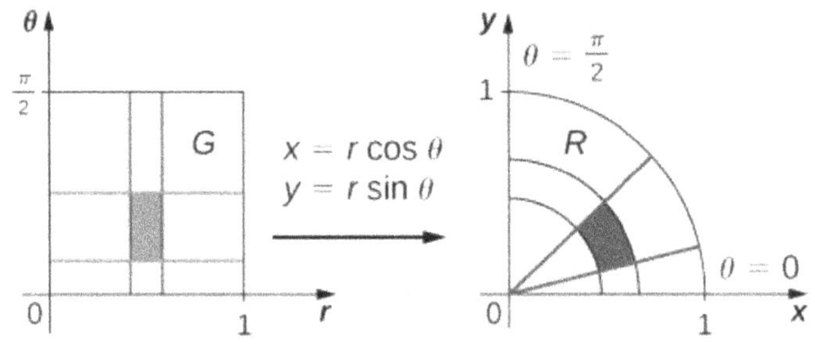

Fig. 2.1-1: Cylindrical coordinates are parametric coordinates.

2.2 Jacobian Matrix

The differentiation of composite functions is required in every parametric finite element study. Let the dependent variable be $\boldsymbol{u(x, y, z)}$ in a domain with the coordinate transformations $= \boldsymbol{f(r, s, t)}$, $\boldsymbol{y = g(r, s, t)}$, and $\boldsymbol{z = h(r, s, t)}$. From the "chain rule" of calculus, the relationship between the parametric derivatives and the physical derivatives are as follows:

$$\begin{aligned}
\frac{\partial u}{\partial r} &= \frac{\partial u}{\partial x}\frac{\partial x}{\partial r} + \frac{\partial u}{\partial y}\frac{\partial y}{\partial r} + \frac{\partial u}{\partial z}\frac{\partial z}{\partial r} \\
\frac{\partial u}{\partial s} &= \frac{\partial u}{\partial x}\frac{\partial x}{\partial s} + \frac{\partial u}{\partial y}\frac{\partial y}{\partial s} + \frac{\partial u}{\partial z}\frac{\partial z}{\partial s} \\
\frac{\partial u}{\partial t} &= \frac{\partial u}{\partial x}\frac{\partial x}{\partial t} + \frac{\partial u}{\partial y}\frac{\partial y}{\partial t} + \frac{\partial u}{\partial z}\frac{\partial z}{\partial t},
\end{aligned} \tag{2.2-1}$$

or in a matrix form, this defines the Jacobian matrix $[\boldsymbol{J}(r,\ s,\ t)]$,

$$\begin{Bmatrix} \frac{\partial u}{\partial r} \\ \frac{\partial u}{\partial s} \\ \frac{\partial u}{\partial t} \end{Bmatrix} = \begin{bmatrix} \frac{\partial x}{\partial r} & \frac{\partial y}{\partial r} & \frac{\partial z}{\partial r} \\ \frac{\partial x}{\partial s} & \frac{\partial y}{\partial s} & \frac{\partial z}{\partial s} \\ \frac{\partial x}{\partial t} & \frac{\partial y}{\partial t} & \frac{\partial z}{\partial t} \end{bmatrix} \begin{Bmatrix} \frac{\partial u}{\partial x} \\ \frac{\partial u}{\partial y} \\ \frac{\partial u}{\partial z} \end{Bmatrix} \equiv [\boldsymbol{J}(r,\ s,\ t)] \begin{Bmatrix} \frac{\partial u}{\partial x} \\ \frac{\partial u}{\partial y} \\ \frac{\partial u}{\partial z} \end{Bmatrix}.$$

The Jacobian matrix is not always square; it has as many rows as parametric coordinates and as many columns as physical coordinates. The relevance of different partitions of the full three-dimensional Jacobian matrix is denoted in the left-hand side of Fig. 2.2-1, and

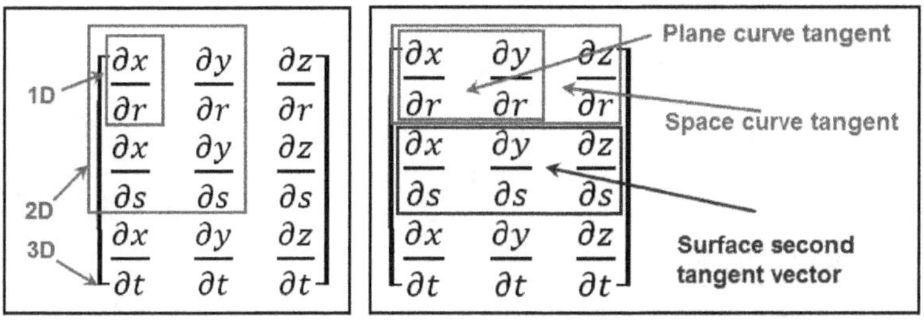

Fig. 2.2-1: Partitions of the transformation Jacobian matrix.

its various rectangular sub-sections are illustrated on the right. In shorthand matrix notation, the parametric partial derivatives, in a parametric space $\boxdot$, are defined in terms of the physical partial derivatives, in a space Ω, given in the full equation and symbolically represented as follows:

$$\frac{\partial u}{\partial \boxdot} = [\boldsymbol{J}(r, s, t)] \frac{\partial u}{\partial \Omega},$$

or since the derivatives can be applied to any function, and not just $u(x, y, z)$, there is a general relationship between parametric derivatives and physical derivatives: $\boldsymbol{\partial}_{\boxdot}() = \boldsymbol{J}(\boxdot)\, \boldsymbol{\partial}_{\Omega}()$. In practice, the element Jacobian matrix, $\boldsymbol{J}^e(\boxdot)$, is usually evaluated numerically as the product of the local derivative of the geometry interpolation, at a specific local point, times the input element physical coordinates as follows:

$$\boldsymbol{J}^e(\boxdot) = \frac{\boldsymbol{\partial H}(\boxdot)}{\boldsymbol{\partial}\boxdot} \boldsymbol{x}^e, \tag{2.2-2}$$

which for one-dimensional problems is simply

$$\boldsymbol{J}^e(r) = \frac{\partial \boldsymbol{H}(\boldsymbol{r})}{\partial r} \boldsymbol{x}^e. \tag{2.2-3}$$

The determinant of the Jacobian of the transformation,

$$J = |\boldsymbol{J}| = \begin{vmatrix} \dfrac{\partial x}{\partial r} & \dfrac{\partial y}{\partial r} & \dfrac{\partial z}{\partial r} \\ \dfrac{\partial x}{\partial s} & \dfrac{\partial y}{\partial s} & \dfrac{\partial z}{\partial s} \\ \dfrac{\partial x}{\partial t} & \dfrac{\partial y}{\partial t} & \dfrac{\partial z}{\partial t} \end{vmatrix} \equiv \frac{\partial(x, y, z)}{\partial(r, s, t)},$$

relates the physical differential volume to the differential parametric volume:

$$d\Omega = |\boldsymbol{J}(\boxdot)| d \boxdot. \tag{2.2-4}$$

For a straight line

$$dx = |\boldsymbol{J}(r)| dr = \left| \frac{\partial x(r)}{\partial r} \right| dr.$$

For a flat area

$$dA = dx\,dy = |\boldsymbol{J}(r,s)|\,dr\,ds = \left(\frac{\partial x}{\partial r}\frac{\partial y(r,\,s)}{\partial s} - \frac{\partial y}{\partial r}\frac{\partial x(r,\,s)}{\partial s}\right) dr\,ds.$$

For a volume

$$dV = dx\,dy\,dz = |\boldsymbol{J}(r,s,t)|\,dr\,ds\,dt.$$

For a non-flat surface, such as a solid element face, it is necessary to use just the top two rows of the Jacobian, in Fig. 2.2-1, along with the mathematical topic of differential geometry to define the vector normal to the surface and to show that the curved surface area is:

$$dS = \sqrt{(x,r\,y,s - y,r\,x,s)^2 + (y,r\,z,s - z,r\,y,s)^2 + (z,r\,x,s - x,r\,z,s)^2} \\ \times dr\,ds.$$

In practical FEA studies, the Jacobian matrix and its (generalized) determinant are evaluated numerically. That is also true for the determinant and the inverse of the Jacobian matrix.

When the Jacobian of a transformation is constant, it is possible to develop closed form exact integrals of parametric polynomials. Several examples of this will be presented in a later chapter for lines, triangles, tetrahedrons, and rectangles. They are useful for simplifying lectures, but for practical FEA, and its automation, it is usually necessary to employ numerical integration. For line integrals of polynomials in unit coordinates, with a constant Jacobian, it is easy to prove that typical terms in the matrix integrals are

$$\int_0^{L^e} r^m\,dx = L^e/(m+1). \tag{2.2-5}$$

Example 2.2-1 Given: Evaluate the Jacobian for a straight quadratic line element with unequal spaces between its three nodes.

Solution: Since only the relative spacing matters, let $x_1 = 0$, $x_2 = \beta\,L^e$, $x_3 = L^e$ for $0.1 \le \beta \le 0.5$. In unit coordinates,

$$x(r) = \boldsymbol{H}(r)\,\boldsymbol{x}^e = (1 - 3r + 2r^2)x_1 + (4r - 4r^2)x_2 + (2r^2 - r)\,x_3.$$

For the node locations,

$$x(r) = \left(4r - 4r^2\right)\beta L^e + \left(2r^2 - r\right)L^e = r\,(4\beta - 1)\,L^e + r^2(2 - 4\beta)L^e.$$

Thus, the variable Jacobian is $\partial x/\partial r = (4\beta - 1)L^e + 2r(2 - 4\beta)\,L^e = \boldsymbol{J}^e(r)$. Note that the Jacobian is only constant within the element when $\beta = 0.5$, that is when the interior node is at the middle of the element. Then $\boldsymbol{J}^e = L^e$, as expected. For $0.25 < \beta \leq 0.5$, the Jacobian is positive (which is good). At $\beta = 1/4$, the Jacobian is zero (which is usually bad). For $\beta < 1/4$, the Jacobian is negative, which is always bad. For distorted elements ($\beta \neq 1/2$), the guideline is that the interior node should be in the center quarter of the element length, $0.4 \leq \beta \leq 0.6$. Ideally, the element will have the interior node exactly at the midpoint. Some programs force that condition by using the average on the end coordinates, $x_2 = (x_1 + x_3)/2$. Likewise, it is easy to show that for a cubic line element the Jacobian will be constant when the interior nodes are placed at the third-points along the length. For a unit coordinate interpolation, the constant is again the element length, L^e.

Example 2.2-2: Repeat Example 2.2-1 using natural coordinates $-1 \leq a \leq 1$ so the quadratic interpolation functions are $\boldsymbol{H}(a) = \left[a(a-1)/2 \;\; (a+1)(1-a) \;\; a(a+1)/2\right]$. Verify that exactly the same result is obtained.

Solution: Since only the relative spacing matters, let $x_1 = 0$, $x_2 = \beta L^e$, $x_3 = L^e$ for $0.1 \leq \beta \leq 0.5$. In natural coordinates:

$$x(a) = \boldsymbol{H}\,(a)\,\boldsymbol{x}^e = x_1 a(a-1)/2 + x_2(a+1)(1-a) + x_3 a(a+1)/2.$$

For the node locations,

$$x(a) = \boldsymbol{H}\,(a)\,\boldsymbol{x}^e = \beta\,L^e + a\,L^e/2 + a^2 L^e(1/2 - \beta).$$

Thus, the variable Jacobian is

$$\partial x/\partial a = L^e/2 + 2aL^e(1/2 - \beta) = \boldsymbol{J}^e(r).$$

Note that the Jacobian is only constant within the element when $\beta = 1/2$, as expected from what has just been mentioned. In natural coordinates, the determinant of the Jacobian becomes $L^e/2$.

Example 2.2-3 Given: A cubic line element has equally spaced nodes of $\boldsymbol{x}^e = [2\ 4\ 6\ 8]$ cm, and interpolates temperatures of $\boldsymbol{u}^e = [2\ 3\ 0\ {-1}]$°C. Evaluate the integral of the nodal data. (In other words, find the area under the curve at the top of Fig. 4.2-10.)

Solution: The integral is

$$I_u = \int_{L^e} u(r)\, dx = \int_0^1 u(r)\, |J(r)|\, dr$$

$$= \int_0^1 \boldsymbol{H}(r)\, \boldsymbol{u}^e\, |J(r)^e|\, dr = \left\{ \int_0^1 \boldsymbol{H}(r)\, |J(r)^e|\, dr \right\} \boldsymbol{u}^e$$

Recall that the Jacobian is constant in an element when the interior nodes are equally spaced. In this case, $J(r)^e = |J(r)^e| = L^e/1 = 6$ cm and the Jacobian can be taken outside the integral, as the nodal constants were

$$I_u = \int_{L^e} u(r)\, dx = L^e \left\{ \int_0^1 \boldsymbol{H}(r)\, dr \right\} \boldsymbol{u}^e.$$

$$1 \times 1 = (1 \times 4)\,(4 \times 1)$$

$$I_u = L^e \left\{ \int_0^1 \left[(2 - 11r + 18r^2 - 9r^3) \quad (18r - 45r^2 + 27r^3) \right.\right.$$

$$\left.\left. (-9r + 36r^2 - 27r^3) \qquad (2r - 9r^2 + 9r^3) \right] /2\, dr \right\} \boldsymbol{u}^e.$$

The first entry in the integral of the interpolation function is

$$\int_0^1 H(r)_1\, dr = \int_0^1 (2 - 11r + 18r^2 - 9r^3)/2\, dr$$

$$= \left(2r - \frac{11r^2}{2} + \frac{18r^3}{3} - \frac{9r^4}{4} \right)/2\ \Big|_0^1 = \frac{1}{8}$$

Evaluating the other three terms gives

$$\int_0^1 \boldsymbol{H}(r)\, dr = [1/8,\ 3/8,\ 3/8,\ 1/8]$$

and the final integral is

$$I_u = \int_{L^e} u(r)\, dx = L^e[1/8,\ 3/8,\ 3/8,\ 1/8]\, \boldsymbol{u}^e.$$

Now, substituting the given data

$$\boldsymbol{u}^{e^T} = \begin{bmatrix} 2 & 3 & 0 & -1 \end{bmatrix}^\circ \mathrm{C}$$

and multiplying the two arrays, we get the final value:

$$I_u = (6\,\mathrm{cm}) \begin{bmatrix} \frac{1}{8}, & \frac{3}{8}, & \frac{3}{8}, & \frac{1}{8} \end{bmatrix} \begin{Bmatrix} 2 \\ 3 \\ 0 \\ -1 \end{Bmatrix} {}^\circ\mathrm{C} = \frac{60^\circ\mathrm{C\,cm}}{8} = 7.5^\circ\mathrm{C}\,c$$

Example 2.2-4 Given: A two-node line segment from $x_1 = 20\,\mathrm{m}$ to $x_2 = 30\,\mathrm{m}$ is subjected to a force per unit length of $p(x)$ that varies linearly from $p_1 = 40\ \mathrm{N/m}$ to $p_2 = 34\,\mathrm{N/m}$. Determine the resultant moment of that line load, with respect to the origin at $x = 0$:

$$M = \int_{x_1}^{x_2} x\,[p(x)dx].$$

Solution: The position and line load can be interpolated with a two-node linear element:

$$x(r) = \boldsymbol{H}(r)\boldsymbol{x}^e = (1-r)x_1 + r\,x_2 = \boldsymbol{x}^{e^T}\boldsymbol{H}(r)^T$$
$$p(r) = \boldsymbol{H}(r)\boldsymbol{p}^e = (1-r)p_1 + r.$$

Substitute the interpolations into the moment integral, and pull the node constants outside that integral and note that for a single element, $dx/dr = x_2 - x_1 = L = L^e$

$$M = \int_{x_1}^{x_2} \boldsymbol{x}^{e^T}\boldsymbol{H}(r)^T\boldsymbol{H}(r)\,\boldsymbol{p}^e\,\boldsymbol{dx} = \boldsymbol{x}^{e^T}\left[\int_0^1 \boldsymbol{H}(r)^T\boldsymbol{H}(r)\frac{dx}{dr}\boldsymbol{dr}\right]\boldsymbol{p}^e.$$

$$M = \boldsymbol{x}^{e^T}\left[\int_0^1 \begin{Bmatrix} (1-r) \\ r \end{Bmatrix}\begin{bmatrix}(1-r) & r\end{bmatrix} L\,dr\right]\boldsymbol{p}^e.$$

$$M = \boldsymbol{x}^{e^T} L^e \int_0^1 \begin{bmatrix} (1-2r+r^2) & (r-r^2) \\ (r-r^2) & r^2 \end{bmatrix} dr\,\boldsymbol{p}^e = L^e\boldsymbol{x}^{e^T}\frac{1}{6}\begin{bmatrix} 2 & 1 \\ 1 & 2 \end{bmatrix}\boldsymbol{p}^e.$$

This can be applied to any such line segment. The specific moment is

$$M = \frac{(x_2 - x_1)}{6} \begin{bmatrix} x_1 & x_2 \end{bmatrix} \begin{bmatrix} 2 & 1 \\ 1 & 2 \end{bmatrix} \begin{Bmatrix} p_1 \\ p_2 \end{Bmatrix}$$

$$= \frac{(30 - 20)m}{6} \begin{bmatrix} 20 & 30 \end{bmatrix} m \begin{bmatrix} 2 & 1 \\ 1 & 2 \end{bmatrix} \begin{Bmatrix} 40 \\ 34 \end{Bmatrix} \frac{\text{N}}{\text{m}},$$

$$M = 9{,}200\,\text{Nm}.$$

Of course, if the interpolations are done using natural coordinate interpolations, the exact same matrix integrals and results are obtained.

Example 2.2-5 Given: Calculate the differential area $dA = dx\,dy$ when converted to polar coordinates using the parametric transformation: $x(R, \theta) = R\cos\theta$, $y(R, \theta) = R\sin\theta$.

Solution: For these two parameters, the Jacobian is

$$\boldsymbol{J} = \begin{bmatrix} \partial x/\partial R & \partial y/\partial R \\ \partial x/\partial \theta & \partial y/\partial \theta \end{bmatrix} = \begin{bmatrix} \cos\theta & \sin\theta \\ -R\sin\theta & R\cos\theta \end{bmatrix},$$

and its determinant is $|J| = R\cos^2\theta + R\sin^2\theta = R$. Therefore, the physical differential area in polar coordinates is $dA = dx\,dy = |J(R, \theta)|\,dR\,d\theta = R\,dR\,d\theta$.

Example 2.2-6 Given: An area of interest is a square with a side length of $\sqrt{2}\,m$ which has been rotated CCW about the origin by 45 degrees. The location of all points in the region can be defined parametrically in unit coordinates as $x(r, s) = (r + s)$ and $y(r, s) = (s - r)$ where r and s are unit coordinates, $0 \le (r, s) \le 1$. Determine the Jacobian and its determinant for that transformation and the physical area of the region.

Solution: By definition the Jacobian matrix is

$$\boldsymbol{J}(r,\, s) = \begin{bmatrix} \partial x/\partial r & \partial y/\partial r \\ \partial x/\partial s & \partial y/\partial s \end{bmatrix}$$

$$= \begin{bmatrix} 1 & -1 \\ 1 & 1 \end{bmatrix} m, \quad |J\,(r,\, s)| = (1)(1) - (-1)(1) = 2\,m^2.$$

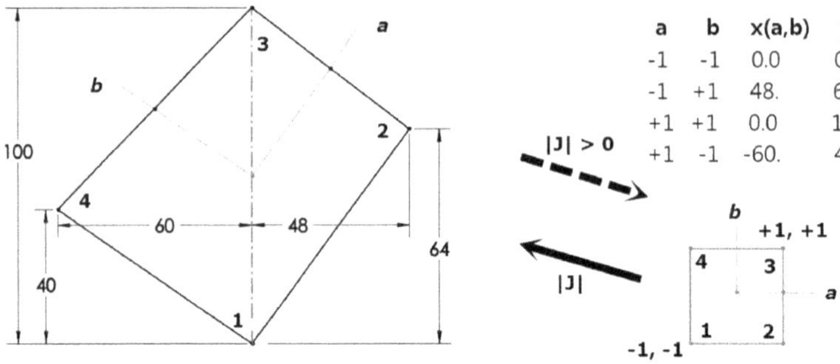

a	b	x(a,b)	y(a,b)
-1	-1	0.0	0.0
-1	+1	48.	64.
+1	+1	0.0	100.
+1	-1	-60.	40.

Fig. 2.2-2: Mapping a natural coordinate square into a general quadrilateral.

The Jacobian is constant because the region in Fig. 2.2-2 has orthogonal straight sides. The area of the physical region is

$$A = \int_A dA = \int_A dx\, dy = \int_0^1 \int_0^1 |J(r,s)|\, dr\, ds$$
$$= 2\,m^2 \int_0^1 \int_0^1 dr\, ds = (2\,m^2)(1).$$

If the interpolations are done using natural coordinate interpolations, the exact same matrix integrals and results are obtained. Such integrals are usually evaluated by numerical integration.

Example 2.2-7 Given: A quadrilateral area in physical space is defined in "natural coordinate" parametric space by the mapping of $x(a,b) = (-3+27\,a-27\,b+3\,ab)$ and $y(a,b) = (51+31\,a+19\,b-ab)$ where $-1 \leq ab \leq +1$. Verify that the variable Jacobian matrix of the mapping is

$$J(a,b) = \begin{bmatrix} (27+3\,b) & (31-b) \\ (-27+3\,a) & (19-a) \end{bmatrix},$$

and determine its determinant.

Solution: Calculating the partial derivatives with respect to a: $\partial x/\partial a = (0+27-0+3\,b)$ and $\partial y/\partial a = (0+31+0-b)$. These are the terms in the first row of the Jacobian matrix. Repeating the process for derivatives with respect to b gives the cited matrix:

$$\boldsymbol{J}(a,b) = \begin{bmatrix} \partial x/\partial a & \partial y/\partial a \\ \partial x/\partial b & \partial y/\partial b \end{bmatrix} = \begin{bmatrix} (27+3\,b) & (31-b) \\ (-27+3\,a) & (19-a) \end{bmatrix}.$$

Thus, $|J(a,b)| = (27+3\,b)(19-a) - (31-b)(-27+3\,a) = 1{,}350 - 120\,a + 30\,b$. The determinant is not constant, but it is positive for the given range of (a,b) values. Since the determinant is positive, $|J(a,b)| > 0$, this mapping is called invertible. Valid finite element shapes should be invertible.

Example 2.2-8 Given: The natural coordinate square $-1 \le a, b \le +1$ is mapped into a physical quadrilateral by

$$x(a,b) = (-3 + 27\,a - 27\,b + 3\,ab) \text{ and}$$
$$y(a,b) = (51 + 31\,a + 19\,b - ab), \text{ in meters.}$$

Evaluate the mapping at the four parametric corners to find the physical coordinates of the corners of the quadrilateral. Use the mapping to determine the physical area of the quadrilateral.

Solution: Directly substituting a variable b at $a = \pm 1$ gives two sides connecting the physical coordinates of the vertices. Substituting a variable a at $b = \pm 1$ defines the quadrilateral in Fig. 2.2-2. The area is given by the integral

$$A = \int_A dA = \int_{-1}^{1}\int_{-1}^{1} |J(a,b)|\, da\, db.$$

The determinant for this area, with the units m^2, was developed in Example 2.2-5. Substituting gives

$$\begin{aligned} A &= \int_A dA = \int_{-1}^{1}\int_{-1}^{1} |J(a,b)|\, da\, db \\ &= m^2 \int_{-1}^{1}\int_{-1}^{1} (1{,}350 - 120\,a + 30\,b)\, da\, db \\ &= 5{,}400\,\mathrm{m}^2. \end{aligned}$$

2.2.1 Linear triangle geometry

The three-noded linear triangle is the simplest two-dimensional element and is probably the most common element presented in the finite element literature. It always has a constant Jacobian. As shown in Fig. 2.2-1 the two-dimensional Jacobian matrix depends on the nodal coordinates of the triangle:

$$\boldsymbol{J}^e(r,\, s) = \begin{bmatrix} \partial x/\partial r & \partial y/\partial r \\ \partial x/\partial s & \partial y/\partial s \end{bmatrix}^e .$$

The corner locations are counted counter-clockwise, starting from any vertex. Since the two coordinates of a physical location of any point are found by interpolation:

$$\begin{aligned} \begin{bmatrix} x(r,\, s) & y(r,\, s) \end{bmatrix} &= \boldsymbol{H}(r,\, s)^e \begin{bmatrix} \boldsymbol{x}^e \,\vdots\, \boldsymbol{y}^e \end{bmatrix} \\ &= \begin{bmatrix} (1-r-s) & r & s \end{bmatrix} \begin{bmatrix} x_1 & y_1 \\ x_2 & y_2 \\ x_3 & y_3 \end{bmatrix}^e . \end{aligned}$$

and the first row of the Jacobian matrix is

$$\begin{aligned} \begin{bmatrix} \partial x/\partial r & \partial y/\partial r \end{bmatrix} &= \begin{bmatrix} (-1) & 1 & 0 \end{bmatrix} \begin{bmatrix} x_1 & y_1 \\ x_2 & y_2 \\ x_3 & y_3 \end{bmatrix}^e \\ &= \begin{bmatrix} (x_2 - x_1) & (y_2 - y_1) \end{bmatrix}^e , \end{aligned}$$

while the second row is

$$\begin{aligned} \begin{bmatrix} \partial x/\partial s & \partial y/\partial s \end{bmatrix} &= \begin{bmatrix} (-1) & 0 & 1 \end{bmatrix} \begin{bmatrix} x_1 & y_1 \\ x_2 & y_2 \\ x_3 & y_3 \end{bmatrix}^e \\ &= \begin{bmatrix} (x_3 - x_1) & (y_3 - y_1) \end{bmatrix}^e . \end{aligned}$$

Of course, the numerical value of the Jacobian for a straight-sided triangle can be obtained by simple matrix multiplication of the two constant matrices: $\boldsymbol{J}^e =$

$$\begin{bmatrix}\partial x/\partial r & \partial y/\partial r\\ \partial x/\partial s & \partial y/\partial s\end{bmatrix}^e = \begin{bmatrix}-1 & 1 & 0\\ -1 & 0 & 1\end{bmatrix}\begin{bmatrix}x_1 & y_1\\ x_2 & y_2\\ x_3 & y_3\end{bmatrix}^e$$

$$= \begin{bmatrix}(x_2 - x_1) & (y_2 - y_1)\\ (x_3 - x_1) & (y_3 - y_1)\end{bmatrix}^e. \tag{2.2-6}$$

Its determinant is also constant with a value of twice the physical area of the triangle:

$$|\boldsymbol{J}^e| = (x_2 - x_1)^e (y_3 - y_1)^e - (x_3 - x_1)^e (y_2 - y_1)^e = 2A^e. \tag{2.2-7}$$

Since the straight-sided triangle has a constant 2×2 matrix, its inverse matrix can be written in closed form as follows:

$$\boldsymbol{J}^{e^{-1}} = \frac{1}{2A^e}\begin{bmatrix}(y_3 - y_1) & (y_1 - y_2)\\ (x_1 - x_3) & (x_2 - x_1)\end{bmatrix}^e. \tag{2.2-8}$$

The differences in corner coordinates occur so often in the literature they have been assigned shorthand notations using subscripts i, j, k that follow a cyclic permutation through 123: $ijk \to 123123$ so the nine element shape constants are

$$a_i^e = x_j^e y_k^e - x_k^e y_j^e, \quad b_i^e = y_j^e - y_k^e, \quad c_i^e = x_k^e - x_j^e, \tag{2.2-9}$$

where an alternate form for the physical area is $2A^e = a_1^e + a_2^e + a_3^e = b_2^e c_3^e - b_3^e c_2^e$.

Example 2.2-9 Given: A triangle has corner (x, y) coordinates of $(0, 0)$, $(4, 0)$, and $(3, 2)$ mm. Determine its geometric constants and physical area.

Solution: First, tabulate the constants

x_i^e	y_i^e	a_i^e	b_i^e	c_i^e
0.	0.	$[4(2) - 3(0)] = 8$	$[0 - 2] = -2$	$[3 - 4] = -1$
4.	0.	$[3(0) - 0(2)] = 0$	$[2 - 0] = 2$	$[4 - 3] = 1$
3.	2.	$[0(0) - 4(0)] = 0$	$[0 - 0] = 0$	$[4 - 0] = 4$

Sum $= 8\,\text{mm}^2 = b_2^e c_3^e - b_3^e c_2^e = 2(4) - 0(1)$, *check*.

Noting that $2A^e$ is the sum of the a_i^e gives $A^e = 4$ mm^2.

2.2.2 Linear tetrahedron

The simplest solid element is the four-noded linear tetrahedron (pyramid). That element has straight edges and flat faces and clearly has a constant Jacobian matrix. The volume of any straight-sided tetrahedron is one-third the base area times the height. In unit coordinates, the unit triangle base area is 1/2 and the parametric tetrahedron has a unit height, therefore its parametric measure (the volume in parametric space) is: $|\boxdot| = (1/3)(1/2)1 = 1/6$, so it will yield the constant determinant of the Jacobian as $|\boldsymbol{J}^e| = |\Omega|/|\boxdot| = V^e/(1/6) = 6V^e$, where V^e is the volume of the tetrahedron in physical space. A process similar to that just applied to the straight-sided triangle gives the constant Jacobian of any straight-edged tetrahedron:

$$\boldsymbol{J}^e = \begin{bmatrix} (x_2 - x_1) & (y_2 - y_1) & (z_2 - z_1) \\ (x_3 - x_1) & (y_3 - y_1) & (z_3 - z_1) \\ (x_4 - x_1) & (y_4 - y_1) & (z_4 - z_1) \end{bmatrix}^e ,$$

and its determinant is six times the physical volume: $|\boldsymbol{J}^e| = 6V^e$.

2.3 Inverse Jacobian

The inverse of the Jacobian matrix is needed when the physical derivatives must be obtained from known parametric derivatives:

$$\boldsymbol{\partial}_\Omega(\,) = \boldsymbol{J}(\boxdot)^{-1}\,\boldsymbol{\partial}_\boxdot(\,),$$

$$\begin{Bmatrix} \dfrac{\partial u}{\partial x} \\ \dfrac{\partial u}{\partial y} \\ \dfrac{\partial u}{\partial z} \end{Bmatrix} = \begin{bmatrix} \dfrac{\partial x}{\partial r} & \dfrac{\partial y}{\partial r} & \dfrac{\partial z}{\partial r} \\ \dfrac{\partial x}{\partial s} & \dfrac{\partial y}{\partial s} & \dfrac{\partial z}{\partial s} \\ \dfrac{\partial x}{\partial t} & \dfrac{\partial y}{\partial t} & \dfrac{\partial z}{\partial t} \end{bmatrix}^{-1} \begin{Bmatrix} \dfrac{\partial u}{\partial r} \\ \dfrac{\partial u}{\partial s} \\ \dfrac{\partial u}{\partial t} \end{Bmatrix}. \tag{2.3-1}$$

In other words, (2.3-1) is the inverse of (2.2-1). In the one-dimensional case, it becomes

$$\frac{\partial}{\partial x} = \frac{1}{\partial x(r)/\partial r}\frac{\partial}{\partial r} = \frac{\partial}{\partial r}\frac{\partial r}{\partial x}.$$

For line elements with equally spaced physical nodes, the Jacobian is a constant proportional to the physical length of the element. A unit-coordinate element with equally spaced nodes has a Jacobian of $\partial x/\partial r = L^e/1$. In such an element, the physical derivative is

$$\frac{\partial}{\partial x} = \frac{1}{L^e/1}\frac{\partial}{\partial r} = \frac{\partial}{\partial r}\frac{1}{L^e},$$

which should have been expected since every derivative with respect to x must introduce a term having the units of length. Likewise, using the popular natural coordinates form, with equal node spacing,

$$\frac{\partial}{\partial x} = \frac{1}{L^e/2}\frac{\partial}{\partial a} = \frac{2}{L^e}\frac{\partial}{\partial a}.$$

For future analytic examples, in two dimensions the inverse Jacobian matrix and its determinant are

$$\boldsymbol{J}^{-1} = \frac{1}{|\boldsymbol{J}|}\begin{bmatrix} \dfrac{\partial y}{\partial s} & -\dfrac{\partial y}{\partial r} \\ -\dfrac{\partial x}{\partial s} & \dfrac{\partial x}{\partial r} \end{bmatrix}, \quad |\boldsymbol{J}| = \left(\frac{\partial x}{\partial r}\frac{\partial y}{\partial s} - \frac{\partial y}{\partial r}\frac{\partial x}{\partial s}\right). \tag{2.3-2}$$

The inverse of the three-dimensional Jacobian is also known analytically, but in practice, it is usually inverted numerically.

Example 2.3-1 Given: Example 2.2-3 describes a square rotated 45 degrees. Evaluate the polar-moment-of-inertia $\int_A (x^2 + y^2)\, dx\, dy$ of the square using the parametric substitution $x(r, s) = (r + s)m$ and $y(r, s) = (s - r)m$, for the unit coordinates $0 \leq (r, s) \leq 1$.

Solution: In Example 2.2-3, the determinant of the Jacobian of that mapping is shown to be a constant $|J| = 2m^2$. The transformation of the integral is

$$\begin{aligned}
\int_A (x^2 + y^2) dx\, dy &= \int_0^1 \int_0^1 \left[x(r,s)^2 + y(r,s)^2\right] |J(r,s)|\, dr\, ds \\
&= \int_0^1 \int_0^1 \left[(r+s)^2 m^2 + (s-r)^2 m^2\right] 2m^2\, dr\, ds \\
&= 2m^4 \int_0^1 \int_0^1 \left[2r^2 + 2s^2\right] dr\, ds
\end{aligned}$$

$$= 2m^4 \int_0^1 \left[\frac{2}{3}r^3 + 2s^2 r\right]_0^1 ds$$

$$= 2m^4 \int_0^1 \left[\frac{2}{3} + 2s^2\right] ds$$

$$\int_A \left(x^2 + y^2\right) dx\, dy = 2m^4 \left[\frac{2}{3}s + \frac{2}{3}s^3\right]_0^1 = 2m^4 \left[\frac{4}{3}\right] = \frac{8}{3}m^4.$$

2.4 Integration by Parts

The use of the powerful Galerkin method of FEA generally requires the use of integration by parts. or Green's Theorem, in two- and three-dimensional space in order to reduce the continuity requirements of the weak solution and to render even order equations to a symmetric integral form. In one dimension, the most commonly used relations are

$$\int_a^b f(x)\, g'(x)\, dx = f(x)\, g(x)|_a^b - \int_a^b f'(x)\, g(x)\, dx,$$

$$\int_a^b f(x)\, g''(x)\, dx = f(x)\, g'(x)|_a^b - \int_a^b f'(x)\, g'(x)\, dx. \quad (2.4\text{-}1)$$

For a volumetric region, V, bounded by the surface, S, Green's Theorem gives the following commonly used relations:

$$\iiint_V A\, \nabla^2 B\, dV = \iint_S A \vec{\nabla} B \cdot \vec{n} dS - \iiint_V \vec{\nabla} A \cdot \vec{\nabla} B\, dV$$

$$= \iint_S A \frac{\partial B}{\partial n} dS - \iiint_V \vec{\nabla} A \cdot \vec{\nabla} B\, dV,$$

$$\iiint_V \left(A\, \nabla^2 B - B\, \nabla^2 A\right) dV = \iint_S \left(A \frac{\partial B}{\partial n} - B \frac{\partial A}{\partial n}\right) dS. \quad (2.4\text{-}2)$$

Example 2.4-1 Given: Evaluate the following integral using integration by parts

$$I = \int_0^L u(x) \left[\frac{d^2 u}{dx^2} + cx \right] dx = 0,$$

Solution: The first term can be integrated by parts

$$\int_0^L u(x) \left[\frac{d^2 u}{dx^2} \right] dx = \left[u \frac{du}{dx} \right]_0^L - \int_0^L \frac{du}{dx} \frac{du}{dx} dx,$$

so an alternate form of the integral formulation is

$$I = \left[u \frac{du}{dx} \right]_0^L - \int_0^L \frac{du}{dx} \frac{du}{dx} dx + \int_0^L u(x)\, cx\, dx = 0.$$

Note that the first term introduces the derivative of the solution normal to the boundary. Often such derivatives appear as nonessential boundary conditions (NBCs). It also lowers the highest derivative in the integrand from the second to the first.

Example 2.4-2 Given: In two dimensions, show how Green's Theorem converts the Galerkin diffusion integral

$$I_k \equiv \int_\Omega u\,(x, y) \left[\boldsymbol{\nabla} \left[\boldsymbol{\kappa} \right] \boldsymbol{\nabla}^{\boldsymbol{T}} u(x, y) \right] d\Omega,$$

into

$$I_k = \int_\Gamma u \, \left[\left[\boldsymbol{\kappa} \right] \boldsymbol{\nabla}^{\boldsymbol{T}} u \right] \cdot \boldsymbol{n}\, d\Gamma - \int_\Omega \boldsymbol{\nabla} u \, \left[\left[\boldsymbol{\kappa} \right] \boldsymbol{\nabla}^{\boldsymbol{T}} u \right] d\Omega.$$

Solution: In two dimensions, the diffusion integral is

$$I_k = \int_\Omega u \left[\frac{\partial}{\partial x} \left(k_{xx} \frac{\partial u}{\partial x} \right) + \frac{\partial}{\partial y} \left(k_{yy} \frac{\partial u}{\partial y} \right) \right] d\Omega,$$

Using the identity $\frac{\partial}{\partial x}\left[u\left(k_{xx}\frac{\partial u}{\partial x}\right)\right]=\frac{\partial u}{\partial x}\left(k_{xx}\frac{\partial u}{\partial x}\right)+u\frac{\partial}{\partial x}\left(k_{xx}\frac{\partial u}{\partial x}\right)$, etc. for y the diffusion integral is re-written as

$$I_K=\int_\Omega\left\{\frac{\partial}{\partial x}\left[u\left(k_{xx}\frac{\partial u}{\partial x}\right)\right]+\frac{\partial}{\partial y}\left[u\left(k_{yy}\frac{\partial u}{\partial y}\right)\right]\right\}d\Omega$$
$$-\int_\Omega\left\{\frac{\partial u}{\partial x}\left(k_{xx}\frac{\partial u}{\partial x}\right)+\frac{\partial u}{\partial y}\left(k_{xx}\frac{\partial u}{\partial y}\right)\right\}d\Omega.$$

The first integral has the form of Green's Theorem:

$$\int_\Omega\{\partial N(x,y)/\partial x-\partial M\,(x,y)/\partial y\}\,d\Omega\equiv\int_\Gamma[Mdx+Ndy].$$

In this case, $N=u\,k_{xx}\,\partial u/\partial x$, $M=-u\,k_{yy}\partial u/\partial y$, and the first part is converted to a boundary integral as follows:

$$\int_\Omega\left\{\frac{\partial}{\partial x}\left[u\left(k_{xx}\frac{\partial u}{\partial x}\right)\right]+\frac{\partial}{\partial y}\left[u\left(k_{yy}\frac{\partial u}{\partial y}\right)\right]\right\}d\Omega\rightarrow I_\Gamma$$
$$=\int_\Gamma\left\{-u\,k_{yy}\frac{\partial u}{\partial y}dx+u\,k_{xx}\frac{\partial u}{\partial x}dy\right\}.$$

At a point on the boundary, the outward unit normal is $\vec{n}=n_x\vec{i}+n_y\vec{j}=\cos\theta_x\vec{i}+\cos\theta_y\vec{j}$. From the geometry of a differential length, ds, along the boundary (see Fig. 2.4-1) the coordinate differential lengths are $-dx=ds\cos\theta_y=n_y\,ds$ and

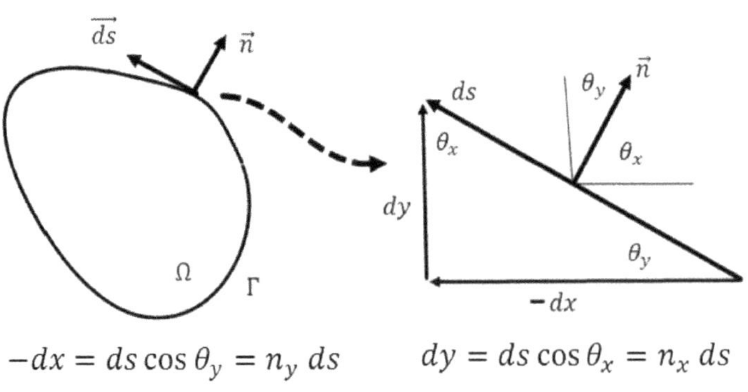

Fig. 2.4-1: Differential lengths along a planar boundary segment.

$dy = ds \cos\theta_x = n_x\, ds$. The boundary integral becomes

$$I_\Gamma = \int_\Gamma u \left\{ k_{yy} \frac{\partial u}{\partial y} n_y\, ds + k_{xx} \frac{\partial u}{\partial x} n_x\, ds \right\}$$
$$= \int_\Gamma u \left\{ [\boldsymbol{\kappa}]\, \boldsymbol{\nabla}^T u \right\} \cdot \boldsymbol{n}\, ds = \int_\Gamma u \left\{ k_{nn} \frac{\partial u}{\partial n} \right\} ds.$$

Therefore, the diffusion integral form becomes

$$I = \int_\Gamma u \left\{ k_{nn} \frac{\partial u}{\partial n} \right\} d\Gamma - \int_\Omega \left\{ \frac{\partial u}{\partial x} \left(k_{xx} \frac{\partial u}{\partial x} \right) + \frac{\partial u}{\partial y} \left(k_{yy} \frac{\partial u}{\partial y} \right) \right\} d\Omega.$$

Example 2.4-3 Given: The Poisson equation, $\nabla^2 u\,(x, y) + Q\,(x, y) = 0$ occurs commonly in engineering and physics applications. The Galerkin weighted residual method approximation begins with the integral $\int_\Omega u\,(x, y) \left[\nabla^2 u\,(x, y) + Q\,(x, y) \right] d\Omega = 0$. By using Green's Theorem reduce the second derivatives in the first integral.

Solution: The first form of the theorem is

$$\int_\Omega u\,(x, y,) \nabla^2 u\ (x, y,) d\Omega$$
$$= \int_\Gamma u\,(x, y,) \frac{\partial u(x, y,)}{\partial n} d\Gamma - \int_\Omega \vec{\nabla} u \cdot \vec{\nabla} u\, d\Omega,$$
$$= \int_\Gamma u\,(x, y,) \frac{\partial\, u(x, y,)}{\partial n} d\Gamma - \int_\Omega \left[\frac{\partial u}{\partial x} \frac{\partial u}{\partial x} + \frac{\partial u}{\partial y} \frac{\partial u}{\partial y} \right] d\Omega.$$

Note that this process automatically brings in the derivative normal to the boundary. Those terms are often specified in the secondary boundary conditions. It also lowers the highest derivative in the integrand from the second to the first.

2.5 Evaluation of Integrals with Constant Jacobian

When the Jacobian of a transformation is constant, it is possible to develop closed-form exact integrals of parametric polynomials. Several examples of this will be presented in the next chapter for lines, triangles, and rectangles. They are useful for simplifying lectures, but for practical FEA, and its automation, it is usually necessary to employ numerical integration. Here, symbolic integrations will be given for the three-noded quadratic line element, with the interior node at its midpoint for

$$\int_0^L f(r)dx = \int_0^1 f(r)\frac{\partial x}{\partial r}dr = \frac{\partial x}{\partial r}\int_0^1 f(r)dr,$$

where the integrand $f(r)$ are the interpolation matrices, their products, and their physical derivatives. Similar exact integrals for common simplex elements (with straight edges) to be used later are given in Table 2.5-1. That table is based on the constant Jacobian unit coordinate parametric line integrals.

Constant Jacobian determinants are usually the ratio of the physical element volume over the parametric element volume. For example, the physical area in general is

$$A^e = \iint_{\boldsymbol{A}}^{e} dA = \iint_{\boxdot} \left|\boldsymbol{J}^e(r,s)\right| d\boxdot = \sum_{\boldsymbol{q=1}}^{\boldsymbol{n_q}} \left|\boldsymbol{J}^e(r,s)\right| w_q.$$

so when the Jacobian determinant is constant, it comes out of the summation as follows:

$$A^e = \left|\boldsymbol{J}^e(r,s)\right| \sum_{\boldsymbol{q=1}}^{\boldsymbol{n_q}} w_q = \left|\boldsymbol{J}^e(r,s)\right| \iint_{\boxdot} d\boxdot, \quad \left|\boldsymbol{J}^e(r,s)\right| = A^e/|\boxdot|.$$

which requires that in a given parametric shape, the sum of the tabulated quadrature weights must equal the measure (non-dimensional

Table 2.5-1: Exact physical integrals for constant Jacobian elements.

Geometry	**Exact integral**
Unit Line	$\int_0^L r^m\, dx = \frac{L}{m+1}$
Unit Triangle	$\int_A r^m\, s^n\, dA = 2A\frac{m!\,n!}{(2+m+n)!}$
Unit Tetrahedron	$\int_V r^m\, s^n t^p\, dV = 6V\frac{m!\,n!\,p!}{(3+m+n+p)!}$

volume) of that shape. For the parametric unit triangle $|\boxdot| = 1/2$ and the proper quadrature weights total to one-half. For the parametric unit square in this example $|\boxdot| = 1$ and the quadrature weights total to one. Had parametric natural coordinates been selected the interpolations for the square, then the sum of the weights would have to match the local measure of $2 \times 2 = 4 = |\boxdot|$ for that choice.

The most useful constant Jacobian elements are triangles or tetrahedra with straight edges and equally spaced nodes. They can still be meshed to accurately model the geometry of any shape. Only degenerate quadrilaterals (rectangles) and hexahedra (bricks) have constant Jacobians when their edges are straight and parallel to the system coordinates. They are less useful in approximating complex shapes. Tables 12.9-1–12.9-5 will give a few closed form integrals of element matrices with constant and/or diagonal Jacobians. In practice, element arrays in two and three dimensions (and four) are obtained by numerical integration.

2.6 Summary

$n_b \equiv$ Number of boundary segments	$n_d \equiv$ Number of system unknowns
$n_e \equiv$ Number of elements	$n_g \equiv$ Number of unknowns per node
$n_i \equiv$ Number of unknowns per element	$n_m \equiv$ Number of mesh nodes
$n_n \equiv$ Number of nodes per element	$n_p \equiv$ Dimension of parametric space
$n_q \equiv$ Number of total quadrature points	$n_s \equiv$ Dimension of physical space
$b =$ boundary segment number	$e =$ element number
$\subset =$ subset of a larger set	$\cup =$ union of two sets

Boundary, element, and system unknowns: $\boldsymbol{\delta}^b \subset_b \boldsymbol{\delta}^e \subset_e \boldsymbol{\delta}$

Boolean extraction arrays: $\boldsymbol{\delta}^b \equiv \boldsymbol{\beta}_b \boldsymbol{\delta},\ \boldsymbol{\delta}^e \equiv \boldsymbol{\beta}_e \boldsymbol{\delta}$

Geometry: $\Gamma^b \subset \Omega^e \equiv$ Boundary segment $\quad \Omega^e \equiv$ Element domain

$\Omega = \cup_e \Omega^e \equiv$ Solution domain $\quad \Gamma = \cup_b \Gamma^b \equiv$ Domain boundary

Element interpolations utilized in this chapter

Element Type	**Example Number**	**Polynomial Degree**	n_p	n_g	n_n	$n_i = n_g \times n_n$	**Continuity Level**
Lagrange L2	2.2-5, 2.6-1,3	1	1	1	2	2	C^0
Lagrange L3	2.1-4, 2.6-2	2	1	1	3	3	C^0
Lagrange L4	2.2-4	3	1	1	4	4	C^0
Lagrange T3	2.2-1	1	2	1	3	3	C^0
Lagrange Q4	2.2-6	1	2	1	4	4	C^0

Matrix multiplication: $\boldsymbol{C} = \boldsymbol{A}\,\boldsymbol{B} \neq \boldsymbol{B}\,\boldsymbol{A}$, $C_{ij} \equiv \sum_k A_{ik} B_{kj}$.

Transpose of a product: $(\boldsymbol{A}\,\boldsymbol{B}\,\boldsymbol{C})^T = \boldsymbol{C}^T\,\boldsymbol{B}^T\,\boldsymbol{A}^T$.

Common constants for straight-sided triangles:

$ijk \to 12312$, cyclic permutations

$a_i^e = x_j^e y_k^e - x_k^e y_j^e$, $b_i^e = y_j^e - y_k^e$,

$c_i^e = x_k^e - x_j^e$, $2A^e = a_1^e + a_2^e + a_3^e$.

Vector cross product: $\boldsymbol{c} = \boldsymbol{a} \times \boldsymbol{b}$ or cyclic permutations.

$c_i = a_j b_k - a_k b_j$, $ijk \to 12312$.

Jacobian matrix:

$$\begin{Bmatrix} \dfrac{\partial u}{\partial r} \\ \dfrac{\partial u}{\partial s} \\ \dfrac{\partial u}{\partial t} \end{Bmatrix} = \begin{bmatrix} \dfrac{\partial x}{\partial r} & \dfrac{\partial y}{\partial r} & \dfrac{\partial z}{\partial r} \\ \dfrac{\partial x}{\partial s} & \dfrac{\partial y}{\partial s} & \dfrac{\partial z}{\partial s} \\ \dfrac{\partial x}{\partial t} & \dfrac{\partial y}{\partial t} & \dfrac{\partial z}{\partial t} \end{bmatrix} \begin{Bmatrix} \dfrac{\partial u}{\partial x} \\ \dfrac{\partial u}{\partial y} \\ \dfrac{\partial u}{\partial z} \end{Bmatrix} \equiv [\boldsymbol{J}(r,\, s,\, t)] \begin{Bmatrix} \dfrac{\partial u}{\partial x} \\ \dfrac{\partial u}{\partial y} \\ \dfrac{\partial u}{\partial z} \end{Bmatrix}.$$

Calculation of element Jacobian:

$$\boldsymbol{J}^e(r) = \frac{\partial \boldsymbol{H}(\boldsymbol{r})}{\partial r} \boldsymbol{x}^e.$$

Jacobian determinant:

$$J = |\boldsymbol{J}| = \begin{vmatrix} \dfrac{\partial x}{\partial r} & \dfrac{\partial y}{\partial r} & \dfrac{\partial z}{\partial r} \\ \dfrac{\partial x}{\partial s} & \dfrac{\partial y}{\partial s} & \dfrac{\partial z}{\partial s} \\ \dfrac{\partial x}{\partial t} & \dfrac{\partial y}{\partial t} & \dfrac{\partial z}{\partial t} \end{vmatrix} \equiv \left| \frac{\partial(x, y, z)}{\partial(r, s, t)} \right|.$$

Differential volume relations: $d\Omega = |J(\boxdot)|\, d\boxdot$

$$dx = |J(r)|dr = \left|\frac{\partial x(r)}{\partial r}\right| dr,$$

$$dA = dx\, dy = |J(r,s)|\, dr\, dsd,$$

$$V = dx\, dy\, dz = |J(r,s,t)|\, dr\, ds\, dt,$$

Tangents to a surface:

$$\boldsymbol{T}_r = \frac{\partial \boldsymbol{R}}{\partial r} = \frac{\partial x}{\partial r}\hat{\imath} + \frac{\partial y}{\partial r}\hat{\jmath} + \frac{\partial z}{\partial r}\hat{k}, \quad \boldsymbol{T}_s = \frac{\partial \boldsymbol{R}}{\partial s} = \frac{\partial x}{\partial s}\hat{\imath} + \frac{\partial y}{\partial s}\hat{\jmath} + \frac{\partial z}{\partial s}\hat{k},$$

$$\begin{bmatrix} \boldsymbol{T}_r \\ \boldsymbol{T}_s \end{bmatrix} = \begin{bmatrix} \partial \boldsymbol{H}^b/\partial r \\ \partial \boldsymbol{H}^b/\partial s \end{bmatrix} \left[\boldsymbol{x}^b \middle| \boldsymbol{y}^b \middle| \boldsymbol{z}^b\right].$$

Surface area normal: $dS^b \boldsymbol{n}\,(r,s) = \boldsymbol{T}_r\,(r,s) \times \boldsymbol{T}_s\,(r,s) dr\, ds.$

Non-flat surface area: $dS^b = \|\boldsymbol{T}_r\,(r,s) \times \boldsymbol{T}_s\,(r,s)\| dr\, ds.$

$$dS^b = \sqrt{(x,r\,y,s - y,r\,x,s)^2 + (y,r\,z,s - z,r\,y,s)^2 + (z,r\,x,s - x,r\,z,s)^2}\, dr\, ds.$$

Inverse Jacobian matrix: $\boldsymbol{\partial}_{\boldsymbol{\Omega}}(\,) = \boldsymbol{J}(\boxdot)^{-1}\boldsymbol{\partial}_{\boxdot}(\,).$

$$\begin{Bmatrix} \dfrac{\partial u}{\partial x} \\ \dfrac{\partial u}{\partial y} \\ \dfrac{\partial u}{\partial z} \end{Bmatrix} = \begin{bmatrix} \dfrac{\partial x}{\partial r} & \dfrac{\partial y}{\partial r} & \dfrac{\partial z}{\partial r} \\ \dfrac{\partial x}{\partial s} & \dfrac{\partial y}{\partial s} & \dfrac{\partial z}{\partial s} \\ \dfrac{\partial x}{\partial t} & \dfrac{\partial y}{\partial t} & \dfrac{\partial z}{\partial t} \end{bmatrix}^{-1} \begin{Bmatrix} \dfrac{\partial u}{\partial r} \\ \dfrac{\partial u}{\partial s} \\ \dfrac{\partial u}{\partial t} \end{Bmatrix}.$$

$$\boldsymbol{J}^{-1} = \frac{1}{|\boldsymbol{J}|} \begin{bmatrix} \dfrac{\partial y}{\partial s} & -\dfrac{\partial y}{\partial r} \\ -\dfrac{\partial x}{\partial s} & \dfrac{\partial x}{\partial r} \end{bmatrix}, \quad |\boldsymbol{J}| = \left(\frac{\partial x}{\partial r}\frac{\partial y}{\partial s} - \frac{\partial y}{\partial r}\frac{\partial x}{\partial s}\right).$$

Integral transformations:

$$\iint_\Omega f\,(x,y) dx\, dy = \iint_\boxdot f\,[x\,(r,s),\, y\,(r,s)]\, |J(r,s)| dr\, ds.$$

Integration by Parts:

$$\int_a^b u\left(\frac{dv}{dx}dx\right) = uv\Big|_a^b - \int_a^b v\left(\frac{du}{dx}dx\right).$$

Green's theorem:

$$\begin{aligned}\iiint_V A\nabla^2 B\,dV &= \iint_S A\vec{\nabla}B\cdot\vec{n}dS - \iiint_V \vec{\nabla}A\cdot\vec{\nabla}B\,dV\\ &= \iint_S A\frac{\partial B}{\partial n}dS - \iiint_V \vec{\nabla}A\cdot\vec{\nabla}B\,dV.\end{aligned}$$

Dirac Delta Distribution:

$$\delta\left(x-x_0\right) \equiv \begin{cases}\infty & \text{at } x = x_0\\ 0 & \text{at } x \neq x_0\end{cases}.$$

$$\int_{-\infty}^{\infty} f\left(x\right)\delta\left(x-x_0\right)dx \equiv f\left(x_0\right).$$

Volume of revolution:

$$V = 2\pi\int_A R\left(r,s\right)dA = 2\pi\int_\Box \boldsymbol{H}\left(r,s\right)\left|J^e(r,s)\right|d\,\Box\,\boldsymbol{R}^e.$$

2.7 Review

1. What are the primary uses of the geometric Jacobian in a typical element?
2. The geometry mapping from a parametric to physical space is done with the _____.

   (a) Determinant of the Jacobian
   (b) Inverse of the Jacobian matrix
   (c) Jacobian matrix
   (d) Interpolation functions
   (e) Derivatives of interpolation functions
   (f) Parametric derivatives

3. The physical differential volume is related to the parametric differential by the _____.

   (a) Determinant of the Jacobian
   (b) Inverse of the Jacobian matrix
   (c) Jacobian matrix
   (d) Interpolation functions
   (e) Derivatives of interpolation functions
   (f) Parametric derivatives

4. When is the Jacobian matrix square and when does it have a rectangular form?
5. The physical partial derivative of a quantity, du/dx, is obtained from the parametric partial derivative, du/dr, of a quantity (when one-to-one) by: _____.

   (a) Adding the Jacobian determinate
   (b) Pre-multiplied by Jacobian inverse
   (c) Pre-multiplied by the Jacobian matrix
   (d) Adding the interpolation functions
   (e) Post-multiplied by the Jacobian matrix
   (f) Post-multiplied by Jacobian inverse

6. Calculate the area of a four node quadrilateral with (x, y) coordinates of $(-1, -0.75)$, $(1, -0.75)$, $(1, 1.25)$, and $(-1, 0.25)$ meters. In natural coordinates with $-1 <= ab <= 1$, its geometric Jacobian matrix is

$$\boldsymbol{J}^e = \frac{1}{4}\begin{bmatrix} 4 & (1+b) \\ 0 & (3+a) \end{bmatrix} \text{m}.$$

7. Briefly explain how you would find a vector normal to a non-flat surface defined by two parametric coordinates.
8. In Example 2.2-3, verify that

$$\int_0^1 H_2(r)\,dr = \int_0^1 \left(18r - 45r^2 + 27r^3\right) dr = 3/8.$$

Chapter 3

Terminology from Differential Equations

3.1 Introduction

The finite element method is always used to solve differential equations but does so using an equivalent integral formulation. However, it does utilize some of the jargon from classes on differential equations, and most importantly a finite element analysis (FEA) must satisfy the essential (Dirichlet) boundary conditions and must include the weaker non-essential (Neumann) boundary conditions associated with the original differential equations. Later chapters mainly illustrate even-order differential equations and their simpler rule for identifying their boundary conditions. An optional section on adjunct operators is included as a reference for how to establish the types of boundary conditions for odd-order differential equations. The most common second-order (Poisson's) equation is selected to show how to identify its essential and non-essential boundary conditions that must be addressed in the FEA.

3.2 Differential Equation Jargon*

An ordinary differential equation (ODE) has a dependent variable, say u, and an independent variable (here usually the spatial coordinate x, or time t). The dependent variable is to be found for all values of the independent variable within some specified length L.

The boundary conditions are applied at the two bounding endpoints of that region.

Let x be the independent variable and let $u(x)$ be the dependent variable to be determined inside a specific range of x. The differential equation is said to be of *order* n if the n-th derivative of u with respect to (wrt) x is the highest derivative in that equation. An ODE of order n can be written as a set of n first-order differential equations. Some authors utilize that approach when applying the least squares FEA. That change allows the calculus required inter-element continuity to be reduced to simply having the function continuous at the interfaces between elements.

Here, we will consider mainly even-order equations, $n = 2m$, in space and first- or second-order in time. A first-order ODE is said to be *linear if* it can be written in the form

$$\frac{du}{dx} + f\left(x\right)u = p\left(x\right),$$

or $u' + f\left(x\right)u = p(x)$, where $()' \equiv du/dx$, and $f(x)$ and $p(x)$ are any given functions of x. When $p(x) = 0$, the equation is said to be *homogeneous*; otherwise it is called *non-homogeneous.* Likewise, a second-order ODE is said to be *linear* if it can be written as

$$\frac{d^2u}{dx^2} + f\left(x\right)\frac{du}{dx} + g\left(x\right)u = p(x),$$

or $u'' + f(x)\,u' + g(x)\,u = p(x)$. For example, $u'' + 2u + \sin(x) = 0$ is linear while $u''u + u' = x$ is *nonlinear* since it contains a product of terms involving the solution and or its derivatives. The previous equations would be nonlinear if their coefficients depended on the solution, for example, if $f\left(x\right) = f(u\left(x\right))$.

Again, if $p(x) = 0$, such an equation is said to be *homogeneous.* The solution of a homogeneous differential equation is called the *homogeneous solution* or *complementary solution.* When $p(x) \neq 0$, the resulting solution is called the *particular solution*. The *general solution* of a differential equation is the sum of the homogeneous solution and the particular solution. A solution is not unique until the boundary conditions have been applied (or enforced) to evaluate the unknown constants in the solution (see Fig. 3.2-1). This requirement carries forward when we replace the differential (strong) form with an

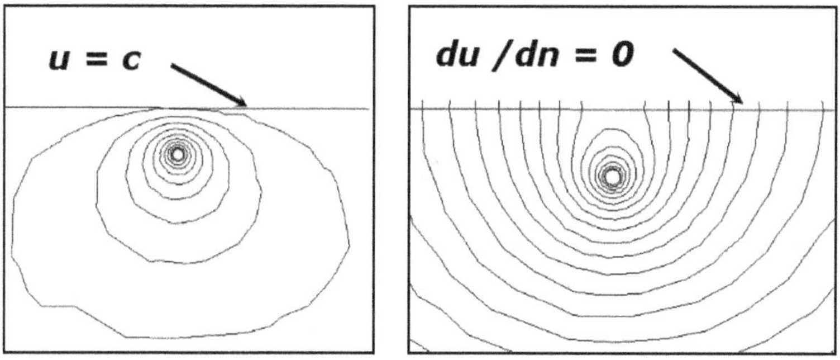

Fig. 3.2-1: An essential (left) and natural boundary condition on the top edge

integral (weak) form. The integral form solution is not unique until it satisfies the essential boundary conditions (EBCs). Likewise, when finite elements are employed to convert an integral form into a matrix form, the matrix system is non-unique (singular) until the matrix system is modified to enforce the EBC. Then the matrix solution can be solved and will yield the unique solution.

It can be proved that a finite element approximation of a differential equation can be only exact at the nodes of the mesh if the piecewise spatial approximation (the element interpolation function) contains at least the homogeneous solution. The solution at other points within the element usually will not be exact but can be exact in some cases. If the element interpolation functions include at least the general solution, then the results are exact everywhere in the element.

3.3 Boundary Conditions

Boundary conditions are extremely important since they must be enforced to describe and obtain a unique solution. There are two classes of boundary conditions; the essential (or *Dirichlet*) conditions and the *secondary boundary* conditions. The EBCs assign known values to the solution, $\boldsymbol{u(x, y, z)}$, at specified regions on the boundary of the geometric shape, inside which the differential defines the solution. The secondary boundary conditions (non-essential boundary condition, NBC) have two versions. The first is the *Neumann condition* which assigns known valves to the derivative of the solution normal (perpendicular) to the boundary, like:

$$a_n \frac{\partial u}{\partial n} = b, \tag{3.3-1}$$

where b is the known boundary condition value, $\vec{n}$ is the direction normal to the boundary, and a_n frequently denotes a known material constitutive term (property) component evaluated in that direction. In the common case where $b = 0$, this becomes a "natural boundary condition" (NatBC) because it is the default on all surfaces in an FEA. It requires no action at all since the integral of zero is zero.

In one-dimensional problems, keep in mind that at $x_{\max}$ the normal derivative of the solution is $\partial u/\partial n = du/dx$, but at $x_{\min}$ it changes sign to $\partial u/\partial n = -du/dx$ because the normal to that end is in the negative x-direction. The Neumann condition becomes a *NatBC* when $b = 0$ because it is the default (finite element) boundary condition on all boundary regions that do not have any other type of boundary condition specified.

The other secondary boundary condition type is the mixed boundary condition (or *Robin* or *Cauchy condition*). In addition to the normal derivative, a mixed condition couples the scaled normal derivative to the unknown value of the solution at the boundary:

$$a \frac{\partial u}{\partial n} + cu = b, \tag{3.3-2}$$

where c is a known boundary property (like a surface-fluid convection coefficient).

Many engineering differential equations are of even-order (second, fourth, or sixth). Consider an even-order PDE of order $2m$ in a domain with EBCs and secondary NBCs:

Let the even order be $n = 2m$ for $m \geq 1$, then the EBCs involve specifying the value of u and its $(m - 1)$ derivatives. The zeroth derivative is the function value. For even-order differential equations, the secondary boundary conditions involve specifying the (m_th) to $(2m-1)$ order derivatives as shown in Table 3.3-1. Two common one-dimensional applications to be studied later are given in Table 3.3-2.

In the case of heat conduction, an example of a mixed boundary condition (surface convection) is: $k_n \partial u/\partial n + cu = b$. An ODE of order n must have n boundary conditions applied. In theory, they

Table 3.3-1: Boundary condition classes for even-order partial differential equations.

Differential equation	$\frac{\partial^{2m} u}{\partial x^{2m}} + \cdots + \frac{\partial u}{\partial x} + g(x)\, u + q(x) = 0$
Essential boundary conditions (EBC)	$u, \frac{\partial u}{\partial x}, \ldots, \frac{\partial^{(m-1)} u}{\partial x^{(m-1)}}$
Non-essential boundary conditions (NBC)	$\frac{\partial^{(m)} u}{\partial x^{(m)}}, \frac{\partial^{(m+1)} u}{\partial x^{(m+1)}}, \ldots, \frac{\partial^{(2m-1)} u}{\partial x^{(2m-1)}}$

Note: $\partial^0 u / \partial x^0 \equiv u$.

Table 3.3-2: Example one-dimensional boundary conditions.

One-dimensional application	**ODE**	n	m	**EBC** $[0$ **to** $m-1]$	**NBC** $[m$ **to** $2m-1]$
Axial conduction	$k\, u'' = p$	2	1	u	$k\, u,n = q$
Beam bending	$EI\, u'''' = p$	4	2	u and u,n	$EI\, u,nn = M$ and $EI\, u,nnn = V$

Note: Where $(\,)_{,n} = \partial(\,)/\partial n$.

can be any mixture of EBCs and NBCs. Applying only NBCs defines the solution only to within an arbitrary constant. In that case, using a finite word length computer, the resulting equations are usually singular and it is necessary to specify an arbitrary value of u on the interior of the region. Then, the true solution is the computed one, relative to that given point, plus an arbitrary constant.

3.4 Adjoint Operator*

If a PDE is not of even-order, then the boundary conditions can be established by formulating the *adjoint* of the PDE. For example, let a homogeneous PDE operator be represented as $L(u) = 0$, and form its "inner product" with another function, say v. That is, integrate the product of the PDE and the second function over the region:

$$\langle L(u), v \rangle \equiv \int_\Omega v\, L(u)\, d\Omega.$$

Integrating by parts (sometimes repeatedly) gives an alternate weak form

$$\langle L(u), v\rangle = \langle u, L^*(v)\rangle + \int_{\Gamma} [F\,(v)\ G\,(u) - F\,(u)\ G^*\,(v)] d\Gamma. \tag{3.4-1}$$

Here, F and G are differential operators that appear naturally from the integration(s) by parts processes. The operator $L^*(v)$ is called the adjoint of $L(u)$ and L is called self-adjoint if $L^*(v) = L(u)$, and u and v are interchanged. Then, $G^*(v) = G(u)$ also.

The $F\,(u)$ terms are the essential (Dirichlet) boundary conditions on Γ_1 and the $G\,(u)$ terms are the non-essential (Neumann) boundary conditions on Γ_2. Self-adjoint operators always lead to a symmetric algebraic system of equations in FEA.

For an even-order PDE, the highest derivative of u occurring in the variational or Galerkin integral form will also be of order m. If the highest derivative of u in any integral, over some region, is of order m, then that integral can alternately be evaluated as the sum of integrals over the same region if, and only if, u and its $(m-1)$ normal derivatives are continuous across the interface of the adjacent sub-regions.

In the integral form, the NBCs are carried into the integrals and the conversion to a matrix system places them in the column matrix with known values. If mixed NBCs are present, then they also contribute known values to the square matrix of the algebraic system.

3.5 Model Second-Order Elliptic PDE

A common two-dimensional PDE often takes the form of a two-dimensional boundary value problem (BVP) in the region $\boldsymbol{\Omega}$ as

$$\frac{\partial}{\partial x}\left(k_{xx}\frac{\partial u}{\partial x}\right) + 2\frac{\partial}{\partial x}\left(k_{xy}\frac{\partial u}{\partial y}\right) + \frac{\partial}{\partial y}\left(k_{yy}\frac{\partial u}{\partial y}\right) + g\,(x, y)\,u + q\,(x, y) = 0. \tag{3.5-1}$$

Here, the coefficients k_{xx}, etc. usually represent directionally dependent material properties of the domain in which the equation is to be solved. The (EBC) of zeroth-order, on boundary region, Γ_1, of the solution region, Ω, is $u = u_{\text{known}}$. On the interior of the region, the quantity

$$k_{xx}\frac{\partial u}{\partial x} = \mp q_x$$

represents the x-component of a vector quantity, q_x, that corresponds to the flux of some quantity per unit area in the x-direction. The y-component is defined in a similar fashion. In heat transfer, Fourier's Law requires the negative sign since the heat, per unit area, flows from higher temperatures to lower temperatures. In ideal fluid flow, using a velocity potential, the plus sign is needed to define the mass flow rate components (or the velocity vector components since the mass density is taken as constant).

On the two-dimensional boundary, having a unit normal vector of $\vec{n} = n_x\vec{i} + n_y\vec{j}$, the dot product of that normal vector with the above flux vector, $\vec{q}$, gives the scalar flow rate per unit area, say q_s, entering or exiting the domain as follows:

$$\left(k_{xx}\frac{\partial u}{\partial x}\right)n_x + \left(k_{yy}\frac{\partial u}{\partial y}\right)n_y = k_n\frac{\partial u}{\partial n} = \mp q_s.$$

This is often given as a NatBC, on Γ_2, of $(k_n \partial u/\partial n) = 0$.

A secondary boundary condition, on boundary region Γ_3, involves coupling the unknown boundary solution with its normal derivative: $(k_n \partial u/\partial n) + cu = b_{\text{known}}$. This type of mixed boundary condition is often called a Cauchy or Robin condition.

The union ($\cup$) of all the boundary regions forms the total boundary of the solution domain $\Gamma = \bigcup_k \Gamma_k$. An example image of a solution with an internal point source with an essential or a NatBC on one boundary was sketched in Fig. 3.2-1.

3.6 Point Singularities*

It is a property of all elliptic PDEs that the boundary of the solution domain often has points where the solution is singular. Such points occur where there is a discontinuity in assigned EBC values, where an EBC jumps to an adjacent NBC, and where the solution domain contains a sharp re-entrant corner. As such points are approached, the solution has an infinite derivative in the radial direction outward

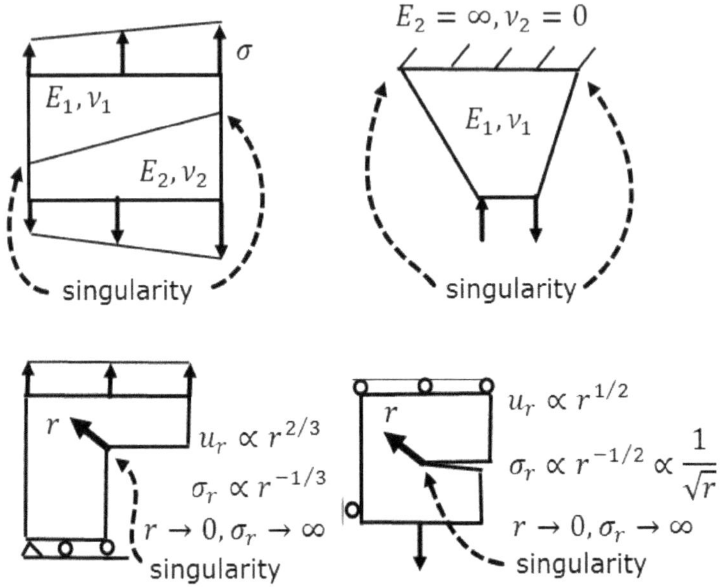

Fig. 3.6-1: Typical singularity point locations.

from the point and tends to change rapidly in the transverse direction. Each type of singularity point (or curve in three-dimensional) has its own "strength measure", with the strongest being at the tip if there is a crack in some solid (Fig. 3.6-1).

3.7 Eigenproblems

Another type of problem is the special case where the PDE convection coefficient, $g(x, y) \equiv \lambda$, in (3.4-1) is an unknown global constant to be determined. This is called an eigenproblem (from the German word *eigen* meaning belonging distinctly to a group). A common PDE containing eigenvalues is

$$\nabla^2 V + \lambda V = 0,$$

which is solved for multiple eigenvalues, λ_n, and a corresponding set of solution eigenvectors, $\boldsymbol{V}_n$. Eigenproblems are addressed in detail in Chapter 14.

3.8 Summary

Boundary condition classes for even-order partial differential equations:

Differential equation	$\frac{\partial^{2m} u}{\partial x^{2m}} + \cdots + \frac{\partial u}{\partial x} + g(x)\, u + q(x) = 0$
Essential (Dirichlet) boundary conditions	$u, \frac{\partial u}{\partial x}, \ldots, \frac{\partial^{(m-1)} u}{\partial x^{(m-1)}}$
Non-essential (Neumann) boundary conditions	$\frac{\partial^{(m)} u}{\partial x^{(m)}}, \frac{\partial^{(m+1)} u}{\partial x^{(m+1)}}, \ldots, \frac{\partial^{(2m-1)} u}{\partial x^{(2m-1)}}$

Note: $\partial^0 u/\partial x^0 \equiv u$

Boundary conditions for PDE $L(u) = 0$ via the adjoint:

$$\int_\Omega L(u(x,y))\, v(x,y)\, d\Omega \equiv \langle L(u), v\rangle = \langle u, L*(v)\rangle$$

$$+ \int_\Gamma [F(v)\, G(u) - F(u)\, G^*(v)] d\Gamma.$$

Essential boundary condition: $F(u)$ on Γ_1.

Non-essential boundary condition: $G(u)$ on Γ_2.

Common one-dimensional boundary conditions:

One-dimensional application	**ODE**	n	m	**EBC [0 to $m-1$]**	**NBC [m to $2m-1$]**
Axial conduction	$k\, u'' = p$	2	1	u	$k\, u, n = q$
Beam bending	$EI\, u'''' = p$	4	2	u and u, n	$EI\, u, nn = M$ and $EI\, u, nnn = V$

Anisotropic material data transformations:

$$\boldsymbol{k}^e(\theta^e)_{\text{Global}} = \boldsymbol{T}(\theta^e)^T\, \boldsymbol{k}^e{}_{\text{Local}}\, \boldsymbol{T}(\theta^e).$$

Typical elliptical two-dimensional PDE:

$$\frac{\partial}{\partial x}\left(k_{xx}\frac{\partial u}{\partial x}\right)+2\frac{\partial}{\partial x}\left(k_{xy}\frac{\partial u}{\partial y}\right)+\frac{\partial}{\partial y}\left(k_{yy}\frac{\partial u}{\partial y}\right)+g\left(x,y\right)u+q\left(x,y\right)=0.$$

Mixed boundary condition: (b and/or c can be zero): $\left(k_n\frac{\partial u}{\partial n}\right)+cu=b$.

3.9 Review

1. A radial model of a gas centrifuge involves a sixth-order elliptical ODE:
   (a) After integration by parts three times, what order of spatial derivative appears in the integral?
   (b) What terms are defined as the essential boundary conditions?
   (c) What terms are defined as the non-essential boundary conditions?
2. What are the essential (Dirichlet) and non-essential (Neumann) boundary conditions for a second-order ordinary differential equation?
3. What analysis method identifies the Neumann boundary conditions if the ODE is not of even-order?

Chapter 4

Parametric Interpolation

4.1 Types of Interpolation

In finite element analysis (FEA), the ability to handle curved shapes rather than straight-sided triangles and rectangles, and their three-dimensional equivalents, requires the use of non-dimensional parametric interpolation to transform or map the element geometry from a straight-sided parametric space to its curved physical shape. The use of parametric coordinates automatically allows the elements to have unique curved edges and curved non-flat faces on solid elements. Using parametric coordinates also allows for the required integration over curvilinear shapes to be automated by numerical integration, as shown in the next chapter.

Here, the engineering approach is used where the interpolation functions are defined on, and inside of, an element volume. They were originally developed by structural engineers and were called "shape functions" because they interpolated the displacements of a part and could be plotted to show its deformed shape. The shape functions define the contribution of each node attached to an element (see Fig. 1.2-1), but only the contribution that falls inside or on the element.

This approach at first appears to be different from the applied mathematics approach that uses node-based "hat functions" that define the contribution of the node to a part, or all, of each element to which it is attached (see Fig. 4.2-5). The "hat function" approach makes it easier to prove certain mathematically important items such as the equivalence of a differential equation (strong form) with its integral (weak) form, etc. Both approaches yield exactly the same governing matrix systems to be solved (after imposing boundary conditions).

Three types of polynomial scalar interpolations will be used in most of the applications given later. The most common ones (Lagrange interpolation and Serendipity interpolation) use only the value of a function at every node on the element. In one dimension, adding another node simply raises the polynomial degree by one. Such elements are usually employed to solve second-order partial differential equations (PDEs). A third approach, Hermite interpolation, uses the value of a function and its spatial derivative(s) at every node on the element. In one dimension, when using the function and just its slope, adding another node raises the polynomial degree by two. Such elements are usually employed to solve fourth-order PDEs. When simulating plates or shells, the nodal degrees of freedom can be extended to include the curvature (second or higher derivatives) at the nodes.

These types of interpolations are classified mathematically by the level of continuity between adjacent regions of interpolation. A function is said to be C^n continuous when the function ($n = 0$) through its nth derivative is continuous. All of the interpolation functions used here are C^∞ on the element interior, but have very low continuity at their boundary with another element. The Lagrange interpolation and Serendipity interpolation functions only have their values (zeroth derivative) shared at the boundary of an adjacent element. Therefore, they are referred to as C^0 elements. The Hermite family has the function and at least the first derivative(s) shared at the boundary with an adjacent element. Therefore, they are at least C^1 elements, but can be C^2 or higher in their continuity. In one dimension it is easy to create C^n elements, but it is very difficult to create them in two and three dimensions (while retaining local support). Hermite C^1 interpolation is typically used on fourth-order PDEs (like beams and plates) and Hermite C^2 interpolation is typically used on sixth-order PDEs (like ideal centrifuge flows).

It is not necessary to require the same number of unknowns at each node, but that common approach will be followed in this book. All of the interpolation functions to be used here have been known for at least 50 years and can be found in handbooks on FEA or handbooks on mathematical analysis. However, experience shows that students do not find them obvious. Therefore, several of them are derived herein and Matlab symbolic scripts are given to illustrate how they can be derived in general.

4.2 Lagrange One-Dimensional Interpolation

Applying Lagrange interpolation requires estimating the values of a function $u(r)$ based on locations r_k for $k = 1, \dots, n$ at which the values u_k are known. In this book, only equally spaced intervals, Δr, will be employed in the parametric space. The expressions for the finite element interpolations are well known and will generally be given without proof. For completeness, the one-dimensional ($n_p = 1$) quadratic C^0 interpolation function, in unit coordinates, will be derived here. Consider a three-noded quadratic line element ($n_n = 3$). A complete quadratic polynomial in one dimension has three constants. In the unit coordinate space ranging from zero to one, the three equally spaced parametric locations are $r_1 = 0$, $r_2 = 1/2$, and $r_3 = 1$, and the non-dimensional measure of the parametric range is $\lambda = (r_3 - r_1) = 1$. Let the polynomial data fit be

$$u(r) = c_1 + c_2 r + c_3 r^2$$

$$= \begin{bmatrix} 1 & r & r^2 \end{bmatrix} \begin{Bmatrix} c_1 \\ c_2 \\ c_3 \end{Bmatrix} \equiv [P(r)]\,\{c\} = \boldsymbol{P}(r)\boldsymbol{c} = \boldsymbol{c}^T \boldsymbol{P}^T(r),$$

where the row matrix $\boldsymbol{P}(r)$ is the assumed polynomial and $\mathbf{c}$ denotes a column matrix of mathematical constants. A quadratic interpolation using three data values is shown in Fig. 4.2-1 (where the interior node x_2 does not have to be L/2, but it usually is).

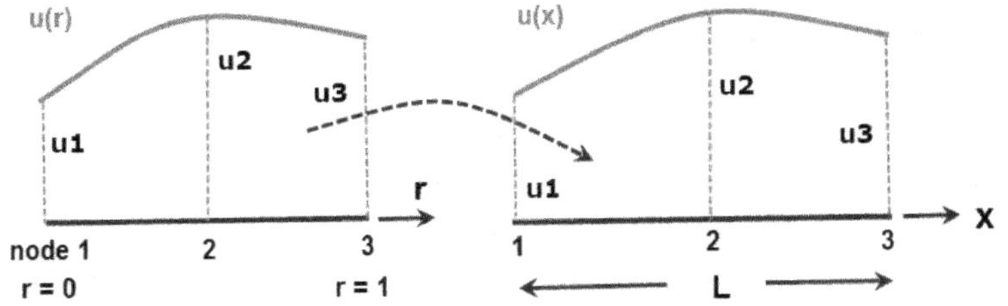

Fig. 4.2-1: A quadratic line interpolation between three values.

The solution could be completed using these mathematical constants, but engineers prefer to relate the solution to the actual solution physical values. To relate the three constants to physical values, note that there is an identity at each local parametric node:

$$u\left(r_k\right) \equiv u_k = c_1 + c_2 r_k + c_3 r_k^2 = \begin{bmatrix} 1 & r_k & r_k^2 \end{bmatrix} \begin{Bmatrix} c_1 \\ c_2 \\ c_3 \end{Bmatrix}, \quad 1 \leq k \leq 3.$$

Evaluate this identity at the three uniformly spaced parametric locations ($r_1 = 0$, $r_2 = 0.5$, $r_3 = 1$), where the three function values (u_1, u_2, u_3) occur, one at each node. These three identities can be written together to yield a matrix identity:

$$\begin{Bmatrix} u(r_1) \\ u(r_2) \\ u(r_3) \end{Bmatrix} \equiv \begin{Bmatrix} u_1 \\ u_2 \\ u_3 \end{Bmatrix} = \begin{bmatrix} 1 & 0 & 0^2 \\ 1 & 0.5 & 0.5^2 \\ 1 & 1 & 1^2 \end{bmatrix} \begin{Bmatrix} c_1 \\ c_2 \\ c_3 \end{Bmatrix}, \quad \text{or} \quad \boldsymbol{u}^e = \boldsymbol{G}\boldsymbol{c},$$

where $\boldsymbol{u}^e$ denotes a column matrix containing the physical value of the solution at the nodes. Each row of the square matrix, $\boldsymbol{G}$, is just the polynomial row matrix evaluated at the local node coordinates:

$$\boldsymbol{G} \equiv \begin{bmatrix} \boldsymbol{P}\left(r_1\right) \\ \boldsymbol{P}\left(r_2\right) \\ \boldsymbol{P}\left(r_3\right) \end{bmatrix} = \begin{bmatrix} 1 & r_1 & r_1^2 \\ 1 & r_2 & r_2^2 \\ 1 & r_3 & r_3^2 \end{bmatrix}.$$

Here, $\boldsymbol{G}$ is non-singular and its inverse is computable, and it lets the initial constants, $\boldsymbol{c}$ be replaced by the spaced physical values, $\boldsymbol{u}^e$:

$$\boldsymbol{c} = \boldsymbol{G}^{-1}\boldsymbol{u}^e = \begin{bmatrix} 1 & 0 & 0 \\ -3 & 4 & -1 \\ 2 & -4 & 2 \end{bmatrix} \boldsymbol{u}^e.$$

Eliminating the non-physical constants in favor of the interpolation data yields the interpolation equations, $\boldsymbol{H}(r)$ in FEA: $u(r) = \boldsymbol{P}(r)\,\boldsymbol{G}^{-1}\boldsymbol{u}^e \equiv \boldsymbol{H}(r)\boldsymbol{u}^e$. These functions are also known as the *shape functions* because in the structural analysis they actually describe the shape of the deformed member. Note that the interpolation (shape) functions are formed from an assumed polynomial, geometrical data about the local non-dimensional placement of the nodes, and the physical values at those nodes:

$$u(r) = \begin{bmatrix}1 & r & r^2\end{bmatrix}\begin{bmatrix}1 & 0 & 0\\ -3 & 4 & -1\\ 2 & -4 & 2\end{bmatrix}\begin{Bmatrix}u_1\\ u_2\\ u_3\end{Bmatrix}$$

$$u(r) = \left[(1-3r+2r^2) \quad (4r-4r^2) \quad (-r+2r^2)\right]\begin{Bmatrix}u_1\\ u_2\\ u_3\end{Bmatrix}$$

$$u(r) = [H_1(r) \quad H_2(r) \quad H_3(r)]\begin{Bmatrix}u_1\\ u_2\\ u_3\end{Bmatrix}. \tag{4.2.1}$$

Since $u(r)$ is a scalar quantity, it is the same as its transpose: $u(r) = u(r)^T = \boldsymbol{u}^{e^T}\boldsymbol{H}(r)^T$.

Also, since the interpolation functions, $\boldsymbol{H}(r)$, are dimensionless, the approximation $u(r)$ takes on the units of the item being interpolated, $\boldsymbol{u}^e$. Having made this selection for the parametric spatial form, the parametric local derivative is also known:

$$\frac{\partial u}{\partial r}(r) = \frac{\partial \boldsymbol{H}(r)}{\partial r}\boldsymbol{u}^e = \left[\frac{\partial H_1}{}\partial r(r) \quad \frac{\partial H_2}{\partial r}(r) \quad \frac{\partial H_3}{\partial r}(r)\right]\begin{Bmatrix}u_1\\ u_2\\ u_3\end{Bmatrix}$$

$$\frac{\partial u}{\partial r}(r) = [(-3+4r) \quad (4-8r)\,(-1+4r)]\begin{Bmatrix}u_1\\ u_2\\ u_3\end{Bmatrix}, \tag{4.2.2}$$

since the derivative of any matrix contains the derivative of each of its terms. The above quadratic interpolation functions and their parametric local derivatives can easily be obtained using symbolic calculations. The symbolic Matlab script equivalent to the above derivation is given in Fig. 4.2-2, while its output is given in Fig. 4.2-3. (*Note*: the latest releases of Matlab have discontinued the use of the keyword "positive" and just use "real".)

```
% Symbolic derivation of a 3-node line element, 0<=r<=1
syms r r_n real                  % symbolic variables
syms c_e c1 c2 c3 real           % symbolic math constants
syms u_e u1 u2 u3 real           % symbolic node values
r_n = [0, 1/2, 1]                % equally spaced node locations
c_e = [c1, c2, c3]'              % set constant vector
u_e = [u1, u2, u3]'              % set physical vector
Poly (r) = [1, r, r^2]           % quadratic polynomial
u(r) = Poly(r) * c_e             % u at any 0 <= r <= 1
% Identity u(r_n) = Poly (r_n) * c_n
for k = 1:3
  G (k, :) = Poly (r_n(k)) ;     % k-th row of U_e to C_e identity
end % for k
display (G)                      % local geometry matrix
% iff the inverse exists, this is a valid polynomial
% and node location combination
G_inv = inv (G)                  % attempt inversion
c_e = G_inv * u_e                % replace math constants
H (r) = Poly (r) * G_inv         % element interpolation functions
DH_Dr (r) = diff (H, r)          % local derivative of H
% u(r) = Poly (r) * G_inv * u_e
u(r) = H (r) * u_e               % physical solution interpolation
Du_Dr (r) = DH_Dr * u_e          % local derivative of u(r)
```

Fig. 4.2-2: Matlab symbolic derivations of the quadratic line interpolations.

```
%      Symbolic derivation of a 3-node line element
Poly (r) = [1, r, r^2]           % unit coordinate quadratic
u(r) = c3*r^2 + c2*r + c1        % math constant interpolation
r_n = 0     0.5000    1.0000     % local node coordinates
G     = [ 1,    0,    0]         % identity 1 for u_e & c_e
        [ 1,  1/2,  1/4]         % identity 3 for u_e & c_e
        [ 1,    1,    1]         % identity 3 for u_e & c_e
G_inv = [ 1,    0,    0]         % inverse of geometry data
        [-3,    4,   -1]
        [ 2,   -4,    2]
u_e = [u1, u2, u3]'              % local solution values
c_e = [u1                ]       % get rid of math constants
      [4*u2 - 3*u1 - u3  ]       % get rid of math constants
      [2*u1 - 4*u2 + 2*u3]'      % get rid of math constants

%              Interpolation functions
H(r) = [2*r^2 - 3*r + 1, - 4*r^2 + 4*r, 2*r^2 - r]
%  Parametric derivative of interpolations
DH_Dr(r) = [(4*r - 3), (4 - 8*r), (4*r - 1)]

%   Interpolated solution from its three node values
u(r) = u1*(2*r^2-3*r+1) + u2*(-4*r^2+4*r) - u3*(-2*r^2+r)
%   Solution parametric derivatives from 3 node values
Du_Dr(r) = u1*(4*r - 3) + u3*(4*r - 1) - u2*(8*r - 4)
```

Fig. 4.2-3: Output for line quadratic interpolation (L3_C0).

This quadratic interpolation also includes the subset for a linear interpolation or a constant value. For a result that is linear, $u_2 = (u_1 + u_3)/2$ and the above quadratic simplifies to a linear interpolation, which depends only on the two end values, namely

$$\begin{aligned} u(r) &= (1 - 3r + 2r^2)u_1 + ((4r - 4r^2)u_1/2 + (4r - 4r^2)u_3/2) \\ &\quad + (-r + 2r^2)u_3, \\ u(r) &= (1 - 3r + 2r^2 + 2r - 2r^2)u_1 + (2r - 2r^2 - r + 2r^2)u_3, \\ u(r) &= (1 - r)\, u_1 + r u_3 = [(1 - r) \quad r] \begin{Bmatrix} u_1 \\ u_3 \end{Bmatrix}. \end{aligned}$$

However, if we wanted just a linear approximation, it is more common just to use a two-node element, as in Fig. 4.2-4, and denote its interpolation as

$$u(r) = [(1 - r) \quad r] \begin{Bmatrix} u_1 \\ u_2 \end{Bmatrix} = [H_1(r) \quad H_2(r)] \begin{Bmatrix} u_1 \\ u_2 \end{Bmatrix}. \tag{4.2.3}$$

Likewise, if all the values are the same constant, then the quadratic interpolation must simplify to that constant. For that to be true, all the interpolation functions must sum to unity for any and all values of r:

$$\sum_k H_k(r) \equiv 1. \tag{4.2.4}$$

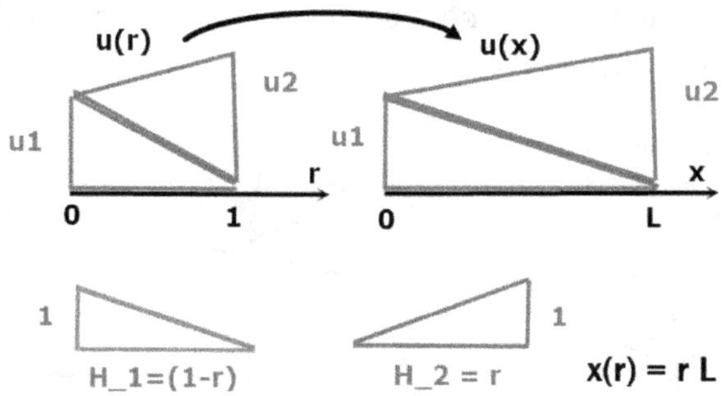

Fig. 4.2-4: Linear line element interpolation (shape) functions (L2_C0).

To illustrate that (convergence) requirement, use the constant data $v = u_1 = u_2 = u_3$. Then the quadratic interpolation degenerates to

$$u(r) = \left(1 - 3r + 2r^2\right)v + \left(4r - 4r^2\right)v + \left(-r + 2r^2\right)v,$$

or simply $u(r) = v$, as expected. These two simplifications of a quadratic interpolation are also confirmed by the Matlab symbolic calculations in Fig. 4.2-5. Since Lagrangian interpolations, H_k, sum to unity at any local point, their values can be thought of as the percent of u_1, u_2, and u_3 that contribute to the total interpolated value of $u(r)$.

Since this interpolation approach exactly matches the data, u_k, at the control points, r_k, this is a Lagrangian interpolation. In this book, linear through cubic C^0 Lagrangian polynomials will be applied to first- and second-order PDEs. Cubic through quintic C^1 Hermite polynomials will be utilized in fourth-order PDEs. In general, a Lagrange interpolation function evaluated at its control point will have a value of unity and it will be zero at any other control point:

$$H_k\left(r_j, s_j, t_j\right) = \begin{cases} 1 & \text{if } j = k \\ 0 & \text{if } j \neq k \end{cases} \equiv \delta_{jk}\,. \tag{4.2.5}$$

Changing the subject, beginners are often confused by the use of a "hat" functions approach to FEA presented in a prior applied mathematics course and how the node "hat" functions differ from the element "shape" functions mentioned earlier. That math view is slightly different from the engineering view, but they represent exactly the same approximation. The math viewpoint makes it easier to prove that the finite element solution is a solution to the differential equation being modeled.

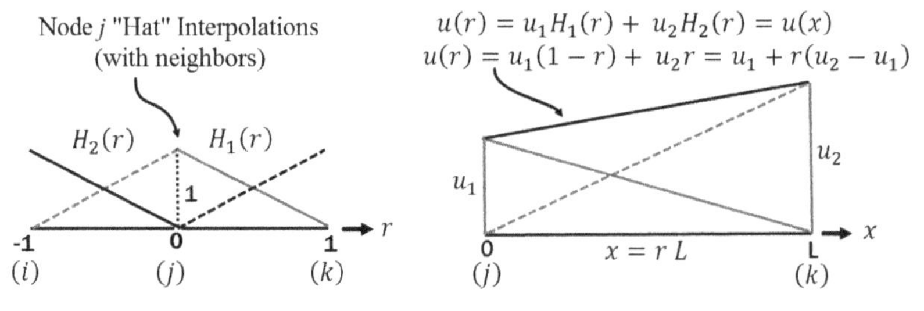

Fig. 4.2-5: The "hat" functions are equivalent to engineering "shape" functions.

A "hat" function multiplied by the node solution value defines the solution in the volume around the node. The "shape" functions, or interpolation functions, use the portions of the "hat" functions of all of the element nodes, but only the portion that falls in and on the element volume. Figure 4.2-5 illustrates this equivalent for linear "hat" functions combined to define the linear "shape" functions over a line element with two nodes.

The process considered so far only gives the interpolation and parametric derivative of the interpolated quantity. Differential equations utilize the physical (x) derivatives of $u(r)$, and once $u(r)$ is known, it is usually necessary to find its gradient, $\partial u/\partial x = \partial u/\partial r\, \partial r/\partial x$. In order to do that, the physical coordinate, x, must be defined in terms of the local parametric coordinate. Then the nodal u_k values are simply replaced by nodal x_k values.

The above quadratic interpolation was described as interpolating a solution value, but it could be applied to interpolating anything that is associated with the three nodes on the element. For a straight line element, only the two end point coordinates are needed for the geometry. A linear geometry interpolation is obtained by having (4.2.3) interpolate the end physical coordinate values instead of solution values:

$$x(r) = [(1-r) \quad r] \begin{Bmatrix} x_1 \\ x_3 \end{Bmatrix} = x_1 + r\,(x_3 - x_1) = x_1 + r\,L, \qquad (4.2.6)$$

where L is the physical length (or measure) of the element. This form automatically occurs (as seen in Fig. 4.2-6) when the interior node is placed exactly at the mid-point of the physical length. That is almost always the preferred way to describe the geometry. The unit coordinate version of the one-dimensional linear, quadratic, and cubic C^0 Lagrangian interpolation functions are given in Matlab script *Lagrangian_1D_library.m* shown in Fig. 4.2-7.

Mathematical terminology defines that a function is C^n continuous when the function and its first n derivatives are continuous. Therefore, the prior Lagrangian elements are called C^0 on their boundaries, but are C^∞ on the interior of the element. Several C^0 interpolation functions for one-, two-, and three-dimensional elements are given in the Matlab script *el_shape_n_local_deriv.m* which is also included in the general library of finite element scripts. A subset of the one-dimensional interpolations is included in *Lagrangian_1D_library.m*, such a function accepts a numerical value

```
% A quadratic line element reduces to a linear solution
syms r positive real              % symbolic variables
syms u_e u1 u2 u3  real           % symbolic nodal values

% Interpolation functions, from previous derivation
H(r) = [2*r^2 - 3*r + 1, -4*r^2 + 4*r, 2*r^2 - r]
u_e = [u1 (u1+u3)/2 u3]'          % linear data
u_(r) = H (r) * u_e               % interpolation for u(r)
u (r) = simplify (u(r))           % interpolation for u(r)

u_e = [u1, u1, u1]'               % constant data
u_(r) = H (r) * u_e               % interpolation for u(r)
u (r) = simplify (u(r))           % interpolation for u(r)

total = sum (H(r))                % interpolation sum

%  Following H, the outputs are
%  u_e =          u1
%       u1/2 + u3/2
%                 u3
%  u(r) = u1*(2*r^2 - 3*r + 1) + (u1/2 + u3/2)*(- 4*r^2 + 4*r)
%       - u3*(- 2*r^2 + r)
%
%  u(r) = u1 - r*u1 + r*u3
%
%  u_e = u1
%        u1
%        u1
%
%  u(r) = u1*(2*r^2 - 3*r + 1) + u1*(- 4*r^2 + 4*r)
%       - u1*(- 2*r^2 + r)
%
%  u(r) = u1
%
%  total = 1
```

Fig. 4.2-6: Constant and linear results are included in quadratic interpolation.

for the parametric coordinate(s) and returns numerical values of the interpolation functions and the (rectangular array) of local derivatives of those interpolation functions. It will be shown later that such scripts are necessary to automate the numerical integration processes almost always needed in a finite element simulation.

In general, for *straight* line elements using equal physical space increments between the nodes causes this linear mapping between parametric and physical spaces. For this common special case, $\partial x/\partial r = L$ and the physical derivative of $u(r)$ in a straight element is

$$\frac{\partial u}{\partial x} = \frac{\partial u}{\partial r}\frac{\partial r}{\partial x} = \frac{\partial u}{\partial r}\frac{1}{L}. \tag{4.2.7}$$

```
function [H, DLH] = Lagrange_1D_library (n_n, r) %===========
% parametric interpolation functions and local derivatives
% at local point r in 1D unit parametric space, 0 <= r <= 1
% H      = element interpolation functions at r
% DLH    = element interpolation local derivatives at r
% n_n    = number of nodes per element
% See qp_rule_unit_Gauss for corresponding tabulated data

switch n_n ; % select from available library of elements
  case {2} ; % two node line element 1----2, L2
    H = [(1 - r),   r] ; DLH = [-1,     1] ;
  case {3} ; % three node line quadratic 1--2--3, L3
    H   = [(1 - 3*r + 2*r^2), (4*r - 4*r^2), (2*r^2 - r)] ;
    DLH = [(-3 + 4 * r),       (4 - 8*r),     (4*r -1)] ;
  case {4} ; % four node line cubic element 1--2--3--4, L4
   H = [(1-r*11/2+9*r^2-9*r^3/2), (9*r-45*r^2/2+27*r^3/2), ...
        (-9*r/2+18*r^2-27*r^3/2), (r-9*r^2/2+9*r^3/2)];
   DLH = [(-11/2+18*r-27*r^2/2),  (9-45*r+81*r^2/2),...
          (-9/2+36*r-81*r^2/2),   (1-9*r+27*r^2/2)];
end ; % switch on number of nodes
% end Lagrange_1D_library % ===================================
```

Fig. 4.2-7: Placing interpolation functions in a script for a library of one-dimensional elements.

Example 4.2-1 Given: A four-noded cubic line element (L4_C0), with equal node x-spacing, has temperature nodal values of $u_1 = 2°\text{C}$, $u_2 = 3°\text{C}$, $u_3 = 2°\text{C}$, and $u_4 = -1°\text{C}$. The physical coordinates are $x_1 = 2\,\text{cm}$, $x_2 = 4\,\text{cm}$, $x_3 = 6\,\text{cm}$, and $x_4 = 8\,\text{cm}$, so the length of the element is $L = 6\,\text{cm}$. Fill in the element degree of freedom vector, u^e, and the element coordinate vector, x^e. At local point $r = 0.7$, find the physical coordinate, x, the interpolated value of $u(r)$, and the physical gradient of the solution, $\partial u/\partial x$.

Solution: The element degrees of freedom are

$$\boldsymbol{u}^{e^T} = [2 \quad 3 \quad 2 \quad -1]\,°\text{C (transposed)}$$

and its coordinates are

$$\boldsymbol{x}^{e^T} = [2 \quad 4 \quad 6 \quad 8]\ \text{cm}.$$

From the script *Lagrange_1D_library.m*, the shape functions are

$$\boldsymbol{H}(\mathrm{r}) = \frac{1}{2}\left[(2 - 11r + 18r^2 - 9r^3) \quad (18r - 45r^2 + 27r^3) \ldots \right.$$
$$\left. (-9r + 36r^2 - 27r^3) \quad (2r - 9r^2 + 9r^3)\right].$$

The equal spacing of the physical nodes causes a linear geometry mapping. That could be seen by doing the actual multiplication, $x(r) = \boldsymbol{H}(r)\boldsymbol{x}^e = (2 + 6r)\,\text{cm} = x_1 + L\,r$. So at $x\,(0.7) = 6.2\,\text{cm}$. In practice, the r coordinate is substituted into $\boldsymbol{H}$ to get its numerical values and then the two arrays are simply multiplied:

$$x(\mathrm{r}=0.7)$$

$$= \boldsymbol{H}(0.7)\boldsymbol{x}^e = [0.0165 \quad -0.0945 \quad 1.0395 \quad 0.0385] \begin{Bmatrix} 2 \\ 4 \\ 6 \\ 8 \end{Bmatrix} \mathrm{cm},$$

$$= 6.200\,\mathrm{cm}.$$

It happens that the $u(r)$ values fall on a parabola, so they are actually quadratic. The cubic interpolation automatically can capture a set of quadratic data, or linear data, or constant. That could be seen by actual multiplication, $u(r) = \boldsymbol{H}(r)\boldsymbol{u}^e = (2 + 6r - 9r^2)°\mathrm{C}$, so at the local point $u(0.7) = 1.79°\mathrm{C}$. Again, in practice, the process is automated by just multiplying the numerical values of $\boldsymbol{H}$ and by the nodal degrees of freedom:

$$u(r=0.7) = \boldsymbol{H}(0.7)\boldsymbol{u}^e$$

$$= [0.0165 \quad -0.0945 \quad 1.0395 \quad 0.0385] \begin{Bmatrix} 2 \\ 3 \\ 2 \\ -1 \end{Bmatrix} °\mathrm{C} = 1.790°\mathrm{C}.$$

Figure 4.2-8 shows the interpolated $u(x)$ curve for these data. The dashed line at the top represents the range of the unit coordinates. The arrows show the interpolated values at the given r value.

To compute the physical gradient, it is necessary to compute the Jacobian and its inverse. Looking up the local derivatives from the same sources for the cubic gives

$$\partial \boldsymbol{H}(r)/\partial \mathrm{r} = \left[(-11 + 36r - 27r^2) \quad (18 - 90r + 81r^2) \cdots \right.$$
$$\left. (-9 + 72r - 81r^2) \quad (2 - 18r + 27r^2)\right]/2.$$

The Jacobian is $J(r) = \partial x/\partial r = \partial \boldsymbol{H}(r)/\partial r\ \boldsymbol{x}^e$. If the actual multiplication is done to get the Jacobian as a function of r, the result (in this case) is $J(r) = 6\,\mathrm{cm}/1$. That is, the Jacobian (matrix) is

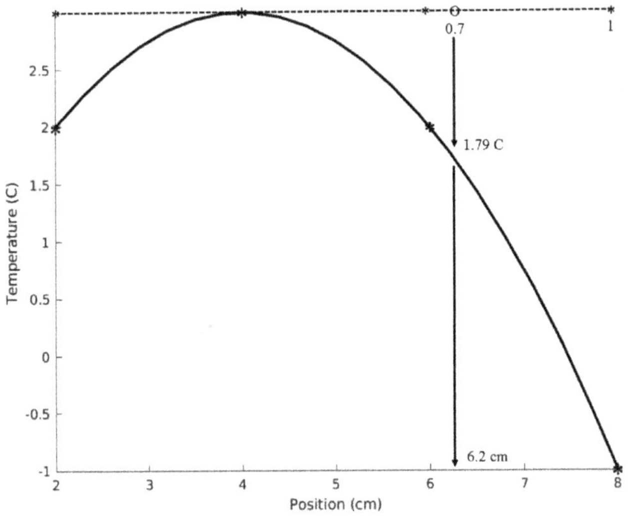

Fig. 4.2-8: Cubic interpolation.

constant. In practice, this process is automated by substituting the numerical value of r into the expression

$$J^{\mathrm{e}}(0.7) = \frac{\partial x}{\partial r} = \frac{\partial \boldsymbol{H}(0.7)}{\partial r}\boldsymbol{x}^{e}$$

$$= [0.485 \quad -2.655 \quad 0.855 \quad 1.315] \begin{Bmatrix} 2 \\ 4 \\ 6 \\ 8 \end{Bmatrix} \mathrm{cm} = 6.000\ \mathrm{cm}/1$$

The determinant and inverse are $J^{\mathrm{e}}(0.7) = |J^{\mathrm{e}}(0.7)|$, and $J^{\mathrm{e}}(0.7)^{-1} = \partial r/\partial x = 1/6\,\mathrm{cm}$. The superscript "e" was added as a reminder that element geometry was used. The local derivative is

$$\frac{\partial u(0.7)}{\partial r} = \partial \boldsymbol{H}(0.7)/\partial r\, \boldsymbol{u}^{e}$$

$$= [0.485 \quad -2.655 \quad 0.855 \quad 1.315] \begin{Bmatrix} 2 \\ 3 \\ 2 \\ -1 \end{Bmatrix} {}^{\circ}\mathrm{C} = -6.600^{\circ}\mathrm{C}/1.$$

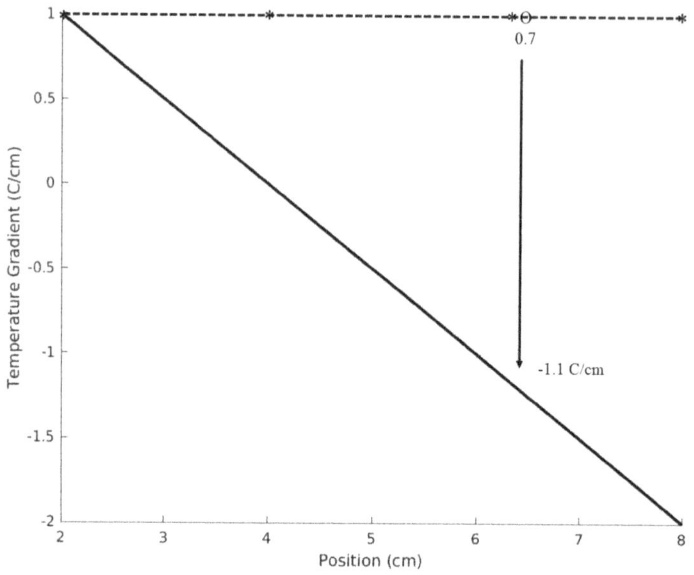

Fig. 4.2-9: Interpolated gradient.

The physical gradient is

$$\begin{aligned}\partial u(r = 0.7)/\partial x &= \partial u(r = 0.7)/\partial r \times \partial r(0.7)/\partial x\\ &= (-6.600°\mathrm{C})\left(\frac{1}{6\,\mathrm{cm}}\right) = -1.100°\mathrm{C/cm}.\end{aligned}$$

Figure 4.2-9 shows the interpolated gradient curve for these data. The dashed line at the top represents the range of the unit coordinates. The arrows show the interpolated values at the given r value. The next example shows how to build such a graph for only one element.

Example 4.2-2 Given: Change the data given in Example 4.2-1 to $u_3 = 0$, and plot the temperature and the temperature gradient.

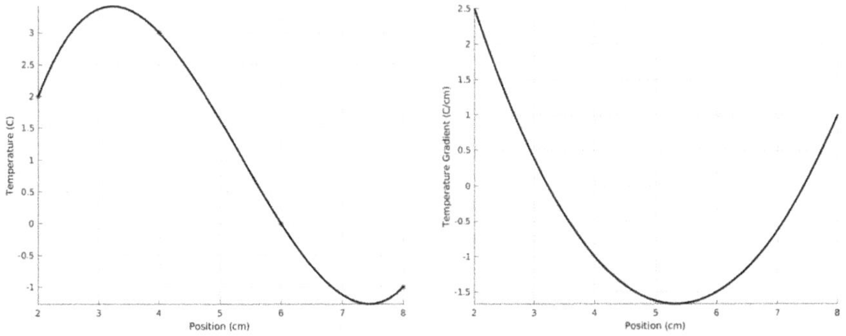

Fig. 4.2-10: Graph of cubic element values (left) and its gradient (right).

Solution: The change in the EBC value means that the full cubic nature is active (since the data no longer fits on a parabola). To create the graph, it is just necessary to loop over the number of points in the parametric domain needed to make the physical domain graph look smooth. At each point in the local coordinate the above example calculations are repeated. The results are shown in Fig. 4.2-10. A script for creating the graph is given in Fig. 4.2-11. If the lines for calculating arrays **H** and **DLH** were replaced with a call to the library of one-dimensional elements, this process would work for any one-dimensional Lagrangian element considered here. Such a script is in the FEA analysis library as script *Lib_1D_graph.m.* (Think about how you could extend this process to plot all elements in the mesh.) Note that if the given requirement was to plot the magnitude of the heat flux vector, then the process would be essentially the same. The material thermal conductivity, K, would have also been input. After the gradient values were computed and stored in its array, Fourier's Law would have been applied: $\vec{q} = -K\vec{\nabla}u$. In other words, the second plot would have its sign changed and height scaled by K.

```
%    Graph the temperature and temperature gradient
%                 in a cubic line element
u_e = [2; 3; 2; -1]   ;                 % 4x1 vector degrees C
x_e = [2; 4; 6; 8]    ;         % 4x1 vector cm (equal spaces)
n_n = size (x_e, 1)   ;           % number of nodes on element
n_gaps = 20           ;         % number of spaces along curve
R = [0:(1/n_gaps):1]  ;                   % graph points in r
for k = 1:(n_gaps+1)  ;                 % loop over all points
  r = R(k)              ;                     % specific point
  % Evaluate local interpolation definition, 0 <= r <= 1
  H=[(1-r*11/2+9*r^2-9*r^3/2), (9*r-45*r^2/2+27*r^3/2), ...
     (-9*r/2+18*r^2-27*r^3/2), (r-9*r^2/2+9*r^3/2)];
  DLH=[(-11/2+18*r-27*r^2/2), (9-45*r+81*r^2/2), ...
       (-9/2+36*r-81*r^2/2),( 1-9*r+27*r^2/2)];
  u(k)  = H * u_e       ;           % interpolate the solution
  x(k)  = H * x_e       ;           % interpolate the position
  J_k   = DLH * x_e     ;               % Jacobian at the point
  J_i   = 1 / J_k       ;       % inverse Jaconian at the point
  dudr  = DLH * u_e     ;           % local derivative of u(r)
  g(k)  = dudr * J_i    ;         % physical gradient of u(r)
end                                           ; % for k points
clf                                       % clear the plot frame
xmin = min (x_e) ; xmax = max (x_e) ;                % x range
ymax = max (u)   ; ymin = min (u)   ;                % u range
grid on                                     % show grid lines
hold on                            % show following in one plot
axis ([xmin, xmax, ymin, ymax])             % set axis limits
xlabel ('Position (cm)')                        % x axis label
ylabel ('Temperature (C)')                      % y axis label
plot (x, u, 'r-', 'LineWidth',2)               % fat red line
plot (x_e, u_e, 'k*')           % node u values as black star
print -dpng Temperature              % save to a png plot file
fprintf ('Created file Temperature.png \n')
hold off                                   % first graph done
clf                                      % clear the plot frame
ymax = max (g) ; ymin = min (g) ;            % gradient range
grid on                                     % show grid lines
hold on                            % show following in one plot
axis ([xmin, xmax, ymin, ymax])             % set axis limits
xlabel ('Position (cm)')                        % x axis label
ylabel ('Temperature Gradient (C/cm)')          % y axis label
plot (x, g, 'r-', 'LineWidth',2)     % gradient fat red line
print -dpng Temp_Gradient            % save to a png plot file
fprintf ('Created file Temp_Gradient.png \n')
hold off                                    % last graph done
```

Fig. 4.2-11: A Matlab script to graph a cubic element ($L4\_C0$).

Example 4.2-3 Given: A 90 degree segment of a circular arc of radius 4 cm is modeled by a single four-noded line element in order to approximately determine the arc length. Plot the curved element in physical space.

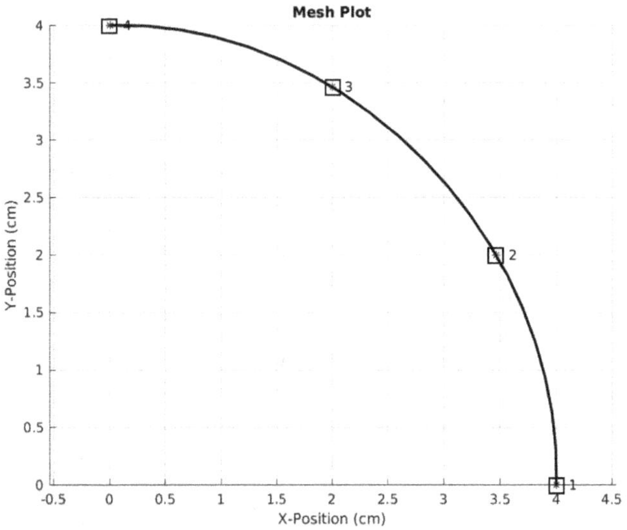

Fig. 4.2-12: Plot of a single curved cubic element.

Solution: Let the arc center point be at the x, y origin. Then the x- and y-coordinates of the four nodes are

$$\boldsymbol{x}^e = [4, \quad 3.464, \quad 2, \quad 0]\,\text{cm}, \quad \boldsymbol{y}^e = [0, \quad 2, \quad 3.464, \quad 4]\,\text{cm}.$$

To plot this one element, just alter the previous temperature graphing script by replacing the u values with the y-values. The mesh curve is in Fig. 4.2-12, and the modified script to plot the curve is in Fig. 4.2-13. The integer node numbers were added for clarity.

4.3 Natural Coordinates*

In addition to the above unit coordinate system, much of the finite element literature also utilizes a parametric system set on $-1 \leq a \leq 1$. Here, this is called a natural coordinate system. The above symbolic process works just as well for deriving the corresponding quadratic interpolation functions in that coordinate system, as shown by the Matlab symbolic script in Fig. 4.3-1. Of course, the two parametric coordinates are related since $r = (a + 1)/2$. Therefore, any interpolation function given in one coordinate system is easily converted to the other. The natural coordinate system is popular in

```
% Graph the position of a cubic approximation to a 90 deg
% circular arc of radius 4
u_e = [2; 3; 0; -1]          ;       % 4x1 vector degrees C
x_e = [4; 3.464; 2; 0]       ;   % 4x1 vector X locations, cm
y_e = [0; 2; 3.464; 4]       ;   % 4x1 vector Y locations, cm
n_n = size (x_e, 1)          ;   % number of nodes on element
n_gaps = 20                  ;    % number of spaces on curve
R = [0:(1/n_gaps):1]         ;        % graph points in r
for k = 1:(n_gaps+1)         ;       % loop over all points
  r = R(k)                   ;          % specific point
  % Evaluate local interpolation definition
  [H_q, DLH_q] = Lagrange_1D_library (n_n, r);   % el lib
  x(k) = H_q * x_e       ;        % interpolate X position
  y(k) = H_q * y_e       ;        % interpolate Y position
end % for k points

clf                                   % clear the plot frame
xmin = min (x_e) ; xmax = max (x_e) ;            % x range
ymin = min (y_e) ; ymax = max (y_e) ;            % y range
grid on                                  % show grid lines
hold on                        % show following in one plot
axis ([xmin, xmax, ymin, ymax])          % set axis limits
axis ('equal')                          % both equal steps
xlabel ('X-Position (cm)')                  % x axis label
ylabel ('Y-Position (cm)')                  % y axis label
title ('Mesh Plot')                          % add a title

% plot element location
plot (x, y, 'r-', 'LineWidth',2)            % fat red line
plot (x_e, y_e, 'k*')         % node u values as black star

for k = 1:n_n                         % add the node numbers
  n_text = sprintf ('   %i', k) ;      % convert to string
  text (x_e(k), y_e(k), n_text) ;       % add text to plot
end % for k nodes

print -dpng Mesh_Geom               % save to a png plot file
fprintf ('Created file Mesh_Geom.png \n')
hold off                                  % first graph done
```

Fig. 4.2-13: Script to plot a single curved parametric element.

part because most of the data required for numerical integration were originally published for such a domain.

4.4 Hermite One-Dimensional Interpolation*

Polynomials that exactly interpolate the data, u_k, and one or more of the physical derivatives at the control points, like $\partial u_k / \partial x = u'_k = \theta_k$, define a C^1 Hermite interpolation. In that case, there are two degrees of freedom at each control point $(n_g = 2)$. Hermite interpolation uses a higher degree on mathematical continuity

```
% Symbolic derivation of a quadratic line element, -1<=a<=1
syms a a_n          real             % symbolic variables
syms c_e c0 c1 c2  real             % symbolic math constants
syms u_e u1 u2 u3  real             % symbolic nodal values
% u(a) = Poly(a) * c_n = c0 + c1*a + c2 * a^2 + ...
% u(a) = H(a) * u_e = H_1*u1 + H_2*u2 + ...
Poly (a) = [1, a, a^2]               % the quadratic polynomial
a_n = [-1, 0, 1]                     % equal spaced node locations
% Identity u_e = u(a_n) = Poly (a_n) * c_n at each node
% G (1, :) = Poly ( a_n(1)) ;       % first row identity
% G (2, :) = Poly ( a_n(2)) ;       % second row identity
% G (3, :) = Poly ( a_n(3)) ;       % third row identity
for k = 1:3                          % loop over nodes
  G (k, :) = Poly (a_n(k)) ;        % k-th row of identity
end % for k
G_inv = inv (G)                      % identity inverse, remove constants
H(a) = Poly(a) * G_inv               % interpolation (shape) functions
total = sum (H(a))                   % interpolation sum
DH_Da(a) = diff (H, a)               % local derivative of H

u_e = [u1, u2, u3]'                  % nodal vector
u (a) = H (a) * u_e                  % the interpolation for u(a)
Du_Da(a) = DH_Da(a) * u_e            % local derivative of u(a)

%  The output results:
%  Poly(a) = [ 1, a, a^2]
%  a_n = -1      0      1
%  G_inv = [    0,  1,    0]
%          [-1/2,  0, 1/2]
%          [ 1/2, -1, 1/2]
%
%  H(a) = [a^2/2 - a/2, 1 - a^2, a^2/2 + a/2]
%  total = 1
%  DH_Da(a) = [a - 1/2, -2*a, a + 1/2]
%
%  u_e = u1
%        u2
%        u3
%  u(a) = u3*(a^2/2 + a/2) - u1*(- a^2/2 + a/2) - u2*(a^2 - 1)
%  Du_Da(a) = u1*(a - 1/2) - 2*a*u2 + u3*(a + 1/2)
```

Fig. 4.3-1: Symbolic Lagrange quadratic line interpolation in natural coordinates.

between the elements. Hermite polynomials are at least $\boldsymbol{C}^1$ on their boundary but also $\boldsymbol{C}^\infty$ on the interior of the element.

The one-dimensional ($n_p = 1$) three-noded ($n_n = 3$) parametric space C^1 Hermite element would have six constants ($n_i = n_g \times n_n = 6$) so the polynomial must be of fifth degree. Since the physical slope is included in the control data, it is necessary to also define $x(r)$. Since x is a scalar, use the same quadratic interpolation process and set $x(r) = \boldsymbol{H}(r)\boldsymbol{x}^e$. Usually, the physical nodes are also equally spaced. In that case, $x_2 = x_1 + L/2$ and $x_3 = x_1 + L$, where L is the length of the region in one-dimensional physical space ($n_s = 1$).

Then, the quadratic terms cancel and the geometry mapping is linear

$$x(r) = (1 - r)x_1 + r\,(x_1 + L) = x_1 + rL.$$

Repeating the above process used for the prior C^0 interpolation functions and inverting the resulting 6×6 $\boldsymbol{G}$ matrix gives the three-node quintic Hermite interpolation:

$$\begin{aligned} u(r) = [&u_1\left(1 - 23r^2 + 66r^3 - 68r^4 + 24r^5\right) \\ &+ \theta_1\left(r - 6r^2 + 13r^3 - 12r^4 + 4r^5\right)L \\ &+ u_2\left(16r^2 - 32r^3 + 16r^4\right) \\ &+ \theta_2\left(-8r^2 + 32r^3 - 40r^4 + 16r^5\right)L \\ &+ u_3\left(7r^2 - 34r^3 + 52r^4 - 24r^5\right) \\ &+ \theta_3\left(-r^2 + 5r^3 - 8r^4 + 4r^5\right)L], \end{aligned} \tag{4.4.1}$$

and its slope (first derivative):

$$\begin{aligned} &\theta(r) = \partial u(r)/\partial x = [u_1\left(-46r + 198r^2 - 272r^3 + 120r^4\right)/L \\ &\theta_1\left(1 - 12r + 39r^2 - 48r^3 + 20r^4\right) + u_2\left(32r - 96r^2 + 64r^3\right)/L \\ &\quad + \theta_2\left(-16r + 96r^2 - 160r^3 + 80r^4\right) \\ &\quad + u_3\left(14r - 102r^2 + 208r^3 - 120r^4\right)/L \\ &\quad + \theta_3\left(-2r + 15r^2 - 32r^3 + 20r^4\right)]. \end{aligned} \tag{4.4.2}$$

Note that Hermite interpolations also depend on the physical element size (L) as well as the parametric measure. The symbolic derivation of this quintic C^1 line element is given in Fig. 4.4-1. This element gives excellent results for beam bending applications and most fourth-order ordinary differential equations.

The simplest element in the C^1 Hermite family is a two-node ($n_n = 2$) straight-line element. It has four nodal constants ($n_i = 4$) and therefore defines a cubic polynomial in one dimension. It is famous for being the first beam bending element and is still widely used for that purpose, even though a three-noded bending element is much more accurate. The symbolic derivation of the cubic C^1 line

```
function [H, DGH, D2GH, D3GH] = Hermite_1D_C1_library ...
                                   (n_n, r, L) %====================
% 1D parametric C1 interpolations and their global derivatives
%       at local point r, in unit coordinates, 0 <= r <= 1
% (See qp_rule_unit_Gauss for corresponding tabulated data)
% DGH  = first physical derivative of H(r), the slope
% D2GH = second physical derivative of H(r), the curvature
% D3GH = second physical derivative of H(r), the curvature rate
% H    = interpolation functions for deflection
% L    = physical length of element
% n_n  = number of nodes per element

r2 = r^2 ; r3 = r^3 ; L2 = L^2 ;
switch n_n % select from available library of elements
 case {2}  % two node classic cubic element, L2_C1 1-----2-->r
  H    = [(1-3*r2+2*r3) (r-2*r2+r3)*L (3*r2-2*r3)   (r3-r2)*L] ;
  DGH  = [(-6*r+6*r2)/L (1-4*r+3*r2)   (6*r-6*r2)/L (3*r2-2*r)] ;
  D2GH = [(12*r-6)/L2   (6*r-4)/L      (6-12*r)/L2  (6*r-2)/L ] ;
  D3GH = [12/L3          6/L2          -12/L3        6/L2     ] ;

 case {3}  % quintic beam element L3_C1 1-----2-----3--> r
  r4 = r^4 ; r5 = r^5 ;
  H    = [(1-23*r2+66*r3-68*r4+24*r5) (r-6*r2+13*r3-12*r4+4*r5)*L ...
          (16*r2-32*r3+16*r4 )        (-8*r2+32*r3-40*r4+16*r5)*L ...
          (7*r2-34*r3+52*r4-24*r5)    (-r2+5*r3-8*r4+4*r5 )*L] ;
  DGH = [(-46*r+198*r2-272*r3+120*r4)/L (1-12*r+39*r2-48*r3+20*r4) ...
          (32*r-96*r2+64*r3)/L           (-16*r+96*r2-160*r3+80*r4) ...
          (14*r-102*r2+208*r3-120*r4)/L (-2*r+15*r2-32*r3+20*r4)] ;
  D2GH = [(-46+396*r-816*r2+480*r3)/L  (-12+78*r-144*r2+80*r3)      ...
           (32-192*r+192*r2 )/L         (-16+192*r-480*r2+320*r3 )  ...
           (14-204*r+624*r2-480*r3)/L   (-2+30*r-96*r2+80*r3)]/L ;
  D3GH = [(396-1632*r+1440*r2)/L       (78-288*r+240*r2) ...
          (-192+384*r)/L               (192-960*r+960*r2) ...
          (-204+1248*r-1440*r2)/L      (30-192*r+240*r2)]/L2 ;
  otherwise
    fprintf ('Current number of element nodes = %i \n', n_n)
    error ('\n Missing parametric functions for that element')
 end % switch
% end Hermite_1D_C1_library % ========================================
```

Fig. 4.4-1: First two C^1 Hermite line interpolations and physical derivatives.

element is also given in Fig. 4.4-2 and yields the interpolations and their derivatives:

$$u(x) = u_1\left(1 - 3r^2 + 2r^3\right) + \theta_1\left(r - 2r^2 + r^3\right)L + u_2\left(3r^2 - 2r^3\right) + \theta_2\left(r^3 - r^2\right)L, \tag{4.4.3}$$

$$\frac{du(x)}{dr}\frac{dr}{dx} = \left[u_1\left(-6r + 6r^2\right) + \theta_1\left(1 - 2r + 3r^2\right)L + u_2\left(6r - 6r^2\right) + \theta_2\left(3r^2 - 2r\right)L\right]/L. \tag{4.4.4}$$

```
function [H, DGH, D2GH, D3GH] = Hermite_1D_C1_library ...
                                    (n_n, r, L) %=====================
% 1D parametric C1 interpolations and their global derivatives
%         at local point r, in unit coordinates, 0 <= r <= 1
% (See qp_rule_unit_Gauss for corresponding tabulated data)
% DGH  = first physical derivative of H(r), the slope
% D2GH = second physical derivative of H(r), the curvature
% D3GH = second physical derivative of H(r), the curvature rate
% H    = interpolation functions for deflection
% L    = physical length of element
% n_n  = number of nodes per element

r2 = r^2 ; r3 = r^3 ; L2 = L^2 ;
switch n_n % select from available library of elements
 case {2}  % two node classic cubic element, L2_C1 1-----2-->r
  H    = [(1-3*r2+2*r3)  (r-2*r2+r3)*L (3*r2-2*r3)   (r3-r2)*L] ;
  DGH  = [(-6*r+6*r2)/L  (1-4*r+3*r2)   (6*r-6*r2)/L (3*r2-2*r)] ;
  D2GH = [(12*r-6)/L2    (6*r-4)/L      (6-12*r)/L2  (6*r-2)/L ] ;
  D3GH = [12/L3          6/L2           -12/L3        6/L2     ] ;

 case {3}  % quintic beam element L3_C1 1-----2-----3--> r
  r4 = r^4 ; r5 = r^5 ;
  H    = [(1-23*r2+66*r3-68*r4+24*r5) (r-6*r2+13*r3-12*r4+4*r5)*L ...
          (16*r2-32*r3+16*r4 )        (-8*r2+32*r3-40*r4+16*r5)*L ...
          (7*r2-34*r3+52*r4-24*r5)    (-r2+5*r3-8*r4+4*r5 )*L] ;
  DGH = [(-46*r+198*r2-272*r3+120*r4)/L (1-12*r+39*r2-48*r3+20*r4) ...
          (32*r-96*r2+64*r3)/L            (-16*r+96*r2-160*r3+80*r4) ...
          (14*r-102*r2+208*r3-120*r4)/L (-2*r+15*r2-32*r3+20*r4)] ;
  D2GH = [(-46+396*r-816*r2+480*r3)/L  (-12+78*r-144*r2+80*r3)      ...
           (32-192*r+192*r2 )/L        (-16+192*r-480*r2+320*r3 ) ...
           (14-204*r+624*r2-480*r3)/L  (-2+30*r-96*r2+80*r3)]/L ;
  D3GH = [(396-1632*r+1440*r2)/L       (78-288*r+240*r2) ...
          (-192+384*r)/L               (192-960*r+960*r2) ...
          (-204+1248*r-1440*r2)/L      (30-192*r+240*r2)]/L2 ;
  otherwise
    fprintf ('Current number of element nodes = %i \n', n_n)
    error ('\n Missing parametric functions for that element')
 end % switch
% end Hermite_1D_C1_library % =======================================
```

Fig. 4.4-2: Symbolic derivation of the cubic C^1 line element interpolation.

Those two C^1 Hermite interpolations are included in the Matlab script *Hermite_1D_C1_library.m*, as shown in Fig. 4.4-1. Given the input of the local coordinate of a point and the physical length of the element, that function returns the numerical values in the interpolation array, $\boldsymbol{H}$, and the numerical values of the physical derivative matrix, $d\boldsymbol{H}/dx$. It also returns the derivatives $d^2\boldsymbol{H}/dx^2$ and $d^3\boldsymbol{H}/dx^3$ because they are usually needed to solve and/or post-process fourth-order differential equations. Also, the Hermite interpolations require the input of the physical length, L, of the element.

4.5 Lagrangian Quadrilateral Elements

The Lagrangian quadrilateral element interpolations are just the products of the above one-dimensional form, used in each parametric direction. Here, the interpolation functions for the Lagrange bilinear four-noded quadrilateral will be developed, in unit coordinates, by using the product of the linear one-dimensional functions. From Fig. 4.5-1, the first two nodes on the quadrilateral have the interpolations at $s = 0$ multiplied times the two r-interpolations, and so on:

$$H_1(r,s) = H_1(r)H_1(s) = (1-r)(1-s) = 1 - r - s + rs,$$
$$H_2(r,s) = H_2(r)H_1(s) = r(1-s) = r - rs,$$
$$H_3(r,s) = H_2(r)H_2(s) = rs,$$
$$H_4(r,s) = H_1(r)H_2(s) = (1-r)s = s - rs,$$

so

$$\boldsymbol{H}(r,s) = [(1 - r - s + rs) \quad (r - rs) \quad (rs) \quad (s - rs)]. \tag{4.5.1}$$

These are identical to those derived by a different approach in Fig. 4.5-2, and they satisfy the requirement that

$$\sum_k H_k(r,s) \equiv 1.$$

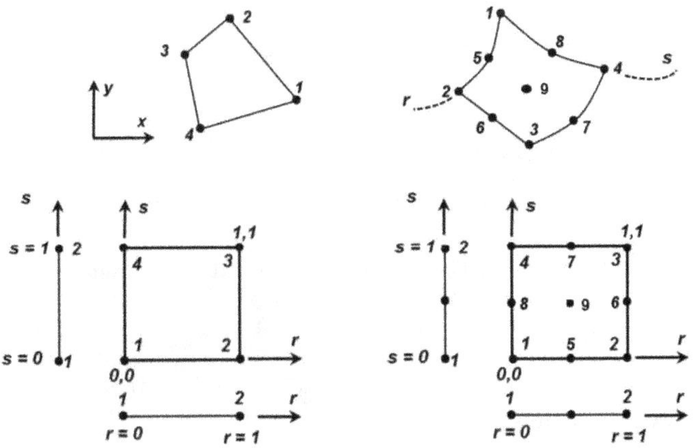

Fig. 4.5-1: Four- and eight-node Lagrangian quadrilaterals in unit coordinates.

```
% Symbolic derivation of a bi-linear quadrilateral element
syms r r_n positive real              % symbolic coords, 0<=r<=1
syms s s_n positive real              % symbolic coords, 0<=s<=1
syms c_e c0 c1 c2 c3 real             % symbolic math constants
syms u_e u1 u2 u3 u4 real             % symbolic nodal values, CCW

% u(r,s) = Poly(r,s) * c_n = c0 + c1*r + c2*s + c3*rs
% u(r,s) = H(r,s) * u_e = H_1*u1 + H_2*u2 + H_3*u3 + H_4*u4

Poly (r, s) = [1, r, s, r*s]          % the quadratic polynomial
r_n = [0, 1, 1, 0]                    % r node CCW locations
s_n = [0, 0, 1, 1]                    % s node CCW locations

% Identity u_e = u(r_n) = Poly (r_n) * c_n at each node
for k = 1:4                           % loop over nodes
  G(k, :) = Poly(r_n(k), s_n(k)) ;    % k-th row of identity
end % for k
% if the inverse of G exists, then this is a valid combination
% of polynomial and local node locations
G_inv = inv (G)                       % identity inverse

H(r,s) = Poly(r,s) * G_inv            % interpolation functions
total = sum (H)

DH_Dr(r,s) = diff (H, r)              % local derivative of H
DH_Ds(r,s) = diff (H, s)              % local derivative of H

u_e = [u1, u2, u3, u4]'               % nodal vector
u (r,s) = H (r,s) * u_e               % the interpolation for u(r)

% The script output
% Poly(r, s) = [ 1, r, s, r*s] % on the unit r-s square
% r_n = 0      1      1      0    % local coords CCW
% s_n = 0      0      1      1    % local coords CCW
%
% G_inv = [  1,  0, 0,  0]     % local u_e to c_e identity
%         [ -1,  1, 0,  0]
%         [ -1,  0, 0,  1]
%         [  1, -1, 1, -1]
%
% H(r, s) = [ r*s - s - r + 1, r - r*s, r*s, s - r*s]
% total(r, s) = 1
%
% DH_Dr(r, s) = [ s - 1, 1 - s, s, -s]
% DH_Ds(r, s) = [ r - 1, -r, r, 1 - r]
%
% u(r, s) = u2*(r - r*s) - u1*(r + s - r*s - 1)
%         + u4*(s - r*s) + r*s*u3
```

Fig. 4.5-2: Symbolic derivation of four-noded Lagrangian quadrilateral interpolations.

This form is useful for lectures, but most quadrilaterals and hexahedra are formulated in natural coordinates, $-1 \leq (a, b) \leq 1$ (because most integration data are tabulated for that space). In natural coordinates, the above $Q4$ Lagrange interpolation functions for

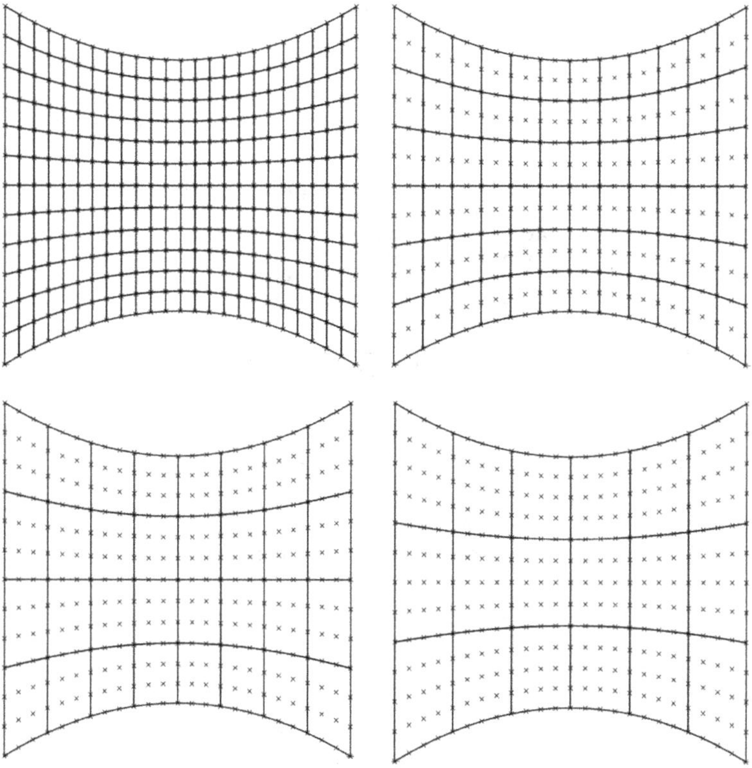

Fig. 4.5-3: Mesh with Lagrangian quadrilaterals $Q4$, $Q9$, $Q16$, and $Q25$.

node k can be expressed simply as

$$H_k(a,b) = \frac{1}{4}(1 + a\,a_k)(1 + b\,b_k), \tag{4.5.2}$$

where $(a_k,\, b_k)$ are the parametric coordinates of the node. That is, $(a_k,\, b_k) = (\pm 1,\, \pm 1)$. The most common quadrilateral elements are shown in a mesh in Fig. 4.5-3. The beginning of the quadrilateral element interpolations is shown in function *Lagrange_quadrilaterals.m* in Fig. 4.5-4.

4.6 Lagrangian Triangular Elements

The linear line, triangular, and tetrahedral elements are "simplex elements" which are defined as having one more node than the

```
function [H, DLH] = Lagrange_quadrilaterals (n_n, r, s) %=====
% Contains Q4, Q8, and Q9 elements
% parametric interpolation functions and local derivatives
% at local point (r, s) in unit coordinat space
% H      = element interpolation functions at r,s,t
% DLH    = element interpolation local derivatives at r,s,t
% n_n    = number of nodes per element

switch n_n % select from available library of elements
 case {4} % four node quadrilateral, -1 <= r,s <= 1, Q4
% (See qp_rule_nat_quad for corresponding data)      % 4  3
% type interpolation functions, 1 x 4, 1-2-3-4 CCW  % 1  2  |r
  H = [ (1 - r)*(1 - s), (1 + r)*(1 - s), ...
        (1 + r)*(1 + s), (1 - r)*(1 + s)] / 4 ;
%               element type parametric derivatives, 2 x 4
  DLH = [ -(1 - s),  (1 - s), (1 + s), -(1 + s); ...   % dH/dr
          -(1 - r), -(1 + r), (1 + r),  (1 - r)] / 4 ; % dH/ds

 case {9}  % nine node quadrilateral, 1 x 9, Q9
%(See qp_rule_nat_quad for corresponding data) % 4 7 3
% corners 1-2-3-4 CCW, mid 5-6-7-8, center 9.  % 8 9 6
% -1 <= r,s <= 1                               % 1 5 2 r
...
```

Fig. 4.5-4: Top of the Lagrange quadrilaterals script.

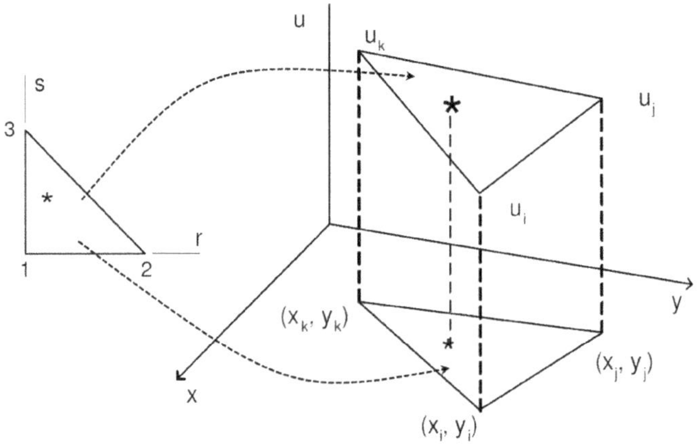

Fig. 4.6-1: Linear unit triangle in two and three dimensions.

dimension of their space. For triangles and tetrahedra, their Lagrange interpolations can be obtained by the same process outlined for the quadratic line element by solving a small system of linear equations. When the parametric nodes are equally spaced, then the required matrix inversion succeeds. These elements are usually expressed in unit coordinates or in baracentric (area or volume) coordinates. This linear triangle is illustrated in Fig. 4.6-1 for three-dimensional (top) and two-dimensional physical studies. In Fig. 4.6-1, it is important to note that the inclined side in the parametric space has the equation $r + s = 1$. That relation is needed when analytic integrals are being evaluated in the parametric space.

Following the procedures in Section 2.6 for developing interpolation functions, begin with a complete linear polynomial related to non-physical constants:

$$u(r,s) = d_1^e + d_2^e r + d_3^e s = [1 \quad r \quad s] \begin{Bmatrix} d_1 \\ d_2 \\ d_3 \end{Bmatrix}^e = \boldsymbol{P}(r,s)\boldsymbol{d}^e.$$

Let the local nodes be located at $(0,0)$, $(1,0)$, and $(0,1)$, respectively. Evaluating the interpolations sequentially at the three nodes gives three identities which relate the non-physical constants to the nodal values. Inverting that 3×3 matrix gives the desired conversion:

$$\begin{Bmatrix} u_1 \\ u_2 \\ u_3 \end{Bmatrix}^e = \begin{bmatrix} 1 & 0 & 0 \\ 1 & 1 & 0 \\ 1 & 0 & 1 \end{bmatrix} \begin{Bmatrix} d_1 \\ d_2 \\ d_3 \end{Bmatrix}^e, \quad \begin{Bmatrix} d_1 \\ d_2 \\ d_3 \end{Bmatrix}^e = \begin{bmatrix} 1 & 0 & 0 \\ -1 & 1 & 0 \\ -1 & 0 & 1 \end{bmatrix} \begin{Bmatrix} u_1 \\ u_2 \\ u_3 \end{Bmatrix}^e.$$

Combining that information with the original parametric form gives the parametric interpolation functions

$$u(r,s) = [1 \quad r \quad s] \begin{bmatrix} 1 & 0 & 0 \\ -1 & 1 & 0 \\ -1 & 0 & 1 \end{bmatrix} \begin{Bmatrix} u_1 \\ u_2 \\ u_3 \end{Bmatrix}^e$$

$$= [(1-r-s) \quad r \quad s] \begin{Bmatrix} u_1 \\ u_2 \\ u_3 \end{Bmatrix}^e = \boldsymbol{H}(r,s)\,\boldsymbol{u}^e.$$

For the complete linear three-noded triangle in unit coordinates, the interpolation functions are

$$H_1(r,s) = 1 - r - s \quad H_2(r,s) = r \quad H_3(r,s) = s, \tag{4.6.1}$$

and they clearly satisfy the Lagrange requirement that $\sum_k H_k(r,s) \equiv 1$.

Lagrangian triangular and tetrahedral elements' interpolations always have the same complete polynomial degree on their interior, on any faces, and along their edges. This assures that adjacent two-dimensional elements of the same degree are continuous along the edges, and that adjacent three-dimensional elements are continuous along their faces The symbolic Matlab script in Fig. 4.4-2 is easily changed to derive the three-noded triangle interpolations.

The values of all three Lagrange interpolation functions, and their sum, are sketched in Fig. 4.6-2. These functions can interpolate the surface that defines the spatial variation of the unknown, $u(r, s)$ between the three vertices. They can also be used to calculate the x- or y-coordinates of any point by interpolating between the nodal coordinates. In the literature, this is called an *isoparametric analysis* because a single (iso) parametric function is used to represent all spatial quantities: the unknown, the coordinates, any spatially dependent properties, etc.

Note that the local derivatives of the three-noded triangle interpolation are constant:

$$\begin{bmatrix} \partial \boldsymbol{H}/\partial r \\ \partial \boldsymbol{H}/\partial s \end{bmatrix} = \begin{bmatrix} -1 & 1 & 0 \\ -1 & 0 & 1 \end{bmatrix}.$$

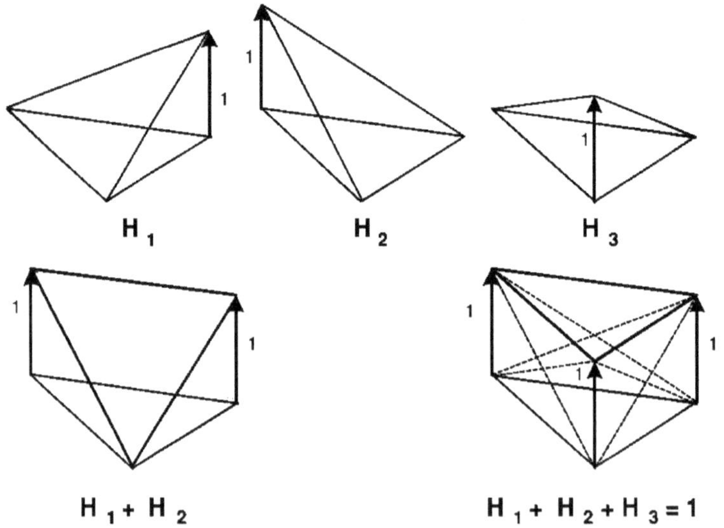

Fig. 4.6-2: Linear triangle dimensionless interpolation and their sums.

That means that the solution in that element will have a constant gradient. In the finite element literature, the three-noded triangle is often called the constant stress triangle (CST). Historically, the earliest CST triangles were interpolated in physical coordinates as

$$H_i(x,y) = \frac{[a_i^e + b_i^e x + c_i^e y]}{2A^e},$$

with a counter-clockwise numbering of the nodes defining the geometric constants as

$$2A^e = a_1^e + a_2^e + a_3^e, \quad \text{and}$$
$$a_i^e = x_j^e y_k^e - x_k^e y_j^e, \quad b_i^e = y_j^e - y_k^e, \quad c_i^e = x_k^e - x_j^e.$$

That form makes clear that this element's physical derivatives are constant.

The symbol T# (like T3, T6, T10, T15) is being used herein to indicate a triangular element with a specific number of nodes that in turn define the degree of its interpolation functions. The most common Lagrange triangular elements can be visualized by referring to the quadrilaterals in Fig. 5.5-3 and placing an edge along the shortest diagonal to see the edge and interior nodes of triangular elements of the same degree. The complete quadratic six-node triangle (T6) interpolations, numbered CCW with the corners first and then the mid-side nodes, are

$$\begin{aligned} &H_1(r,s) = 1 - 3r + 2r^2 - 3s + 4rs + 2s^2 \quad H_2(r,s) = -r + 2r^2, \\ &H_4(r,s) = 4r - 4r^2 - 4rs \quad H_5(r,s) = 4rs \\ &H_6(r,s) = 4s - 4rs - 4s^2. \end{aligned} \tag{4.6.2}$$

They are derived symbolically in Figs. 4.6-3 and 4.6-4, which shows the beginning of the Matlab script *Lagrangian_triangles.m* that contains the above two interpolations functions. Those interpolations are also included in the script *el_shape_n_local_deriv.m*, which contains all of the C^0 interpolation functions.

```
% Symbolic derivation of a quadratic triangle with 6 nodes
syms r r_n positive real            % symbolic coords, 0<=r<=1
syms s s_n positive real            % symbolic coords, 0<=s<=1
syms c_e c0 c1 c2 c3 c4 c5 real     % symbolic math constants
syms u_e u1 u2 u3 u4 u5 u6 real     % symbolic nodal values, CCW

% u(r,s) = c0 + c1*r + c2*s + c3*rs + c4*r^2 + c5*s^2
% u(r,s) = H_1*u1 + H_2*u2 + H_3*u3 + H_4*u4 + H_5*u5 + H_6*u6

Poly (r, s) = [1, r, s, r*s, r^2, s^2] % the quadratic polynomial
r_n = [0, 1, 0, 0.5, 0.5, 0]        % r node CCW vertex & midsides
s_n = [0, 0, 1, 0, 0.5, 0.5]        % s node CCW vertex & midsides

% Identity u_e = u(r_n) = Poly (r_n) * c_n at each node
for k = 1:6                         % loop over nodes
  G(k, :) = Poly(r_n(k), s_n(k)) ; % k-th row of identity
end % for k
% if the inverse of G exists, then this is a valid combination
% of polynomial and local node locations
G_inv = inv (G)                     % identity inverse

H(r,s) = Poly(r,s) * G_inv          % interpolation functions
total = sum (H)                     % must = 1

DH_Dr(r,s) = diff (H, r)            % local derivative of H
DH_Ds(r,s) = diff (H, s)            % local derivative of H

u_e = [u1, u2, u3, u4, u5, u6]'     % nodal vector
u (r,s) = H (r,s) * u_e             % interpolation for u(r,s)

% Poly(r, s) = [ 1, r, s, r*s, r^2, s^2]
% r_n = 0    1.0000         0    0.5000    0.5000         0
% s_n = 0         0    1.0000         0    0.5000    0.5000
%
% G_inv = [  1,  0,  0,  0, 0,  0]
%         [ -3, -1,  0,  4, 0,  0]
%         [ -3,  0, -1,  0, 0,  4]
%         [  4,  0,  0, -4, 4, -4]
%         [  2,  2,  0, -4, 0,  0]
%         [  2,  0,  2,  0, 0, -4]
%
% H(r, s) = [ 2*r^2 + 4*r*s - 3*r + 2*s^2 - 3*s + 1, 2*r^2 - r,
%             2*s^2 - s, 4*r - 4*r*s - 4*r^2,
%             4*r*s, 4*s   4*r*s   4*s^2]
% total(r, s) = 1
%
% DH_Dr(r, s) = [ 4*r + 4*s - 3, 4*r - 1, 0, 4 - 4*s - 8*r, 4*s, -4*s]
% DH_Ds(r, s) = [ 4*r + 4*s - 3, 0, 4*s - 1, -4*r, 4*r, 4 - 8*s - 4*r]
%
% u(r, s) = u1*(2*r^2 + 4*r*s - 3*r + 2*s^2 - 3*s + 1) - u2*(-2*r^2 + r)
%          - u3*(-2*s^2 - s) - u4*(4*r*s - 4*r + 4*r^2)
%          + 4*r*s*u5 - u6*(4*r*s - 4*s - 4*s^2)
```

Fig. 4.6-3: Symbolic derivation for a Lagrangian quadratic triangle.

```
function [H, DLH] = Lagrange_triangles (n_n, r, s) %=====
% Contains T3, T6, T10 elements
% parametric interpolations and their local derivatives
% at local point (r, s) in unit coordinat space
% H     = element interpolation functions at r,s
% DLH   = element interpolation local derivatives at r,s
% n_n   = number of nodes per element
% (See qp_rule_unit_tri for corresponding tabulated data)

switch n_n % select from available library of elements
 case {3}  % three node triangle, 0 <= r, s <= 1, T3
% element interpolation functions, 1 x 3, 1-2-3 CCW
  H = [ (1 - r - s), r, s ] ;
% element parametric derivatives, 2 x 3       % s
  DLH = [ -1, 1, 0 ; ... % dH/dr              % 3
          -1, 0, 1 ] ;   % dH/ds              % 1  2 r

  case {6}  % six node triangle, 0 <= r, s <= 1, T6
%  element interpolations, 1 x 6,              % 3
%  corners 1-2-3                               % 6 5
%  then mid-sides 4-5-6                        % 1 4 2 r
...
```

Fig. 4.6-4: Top of a script to access Lagrange triangle interpolations.

Example 4.6-1 Given: A parametric triangle is defined in the unit coordinate space. Find its non-dimensional area (measure) by analytic integration and check the result using basic geometry.

Solution: The analytic integral for the non-dimensional area is

$$\boxdot = \int_0^1 \int_0^{1-r} ds\, dr = \int_0^1 s \Big|_0^{(1-r)} dr$$

$$= \int_0^1 (1-r)dr = \left[r - r^2/2\right]\Big|_0^1 = \frac{1}{2}\,.$$

The parametric triangle is a right triangle. From geometry, the area of a right triangle is simply half of the base, Δr, times the height, Δs. But the base and height both have dimensionless unit values, so its parametric measure is also dimensionless:

$$\boxdot = \frac{1}{2}\,\text{base} \times \text{height} = \frac{1}{2}(1)(1) = \frac{1}{2}.$$

4.7 Tetrahedral Elements in Unit Coordinates*

The extension of the three-noded triangular elements to the solid pyramid four-noded tetrahedra (P4), shown in Fig. 4.7-1, is straightforward. The tetrahedron interpolation functions are often written in a condensed form using the four coordinates of a baracentric (volume) coordinate system rather than the unit coordinate system with three local coordinates employed here. The four-noded linear tetrahedron Lagrange interpolation functions and their derivatives in unit coordinates, $0 \leq r, s, t \leq 1$, with nodes at $(0,0,0)$, $(1,0,0)$, $(0,1,0)$, and $(0,0,1)$ are

$$\boldsymbol{H}(r,s,t) = [(1-r-s-t) \quad (r) \quad (s) \quad (t)].$$

The four-noded tetrahedra always have straight edges and flat faces. Thus, they have a constant Jacobian matrix. The ten-node tetrahedra can either have curved edges and faces or straight edges and flat faces. The ten-noded quadratic tetrahedron Lagrange interpolation functions (Fig. 4.7-2) are

$$\begin{aligned}\boldsymbol{H}(r,s,t) = \big[&(2r^2+4rs+4rt-3r+2s^2+4st-3s+2t^2-3t+1),\\ &r(2r-1), \quad s(2s-1), \quad t(2t-1),\\ &-4r(r+s+t-1), \quad (4rs), \quad -4s(r+s+t-1),\\ &-4t(r+s+t-1), \quad (4rt), \quad (4st)\big],\end{aligned}$$

with four local nodes at corner coordinates of $(0,0,0)$, $(1,0,0)$, $(0,1,0)$, $(0,0,1)$, and with six mid-edge coordinates of $(0.5,0,0)$, $(0.5,0.5,0)$, $(0,0.5,0)$, $(0,0,0.5)$, $(0.5,0,0.5)$, and $(0,0.5,0.5)$. When the coordinates are restricted to any face, like $t=0$, the interpolations reduce to those on a triangle.

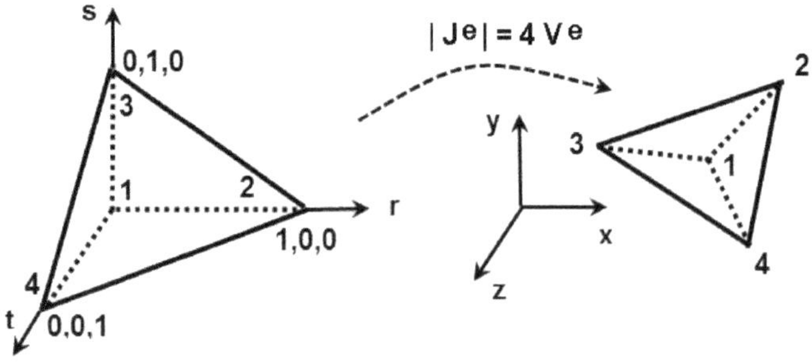

Fig. 4.7-1: The linear tetrahedra simplex element (P4_C0).

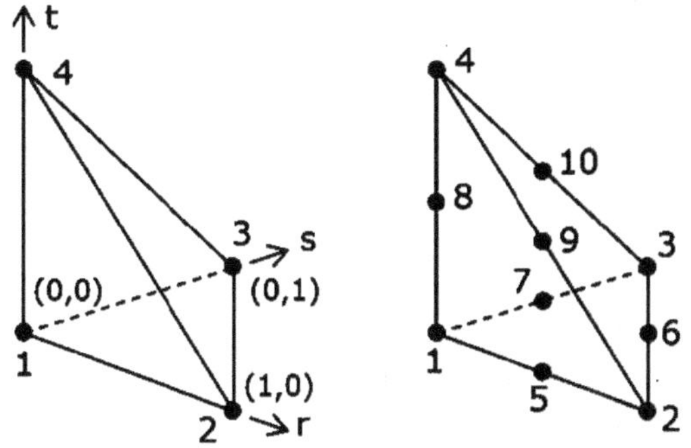

Fig. 4.7-2: The unit tetrahedral coordinate system for P4 and P10 elements.

For any straight-edged, and thus flat-faced, tetrahedral element, the geometric Jacobian matrix is a constant given by

$$\boldsymbol{J}^e = \begin{bmatrix} (x_2 - x_1) & (x_3 - x_1) & (x_4 - x_1) \\ (y_2 - y_1) & (y_3 - y_1) & (y_4 - y_1) \\ (z_2 - z_1) & (z_3 - z_1) & (z_4 - z_1) \end{bmatrix}^e, \quad |\boldsymbol{J}^e| = 6V^e.$$

Since the determinate of this constant Jacobian is the ratio of the physical volume, V^e, divided by the non-dimensional volume in the parametric coordinates, which is one-third the height times the base area: $\boxdot = 1/3\,(1)1/2 = 1/6$.

4.8 Serendipity Quadrilaterals*

In the very earliest days of FEA, computers had very severe limits on the available memory. Since the internal nodes of the Lagrangian elements do not contribute to the required inter-element compatibility, matrix algebra was used to "condense" them out before assembly and to recover them after the solution was obtained. Studies were undertaken to find higher-order quadrilaterals that had few, if any, internal nodes. The interpolation functions were found accidentally, so they were named after the lucky men in the fairy tale called *The Three Princes of Serendip*.

The natural coordinates polynomial variation for Serendipity quadrilaterals are incomplete. The polynomials for the first three members are

$$
\begin{aligned}
P(a,b) &= c_1 + c_2 a + c_3 b + c_4 ab && \text{(for SQ4)},\\
&\quad + c_5 a^2 + c_6 b^2 + c_7 a^2 b + c_8 ab^2 && \text{(for SQ8)},\\
&\quad + c_9 a^3 + c_{10} b^3 + c_{11} a^3 b + c_{12} ab^3 && \text{(for SQ12)}.
\end{aligned}
$$

The corresponding interpolation arrays were first published in 1967. Unfortunately, the widely published interpolation functions for the SQ12 are incorrect due to a topographical error in the original article. The incorrect functions do NOT satisfy the necessary condition that they must sum to unity at any interior point, $\sum_k H_k(a,b) \equiv 1$. The correct forms can be calculated symbolically (like the algorithm in Fig. 4.6-4). Due to those widespread SQ12 errors, the correct interpolations are given here. For the SQ8:

$$
\begin{aligned}
H_1(a,b) &= (1-2a-2b)(1-a)(1-b),\\
H_2(a,b) &= (1-2a+2b)(b-1)a,\\
H_3(a,b) &= ab(2a+2b-3),\\
H_4(a,b) &= b(a-1)(2a-2b+1),\\
H_5(a,b) &= (b-1)((2a-1)^2-1),\\
H_6(a,b) &= a(1-(2b-1)^2),\\
H_7(a,b) &= b(1-(2a-1)^2),\\
H_8(a,b) &= (a-1)((2b-1)^2-1).
\end{aligned}
\tag{4.8.1}
$$

For the SQ12:

$$
\begin{aligned}
H_1(a,b) &= (9a^2+9b^2-10)(1-a)(1-b)/32,\\
H_2(a,b) &= (9a^2+9b^2-10)(1+a)(1-b)/32,\\
H_3(a,b) &= (9a^2+9b^2-10)(1+a)(1+b)/32,\\
H_4(a,b) &= (9a^2+9b^2-10)(1-a)(1+b)/32,\\
H_5(a,b) &= (1-3a-a^2+3a^3)(1-b)9/32,\\
H_6(a,b) &= (1-3b-b^2+3b^3)(1+a)9/32,\\
H_7(a,b) &= (1+3a-a^2-3a^3)(1+b)9/32,\\
H_8(a,b) &= (1+3b-b^2-3b^3)(1-a)9/32,
\end{aligned}
$$

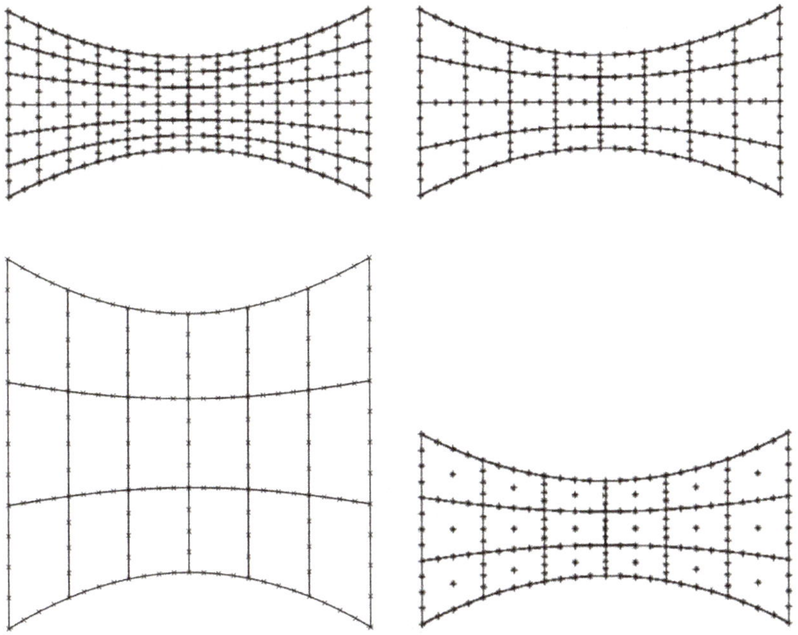

Fig. 4.8-1: Mesh of Serendipity quadrilaterals SQ8, SQ12, SQ16, and SQ17.

$$
\begin{aligned}
H_9(a,b) &= (1+3a-a^2-3a^3)(1-b)9/32,\\
H_{10}(a,b) &= (1+3b-b^2-3b^3)(1+a)9/32,\\
H_{11}(a,b) &= (1-3a-a^2+3a^3)(1+b)9/32,\\
H_{12}(a,b) &= (1-3b-b^2+3b^3)(1-a)9/32. \qquad (4.8.2)
\end{aligned}
$$

Of course, the SQ4 interpolation is identical to the Lagrangian Q4 given in (4.5.2). The Serendipity quadrilateral elements SQ4, SQ8, and SQ12 are included in the provided element library in function *Serendipity_quads.m*. A mesh with the most common Serendipity quadrilaterals is shown in Fig. 4.8-1.

In the above equations and figures, the two-dimensional elements have their nodes numbered in a counter-clockwise order with the vertices first, then the first edge node is numbered around the edges, like Figs. 4.5-1 and 4.7-2. If other edge nodes are present, they are numbered in a similar way. For the SQ17 element, the last node is placed at the centroid of the parametric element.

Example 4.8-1 Given: An eight-node quadratic quadrilateral element, SQ8, has three nodes on each edge. In unit coordinates along the edge where $r = 1$ the interpolation degenerates to $\boldsymbol{H}^b(s) = \left[(1-3s+2s^2) \;\; (4s-4s^2) \;\; (-s+2s^2)\right]$, just like (4.2.1). The system node numbers on that edge happen to be 2, 7, and 9, respectively. Determine the shape of that edge.

Solution: Interpolate the x- and y-positions along the edge;

$$x(s) = \boldsymbol{H}^b(s)\boldsymbol{x}^b$$
$$= (1-3s+2s^2)x_2 + (4s-4s^2)x_7 + (-s+2s^2)x_9,$$
$$x(s) = x_2 + s(4x_7 - 3x_2 - x_9) + s^2(2x_2 - 4x_7 + 2x_9).$$

Likewise, the y-coordinate has the same form. Evaluating at the local nodes of $s = 0$, $s = 0.5$ and $s = 1$ shows that the edge shape goes exactly through the input positions of nodes 2, 7, and 9, respectively. The quadratic change in both the x- and y-coordinates means that, in general, the edge shape is a segment of a parabola going through the three nodes. If the user input the coordinate data such that node 7 was exactly the midpoint between nodes 2 and 9, then a special case occurs with $x_7 = (x_2 + x_9)/2$. Then the s^2 term drops out and

$$x(s) = x_2 + s(2x_2 + 2x_9 - 3x_2 - x_9) = x_2 + s(x_9 - x_2),$$

etc. for $y(s)$ and the edge shape becomes a straight line between the two end nodes.

4.9 Why Parametric Coordinates*

Very early in the development of finite element studies, engineers attempted to interpolate items over curvilinear solids by using physical coordinates. That approach had worked for the two-node line, three-noded straight-sided triangle, and the four-noded straight edge and flat face tetrahedral elements. But when a shape involved curvature, then those attempts failed and yielded non-unique solutions. They were successfully replaced by parametric interpolations introduced in the above sections. An insight to the reasons why physical

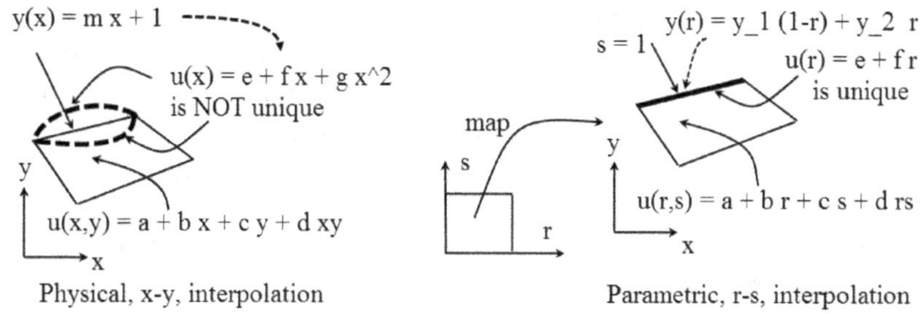

Fig. 4.9-1: Element uniqueness is lost with physical coordinate interpolations.

coordinate interpolations failed is illustrated in Fig. 4.9-1, and the following discussion.

Attempt to use the physical x- and y-coordinates to interpolate the straight-sided two-dimensional four-noded quadrilateral shown in Fig. 4.1-1. The derivation of any set of interpolation functions would follow the process given in Section 4.2. Begin with the incomplete quadratic polynomial assumption to interpolate between the four nodal values of a solution, $u(x, y)$, in terms of the physical coordinates:

$$u(x, y) = c_1 + c_2 x + c_3 y + c_4 xy = \boldsymbol{P}(x, y)\boldsymbol{c}.$$

The failure of this approach is quickly foreseen. All edges have been given to be straight. Thus, on the edge between nodes 2 and 3, the y-coordinate is described by the slope-intercept equation: $y_{23}(x) = b_{23} + m_{23}x$, where the slope, m_{23}, and the y-intercept, b_{23}, are geometric constants. The solution for u along that edge (that is, the boundary interpolation) degenerates to a function of x alone:

$$u_{23}(x) = u(x, y_{23}(x)) = c_1 + c_2 x + c_3(b_{23} + m_{23}x) + c_4 x(b_{23} + m_{23}x),$$
$$u_{23}(x) = (c_1 + c_3 b_{23}) + x\,(c_2 + c_3 m_{23} + c_4 b_{23}) + x^2(c_4 m_{23}),$$
$$u_{23}(x) \equiv d_1 + d_2 x + d_3 x^2.$$

Three values of u are needed on that edge to uniquely determine these three constants, but only the two u_2 and u_3 values are available on that edge. The same conclusion is reached on the other three edges. In other words, global coordinate interpolation for general quadrilaterals fails to give unique results, unless all of the sides are parallel to the global axes. Global coordinate interpolation is valid only for straight-edged triangles and tetrahedra, and was used with those elements in the earliest finite element literature.

Example 4.9-1 Given: Consider the four-noded quadrilateral element as in Fig. 4.9-1. In unit coordinates the interpolations are

$$u(r,s) = (1 - r - s + rs)u_1 + (r - rs)u_2 + rs\,u_3 + (s - rs)u_4.$$

Evaluate the bilinear parametric form on (right) edge 2-3.

Solution: On edge 2-3, the r coordinate is constant, $r_{23} = 1$, so the interpolation degenerates to (the edge interpolation)

$$u_{23}(s, r = 1) = (1 - 1 - s + 1s)u_1 + (1 - 1s)u_2 + s\,u_3 + (s - 1s)u_4,$$

or

$$u_{23}(s) = 0 + (1 - s)u_2 + s\,u_3 + 0 = (1 - s)u_2 + s\,u_3,$$

which is a unique linear function dependent only on the two nodal values, u_2 and u_3, on that edge. An adjacent element having only two edge nodes (quadrilateral or triangle) would have the exact same linear parametric interpolation, and thus there is no gap or discontinuity in the solution value across the elements interface.

4.10 Most Common One-Dimensional Element Integrals

Looking ahead to the applications presented beginning in Chapter 8, there are four element matrix integrals that appear repeatedly. For very common special case of a line element with constant properties, and with equally spaced nodes (constant Jacobians) those integrals can be written in closed form. Tables 4.10-1 and 4.10-2 give the

Table 4.10-1: Interpolation column and symmetric matrix integrals for constant Jacobian line elements.

Type	$\int_\Omega \boldsymbol{H}^T d\Omega$	$\int_\Omega \boldsymbol{H}^T \boldsymbol{H} d\Omega$	$\int_\Omega \vec{\nabla}\boldsymbol{H}^T \vec{\nabla}\boldsymbol{H} d\Omega$
L2C0	$\frac{L^e}{2}\begin{Bmatrix}1\\1\end{Bmatrix}$	$\frac{L^e}{6}\begin{bmatrix}2 & 1\\1 & 2\end{bmatrix}$	$\frac{1}{L^e}\begin{bmatrix}1 & -1\\-1 & 1\end{bmatrix}$
L3C0	$\frac{L^e}{6}\begin{Bmatrix}1\\4\\1\end{Bmatrix}$	$\frac{L^e}{30}\begin{bmatrix}4 & 2 & -1\\2 & 16 & 2\\-1 & 2 & 4\end{bmatrix}$	$\frac{1}{3L^e}\begin{bmatrix}7 & -8 & 1\\-8 & 16 & -8\\1 & -8 & 7\end{bmatrix}$
L4C0	$\frac{L^e}{8}\begin{Bmatrix}1\\3\\3\\1\end{Bmatrix}$	$\frac{L^e}{1680}\begin{bmatrix}128 & 99 & -36 & 19\\99 & 648 & -81 & -36\\-36 & -81 & 648 & 99\\19 & -36 & 99 & 128\end{bmatrix}$	$\frac{1}{40L^e}\begin{bmatrix}148 & -189 & 54 & -13\\-189 & 432 & -297 & 54\\54 & -297 & 432 & -189\\-13 & 54 & -189 & 148\end{bmatrix}$
L5C0	$\frac{L^e}{90}\begin{Bmatrix}7\\32\\12\\32\\7\end{Bmatrix}$	$\frac{L^e}{5670}\begin{bmatrix}292 & 296 & -174 & 56 & -29\\296 & 1792 & -384 & 256 & 56\\-174 & -384 & 1892 & -384 & -174\\56 & 256 & -384 & 1792 & 296\\-29 & 56 & -174 & 296 & 292\end{bmatrix}$	$\frac{1}{945L^e}\begin{bmatrix}4925 & -6848 & 3048 & -1472 & 347\\-6848 & 16640 & -14208 & 5888 & -1472\\3048 & -14208 & 22320 & -14208 & 3048\\-1472 & 5888 & -14208 & 16640 & -6848\\347 & -1472 & 3048 & -6848 & 4925\end{bmatrix}$

Notes: Line elements have a constant Jacobian only if the physical nodes are equally spaced, like the parametric nodes, along a straight physical line. Curved line elements do not have a constant Jacobian and require numerical integration.

If an integral includes constant properties, then the element matrices are simply obtained by multiplying the above integrals by that property.

For the first two integrals, the sum of all the terms in the brackets is one. In the last integral the sum of all the terms in brackets is zero.

closed form expressions of those matrices for linear, quadratic, and cubic line elements. The tabulated matrix integrals are usually pre-multiplied by a constant scalar property; and/or matrix multiplied by nodal values associated with the element.

Table 4.10-2: Non-symmetric constant Jacobian line element integrals: $\boldsymbol{U} = \int_\Omega \boldsymbol{H}^T \vec{\nabla} \boldsymbol{H} d\Omega$.

L2C0	L3C0	L4C0	L5C0
$\frac{1}{2}\begin{bmatrix} -1 & 1 \\ -1 & 1 \end{bmatrix}$	$\frac{1}{6}\begin{bmatrix} -3 & 4 & -1 \\ -4 & 0 & 4 \\ 1 & -4 & 3 \end{bmatrix}$	$\frac{1}{80}\begin{bmatrix} -40 & 57 & -24 & 7 \\ -57 & 0 & 81 & -24 \\ 24 & -81 & 0 & 57 \\ -7 & 24 & -57 & 40 \end{bmatrix}$	

$$\frac{1}{1890}\begin{bmatrix} -945 & 1472 & -804 & 384 & -107 \\ -1472 & 0 & 2112 & -1024 & 384 \\ 804 & -2112 & 0 & 2112 & -804 \\ -384 & 1024 & -2112 & 0 & 1472 \\ 107 & -384 & 804 & -1472 & 945 \end{bmatrix}$$

Notes: Line elements have a constant Jacobian only if the physical nodes are equally spaced, like the parametric nodes, along a straight physical line. Curved line elements do not have a constant Jacobian and require numerical integration.

If an integral includes constant properties, then the element matrices are simply obtained by multiplying the above integrals by that property. The sum of the row terms for this matrix is zero.

Example 4.10-1 Given: Sometimes after a solution has been obtained the integral of that solution has physical importance requiring the post-processing step of evaluating that integral. Determine the integral of the cubic line element solution for equally spaced nodes.

Solution: Example 2.2-2 gives the detailed steps for evaluating that integral for an element of length $L^e = 6\,cm$ and nodal values of $\boldsymbol{u}^e = [2\ 3\ 0\ -1]^T\,°C$. Use Table 4.10-1 for the integral of the interpolation functions.

$$I_u = \int_{L^e} u(r)\,dx = L^e \left\{ \int_0^1 \boldsymbol{H}(r)\,dr \right\} \boldsymbol{u}^e.$$

$$1 \times 1 = (1 \times 4)(4 \times 1),$$

and compare the result to that example.

Solution: The integral is the transpose of the tabulated one. Substituting transposing the tabulated integral and post-multiplying by the solution nodal values gives

$$I_u = \frac{L^e}{8} \begin{Bmatrix} 1 \\ 3 \\ 3 \\ 1 \end{Bmatrix}^T \boldsymbol{u}^e = (6\,\text{cm}) \begin{bmatrix} \frac{1}{8}, & \frac{3}{8}, & \frac{3}{8}, & \frac{1}{8} \end{bmatrix} \begin{Bmatrix} 2 \\ 3 \\ 0 \\ -1 \end{Bmatrix} {}^\circ\text{C}$$

$$= \frac{60^\circ\ \text{cm}}{8} = 7.5^\circ\ \text{cm}.$$

Example 4.10-2 Given: The moment, with respect to the origin at $x = 0$, caused by a pressure changing linearly over a specific line segment, was written using matrix products in Example 2.2-3 as

$$M = \int_{x_1}^{x_2} x[p(x)dx] = \boldsymbol{x}^{e^T} \left[\int_{x_1}^{x_2} \boldsymbol{H}(r)^T\, \boldsymbol{H}(r)\, dx \right] \boldsymbol{p}^e,$$

where the two-node coordinates and pressure values are

$$\boldsymbol{x}^e = \begin{Bmatrix} 20 \\ 30 \end{Bmatrix} \text{m} \quad \text{and} \quad \boldsymbol{p}^e = \begin{Bmatrix} 40 \\ 34 \end{Bmatrix} \frac{\text{N}}{\text{m}},$$

respectively. Use the tabulated square matrix in Table 4.10-1, multiplied by the nodal data to obtain the moment and compare it to that example.

Solution: From the table

$$\int_\Omega \boldsymbol{H}^T \boldsymbol{H} d\Omega = \int_{x_1}^{x_2} \boldsymbol{H}(r)^T\, \boldsymbol{H}(r)\, dx = \frac{L^e}{6} \begin{bmatrix} 2 & 1 \\ 1 & 2 \end{bmatrix},$$

$$M = \begin{bmatrix} 20 & 30 \end{bmatrix} \text{m} \frac{(10)m}{6} \begin{bmatrix} 2 & 1 \\ 1 & 2 \end{bmatrix} \begin{Bmatrix} 40 \\ 34 \end{Bmatrix} \frac{\text{N}}{\text{m}} = 9{,}200\,\text{Nm},$$

as before.

4.11 Summary

$n_b \equiv$ Number of boundary segments
$n_e \equiv$ Number of elements
$n_g \equiv$ Number of generalized DOF per node
$n_i \equiv$ Element independent DOF
$n_m \equiv$ Number of mesh nodes
$n_n \equiv$ Number of nodes per element
$n_p \equiv$ Dimension of parametric space
$n_s \equiv$ Dimension of physical space
$b =$ Boundary segment number
$e =$ Element number

Element interpolation functions given in this chapter

Element Type	**Example or (Equation)**	**Polynomial Degree**	n_p	n_g	n_n	n_i	**Continuity Level**
Lagrange L2	(4.2.6)	1	1	1	2	2	C^0
Lagrange L3	(4.2.1)	2	1	1	3	3	C^0
Lagrange L4	4.2-1,2,3	3	1	1	4	4	C^0
Hermite L2C1	(4.4.3)	3	1	2	2	4	C^1
Hermite L3C1	(4.4.1)	5	1	2	3	6	C^1
Hermite L2C2	Summary	5	1	3	2	6	C^2
Lagrange T3	4.6-1 (4.6.1)	1	2	1	3	3	C^0
Lagrange T6	(4.6.2)	2	2	1	6	6	C^0
Lagrange Q4	(4.5-1,2)	1+	2	1	4	4	C^0
Serendipity SQ8	(4.7-1)	2+	2	1	8	8	C^0
Serendipity SQ12	(4.7-2)	3+	2	1	12	12	C^0
Lagrange P4	4.6, S	1	3	1	4	4	C^0
Lagrange P10	Summary	2	3	1	10	10	C^0
Lagrange H8	Summary	1	3	1	8	8	C^0

Transpose of a product: $(\boldsymbol{A}\,\boldsymbol{B}\,\boldsymbol{C})^T = \boldsymbol{C}^T\,\boldsymbol{B}^T\,\boldsymbol{A}^T$

Parametric interpolations: $u(r) = \boldsymbol{H}(r)\boldsymbol{\delta}^e = \sum_k H_k(r)\,\delta_k^e = \boldsymbol{\delta}^{e^T}\boldsymbol{H}(r)^T$

Natural line coordinates: $-1 \leq a \leq +1$; etc. b, c, so $r = (a+1)/2$ etc. s, t.

Unit coordinates:	$0 \le r \le 1$; etc. s, t, so $a = (2r - 1)$ etc. b, c.
Measure of unit coordinate line:	$\boxdot = \int_0^1 dr = 1$
Measure of natural coordinate line:	$\boxdot = \int_{-1}^1 da = 2$
Measure of unit coordinate triangle:	$\boxdot = \int_0^1 \int_0^{1-r} ds\, dr = 1/2$
Measure of unit coordinate square:	$\boxdot = \int_0^1 \int_0^1 ds\, dr = 1$
Measure of natural coordinate square:	$\boxdot = \int_{-1}^1 \int_{-1}^1 da\, db = 4$

Lagrange linear C^0 line interpolations ($n_p = 1$), in unit coordinates:

$$\boldsymbol{H}(r) = [(1-a)/2 \quad (1+a)/2], \text{ local nodes at } (-1) \text{ and } (1),$$
$$n_n = 2,\ n_g = 1,\ \boldsymbol{\delta}^{\boldsymbol{e}^T} = [u_1 \quad u_2].$$

Lagrange linear C^0 line interpolations ($n_p = 1$), in natural coordinates:,

$$\boldsymbol{H}(a) = [(1-r) \quad r], \text{ local nodes at } (0) \text{ and } (1),\ n_n = 2,\ n_g = 1,$$
$$\boldsymbol{\delta}^{\boldsymbol{e}^T} = [u_1 \quad u_2].$$

Lagrange quadratic C^0 line interpolations ($n_p = 1$), in unit coordinates:

$$\boldsymbol{H}(r) = \big[(1 - 3r + 2r^2) \quad (4r - 4r^2) \quad (-r + 2r^2)\big], \text{local nodes at}$$
$$(0),\ (1/2),\ (1),\ n_n = 3,\ n_g = 1,\ \boldsymbol{\delta}^{\boldsymbol{e}^T} = \big[u_1 \quad u_2 \quad u_3\big].$$

Lagrange cubic C^0 line interpolations ($n_p = 1$), in unit coordinates:

$$\boldsymbol{H}(r) = \frac{1}{2}\big[\,(2 - 11r + 18r^2 - 9r^3) \quad (18r - 45r^2 + 27r^3)$$
$$(-9r + 36r^2 - 27r^3) \cdots (2r - 9r^2 + 9r^3)\,\big],$$

local nodes at $(0), (1/3), (2/3)$, and (1), $n_n = 4$, $n_g = 1$, $\boldsymbol{\delta}^{\boldsymbol{e}^T} = \big[u_1 \quad u_2 \quad u_3 \quad u_4\big]$.

Lagrange linear triangle C^0 interpolation ($n_p = 2$), in unit coordinates:

$$\boldsymbol{H}(rs) = [(1-r-s) \quad (r) \quad (s)], \text{ local nodes at } (0,0), (1,0), \text{ and } (0,1), n_n = 3,\ n_g = 1,\ \boldsymbol{\delta}^{e^T} = [u_1 \quad u_2 \quad u_3].$$

Lagrange linear triangle C^0 interpolation in physical coordinates

$$\boldsymbol{H} = [H_1 \quad H_2 \quad H_3]; \quad H_i(x,y) = \frac{1}{2A^e}[a_i + b_i x + c_i y]$$

$$2A^e = a_1 + a_2 + a_3 = b_2 c_3 - b_3 c_2 : \quad ijk \to 123 \to 231 \to 312$$

$$\begin{aligned}
a_i &= x_j y_k - x_k y_j, & b_i &= y_j - y_k, & c_i &= x_k - x_j \\
a_1 &= x_2 y_3 - x_3 y_2, & a_2 &= x_3 y_1 - x_1 y_3, & a_3 &= x_1 y_2 - x_2 y_1 \\
b_1 &= y_2 - y_3, & b_2 &= y_3 - y_1, & b_3 &= y_1 - y_2 \\
c_1 &= x_3 - x_2, & c_2 &= x_1 - x_3, & c_3 &= x_2 - x_1.
\end{aligned}$$

Lagrange quadratic triangle C^0 interpolation ($n_p = 2$), in unit coordinates:

$$\begin{aligned}\boldsymbol{H}(r,s) = \big[&(1 - 3r + 2r^2 - 3s + 4rs + 2s^2) \quad (-r + 2r^2) \quad (-s + 2s^2) \\ &(4r - 4r^2 - 4rs) \quad (4rs) \quad (4s - 4rs - 4s^2)\big],\end{aligned}$$

local corner vertices at $(0,0)$, $(1,0)$, and $(0,1)$, $n_n = 6$, $n_g = 1$, $\boldsymbol{\delta}^{e^T} = [u_1 \quad u_2 \quad u_3 \quad u_4 \quad u_5 \quad u_6]$.

Lagrange bi-linear quadrilateral C^0 interpolation ($n_p = 2$), in unit coordinates:

$$\boldsymbol{H}(r,s) = [(1 - r - s + rs) \quad (r - rs) \quad (rs) \quad (s - rs)],$$

local nodes at $(0,0)$, $(1,0)$, $(1,1)$ and $(0,1)$, $n_n = 4$, $n_g = 1$.

Lagrange bi-linear quadrilateral C^0 interpolation ($n_p = 2$), in natural coordinates (a,b): $-1 \le a, b \le 1$; $H_k(a,b) = \frac{1}{4}(1 + a\, a_k)$

$(1 + b\,b_k)$, 1,

$$a_k = \pm b_k = \pm 1,\ \boldsymbol{\delta}^{e^T} = [u_1 \quad u_2 \quad u_3 \quad u_4].$$

Lagrange Tri-linear hexahedra C^0 interpolation ($n_p = 3$), in natural coordinates (a, b, c):

$$H_k(a,b,c) = \frac{1}{8}\,(1 + a\,a_k)\,(1 + b\,b_k)\,(1 + c\,c_k),\ a_k = \pm 1,\ b_k = \pm 1,$$
$$c_k = \pm 1,\ \boldsymbol{\delta}^{e^T} = [u_1 \quad u_2 \quad u_3 \quad u_4 \quad u_5 \quad u_6 \quad u_7 \quad u_8].$$

Lagrange linear tetrahedron Lagrange interpolation ($n_p = 3$), in unit coordinates:

$$\boldsymbol{H}(r,s,t) = [(1 - r - s - t) \quad (r) \quad (s) \quad (t)],$$

nodes at $(0,0,0)$, $(1,0,0)$, $(0,1,0)$, and $(0,0,1)$, $n_n = 4$, $n_g = 1$, $\boldsymbol{\delta}^{e^T} = [u_1 \quad u_2 \quad u_3 \quad u_4]$.

Lagrange quadratic tetrahedron Lagrange interpolation ($n_p = 3$), in unit coordinates:

$$\begin{aligned}\boldsymbol{H}(r,s,t) = [&(2r^2 + 4rs + 4rt - 3r + 2s^2 + 4st - 3s + 2t^2 - 3t + 1),\\ &r(2r-1), \quad s(2s-1), \quad t(2t-1), \quad -4r(r+s+t-1),\\ &(4rs), \quad -4s(r+s+t-1), \quad -4\mathrm{t}(r+s+t-1),\\ &(4rt), \quad (4st)]\end{aligned}$$

local nodes at $(0,0,0)$, $(1,0,0)$, $(0,1,0)$, $(0,0,1)$, $(0.5,0,0)$, $(0.5,0.5,0)$, $(0,0.5,0)$, $(0,0,0.5)$, $(0.5,0,0.5)$, and $(0,0.5,0.5)$, $n_n = 4$, $n_g = 1$, $\boldsymbol{\delta}^{e^T} = [u_1 \quad u_2 \quad \cdots \quad u_{10}]$.

Hermite cubic C^1 line interpolations ($n_p = 1$), in unit coordinates (L is physical length):

$$\boldsymbol{H}(r) = [(1 - 3r^2 + 2r^3) \quad (r - 2r^2 + r^3)L \quad (3r^2 - 2r^3) \quad (r^3 - r^2)L],$$

local nodes at (0) and (1), $n_n = 2$, $n_g = 2$, $\boldsymbol{\delta}^{e^T} = [u_1 \quad \theta_1 \quad u_2 \quad \theta_2]$, $\theta = du/dx$.

Hermite quintic C^1 line interpolations ($n_p = 1$), in unit coordinates (L physical length):

$$\boldsymbol{H}(r) = \Big[\left(1 - 23r^2 + 66r^3 - 68r^4 + 24r^5\right) \quad \left(r - 6r^2 + 13r^3 - 12r^4 + 4r^5\right)L \cdots$$

$$\left(16r^2 - 32r^3 + 16r^4\right) \quad \left(-8r^2 + 32r^3 - 40r^4 + 16r^5\right)L \cdots$$

$$\left(7r^2 - 34r^3 + 52r^4 - 24r^5\right) \quad \left(-r^2 + 5r^3 - 8r^4 + 4r^5\right)L\Big],$$

local nodes at (0), (1/2) and (1), $n_n = 3$, $n_g = 2$, $\boldsymbol{\delta}^{e^T} = [u_1 \quad \theta_1 \quad u_2 \quad \theta_2 \quad u_3 \quad \theta_3]$.

Hermite quintic C^2 line interpolations ($n_p = 1$), in unit coordinates (L is physical length):

$$\boldsymbol{H}(r) = \big[(1 - 10r^3 + 15r^4 - 6r^5) \quad (r - 6r^3 + 8r^4 - 3r^5)L \cdots$$

$$(r^2 - 3r^3 + 3r^4 - r^5)L^2 \quad (10r^3 - 15r^4 + 6r^5)$$

$$(7r^4 - 3r^5 - 4r^3)\,L \quad (r^3 - 2r^4 + r^5)\,L^2\big],$$

local nodes at (0) and (1), $n_n = 2$, $n_g = 3$,

$$\boldsymbol{\delta}^{e^T} = [u_1 \quad \theta_1 \quad \kappa_1 \quad u_2 \quad \theta_2 \quad \kappa_2], \quad \theta = du/dx, \quad \kappa = d^2u/dx^2.$$

4.12 Review

1. A straight line runs from point x_1 to point x_2 and has a linear line load running with a value of p_1 at the first end to point value p_2 at the other end. Their data are as follows:

Node k	r_k	x_k **(m)**	$p_k(N/m)$
1	0.0	20	40
2	1.0	30	3

Using parametric linear interpolation, of a two-node element, find the position and value of the line load at a point 35% along the length, from the first node.

2. For the above data find the non-dimensional pressure derivative, $\partial p/\partial r$ at the same point.
3. A straight line runs from x_1 to midpoint x_2 to x_3 and has a line load running with a value of p_1 at the first end to point value p_2 at the mid-point to a value of p_3 at the other end. Their data are

Node k	r_k	x_k (m)	p_k (N/m)
1	0.0	20	40
2	0.5	25	46
3	1.0	30	34

Using parametric linear interpolation, find the position, line load value, and local derivative, $\partial p/\partial r$, of the line load at a point 35% along the length, from the first node.
4. A linear triangle has a normal pressure ranging from $p_1 = 40$ to $p_2 = 46$ to $p_3 = 34\,\text{N/m}^2$ at its three corners. The local nodes are at $(0, 0)$, $(1, 0)$, and $(0, 1)$, respectively. Using parametric unit coordinate linear interpolation, for a T3 element, find the pressure value, and the parametric pressure gradient, $\partial p/\partial r$ and $\partial p/\partial s$, at a non-dimensional interior point ($r = 0.32$, $s = 0.43$).
5. How are the physical derivatives of the interpolation functions, dH^e/dx, evaluated at a point within an element?
6. What is the sum of the terms in the element Lagrangian interpolation matrix, H^e?
7. One must usually numerically evaluate the geometric Jacobian matrix at a quadrature point (along with its determinant and inverse). How is the Jacobian matrix actually numerically evaluated, or constructed, within a typical element?
8. The geometry mapping from a parametric space to physical space is done with which of the following matrix functions? _____.

   (a) Determinant of the Jacobian
   (b) Inverse of the Jacobian matrix
   (c) Jacobian matrix
   (d) Interpolation functions
   (e) Derivatives of interpolation functions
   (f) Parametric derivatives

9. What are the basic concepts for isoparametric elements?
10. A distorted (non-constant Jacobian) three node line element has node x-coordinates of $\boldsymbol{x}^{e^T} = [0 \quad 0.3L \quad L]$. Evaluate $\partial x/\partial r$ for the element.
11. A three node unit triangle has corner x-coordinates of $\boldsymbol{x}^{e^T} = [x_1 \quad x_2 \quad x_3]$. Determine the x-coordinate value, $x(r,s) = \boldsymbol{H}(r,s)\boldsymbol{x}^e$, at the interior point (0.2, 0.3), in unit coordinates.
12. For a uniform temperature increase of ΔT and a coefficient of thermal expansion of α, the axial thermal strain is $\varepsilon_\alpha = \alpha\nabla T$. The resultant of the element nodal thermal forces are defined by the element integral

$$\boldsymbol{C}^e_\alpha = \int_{L^e} \frac{d\boldsymbol{H}^{e^T}}{dx} E^e \varepsilon^e_\alpha A^e \, dx.$$

Evaluate this integral for a uniform three node axial element that has a constant Jacobian.
13. An isoparametric three node triangle has nodal property values of $\boldsymbol{P}^{e^T} = [10 \quad 12 \quad 15.5]\, MPa$. What is the corresponding property value at the interior point $(0.3, 0.4)$, in unit coordinates?
14. A planar curve is interpolated with a quadratic line element. The nodal coordinates of its three (x, y) points are $(4, 2)$, $(3.2, 3.5)$, and $(2, 4)$m. Calculate the unit tangent vector to the curve at local point $r = 0.5$.
15. Can a mesh with a mixture of three-noded lines, six-node triangles, eight-node Quadrilaterals, and nine-node quadrilaterals be a compatible mixture of element types? If yes, explain why.
16. Resolve Example 4.2-1 using only natural coordinate interpolations and verify that the resulting physical gradient value is unchanged.

Chapter 5

Numerical Integration

5.1 One-Dimensional Quadratures

Since the finite element method is based on integral relations, it is logical to expect that one should strive to carry out the integrations as efficiently as possible. In rare cases, exact integration can be used. In most cases, the integrals can become too complicated to integrate exactly. In such cases, the use of numerical integration proves useful or essential. The important topics of local coordinate integration and Gaussian quadratures will be introduced here. They will prove useful when dealing with higher-order interpolation functions in complicated element integrals and allow the whole process to be automated.

Numerical integration is simply a procedure that approximates an integral by a summation. However, it can yield the exact integral and often does when the integrand is a polynomial. The famous mathematician Gauss posed this question: What is the minimum number of points, say n_q, in a summation required to exactly integrate a polynomial, and what are the corresponding non-dimensional abscissae (locations) and weights for those points? His solutions provided analytical locations and weights that are tabulated numerically for practical use. The n_q Gaussian one-dimensional quadrature points are symmetrically placed with respect to the center of the interval, and will exactly integrate a polynomial of degree $D = (2n_q - 1)$. The Gauss rule data are usually tabulated for a non-dimensional unit coordinate range of $0 \le r \le 1$, or for a natural coordinate range of $-1 \le a \le 1$, which are both tabulated in Table 5.1-1. Let the symbol $\boxdot$ denote any non-dimensional space over which an integral is to be evaluated. Then the Gauss integration equation is

$$I_{\boxdot} = \int_{\boxdot} F(r) d\boxdot \approx \sum_{q=1}^{n_q} F(r_q) w_q. \tag{5.1-1}$$

If the function $F(r)$ is a polynomial in r, then the approximately equal sign can be replaced with an equal sign if the number of summation points, n_q, is greater than or equal to $(D+1)/2$. In FEA, the function is usually a matrix, $F(r) \to \boldsymbol{F}(r)$. That just means that the above summation is applied to every term in the matrix.

Gauss obtained the results as numbers defined by square roots or combinations thereof. For example, the two-point rule in natural

Table 5.1-1: Abscissas and weights for Gaussian Quadrature in Unit Coordinates.

$$\int_0^1 f(x)dx = \sum_{i=1}^{n} w_i f(x_i)$$

x_i		w_i
0.50000 00000 00000 00000 000	$n=1$	1.00000 00000 00000 00000 000
0.21132 48654 05187 11774 543	$n=2$	0.50000 00000 00000 00000 000
0.78867 51345 94812 88225 457		0.50000 00000 00000 00000 000
0.11270 16653 79258 31148 208	$n=3$	0.27777 77777 77777 77777 778
0.50000 00000 00000 00000 000		0.44444 44444 44444 44444 444
0.88729 83346 20741 68851 792		0.27777 77777 77777 77777 778
0.06943 18442 02973 71238 803	$n=4$	0.17392 74225 68726 92868 653
0.33000 94782 07571 86759 867		0.32607 25774 31273 07131 347
0.66999 05217 92428 13240 133		0.32607 25774 31273 07131 347
0.93056 81557 97026 28761 197		0.17392 74225 68726 92868 653
0.04691 00770 30668 00360 119	$n=5$	0.11846 34425 28094 54375 713
0.02307 65344 94715 84544 818		0.23931 43352 49683 23402 065
0.50000 00000 00000 00000 000		0.28444 44444 44444 44444 444
0.76923 46550 52841 54551 816		0.23931 43352 49683 23402 065
0.95308 99229 69331 99639 881		0.11846 34425 28094 54375 713

coordinates ($-1 \le a \le 1$) gave $a_k = \pm 1/\sqrt{3}, w_k = 1$. For efficiency and fast access, all quadrature data are tabulated as finite numbers with many significant figures. The center point location is included in the abscissae list only when n_q is odd, and the end points are never utilized in a Gauss rule. Some Gauss points are illustrated in Fig. 5.1-1.

In the software provided here, the unit coordinate Gauss point values are tabulated in the Matlab function *qp_rule_unit_Gauss.m* (Fig. 5.1-2), a portion of which is shown in Table 5.1-1. The natural coordinate values of the quadrature data are stored in function *qp_rule_Gauss.m* (Fig. 5.1-3). The number of integration points is

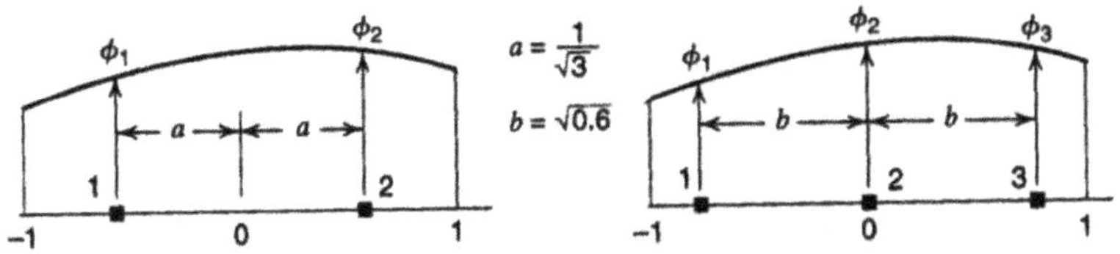

Fig. 5.1-1: Natural 2- and 3-point quadrature points on a line.

```
function [r_q, w_q] = qp_rule_unit_Gauss (n_q) % ======
%  tables of quadrature point locations and weights
%  for lines interpolated in unit coordinates.
%              0 <= r <= 1,     sum (w_q) == 1
% n_q = number of quadrature points required
% r_q = all of first parametric quadrature coordinates
% w_q = weight at all quadrature points in n_p
switch n_q ;
 case 1 ; % precision: exact for polynomial of degree 1
   r_q (1) = 0.5 ; w_q = 1 ;

 case 2 ; % precision: exact for polynomial of degree 3
   r_q (1) = 2.1132486540518711774543e-01 ;
   r_q (2) = 7.8867513459481288225457e-01 ;
   w_q (1) = 5.0000000000000000000000e-01 ;
   w_q (2) = 5.0000000000000000000000e-01 ;

 case 3 ; % precision: exact for polynomial of degree 5
   r_q (1) = 1.1270166537925831148208e-01 ;
   r_q (2) = 5.0000000000000000000000e-01 ;
   r_q (3) = 8.8729833462074168851792e-01 ;
   w_q (1) = 2.7777777777777777777778e-01 ;
   w_q (2) = 4.4444444444444444444445e-01 ;
   w_q (3) = 2.7777777777777777777778e-01 ;
 . . .
end % switch number of quadrature points
```

Fig. 5.1-2: Portion of the unit coordinate line quadrature data.

```
function [r_q, w_q] = qp_rule_Gauss (n_q) % ===========
%  tables of quadrature point locations and weights
%  for lines interpolated in natural coordinates
%              -1 <= r <= 1,     sum (w_q) == 2
% n_q = number of quadrature points required
% r_q = all of first parametric quadrature coordinates
% w_q = weight at all quadrature points in n_p
 switch n_q
  case 1 % precision: exact for polynomial of degree 1
    r_q (1) = 0 ; w_q = 2 ;

  case 2 % precision: exact for polynomial of degree 3
    r_q (1) = -0.577350269189625764509149 ;
    r_q (2) =  0.577350269189625764509149 ;
    w_q (1) = 1                  ; w_q (2) = 1 ;

  case 3 % precision: exact for polynomial of degree 5
    r_q (1) = -0.774596669241483377035835 ;
    r_q (2) =  0.000000000000000000000000 ;
    r_q (3) =  0.774596669241483377035835 ;
    w_q (1) =  0.555555555555555555555556 ;
    w_q (2) =  0.888888888888888888888889 ;
    w_q (3) =  0.555555555555555555555556 ;
...
end % switch
```

Fig. 5.1-3: Portion of the natural coordinate tabulated data.

the input argument, and the arrays of positions and weights are the returned items, ready to be used in an integration loop.

Of course, most engineering applications are defined in physical space, and not in non-dimensional space. Thus, most finite element matrices are defined by the integrals of matrices over physical space, not in non-dimensional space. The physical space must be mathematically mapped into a non-dimensional space before the integrals can be evaluated. The process is like relating rectangular coordinates to cylindrical coordinates. The next chapter on a review of calculus will show that the general process requires defining a three-dimensional "Jacobian Matrix", $[\boldsymbol{J}^e]$, that relates the differential lengths and volume in the first coordinate system to the differential lengths and volume in the second coordinate system.

However, for now, only examples of the special cases where that process degenerates to a single scaling constant, $|\boldsymbol{J}^e|$, will be illustrated. That occurs for a straight line and/or a straight-sided triangle, each with equally spaced nodes. For a straight physical line with a scaling of $x(r) \equiv rL^e$ and $dx/dr = L^e$, an integral over that line changes (5.1-1) slightly to the form usually used in FEA:

$$\boldsymbol{I} = \int_{\boldsymbol{0}}^{\boldsymbol{1}} \boldsymbol{F}(r)\, |\boldsymbol{J}^e|\, d\boxdot = \int_0^1 \boldsymbol{F}(r) \left(\frac{dx}{dr} dr\right) = L^e \int_0^1 \boldsymbol{F}(r) dr,$$

or

$$\boldsymbol{I} \approx L^e \sum_{q=1}^{n_q} \boldsymbol{F}(r_q) w_q$$

The following few examples will illustrate the special cases of a constant Jacobian matrix.

Example 5.1-1 Given: Using numerical integration determine the physical length

$$L^e = \int_{x_1}^{x_2} dx = \int_0^1 |J^e(r)|\, dr = \int_0^1 \frac{dx(r)}{dr} dr = \sum_{q=1}^{n_q} \frac{dx(r_q)}{dr} w_q,$$

of the cubic line element in Example 2.2-1 with straight-line coordinates of $\boldsymbol{x}^{e^T} = [2\ 4\ 6\ 8]\,\text{cm}$.

Solution: Since the physical nodes are equally spaced on a straight line, the physical length only depends on the first and last node. In other words, the geometry mapping degenerates to a linear interpolation

$$x(r) = (1-r)x_1 + r x_4 = (1-r)(2\,\text{cm}) + r(8\,\text{cm}) = 2\,\text{cm} + r(6\,\text{cm})$$

and its constant Jacobian is $dx/dr = 6\,\text{cm}$. The integrand is of degree 0, so only one quadrature point is needed and the element length is thus

$$L^e = \int_0^1 (6\,\text{cm}) dr = \sum_{q=1}^{n_q=1} (6\,\text{cm}) w_q.$$

Here the integrand is just a constant. For a linear polynomial or a constant, the exact integration requires only one Gauss quadrature point. For a one-point rule, in the unit coordinate space, the tabulated integration data are $r_1 = 0.5000$, $w_1 = 1.0000$. Of course, summations begin with a starting value of zero, so the numerical integration gives

$$L^e = 0 + (6\,\text{cm})(1.0000) = 6\,\text{cm}.$$

Example 5.1-2 Given: Using numerical integration determine the physical length of the cubic line element in Example 2.2-1 by interpolating the $x(r)$ location from the straight line coordinates of $\boldsymbol{x}^{\boldsymbol{e}^T} = [2\ 4\ 6\ 8]\text{cm}$, while not assuming that the physical spacing is uniform. That is, do not assume the Jacobian is constant.

Solution: The length is

$$L^e = \int_{x_1}^{x_2} dx = \int_0^1 |J^e(r)| dr = \int_0^1 \frac{dx(r)}{dr} dr = \sum_{q=1}^{n_q} \frac{dx(r_q)}{dr} w_q.$$

Recall that the interpolation function and its derivative are

$$\begin{aligned} \boldsymbol{H}(r) = [&(2 - 11r + 18r^2 - 9r^3)\ (18r - 45r^2 + 27r^3) \\ &\cdots (-9r + 36r^2 - 27r^3)\ (2r - 9r^2 + 9r^3)]/2, \end{aligned}$$

and

$$\begin{aligned} \partial \boldsymbol{H}(r)/\partial r = [&(-11 + 36r - 27r^2)\ (18 - 90r + 81r^2) \\ &\cdots (-9 + 72r - 81r^2)\ (2 - 18r + 27r^2)]/2. \end{aligned}$$

Since the coordinate is interpolated by the above cubic polynomial, $x(r) = \boldsymbol{H}(r)\boldsymbol{x}^{\boldsymbol{e}}$, the degree of the integrand, $dx(r)/dr$, is 2 and the number of Gauss points is only $n_q \geq (2+1)/2 = 2$ to get the exact answer. The numerical integration is

$$L^e = \int_0^1 \frac{dx(r)}{dr}dr = \sum_{q=1}^{n_q=2} \frac{dx(r_q)}{dr}w_q = \sum_{q=1}^{n_q=2} \frac{d\boldsymbol{H}\boldsymbol{x}^{\boldsymbol{e}}}{dr}(r_q)w_q,$$

$$L^e = \left[\sum_{q=1}^{n_q=2} = \frac{d\boldsymbol{H}}{dr}(r_q)w_q\right]\boldsymbol{x}^{\boldsymbol{e}},$$

where the determinant of the Jacobian at each point in the summation is

$$|J^e(r_q)| = \frac{dx(r_q)}{dr} = \frac{d\boldsymbol{H}}{dr}(r_q)\boldsymbol{x}^{\boldsymbol{e}}.$$

Note that the constant vector of element coordinates, $\boldsymbol{x}^{\boldsymbol{e}}$, factors out of the integral and the matrix sum. Here, that product will be evaluated at each quadrature point. The two tabulated quadrature locations in unit coordinates are $r_1 = 0.21132$ and $r_2 = 0.78868$, and the two tabulated weights are the same, $w_1 = w_2 = 0.50000$. Set the sum total initially to zero, $L = 0$, and begin the summation loop: set $q = 1$, substituting $r = r_1 = 0.21132$ into the derivative the Jacobian is

$$\boldsymbol{J}(r = 0.21132)^e = [-2.2990\ 1.2990\ 1.2990\ -0.2990] \times \begin{Bmatrix} 2 \\ 4 \\ 6 \\ 8 \end{Bmatrix} \text{cm} = 6.0000 \text{ cm}.$$

Multiply by the tabulated weight and add to the sum as follows:

$$L^e = 0 + \boldsymbol{J}(r_1)^e w_1 = 0 + (6.0000\,\text{cm})0.5000 = 3.0000 \text{ cm}.$$

At the second point, $r = r_2$, the Jacobian is

$$\boldsymbol{J}(r = 0.78868)^e = [0.2990 \quad -1.2990 \quad -1.2990 \quad 2.2990] \begin{Bmatrix} 2 \\ 4 \\ 6 \\ 8 \end{Bmatrix} \text{cm} = 6.0000 \text{ cm}.$$

Multiply this by the tabulated weight and add to the previous sums,

$$L^e = 3.0000\,\text{cm} + \boldsymbol{J}(r_2)^e w_2 = 3.0000 + (6.0000\,\text{cm})0.5000$$
$$= 6.0000\,\text{cm}.$$

That yields the exact physical length of the cubic line element.

A Matlab script for the same "hard coded" calculation is given in Fig. 5.1-4. That script can be easily generalized to any one-dimensional Lagrangian elements by calling the element library and

```
% Integrate the temperature over a cubic line element
u_e = [2; 3; 0; -1]          ;         % 4x1 vector degrees C
x_e = [2; 4; 6;  8]          ; % 4x1 vector cm (equal spaces)
n_q = 2                      ;  % number of quadrature points
r_q = [2.113248654051871177e-01, 7.886751345948128822e-01]  ;
w_q = [5.000000000000000000e-01, 5.000000000000000000e-01]  ;
I_u = 0                     ; % initialize the integral value

for k = 1:n_q                          % loop over all points
  r = r_q (k)               ;             % specific location
  w = w_q (k)               ;               % specific weight
  % Evaluate local interpolation definitions
  H_q=[(1-r*11/2+9*r^2-9*r^3/2), (9*r-45*r^2/2+27*r^3/2), ...
       (-9*r/2+18*r^2-27*r^3/2), (r-9*r^2/2+9*r^3/2)]
  DLH_q=[(-11/2+18*r-27*r^2/2),  (9-45*r+81*r^2/2), ...
        (-9/2+36*r-81*r^2/2),    (1-9*r+27*r^2/2)]
  J_q = DLH_q * x_e                     % Jacobian at the point
  u_q = H_q * u_e                       % Function at the point
  I_q = u_q * J_q * w_q             % Contribution from this point
  I_u = I_u + I_q             % Update the integration sum value
end % for k quadrature points

fprintf ('Integral of nodal values = %8.3e \n', I_u)
% end of integration
```

Fig. 5.1-4: Evaluating Example 5.1-1 by explicit numerical integration.

```
%    Integrate the temperature over a cubic line element
%        using interpolation and quadrature libraries
u_e = [2; 3; 0; -1]           ;            % 4x1 vector degrees C
x_e = [2; 4; 6;  8]           ; % 4x1 vector cm (equal spaces)
n_n = size (x_e, 1)           ;             % the number of nodes
deg = n_n - 1                 ;            % degree of polynomial
n_q = ceil ((deg+1)/2)        ;  % number of quadrature points
[r_q, w_q] = qp_rule_unit_Gauss (n_q) ;     % data from tables
I_u = 0                       ; % initialize the integral value

for k = 1:n_q % ---> ---> ---> --->        % loop over all points
  r = r_q (k)                 ;                % specific location
  w = w_q (k)                 ;                  % specific weight
  % Evaluate local interpolation definitions at point
  [H_q, DLH_q] = Lagrange_1D_library (n_n, r) ;  % el library
  J_q = DLH_q * x_e            ;           % Jacobian at the point
  u_q = H_q * u_e              ;           % Function at the point
  I_q = u_q * J_q * w_q        ;   % Contribution from this point
  I_u = I_u + I_q              ;   % Update integration sum value
end % for k quadrature points % <--- <--- <--- <---

fprintf ('Integral of nodal values = %8.3e \n', I_u)
% end of integration
```

Fig. 5.1-5: Numerical line integration using tables and the element library.

the quadrature library as shown in Fig. 5.1-5. At each stage in the integration loop, the location, r, and the number of nodes per element, $n\_n \longleftrightarrow n_n$, are supplied as arguments. The value of n_n is used to select which interpolation member of the element library is desired. Then the interpolation functions, and their parametric derivative, are evaluated at the input local coordinate and those two arrays of numbers are the returned items from the function. The script in Fig. 5.1-5 is actually shorter than the hard-coded script. By changing the third line data, any interpolated one-dimensional cubic quantity can be integrated numerically.

Example 5.1-3 Given: Extend Example 4.2-by integrating the cubic solution with nodal values of $\boldsymbol{u}^{e^T} = [2\ 3\ 0\ -1]°\text{C}$ and nodal coordinates of $\boldsymbol{x}^{e^T} = [2\ 4\ 6\ 8]\,\text{m}$ by applying Gaussian quadrature in the unit coordinate space.

Solution: The integral is

$$I_u = \int_{L^e} u(r)dx = \int_0^1 u(r)\,|J(r)|\,dr = \left[\int_0^1 \boldsymbol{H}(r)\,|J(r)^e|\,dr\right]\boldsymbol{u}^e.$$

Previously, it was noted that the Jacobian in this example is constant (L^e), but this example will treat it as a variable. The degree of the polynomial is $2+1=3$. The number of necessary quadrature points is determined from Degree $\leq (2n_q - 1)$, so two quadrature points are required (and more are okay). The integral becomes

$$I_u = \left[\int_0^1 \boldsymbol{H}(r)\,|J(r)^e|\,dr\right]\boldsymbol{u}^e = \left[\sum_{q=1}^{n_q=2} \boldsymbol{H}(r_q)\,|\boldsymbol{J}(r_q)|\,w_q\right]\boldsymbol{u}^e,$$

where, in general, the Jacobian matrix at the quadrature point is calculated (numerically) as the product of the local derivative of the interpolation functions times the input nodal coordinate vector:

$$\boldsymbol{J}(r_q)^e = \frac{\partial x(r_q)}{\partial r} = \frac{\partial \boldsymbol{H}(r_q)}{\partial r}\boldsymbol{x}^e.$$

Here, that product will be evaluated at each quadrature point. The analytic expressions for $\boldsymbol{H}(r)$ and $\partial \boldsymbol{H}(r_q)/\partial r$ are given in Example 4.2-1 as

$$\begin{aligned}\boldsymbol{H}(r) &= [(2 - 11r + 18r^2 - 9r^3)\ (18r - 45r^2 + 27r^3) \\ &\quad \cdots (-9r + 36r^2 - 27r^3)\ (2r - 9r^2 + 9r^3)]/2, \\ \partial \boldsymbol{H}(r)/\partial \mathrm{r} &= [(-11 + 36r - 27r^2)\ (18 - 90r + 81r^2) \\ &\quad \cdots (-9 + 72r - 81r^2)\ (2 - 18r + 27r^2)]/2.\end{aligned}$$

Here the arrays are evaluated numerically at each point. The two tabulated quadrature locations in unit coordinates are $r_1 = 0.21132$ and $r_2 = 0.78868$, and the two tabulated weights are the same, $w_1 = w_2 = 0.50000$. Begin the summation loop: set $q = 1$, the Jacobian there is

$$\boldsymbol{J}(r_1)^e = [-2.2990\ 1.2990\ 1.2990\ -0.2990]\begin{Bmatrix} 2 \\ 4 \\ 6 \\ 8 \end{Bmatrix}\mathrm{cm} = 6.0000\,\mathrm{cm}.$$

The function at the point is

$$u(r_1) = [0.1972\ 1.0245\ \ -0.2745\ 0.0528] \begin{Bmatrix} 2 \\ 3 \\ 0 \\ -1 \end{Bmatrix} {}^\circ\mathrm{C} = 3.4151^\circ\mathrm{C}$$

and the contribution from this point is

$$\begin{aligned} I_q &= u(r_1)\boldsymbol{J}(r_1)^e\ w_q = (6.0000\,\mathrm{cm})(3.4151^\circ\mathrm{C})0.5000 \\ &= 10.2452^\circ\mathrm{C\ cm}. \end{aligned}$$

Set $q = 2$, the Jacobian there is

$$\boldsymbol{J}(r_2)^e = [0.2990\ -1.2990\ -1.2990\ 2.2990] \begin{Bmatrix} 2 \\ 4 \\ 6 \\ 8 \end{Bmatrix} \mathrm{cm} = 6.0000\,\mathrm{cm}.$$

The function at the point is $u(r_1) = [0.0528\ -0.2745\ 1.0245\ 0.1972]$ $\begin{Bmatrix} 2 \\ 3 \\ 0 \\ -1 \end{Bmatrix}$ °C so $u(r_1) = -0.9151^\circ$C and the contribution from this point is

$$\begin{aligned} I_q &= u(r_1)\boldsymbol{J}(r_1)^e\ w_q = (6.0000\,\mathrm{cm})(-0.9151^\circ\mathrm{C})0.5000 \\ &= -2.7452^\circ\mathrm{C\,cm}. \end{aligned}$$

Therefore, the total integral is $I_u = 10.2452^\circ\mathrm{C\,cm} - 2.7452^\circ\mathrm{C\,cm} = 7.5000^\circ$ cm, which agrees with the analytically integrated value.

Example 5.1-4 Given: Using numerical integration determine the physical y-moment of inertia of the cubic line element in prior Example 5.1-2 with nodal coordinates of $\boldsymbol{x}^{e^T} = [2,\ 4,\ 6,\ 8]$ cm with respect to the first node.

Solution: The definition of the moment of inertia with respect to the y-axis (x-origin) is

$$I_Y = \int_{L^e} x^2\, dx = \int_0^1 x(r)^2 \frac{dx(r)}{dr} dr = \sum_{q=1}^{n_q} x(r_q)^2 \frac{dx(r_q)}{dr} w_q$$

The exact integral for a specific element is $I_Y^e = L^e x_1^2 + L^{e^2} x_1 + L^{e^3} \big/ 3 = 168\,\text{cm}^3$. For equal spaced physical nodes on a straight line, the geometry is linear:

$$x(r) = (1-r)x_1^e + r x_4^e = [(1-r)\ r] \begin{Bmatrix} x_1 \\ x_4 \end{Bmatrix}^e, \quad \text{and}$$

$$\frac{dx(r)}{dr} = (x_4^e - x_1^e) \equiv L^e.$$

Since $x(r)$ is degree one, and the Jacobian is constant (degree 0) the total polynomial degree to be integrated is $(1 + 1 + 0) = 2$, so a two-point rule ($n_q = 2$) will exactly integrate the moment of inertia. Recalling that in matrix notation

$$x(r)^2 = x(r)^T x(r) = \left[[(1-r)\ r] \begin{Bmatrix} x_1 \\ x_4 \end{Bmatrix}^e \right]^T [(1-r)\ r] \begin{Bmatrix} x_1 \\ x_4 \end{Bmatrix}^e$$

$$x(r)^2 = [x_1\ x_4]^e \begin{Bmatrix} (1-r) \\ r \end{Bmatrix} [(1-r)\ r] \begin{Bmatrix} x_1 \\ x_4 \end{Bmatrix}^e$$

$$x(r)^2 = [x_1\ x_4]^e \begin{bmatrix} (1-r)^2 & (1-r)r \\ (1-r)r & r^2 \end{bmatrix} \begin{Bmatrix} x_1 \\ x_4 \end{Bmatrix}^e.$$

Now, for the first time, the integrand is a square matrix and the resultant scalar will come from a row matrix times the square matrix times a column matrix. Namely,

$$I_Y^e = \int_0^1 x(r)^2 \frac{dx(r)}{dr} dr = [x_1\ x_4]^e$$
$$\times \int_0^1 \begin{bmatrix} (1-r)^2 & (1-r)r \\ (1-r)r & r^2 \end{bmatrix} L^e dr \begin{Bmatrix} x_1 \\ x_4 \end{Bmatrix}^e.$$

Let $\boldsymbol{S}^e$ be the square matrix:

$$\boldsymbol{S}^e = L^e \int_0^1 \begin{bmatrix} (1-r)^2 & (1-r)r \\ (1-r)r & r^2 \end{bmatrix} dr = \frac{L^e}{6} \begin{bmatrix} 2 & 1 \\ 1 & 2 \end{bmatrix}.$$

Then the matrix notation of the exact moment of inertia is

$$I_Y^e = [x_1 \ x_4]^e \frac{L^e}{6} \begin{bmatrix} 2 & 1 \\ 1 & 2 \end{bmatrix} \begin{Bmatrix} x_1 \\ x_4 \end{Bmatrix}^e$$

$$(1 \times 1) = (1 \times 2)(2 \times 2)(2 \times 1).$$

The given statement requires the integration (of $\boldsymbol{S}^e$) to be done numerically.

$$\boldsymbol{S}^e = L^e \sum_{q=1}^{n_q=2} \begin{bmatrix} (1-r_q)^2 & (1-r_q)r_q \\ (1-r_q)r_q & r_q^2 \end{bmatrix} w_q.$$

Again, $r_1 = 0.21132$ and $r_2 = 0.78868$, and $w_1 = w_2 = 0.50000$. The numerical integral is

$$\boldsymbol{S}^e = \boldsymbol{0} + L^e \begin{bmatrix} (1-0.21132)^2 & (1-0.21132)0.21132 \\ (1-0.21132)0.21132 & 0.21132^2 \end{bmatrix} 0.5000$$

$$+ L^e \begin{bmatrix} (1-0.78868)^2 & (1-0.78868)0.78868 \\ \text{symmetric} & 0.78868^2 \end{bmatrix} 0.5000$$

$$= L^e \begin{bmatrix} 0.3333 & 0.1667 \\ 0.1667 & 0.3333 \end{bmatrix}.$$

Finally, substituting the other numerical constants,

$$I_Y^e = [2 \ 8]\,\text{cm}\ (6\,\text{cm}) \begin{bmatrix} 0.3333 & 0.1667 \\ 0.1667 & 0.3333 \end{bmatrix} \begin{Bmatrix} 2 \\ 8 \end{Bmatrix} \text{cm} = 168.0\,\text{cm}^3.$$

Of course, if the interpolations are done using natural coordinate interpolations, the exact same matrix integrals and results are obtained (try it).

Example 5.1-5 Given: The generalized mass matrix for a line element is defined (later) as

$$\boldsymbol{M}^e = \int_{x_1}^{x_3} \boldsymbol{H}(r)^{\boldsymbol{T}} c(x) \boldsymbol{H}(r) dx,$$

where $c(x)$ is a known property (like the mass per unit length). Evaluate this integral for a quadratic line element, with constant property c, by using exact numerical integration.

Solution: In parametric coordinate space, the definition of the matrix is

$$\boldsymbol{M}^e = \int_0^1 \boldsymbol{H}(r)^{\boldsymbol{T}} c(r) \boldsymbol{H}(r) \frac{dx}{dr} dr.$$

First, it is necessary to establish the polynomial degree of the integrand. Here, $\boldsymbol{H}(r)$ is of degree 2 (quadratic):

$$\boldsymbol{H}(r) = [(1 - 3r + 2r^2)\ (4r - 4r^2)\ (-r + 2r^2)].$$

The source term $c(r)$ is constant (degree 0). Require equal physical node spacing so the determinant of element Jacobian is also constant (degree 0), $|J(r)^e| = L^e$. For these restrictions, the degree of the polynomial to be integrated is

$$\text{Degree} = (2 + 0 + 2 + 0) = 4 \leq (2n_q - 1)$$
$$5 \leq 2n_q, n_q = 2.5, \text{ rounding up } n_q = 3.$$

Therefore,

$$\boldsymbol{M}^e = \sum_{q=1}^{n_q} \boldsymbol{H}(r_q)^{\boldsymbol{T}} c \boldsymbol{H}(r_q) |J(r_q)^e|\ w_q$$

$$= c^e L^e \sum_{q=1}^{n_q=3} \boldsymbol{H}(r_q)^{\boldsymbol{T}} \boldsymbol{H}(r_q) w_q$$

$$(3 \times 3) = \sum [(3 \times 1)(1 \times 1)(1 \times 3)(1 \times 1)],$$

where the tabulated locations and weights, in unit coordinates, are

$$\boldsymbol{r_q} = \begin{Bmatrix} 1.1270166537925831148e-01 \\ 5.0000000000000000000e-01 \\ 8.8729833462074168852e-01 \end{Bmatrix},$$

$$\boldsymbol{w_q} = \begin{Bmatrix} 2.7777777777777777778e-01 \\ 4.4444444444444444445e-01 \\ 2.7777777777777777778e-01 \end{Bmatrix}.$$

Starting with $\boldsymbol{M}^e = \boldsymbol{0}$, loop over each Gaussian quadrature point, numerically form $\boldsymbol{H}(r_q)$, numerically calculate the matrix product, $\boldsymbol{H}(r_q)^T \boldsymbol{H}(r_q)$, add that matrix to $\boldsymbol{M}^e$. After that loop, multiply (numerically) the final square matrix by the element constants for the final result which approximates the exact integral:

$$\boldsymbol{M}^e = c^e L^e \begin{bmatrix} 0.13333 & 0.06667 & -0.03333 \\ 0.06667 & 0.53333 & 0.06667 \\ -0.03333 & 0.06667 & 0.13333 \end{bmatrix}$$

$$\approx \frac{c^e L^e}{30} \begin{bmatrix} 4 & 2 & -1 \\ 2 & 16 & 2 \\ -1 & 2 & 4 \end{bmatrix}.$$

Note: In higher space dimensions the Jacobian is usually not a constant. However, in practical problems where the mesh has many small elements, the Jacobian will be very close to a constant. Thus, the number of quadrature points is often increased by one to account for a not exactly constant Jacobian.

Example 5.1-6 Given: In Example 4.2-3, a segment of a circular arc is modeled as a planar curve by a single four-noded line element in order to approximately determine its shape. The planar curve

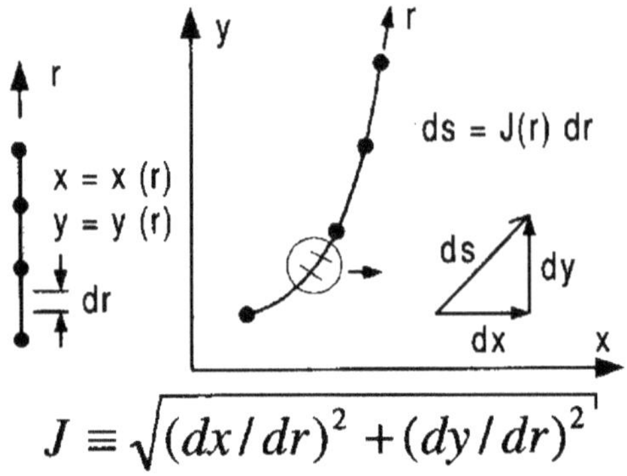

Fig. 5.1-6: Rectangular variable Jacobian curve matrices.

was plotted in Fig. 4.2-12. Outline how to determine the length of any planar curve, such as that arc.

Solution: The length of a planar curve is $L = \int_L^{ds} = \int_0^1 \frac{ds}{dr} dr$, where the physical differential arc length is $ds^2 = dx^2 + dy^2$ and since both x and y are functions of the change of variable, r, this extends to

$$\left(\frac{ds}{dr}\right)^2 = \left(\frac{dx}{dr}\right)^2 + \left(\frac{dy}{dr}\right)^2 \rightarrow \frac{ds}{dr} = \sqrt{\left(\frac{dx}{dr}\right)^2 + \left(\frac{dy}{dr}\right)^2},$$

as shown in Fig. 5.1-6, and the length in general is

$$L = \int_L^{ds} = \int_0^1 \sqrt{\left(\frac{dx}{dr}\right)^2 + \left(\frac{dy}{dr}\right)^2}\, dr.$$

This shows that when the number of physical space dimensions exceeds the number of parametric dimensions, then the Jacobian matrix is rectangular, as illustrated in Fig. 2.2-1, and almost always variable. The above two squared terms are components to the (non-unit) tangent vector of the planar curve, at local position r.

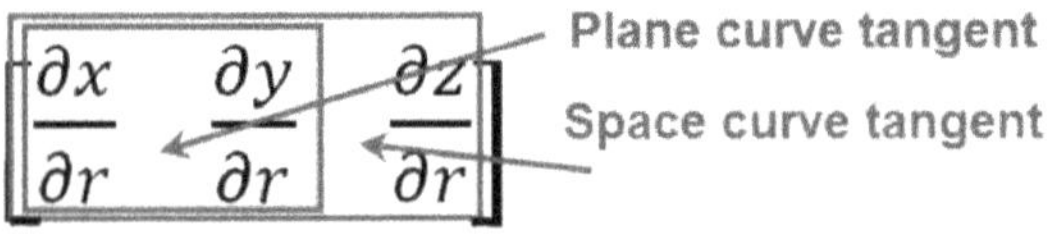

In a FEA, those gradients are simply the local derivatives of the interpolations times their respective input coordinated:

$$\frac{dx(r)}{dr} = \frac{\partial \boldsymbol{H}(r)}{\partial r}\boldsymbol{x}^e \quad \text{and} \quad \frac{dy(r)}{dr} = \frac{\partial \boldsymbol{H}(r)}{\partial r}\boldsymbol{y}^e,$$

so

$$L = \int_L ds = \int_0^1 \sqrt{\left(\frac{\partial \boldsymbol{H}(r)}{\partial r}\boldsymbol{x}^e\right)^2 + \left(\frac{\partial \boldsymbol{H}(r)}{\partial r}\boldsymbol{y}^e\right)^2}\, dr.$$

However, that is a complicated integral to integrate analytically, so apply numerical integration as follows:

$$L = 0 + \sum_{q=1}^{q=n_q} \sqrt{\left(\frac{\partial \boldsymbol{H}(r_q)}{\partial r}\boldsymbol{x}^e\right)^2 + \left(\frac{\partial \boldsymbol{H}(r_q)}{\partial r}\boldsymbol{y}^e\right)^2}\, w_q,$$

where the r_q and w_q are tabulated for each q in the chosen parametric space. At each quadrature point, q, the row matrix $\partial \boldsymbol{H}(r_q)/\partial \mathrm{r}$ is numerically evaluated; then numerically multiplied by the column of coordinate data, say $\boldsymbol{x}^e$; resulting in a scalar contribution $dx(r_q)/dr$ which is numerically squared and added to the square of the similar $dy(r_q)/dr$ term; and then the square root is taken numerically. Finally, that number is multiplied by the numerical value of the tabulated weight, w_q; the numerical sum is updated and the process is repeated at the next quadrature point.

Example 5.1-7 Given: In Example 4.2-3, a 90-degree segment of a circular arc was modeled as a planar curve by a single four-noded cubic line element in order to approximately plot it in Fig. 4.2-12. If the arc center point is at the x, y origin, and the exact x- and y-coordinates of the four nodes of the cubic element are located at $\boldsymbol{x}^e = [4,\ 3.464,\ 2,\ 0]'\,\mathrm{cm}$, and $\boldsymbol{y}^e = [0,\ 2,\ 3.464,\ 4]'\,\mathrm{cm}$, determine the length of that planar curve by numerical integration.

Solution: From Example 5.1-6 that length is

$$L = \sum_{q=1}^{q=n_q} \sqrt{\left(\frac{\partial \boldsymbol{H}(r_q)}{\partial r}\boldsymbol{x}^e\right)^2 + (\frac{\partial \boldsymbol{H}(r_q)}{\partial r}\boldsymbol{y}^e)^2 w_q}.$$

The first step is to determine the number of quadrature points required, and that is defined by the degree of the polynomial being integrated. Recall that the local derivatives of the cubic line element in unit coordinates are

$$\frac{\partial \boldsymbol{H}(r)}{\partial r} = [(-11 + 36r - 27r^2)\ (18 - 90r + 81r^2) \cdots$$
$$(-9 + 72r - 81r^2)\ (2 - 18r + 27r^2)]/2.$$

Since the coordinate is interpolated by the above cubic polynomial, the polynomial degree of the derivative, $dx(r)/dr$, is 2. Squaring the terms and then taking the square root of their sum could give back a polynomial degree of 2, but the square root operator likely does not yield a polynomial result. So the degree of the integrand is an unclear 2+, but not 3. A rule with n_q points exactly integrates a polynomial of degree $D = (2n_q - 1)$. A one-point rule would not be enough here; a two-point rule should be sufficient, and a three-point rule is fine but inefficient. The two-point tabulated quadrature locations in unit coordinates are $r_1 = 0.21132$ and $r_2 = 0.78868$, and the two tabulated weights are the same, $w_1 = w_2 = 0.50000$. At the first point

$$\frac{dx(r_1)}{dr} = \frac{\partial \boldsymbol{H}(r_1)}{\partial \text{r}}\boldsymbol{x}^e = [-2.299\ 1.299\ 1.299\ -0.299] \begin{Bmatrix} 4 \\ 3.424 \\ 2 \\ 0 \end{Bmatrix}$$
$$= -5.8498\,\text{cm}.$$

Likewise, $dy(r_1)/dr = 2.0982\,\text{cm}$ so the incremental addition to the length is 3.1074 cm and the second point gives a similar increment for a total planar cubic length of 6.2480 cm, versus the exact arc length of 6.2832 cm. Using more elements increases the accuracy of the curve length.

```
function [] = planar_curve_segment ()      % via cubic
r_q (1) = 2.113248654051871177454 3e-01    ; % qp data
r_q (2) = 7.886751345948128822545 7e-01    ; % qp data
w_q (1) = 5.0000000000000000000000e-01     ; % qp data
w_q (2) = 5.0000000000000000000000e-01     ; % qp data
n_q = 2 ; L = 0 ;                          % initialize
x = [4; 3.424; 2; 0]; y = [0; 2; 3.464; 4]; % curve
for q = 1:n_q     ; % loop over all quadrature points
 r =  r_q (q)               ; % gather tabulated data
 DLH = [(-11/2+18*r-27*r^2/2), (9-45*r+81*r^2/2),...
        (-9/2+36*r-81*r^2/2),   (1-9*r+27*r^2/2)]
 dx_dr = DLH * x    ; % x component of tangent vector
 dy_dr = DLH * y    ; % y component of tangent vector
 dL = sqrt ( dx_dr^2 + dy_dr^2) * w_q(q) ; % segment
 L = L + dL   ; % add segment to planar curve length
end                       ; % for all quadrature points
fprintf ('Curve length = %10.4e \n', L ); % list FEA
R = 4 ; L = R * pi() / 2 ;                 % exact arc
fprintf ('Arc length   = %10.4e \n', L ); % list arc
% end planar_curve_segment via cubic
```

Fig. 5.1-7: Planar curve segment length by numerical integration.

Example 5.1-8 Given: Implement Example 5.1-7 via a Matlab script.

Solution: See Fig. 5.1-7.

5.2 Two- and Three-Dimensional Quadratures

The quadrature rules for quadrilaterals and hexahedra are simply products of the one-dimensional rule appropriate for the degree of a polynomial in each direction (which are almost always the same degree). The products of two- and three-point rules (in each parametric direction) in a quadrilateral are illustrated in Fig. 5.2-1.

The Matlab script *qp_rule_nat_quad.m* shown in Fig. 5.2-2 creates the numerical integration data for a quadrilateral in natural coordinates. The only input argument is the *total* number of two-dimensional integration points. That value is the square of the number of one-dimensional integration points to be used in each parametric direction. The return items are the two parametric coordinates and the combined weight at each quadrature point. Only one line needs to be changed to create equivalent unit coordinate quadrature data. For a hexahedron a similar script would just use three loops. Of course, its input argument would have to be the *cube*

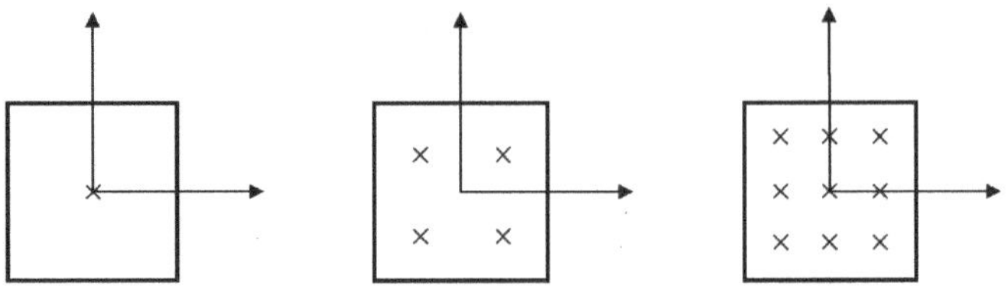

(a) 1×1 (b) 2×2 (c) 3×3

Fig. 5.2-1: Product of 1, 2, and 3 quadrature point rules in a square.

```
function [r_q, s_q, w_q] = qp_rule_nat_quad (n_q) % ===============
%  tables of quadrature point locations and weights for
%  quadrilaterals interpolated in natural coords, -1 <= r,s <= 1
% n_q = 2-D number of quadrature points required, = n_1^2
% r_q = all of first parametric quadrature coordinates
% s_q = all of second parametric quadrature coordinates
% w_q = weight at all quadrature points in n_p
% n_1 = number of 1-D points in each direction

if ( n_q == 1 )          ; % exact for constant or linear polynomial
  r_q = [ 0 ] ; s_q = [ 0 ] ; w_q = [ 4 ] ;   % centroid point data

% tensor products of 1-D rule
elseif ( n_q == 4 | n_q == 9 | n_q == 16 | n_q == 25 ); % tabulated
  n_1 = fix ( sqrt ( n_q ) )                      ; % size of 1-D rule
  [r_1, w_1] = qp_rule_Gauss (n_1)               ; % get 1-D rule data
  k = 0                                   ; % initialize point number
  for i = 1 : n_1                      ; % loop over points in s-direction
    for j = 1 : n_1                    ; % loop over points in r-direction
      k = k + 1                      ; % point number in the quadrilateral
      w_q (k) = w_1 (i) * w_1 (j)           ; % product of 1-D weights
      r_q (k) = r_1 (j)                ; % r-coordinate in qudrilateral
      s_q (k) = r_1 (i)                ; % s-coordinate in qudrilateral
    end                                ; % for j point in quadrilateral
  end                                  ; % for i point in quadrilateral
else % update the tables
  error ('\nERROR quadrature rule not tabulated for these points')
end % if number of quadrature points
% end qp_rule_nat_quad % ===========================================
```

Fig. 5.2-2: Creating quadrilateral integration rule from the one-dimensional rule.

of the number of one-dimensional points used in each parametric direction.

It is not unusual for a FEA to include over a million elements. Then, the numerical integration loop involves a significant amount of computations. Therefore, some specialized integration rules have been developed that give the same accuracy with fewer points. For example, in a hexahedra element, the Gauss process often requires 27 points, but there is a special rule that uses only 14 points for the same accuracy.

The quadrature rules for triangles and tetrahedra do not have a simple equation relating the number of quadrature points to the polynomial degree. The quadrature points in triangles fall along the lines that bisect the corner angles of the element, as shown in Fig. 5.2-3.

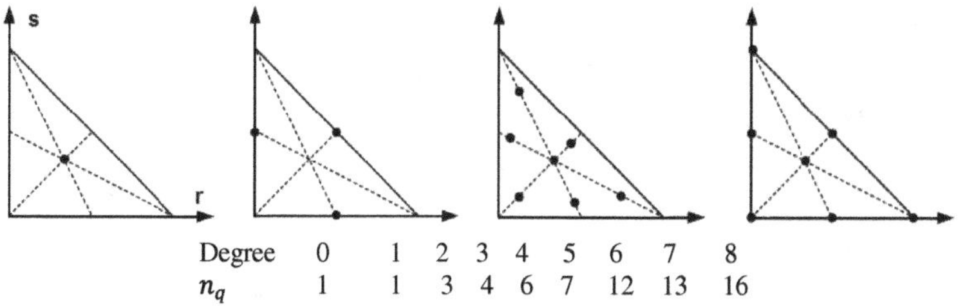

Fig. 5.2-3: Some symmetric quadrature locations for unit right triangle.

```
function [r_q, s_q, w_q] = qp_rule_unit_tri (n_q) % ============
% Tables of quadrature point locations and weights for triangles
% interpolated in unit coordinates, 0 <= r,s <= 1, to n_q = 16.
% For degree = 1,2,3,4,5, 6, 7, 8, 9,10,11,12,13,14,15,16,17
% need n_q   = 1,3,4,6,7,12,13,16,19,25,27,33,37,42,48,52,61
. . .
if ( n_q == 1 )          % exact for constant or linear polynomial
  r_q = [ 1 / 3.] ; s_q = [ 1 / 3.] ; w_q = [ 1 / 2.] ;
elseif ( n_q == 3 )            % exact for 2-nd degree polynomials
  r_q = [6.6666666666666667e-01, 1.6666666666666667e-01, ...
         1.6666666666666667e-01 ] ;
  s_q = [1.6666666666666667e-01, 6.6666666666666667e-01, ...
         1.6666666666666667e-01 ] ;
  w_q = [1.6666666666666666e-01,  1.6666666666666667e-01, ...
         1.6666666666666667e-01 ] ;
elseif ( n_q == 4 )            % exact for 3-rd degree polynomials
. . .
elseif ( n_q == 6 )            % exact for 4-th degree polynomials
. . .
elseif ( n_q == 7 )            % exact for 5-th degree polynomials
  r_q = [0.10128651, 0.47014206, 0.79742699, 0.47014206, ...
         0.10128651, 0.05971587, 0.33333333 ] ;
  s_q = [0.10128651, 0.05971587, 0.10128651, 0.47014206, ...
         0.79742699, 0.47014206, 0.33333333 ] ;
  w_q = [0.06296959, 0.06619708, 0.06296959, 0.06619708, ...
         0.06296959, 0.06619708, 0.11250000 ] ;
elseif (n_q == 12 )            % exact for 6-th degree polynomials
. . .
elseif (n_q == 13 )            % exact for 7-th degree polynomials
. . .
elseif (n_q == 16 )            % exact for 8-th degree polynomials
. . .
else                                         % update the tables
  fprintf ('ERROR: In qp_rule_unit_tri n_q = %i \n', n_q)
  error ('quadrature rule not tabulated for these points')
end % if number of quadrature points
% end qp rule unit tri % ====================================
```

Fig. 5.2-4: Selected triangular quadrature data values.

The number of quadrature points in a triangle required to integrate polynomials from degrees 1 to 8 can be shown to be 1, 3, 4, 6, 7, 12, 13, and 16, respectively. They are available from the Matlab function *qp_rule_unit_tri.m* (Fig. 5.2-4), and data for higher degrees are in function *qp_rule_high_unit_tri.m*. In each case, the single argument to the script is the total number of required quadrature points in the triangle (and *not* the degree of the polynomial being integrated).

The two simplest quadrature rules are the internal (versus internal and boundary points) one-point rule ($n_q = 1$) located at the centroid with $r_1 = 1/3 = s_1$ and $w_1 = 1/2$ for integrating constant and linear functions; and the mid-angle symmetric three-point rule (for degree ≤ 2) with $r_1 = 1/6$, $s_1 = 1/6$; $r_2 = 4/6$, $s_2 = 1/6$, and $r_3 = 1/6$, $s_3 = 4/6$, and $w_1 = w_2 = w_3 = 1/6$.

Example 5.2-1 Given: For a four-noded square element in local natural coordinates, centered on the square, evaluate the local moment of inertia with respect to the a-axis:

$$I_{aa} = \int_{\boxdot} b^2 d\boxdot = \iint_{-1}^{1} b^2 da\, db = \int_{-1}^{1} b^2 \left(\int_{-1}^{1} da \right) db = 2\, \frac{b^3}{3} \bigg|_{-1}^{1}$$
$$= 2 \frac{1^3 - (-1)^3}{3} = \frac{4}{3},$$

by numerical integration and check it with handbook values for right-angled rectangles.

Solution: The integral is quadratic in b, so a two-point rule in each local direction will give the exact results. That is, use the four-point rule ($n_q = 4$) like Fig. 5.2-1:

$$I_{aa} = \int b^2\, d\boxdot = \int_{-1}^{1} \int_{-1}^{1} b^2\, da\, db = \sum_{q=1}^{n_q=4} b_q^2\, w_q.$$

From the Introduction and Summary, the points at a_q and b_q are located at $a_q = \pm 1/\sqrt{3}$ and all have a weight of $w_q = 1$. Summing:

$$I_{aa} = 0 + \left(\frac{-1}{\sqrt{3}} \right)^2 \times 1 + \left(\frac{-1}{\sqrt{3}} \right)^2 \times 1 + \left(\frac{1}{\sqrt{3}} \right)^2 \times 1 + \left(\frac{1}{\sqrt{3}} \right)^2 \times 1 = \frac{4}{3}.$$

Checking a geometric properties table for common shapes gives the inertia of a right rectangle with respect to its centerline as $I_{aa} = \frac{1}{12} \mathit{base}\, \text{height}^3 = \frac{1}{12}(2)(2)^3 = \frac{4}{3}$.

Example 5.2-2 Given: All straight-sided triangles have a constant Jacobian matrix and determinant. Use this fact to calculate the area of the triangle.

Solution: The integration of a constant is simple and the exact result, for comparison, is

$$\begin{aligned} A^e &= \int_A^e dA = \int_{A^e} dx\, dy = \int_{\boxdot} |\boldsymbol{J}^e|\, d\boxdot = |\boldsymbol{J}^e| \int_{\boxdot} d\boxdot \\ &= |\boldsymbol{J}^e| \int_0^1 \int_0^{1-r} ds\, dr \\ &= |\boldsymbol{J}^e| \frac{1}{2} \rightarrow |\boldsymbol{J}^e| = 2A^e, \end{aligned}$$

and any constant can be integrated exactly by a one-point rule ($n_q = 1$). Here, the chapter summary shows that the one-point weight is 0.5 (evaluated at the centroid of the parametric triangle) so the triangle physical area numerical integration reduces to

$$A^e = |\boldsymbol{J}^e| \int_{\boxdot} d\boxdot = |\boldsymbol{J}^e| \sum_{q=1}^{n_q=1} w_q = |\boldsymbol{J}^e| \frac{1}{2} \rightarrow |\boldsymbol{J}^e| = 2A^e.$$

Another way of saying this is that the determinant of the Jacobian of all straight-sided triangles is just twice the physical area of the triangle $|\boldsymbol{J}^e| = 2A^e$ (for straight triangles only). In the following chapters, it will be shown that using the coordinates of the three vertices reduces the constant Jacobian determinant to

$$|\boldsymbol{J}^e| = (x_2 - x_1)^e (y_3 - y_1)^e - (x_3 - x_1)^e (y_2 - y_1)^e = 2A^e,$$

when the corners are numbered counter-clockwise.

Example 5.2-3 Given: For a linear unit triangle element, evaluate the local polar moment of inertia

$$I_{rs} = \int_{\boxdot} rs d\boxdot,$$

and check it with handbook values for right triangles.

Solution: The integral is only linear in r and s, so it is of degree 2. Thus, either the one-point or the three-point rule will give the exact results. Use the three-point rule ($n_q = 3$):

$$I_{rs} = \int_{\boxdot} r\ s\ d\boxdot = \int_0^1 \int_0^{1-r} r\, s\, ds\, dr = \sum_{q=1}^{n_q=3} r_q s_q w_q,$$

$$I_{rs} = 0 + \frac{1}{6}\frac{1}{6}\frac{1}{6} + \frac{4}{6}\frac{1}{6}\frac{1}{6} + \frac{1}{6}\frac{4}{6}\frac{1}{6} = \frac{9}{216} = \frac{1}{24}.$$

Checking a geometric properties table for common shapes gives the polar inertia of a right triangle with respect to the right angle corner as

$$I_{rs} = \frac{1}{24}\text{base}^2\text{height}^2 = \frac{1}{24}1^2 1^2 = \frac{1}{24}.$$

5.3 Summary

Notation

n_e ≡ Number of elements

n_m ≡ Number of mesh nodes

n_p ≡ Dimension of parametric space

n_s ≡ Dimension of physical space

n_g ≡ Number of generalized DOF per node

n_n ≡ Number of nodes per element

n_q ≡ Number of total quadrature points

Element interpolations utilized in this chapter

Element Type	Example Number	Polynomial Degree	n_p	n_g	n_n	$n_i = n_g \times n_n$	Continuity Level
Lagrange L3	5.1-4	2	1	1	3	3	C^0
Lagrange L4	5.1-1, 5.1-2, 5.1-3	3	1	1	4	4	C^0
Lagrange T3	5.2-2, 5.2-3, 5.3-1	1	2	1	3	3	C^0
Lagrange Q4	5.2-1, 5.2-4	1	2	1	4	4	C^0

Definition of Jacobian:

$$[\boldsymbol{J}] \equiv \left[\frac{\partial(x,y,z)}{\partial(r,s,t)}\right], \quad 1-D:\ [\boldsymbol{J}] \equiv \left[\frac{\partial x(r)}{\partial r}\right],$$

$$2-D:[\boldsymbol{J}] \equiv \begin{bmatrix} \partial x/\partial r & \partial y/\partial r \\ \partial x/\partial s & \partial y/\partial s \end{bmatrix}.$$

Numerical integration:

$$\int_{\boxdot} \boldsymbol{F}(r)d\boxdot \approx \sum_{q=1}^{n_q} \boldsymbol{F}(r_q)w_q$$

$$\int_{\Omega} \boldsymbol{F}(r)d\Omega = \int_{\boxdot} \boldsymbol{F}(r)\left|\boldsymbol{J}^e\right|d\boxdot \approx \sum_{q=1}^{n_q} \boldsymbol{F}(r_q)\left|\boldsymbol{J}^e(r_q)\right|w_q.$$

Exact unit coordinate integral for the straight triangle (only):

$$I = \int_A^e r^m s^n dA = 2A^e m!n!/(2+m+n)!.$$

Number of quadrature points for exact one-dimensional polynomial numerical integration:

$$\text{Degree} \le (2n_q - 1).$$

Gaussian one-dimensional one-point line rule data, in unit coordinates and natural coordinates:

$$r_1 = 0.5, \quad w_1 = 1; \qquad a_1 = 0, \quad w_1 = 2.$$

Gaussian one-dimensional two-point line rule data, in unit coordinates and natural coordinates:

$$r_1 = (1 - 1/\sqrt{3})/2 = 0.21132, r_2 = (1 + 1/\sqrt{3})/2 = 0.78867,$$

$$w_1 = w_2 = 0.50000,$$

$$a_1 = -1/\sqrt{3} = -0.57735, a_2 = 1/\sqrt{3} = 0.57735,$$

$$w_1 = w_2 = 1.00000.$$

Number of points needed for integrating polynomials on triangles:

Degree	0	1	2	3	4	5	6	7	8
n_q	1	1	3	4	6	7	12	13	16.

Quadrature unit triangle one-point rule (for degree ≤ 1):

$$r_1 = 1/3, \quad s_1 = 1/3, \quad w_1 = 1/2.$$

Quadrature unit triangle three-point rule (for degree ≤ 2)

$$r_1 = 1/6, \quad s_1 = 1/6, \quad w_1 = 1/6,$$

$$r_2 = 4/6, \quad s_2 = 1/6, \quad w_2 = 1/6,$$

$$r_3 = 1/6, \quad s_3 = 4/6, \quad w_3 = 1/6.$$

Lagrange linear C^0 line interpolations ($n_p = 1$), in unit coordinates:

local nodes at ($r = 0$) and ($r = 1$), $n_n = 2$, $n_g = 1$, $\boldsymbol{\delta}^{\boldsymbol{e}^T} = [u_1\ u_2]$,

$$\boldsymbol{H}(r) = [(1-r)r], \quad \partial \boldsymbol{H}(r)/\partial r = [-1 \quad 1].$$

Lagrange quadratic C^0 line interpolations ($n_p = 1$), in unit coordinates:

local nodes at ($r = 0$), ($r = 1/2$) and ($r = 1$), $n_n = 3$, $n_g = 1$, $\boldsymbol{\delta}^{\boldsymbol{e}^T} = [u_1\ u_2\ u_3]$

$$\boldsymbol{H}(r) = \left[(1 - 3r + 2r^2)(4r - 4r^2)(-r + 2r^2)\right],$$

$$\partial \boldsymbol{H}(r)/\partial r = [(3 + 4r)(4 - 8r)(-1 + 4r)].$$

Lagrange cubic C^0 line interpolations ($n_p = 1, n_n = 4$), in unit coordinates:

with local nodes at ($r = 0$), ($r = 1/3$), ($r = 2/3$) and ($r = 1$). DOF,

$$\boldsymbol{\delta}^{\boldsymbol{e}^T} = [u_1\ u_2\ u_3\ u_4]$$

$$\boldsymbol{H}(r) = \frac{1}{2}[(2 - 11r + 18r^2 - 9r^3)\ (18r - 45r^2 + 27r^3) \cdots$$
$$(-9r + 36r^2 - 27r^3)\ (2r - 9r^2 + 9r^3)]$$

$$\partial \boldsymbol{H}(r)/\partial r = \frac{1}{2}[(-11 + 36r - 27r^2)\ (18 - 90r + 81r^2) \cdots$$
$$(-9 + 72r - 81r^2)\ (2 - 18r + 27r^2)].$$

Lagrange linear triangle C^0 interpolation ($n_p = 2$, $n_n = 3$, $n_g = 1$), in unit coordinates: with local nodes at ($r = 0$, $s = 0$), ($r = 1$, $s = 0$), and $(r = 0,\ s = 1)$.

$$\boldsymbol{H}(r,s) = [(1-r-s)\ (r)\ (s)]\,, \quad \begin{bmatrix} \partial \boldsymbol{H}/\partial r \\ \partial \boldsymbol{H}/\partial s \end{bmatrix} = \begin{bmatrix} -1 & 1 & 0 \\ -1 & 0 & 1 \end{bmatrix}.$$

Lagrange linear line element consistent mass matrix: $\boldsymbol{M^e} = \frac{\rho^e A^e L^e}{6} \begin{bmatrix} 2 & 1 \\ 1 & 2 \end{bmatrix}$.

Lagrange quadratic line consistent mass:

$$\boldsymbol{M^e} = \frac{\rho^e A^e L^e}{30} \begin{bmatrix} 4 & 2 & -1 \\ 2 & 16 & 2 \\ -1 & 2 & 4 \end{bmatrix} = \frac{m^e}{30} \begin{bmatrix} 4 & 2 & -1 \\ 2 & 16 & 2 \\ -1 & 2 & 4 \end{bmatrix}.$$

Lagrange cubic line element consistent mass matrix:

$$\boldsymbol{M^e} = \frac{\rho^e A^e L^e}{1680} \begin{bmatrix} 128 & 99 & -36 & 19 \\ 99 & 648 & -81 & -36 \\ -36 & -81 & 648 & 99 \\ 19 & -36 & 99 & 128 \end{bmatrix}.$$

Lagrange linear triangle consistent mass matrix:

$$\boldsymbol{M^e} = \frac{\rho^e A^e t^e}{12} \begin{bmatrix} 2 & 1 & 1 \\ 1 & 2 & 1 \\ 1 & 1 & 2 \end{bmatrix} = \frac{m^e}{12} \begin{bmatrix} 2 & 1 & 1 \\ 1 & 2 & 1 \\ 1 & 1 & 2 \end{bmatrix}.$$

5.4 Review

1. Repeat Example 5.3-1 using a one-point quadrature rule.
2. Use numerical integration to verify that the local inertia of a unit triangle, with respect to the r-axis, is

$$I_{rr} = \int_{\boxdot} s^2 d\boxdot = \int_0^1 \int_0^{1-r} s^2 ds\, dr = \frac{1}{12}.$$

3. Use numerical integration to verify that the local inertia of a unit triangle, with respect to the s-axis, is

$$I_{ss} = \int_{\boxdot} r^2 d\boxdot = \int_0^1 \int_0^{1-r} r^2 ds\, dr = \frac{1}{12}.$$

4. Use numerical integration to form the 2×2 Lagrange linear line element consistent mass matrix given in the summary as

$$\boldsymbol{M}^e = \rho^e A^e \int_L^e \boldsymbol{H}^T \boldsymbol{H} dx = \frac{\rho^e A^e L^e}{6} \begin{bmatrix} 2 & 1 \\ 1 & 2 \end{bmatrix}$$

where $\boldsymbol{H}(r) = [(1-r)r]$.

5. Use numerical integration to form the 4×4 Lagrange cubic line element consistent mass matrix given in the summary as

$$\boldsymbol{M}^e = \rho^e A^e \int_L^e \boldsymbol{H}^T \boldsymbol{H} dx = \frac{\rho^e A^e L^e}{30} \begin{bmatrix} 4 & 2 & -1 \\ 2 & 16 & 2 \\ -1 & 2 & 4 \end{bmatrix},$$

where $\boldsymbol{H}(r) = \left[(1-3r+2r^2)(4r-4r^2)(-r+2r^2)\right]$.

6. If a uniform line element utilizes n_q quadrature points, what degree of polynomial will it exactly integrate?
7. Explain why the sum of the one-dimensional Gaussian quadrature weights tabulated over $0 <= r <= 1$ must equal unity, while those tabulated over $-1 <= a <= 1$ must sum to 2.
8. The consistent mass matrix for any element is $\boldsymbol{m}^e = \int_L \boldsymbol{H}^{e^T} \rho \boldsymbol{H}^e dx$. For a four-noded line element (L4) in the unit space, $0 <= r <= 1$, explain how many quadrature points would be required to integrate this matrix exactly for equally spaced physical nodes if the density ρ is $\rho = \rho_0 x^2$.
9. One must usually numerically evaluate the geometric Jacobian matrix at a quadrature point (along with its determinant and inverse). How is the Jacobian matrix actually evaluated, or constructed, within a typical element?
10. How does classic algebra define the polynomial degree of the product of polynomials?
11. The geometric inertia of a rigid straight bar, with respect to $x = 0$, is $I_{yy} = \int_{x_1}^{x_2} x^2 dx$. Interpolate the position as $x(r) = \boldsymbol{H}(r)\boldsymbol{x}^e$ where the end coordinates are $\boldsymbol{x}^e = [x_1 \ x_2]^{\mathrm{T}}$.

   (a) Evaluate the Jacobian of the geometric mapping.
   (b) What is the polynomial degree of the square matrix integrand?

Chapter 6

Equivalent Integral Forms

6.1 Introduction

Most engineering education in the United States places the emphasis on deriving differential equations that govern a physical problem. A course in differential equations provides a few theoretical tools for solving such equations. Today, finite element analysis (FEA) is the most common way to solve differential equations over practical engineering shapes. However, FEA always starts with the governing equation written as an integral over the solution domain and its boundary. Usually, the integral form is one that can be proven to give the same results as some differential equation. In rare cases, the integral form defines a conservation law. The equivalent integral forms for most linear problems in engineering and physics have been known since about the 1750s. For most of the applications to be considered herein, the integral forms are stated without proof.

For linear elliptical partial differential equations, there are two types of integral forms that have the same boundary conditions and whose solutions can be shown to be an exact solution of the PDE. Those two forms are Euler's historical Theorem of Variational Calculus (circa 1750), and the Galerkin Weighted Residual Method (circa 1915). Those two forms yield identical definitions for the finite element matrices. The Galerkin method, mainly used herein, can be used to derive an integral form for nonlinear problems, like fluid flow. Another Method of Weighted Residuals which is also used for FEA is the Least Squares Method, but it has continuity requirements that are difficult to satisfy in two and three dimensions.

The following sections are optional and mainly intended for readers who feel a need to understand some of the mathematics of how equivalent integral forms can be developed for any partial differential equation. Since Galerkin's method is most widely used herein, a brief optional description of that process is given first.

6.2 Galerkin's Method

Let the governing differential equation in a domain, Ω, of physical problems be written symbolically as: $L_\Omega u^* - f^* = 0$, in Ω where the differential operator acting on the exact solution, u^*, is denoted as L_Ω and where f^* is a known source term in Ω Typically, L_Ω is an even order derivative like $\partial^2 u/\partial x^2$. Further, let the Dirichlet essential boundary condition (EBC) on the boundary Γ_{E} be $u = u_E$ on Γ_{E}. The goal is to find (guess) an approximate solution, say u, where the residual error in space

$$R \equiv L_\Omega\, u - f \neq 0, \tag{6.2-1}$$

is reduced to an optimal level. Since that residual error is almost never zero over the total domain, Galerkin's concept was to make the approximate solution, u, "orthogonal to" the residual error it causes.

In mathematical jargon, "orthogonal to" means setting the integral of their product to zero, and there is a standard symbol for that operation. It defines the governing Galerkin integral to be

$$I_G = \langle u, R \rangle \equiv \int_\Omega u R \, d\Omega = 0. \tag{6.2-2}$$

Historically (before FEA), the Galerkin method required assuming a single spatial approximation, containing unknown constants, which identically satisfied all of the Dirichlet and Neumann boundary conditions. That can be very difficult to do in two or three dimensions. The FEA changed the original Galerkin procedure in several ways starting with using piecewise spatial approximations, connected to unknown solution values, which do not satisfy any of the boundary conditions in advance. Those piecewise approximations cover a mesh of non-overlapping finite sized sub-regions of the solution domain, which is the union of all of those finite domains, or elements:

$$\Omega \equiv \cup_e \Omega^e. \tag{6.2-3}$$

That in turn splits the original Galerkin integral into the sum of the integrals over all of the elements

$$I_G = \int_\Omega u\, R\, d\Omega = \sum_{e=1}^{n_e} \int_{\Omega^e} u^e R^e\, d\Omega = 0, \tag{6.2-4}$$

Within each finite element region, Ω^e, a local approximation is taken as the product of a spatial form and constants associated with that element, say $u^e(x) = \boldsymbol{H}^e(x)\,\boldsymbol{\delta}^e = \boldsymbol{\delta}^{e^T}\boldsymbol{H}^e(x)^T$. That makes the residual error in the element depend on that choice

$$R^e \to R^e\left(\frac{\partial^n \boldsymbol{H}^e}{\partial x^n}, \boldsymbol{H}^e, f, \boldsymbol{\delta}^e\right),$$

where n is the order of the highest derivative in the operator, L_Ω. Since both the solution and the residual error both have linear dependence on the unknowns, there will always be a quadratic matrix form (square matrix) coming from the derivatives in the differential equation, and if the source, f, is not zero, there will also be a linear form (column matrix) coming from that source.

The element's unknown solution values, say $\boldsymbol{\delta}^e \subset \boldsymbol{\delta}$, connected to the approximate solution, u, will also appear in the residual term, R. As a vector of constants, they can be removed from both sides of the spatial integral and that converts the FEA Galerkin method into a square matrix defined by the operator, and one or more column matrices defined by the source(s):

$$\begin{aligned} I_G &= \sum_{e=1}^{n_e} \boldsymbol{\delta}^{e^T} \int_{\Omega^e} \boldsymbol{H}^{e^T} R^e\left(\frac{\partial^n \boldsymbol{H}^e}{\partial x^n}, \boldsymbol{H}^e, f, \boldsymbol{\delta}^e\right) d\Omega. \\ I_G &\equiv \sum_{e=1}^{n_e} \boldsymbol{\delta}^{e^T} [\boldsymbol{S}]^e_{L_\Omega}\, \boldsymbol{\delta}^e - \sum_{e=1}^{n_e} \boldsymbol{\delta}^{e^T} \{\boldsymbol{c_f}\}^e = 0. \end{aligned} \tag{6.2-5}$$

Writing the Boolean relation, $\boldsymbol{\delta}^e \subset \boldsymbol{\delta}$, as a matrix identity (given in Section 7.2) the scattering (assembly) of the small element matrices into the large system matrices gives the final conversion of the governing differential equation into the governing matrix form:

$$I_G = \boldsymbol{\delta}^T [\boldsymbol{S}]\,\boldsymbol{\delta} + \boldsymbol{\delta}^T \{\boldsymbol{c_f}\} = \boldsymbol{\delta}^T \{[\boldsymbol{S}]\,\boldsymbol{\delta} - \{\boldsymbol{c_f}\}\} = 0. \tag{6.2-6}$$

However, for this matrix result to be true for arbitrary geometry, properties, and sources, the last column matrix must be a null (zero) vector so

$$[\boldsymbol{S}]\,\boldsymbol{\delta} - \{\boldsymbol{c_f}\} = \{\boldsymbol{0}\} \rightarrow [\boldsymbol{S}]\,\boldsymbol{\delta} = \{\boldsymbol{c_f}\}, \tag{6.2-7}$$

is the governing matrix system, before boundary conditions, to be solved for the unknown constants, $\boldsymbol{\delta}$.

However, this matrix system cannot be solved until it is modified to include the Dirichlet EBC's (Section 7.4) and any Neumann or Mixed conditions that make the answer unique. Usually, the non-essential (Neumann) boundary conditions (NBCs) are included in the column matrix, $\{\boldsymbol{c_f}\}$, and any mixed conditions are included in both matrices, $[\boldsymbol{S}]$ and $\{\boldsymbol{c_f}\}$.

Example 6.2-1 Given: The first-order ODE $\frac{du}{dx} + Au(x) = F$ subjected to the Dirichlet condition $u(0) = 0$ has the exact solution $u(x) = \left(1 - e^{-Ax}\right) F/A$. Obtain the element matrices for a Galerkin FEA approximation.

Solution: Let the spatial approximation in each element be

$$u(x) = \boldsymbol{H}^e(x)\,\boldsymbol{\delta^e} = H_1(x)\,\delta_1^e + \cdots + H_m(x)\,\delta_m^e = \boldsymbol{\delta^{e^T}}\,\boldsymbol{H}^e(x)^T,$$

the derivative is

$$\frac{du(x)}{dx} = \frac{d\boldsymbol{H}^e(x)}{dx}\boldsymbol{\delta^e} = \frac{dH_1(x)}{dx}\delta_1^e + \cdots + \frac{dH_m(x)}{dx}\delta_m^e,$$

and the residual error, $R(x)$, in an element then is

$$R(x)^e = \frac{du}{dx} + Au(x) - F = \frac{d\boldsymbol{H}^e(x)}{dx}\boldsymbol{\delta^e} + A\boldsymbol{H}^e(x)\,\boldsymbol{\delta^e} - F,$$

$$R(x)^e = \left[\frac{d\boldsymbol{H}^e(x)}{dx} + A\boldsymbol{H}^e(x)\right]\boldsymbol{\delta^e} - F.$$

The integral is

$$I_G = \int_\Omega u\,R\,d\Omega = \sum_{e=1}^{n_e}\int_{\Omega^e}\boldsymbol{\delta^{e^T}}\,\boldsymbol{H}^e(x)^T$$

$$\times\left(\left[\frac{d\boldsymbol{H}^e(x)}{dx} + A\boldsymbol{H}^e(x)\right]\boldsymbol{\delta^e} - F\right)d\Omega = 0,$$

$$(1\times 1) = (1\times 2)\,(2\times 1)\,(1\times 2)\,(2\times 1) - (1\times 1)\,(1\times 2)\,(2\times 1),$$

$$I_G = \sum_{e=1}^{n_e=2} \boldsymbol{\delta}^{e^T} \int_{\Omega^e} \boldsymbol{H}^e(x)^T \left[\frac{d\boldsymbol{H}^e(x)}{dx} + A\boldsymbol{H}^e(x)\right] d\Omega \boldsymbol{\delta}^e$$

$$- \sum_{e=1}^{n_e=2} \boldsymbol{\delta}^{e^T} \int_{\Omega^e} \boldsymbol{H}^e(x)^T F \, d\Omega = 0$$

This leads to a square matrix from the differential operator and a column matrix from source terms:

$$\int_{\Omega} u \, R \, d\Omega \equiv \sum_{e=1}^{n_e=2} \boldsymbol{\delta}^{e^T} [\boldsymbol{S}^e] \boldsymbol{\delta}^e - \sum_{e=1}^{n_e=2} \boldsymbol{\delta}^{e^T} \boldsymbol{c}^e = 0,$$

where $[\boldsymbol{S}^e] \equiv \int_{\Omega^e} \boldsymbol{H}^e(x)^T \left[\frac{d\boldsymbol{H}^e(x)}{dx} + A\boldsymbol{H}^e(x)\right] d\Omega$ and $\boldsymbol{c}_{\boldsymbol{F}}^{\boldsymbol{e}} \equiv \int_{\Omega^e} \boldsymbol{H}^e (x)^T F \, d\Omega$.

Since each set of element unknowns is a subset of all of the solution values, $\boldsymbol{\delta}^e \subset \boldsymbol{\delta}$, it will be shown later (Section 7.2) that those summations (assemblies) of each element result in a system-level Galerkin governing matrix form

$$\int_{\Omega} u \, R \, d\Omega = \boldsymbol{\delta}^T [\boldsymbol{S}] \boldsymbol{\delta} - \boldsymbol{\delta}^T \mathbf{c} = 0 = \boldsymbol{\delta}^T \{[\boldsymbol{S}] \boldsymbol{\delta} - \mathbf{c}\}, \rightarrow [\boldsymbol{S}] \boldsymbol{\delta} = \mathbf{c}.$$

But, this system is not unique until it is modified to include the Dirichlet boundary condition.

Example 6.2-2 Given: Evaluate the element matrix forms developed in Example 6.2-1 for $\frac{du}{dx} + Au(x) = F$ using a two-noded line element having a linear spatial interpolation.

Solution: For a line element of length L^e, the physical location in the element can be defined with a non-dimensional coordinate $0 \leq r \leq 1$ as $x(r) = x_1^e + rL^e$. The two coordinates are further related by $dx/dr = L^e$, and its inverse $dr/dx = 1/L^e$. A linear interpolation matrix for a two-node line element can be defined as $\boldsymbol{H}^e(x) = [(1-r)\, r]$. In other words,

$$u(x) = \boldsymbol{H}^e(x)\, \boldsymbol{\delta}^e = [(1-r)\; r] \begin{Bmatrix} \delta_1^e \\ \delta_2^e \end{Bmatrix} = (1-r)\delta_1^e + r\delta_2^e,$$

and its gradient is

$$\frac{du(x)}{dx} = \frac{du(r)}{dr}\frac{dr}{dx} = \frac{du}{dr}\frac{1}{L^e} = \frac{1}{L^e}\frac{d\boldsymbol{H}^e(r)\boldsymbol{\delta^e}}{dr}$$
$$= \frac{1}{L^e}[-1 \ \ +1]\begin{Bmatrix} \delta_1^e \\ \delta_2^e \end{Bmatrix} = \frac{-\delta_1^e + \delta_2^e}{L^e}.$$

For this element type, its square matrix from the residual error is split as

$$[\boldsymbol{S^e}] = \int_{L^e} \boldsymbol{H}^e(x)^T \frac{d\boldsymbol{H}^e(x)}{dx} \mathrm{dx} + \int_{L^e} \boldsymbol{H}^e(x)^T A \boldsymbol{H}^e(x) \mathrm{dx}.$$

Inserting the interpolations

$$[\boldsymbol{S^e}] = \left[\int_0^1 \begin{Bmatrix} 1-r \\ r \end{Bmatrix} \frac{1}{L^e}[-1 \ \ +1](L^e dr)\right.$$
$$\left. + \int_0^1 \begin{Bmatrix} 1-r \\ r \end{Bmatrix} A[(1-r) \ \ r](L^e dr)\right],$$
$$[\boldsymbol{S^e}] = \left[\int_0^1 \begin{bmatrix} (r-1) & (1-r) \\ -r & r \end{bmatrix} dr\right.$$
$$\left. + \mathrm{A}\int_0^1 \begin{bmatrix} (1-r)^2 & r(1-r) \\ r(1-r) & r^2 \end{bmatrix} (L^e dr)\right],$$
$$[\boldsymbol{S^e}] = \left[\left[\begin{matrix} (r^2/2 - r) & (r - r^2/2) \\ -r^2/2 & r^2/2 \end{matrix}\right]_0^1 \cdots\right.$$
$$\left. + AL^e \left[\begin{matrix} (1 - 2r^2/2 + r^3/3) & (r^2/2 - r^3/3) \\ (r^2/2 - r^3/3) & r^3/3 \end{matrix}\right]_0^1\right]$$
$$[\boldsymbol{S^e}] = \left[\frac{1}{2}\begin{bmatrix} -1 & 1 \\ -1 & 1 \end{bmatrix} + \frac{AL^e}{6}\begin{bmatrix} 2 & 1 \\ 1 & 2 \end{bmatrix}\right],$$

its source vector, for constant F, is

$$\{\boldsymbol{c^e}\} \equiv \int_{\Omega^e} \boldsymbol{H}^e(x)^T F \, d\Omega = F \int_{L^e} \boldsymbol{H}^e(x)^T \mathrm{dx}$$

$$= F\int_0^1 \boldsymbol{H}^e(r)^T (L^e dr),$$

$$\{\boldsymbol{c}^e\} = FL^e \int_0^1 \begin{Bmatrix} 1-r \\ r \end{Bmatrix} dr = FL^e \begin{Bmatrix} r - r^2/2 \\ r^2/2 \end{Bmatrix}\Bigg|_0^1 = \frac{FL^e}{2}\begin{Bmatrix} 1 \\ 1 \end{Bmatrix}.$$

Example 6.2-3 Given: Using the linear line element matrices in Example 6.2-2 for $\frac{du}{dx} + Au(x) = F$ with $u(0) = 0$ form a two-element (three nodes) model and assemble the system matrix form for the three degrees of freedom. Apply the Dirichlet boundary condition to form the unique matrix system for the remaining two degrees of freedom.

Solution: The data for a mesh with sequential node and element numbers are

```
Elem        1         2
      *---------*---------*        Elem.  Connections
Node  1         2         3          1       1, 2
DOF   δ1        δ2        δ3         2       2, 3
x     0         L/2       L
```

For arbitrary data and operators, the final result in Example 6.2-1 requires that $[\boldsymbol{S}]\boldsymbol{\delta} - \boldsymbol{c} = \boldsymbol{0}$, and the final 3×3 matrix system $[\boldsymbol{S}]\,\boldsymbol{\delta} = \boldsymbol{c}$ still must satisfy the EBC before they can be solved. The system initially has three degrees of freedom. From the element connections list, the terms from the first element add into rows 1 and 2 of the system matrices, while the second element's contributions add into rows 2 and 3 of the matrices:

$$[\boldsymbol{S}]\,\boldsymbol{\delta} = \boldsymbol{c} \rightarrow \left[\frac{1}{2}\begin{bmatrix} -1 & 1 & 0 \\ -1 & (1-1) & 1 \\ 0 & -1 & 1 \end{bmatrix} + \frac{AL^e}{6}\begin{bmatrix} 2 & 1 & 0 \\ 1 & (2+2) & 1 \\ 0 & 1 & 2 \end{bmatrix}\right]$$

$$\times \begin{Bmatrix} \delta_1 \\ \delta_2 \\ \delta_3 \end{Bmatrix} = \frac{FL^e}{2}\begin{Bmatrix} 1 \\ (1+1) \\ 1 \end{Bmatrix}.$$

So the equivalent matrix form is

$$\left[\frac{1}{2}\begin{bmatrix}-1 & 1 & 0\\ -1 & 0 & 1\\ 0 & -1 & 1\end{bmatrix} + \frac{AL^e}{6}\begin{bmatrix}2 & 1 & 0\\ 1 & 4 & 1\\ 0 & 1 & 2\end{bmatrix}\right]\begin{Bmatrix}\delta_1\\ \delta_2\\ \delta_3\end{Bmatrix} = \frac{FL^e}{2}\begin{Bmatrix}1\\ 2\\ 1\end{Bmatrix}.$$

This system does not include the Dirichlet condition required for a unique solution and thus it cannot be solved (because the square matrix is singular). That condition is applied at $x = 0$ which corresponds to node 1 in the mesh model and the solution value at that node is δ_1. Therefore, the required Dirichlet boundary condition is $\delta_1 = u(0) = 0$. That means that rows 2 and 3 are the only independent equations for the remaining unknowns. Also, the now known value of δ_1 multiples the first column in those rows and those values must be carried to the right-hand side:

$$\left[\frac{1}{2}\begin{bmatrix}0 & 1\\ -1 & 1\end{bmatrix} + \frac{AL^e}{6}\begin{bmatrix}4 & 1\\ 1 & 2\end{bmatrix}\right]\begin{Bmatrix}\delta_2\\ \delta_3\end{Bmatrix}$$
$$= \frac{FL^e}{2}\begin{Bmatrix}2\\ 1\end{Bmatrix} - \delta_1\frac{1}{2}\begin{Bmatrix}-1\\ 0\end{Bmatrix} - \delta_1\frac{AL^e}{6}\begin{Bmatrix}1\\ 0\end{Bmatrix}.$$

Note that the Dirichlet condition could have been set to any non-zero value.

$$\frac{1}{6}\begin{bmatrix}(4AL^e) & (3 + AL^e)\\ (-3 + AL^e) & (3 + 2AL^e)\end{bmatrix}\begin{Bmatrix}\delta_2\\ \delta_3\end{Bmatrix} = \frac{FL^e}{2}\begin{Bmatrix}2\\ 1\end{Bmatrix},$$

which can be solved in closed form, but usually the numerical data are inserted to solve for the unknowns.

Example 6.2-4 Given: Using the numerical values of $A = 2$ and $F = 10$ over a domain with $L = 0.5$, and the mesh data in Example 6.2-3, solve the final unique matrix form for the final degrees of freedom and graph the result along with the exact solution listed in Example 6.2-1.

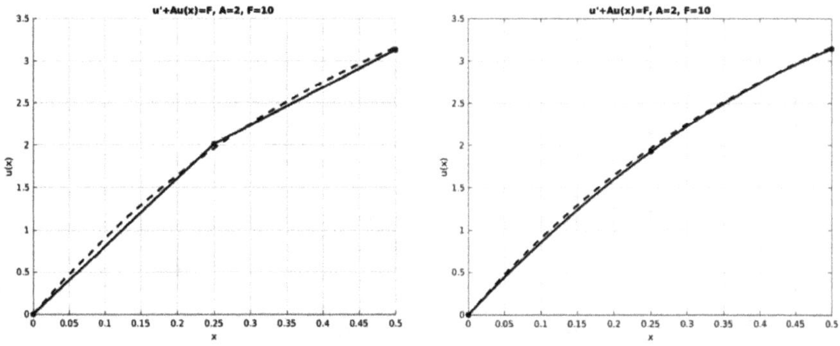

Fig. 6.2-1: Exact (dashed), a two linear (left), and one quadratic element solution (right).

Solution: For this mesh, note that the element length is $L^e = L/2 = 1/4$. Substituting the above coefficients gives the following numerical form:

$$\frac{1}{6}\begin{bmatrix} (4AL^e) & (3+AL^e) \\ (-3+AL^e) & (3+2AL^e) \end{bmatrix}\begin{Bmatrix} \delta_2 \\ \delta_3 \end{Bmatrix} = \frac{FL^e}{2}\begin{Bmatrix} 2 \\ 1 \end{Bmatrix},$$

$$\frac{1}{6}\begin{bmatrix} (4)(2)(1/4) & (3+(2)(1/4)) \\ (-3+(2)(1/4)) & (3+2\,(2)(1/4)) \end{bmatrix}\begin{Bmatrix} \delta_2 \\ \delta_3 \end{Bmatrix} = \frac{10(1/4)}{2}\begin{Bmatrix} 2 \\ 1 \end{Bmatrix},$$

$$\frac{1}{12}\begin{bmatrix} 4 & 7 \\ -5 & 8 \end{bmatrix}\begin{Bmatrix} \delta_2 \\ \delta_3 \end{Bmatrix} = \frac{10}{8}\begin{Bmatrix} 2 \\ 1 \end{Bmatrix} \to \begin{Bmatrix} \delta_2 \\ \delta_3 \end{Bmatrix}$$

$$= \frac{1}{67}\begin{bmatrix} 8 & -7 \\ 5 & 4 \end{bmatrix}\frac{120}{8}\begin{Bmatrix} 2 \\ 1 \end{Bmatrix} = \begin{Bmatrix} 2.015 \\ 3.134 \end{Bmatrix}.$$

Figure 6.2-1 graphs the results which are

x	Exact	FEA	%Error
0.00	0	0	0
0.25	1.967	2.015	2.44
0.50	3.161	3.134	−0.85.

Example 6.2-5 Given: Repeat the numerical analysis in Examples 6.2-1–6.2-4 using a single three-noded quadratic element.

Solution: From (4.2-1) the interpolations are

$$u(r) = \left[\left(1 - 3r+2r^2\right) \left(4r-4r^2\right) \left(-r+2r^2\right) \right] \begin{Bmatrix} \delta_1 \\ \delta_2 \\ \delta_3 \end{Bmatrix}$$

From Tables 4.10-1 and 4.10-2 the integrals are:

$$\int_\Omega \boldsymbol{H}^T \vec{\nabla} \boldsymbol{H} d\Omega = \frac{1}{6} \begin{bmatrix} -3 & 4 & -1 \\ -4 & 0 & 4 \\ 1 & -4 & 3 \end{bmatrix},$$

$$\int_\Omega \boldsymbol{H}^T \boldsymbol{H} d\Omega = \frac{L^e}{30} \begin{bmatrix} 4 & 2 & -1 \\ 2 & 16 & 2 \\ -1 & 2 & 4 \end{bmatrix},$$

and $\int_\Omega \boldsymbol{H}^T d\Omega = \frac{L^e}{6} \begin{Bmatrix} 1 \\ 4 \\ 1 \end{Bmatrix}$. Before enforcing the Dirichlet condition the governing matrix form becomes

$$\left[\frac{1}{6} \begin{bmatrix} -3 & 4 & -1 \\ -4 & 0 & 4 \\ 1 & -4 & 3 \end{bmatrix} + \frac{AL^e}{30} \begin{bmatrix} 4 & 2 & -1 \\ 2 & 16 & 2 \\ -1 & 2 & 4 \end{bmatrix} \right] \begin{Bmatrix} \delta_1 \\ \delta_2 \\ \delta_3 \end{Bmatrix} = \frac{FL^e}{6} \begin{Bmatrix} 1 \\ 4 \\ 1 \end{Bmatrix}$$

Here, the single element covers the entire region so $L^e = L = 1/2$, and again $A = 2$, and $F = 10$, giving

$$\left[\frac{1}{6} \begin{bmatrix} -3 & 4 & -1 \\ -4 & 0 & 4 \\ 1 & -4 & 3 \end{bmatrix} + \frac{1}{30} \begin{bmatrix} 4 & 2 & -1 \\ 2 & 16 & 2 \\ -1 & 2 & 4 \end{bmatrix} \right] \begin{Bmatrix} \delta_1 \\ \delta_2 \\ \delta_3 \end{Bmatrix} = \frac{5}{6} \begin{Bmatrix} 1 \\ 4 \\ 1 \end{Bmatrix}.$$

Enforcing the Dirichlet condition on δ_1 gives the reduced unique governing matrix

$$\left[\frac{1}{6}\begin{bmatrix}0 & 4\\ -4 & 3\end{bmatrix} + \frac{1}{30}\begin{bmatrix}16 & 2\\ 2 & 4\end{bmatrix}\right]\begin{Bmatrix}\delta_2\\ \delta_3\end{Bmatrix}$$

$$= \frac{5}{6}\begin{Bmatrix}4\\ 1\end{Bmatrix} - \delta_1\frac{1}{6}\begin{Bmatrix}-4\\ 1\end{Bmatrix} - \delta_1\frac{1}{30}\begin{Bmatrix}2\\ -1\end{Bmatrix}$$

$$\frac{1}{30}\begin{bmatrix}16 & 22\\ -18 & 19\end{bmatrix}\begin{Bmatrix}\delta_2\\ \delta_3\end{Bmatrix} = \frac{5}{6}\begin{Bmatrix}4\\ 1\end{Bmatrix} \to \begin{Bmatrix}\delta_2\\ \delta_3\end{Bmatrix}$$

$$= \frac{1}{700}\begin{bmatrix}19 & -22\\ 18 & 16\end{bmatrix}\frac{150}{6}\begin{Bmatrix}4\\ 1\end{Bmatrix} = \begin{Bmatrix}1.928\\ 3.143\end{Bmatrix}.$$

This solution is also graphed in Fig. 6.2-1.

Example 6.2-6 Given: In Example 6.2-2, the element square matrix was shown to be

$$[\boldsymbol{S^e}] = \int_{L^e} \boldsymbol{H}^e(x)^T \frac{d\boldsymbol{H}^e(x)}{dx} dx + \int_{L^e} \boldsymbol{H}^e(x)^T A \boldsymbol{H}^e(x)\, dx.$$

Changing variables

$$[\boldsymbol{S^e}] = \int_0^1 \boldsymbol{H}^e(r)^T \frac{d\boldsymbol{H}^e(r)}{dr}\frac{dr}{dx}\left(\frac{dx}{dr}dr\right) + \int_0^1 \boldsymbol{H}^e(r)^T A\boldsymbol{H}^e(r)\left(\frac{dx}{dr}dr\right),$$

and assuming a constant Jacobian from uniformly spaced nodes so that $|J^e| = \frac{dx}{dr} = L^e$:

$$[\boldsymbol{S^e}] = \int_0^1 \boldsymbol{H}^e(r)^T \frac{d\boldsymbol{H}^e(r)}{dr}\frac{1}{L^e}(L^e dr) + \int_0^1 \boldsymbol{H}^e(r)^T A\boldsymbol{H}^e(r)(L^e dr).$$

Integrating this matrix numerically

$$[\boldsymbol{S^e}] = \sum_{q=1}^{q=n_q}\left[\boldsymbol{H}^e(r_q)^T \frac{d\boldsymbol{H}^e(r_q)}{dr} + \boldsymbol{H}^e(r_q)^T A L^e \boldsymbol{H}^e(r_q)\right] w_q,$$

$$[\boldsymbol{S^e}] = \sum_{q=1}^{q=n_q} \boldsymbol{H}^e(r_q)^T \left[\frac{d\boldsymbol{H}^e(r_q)}{dr} + AL^e \boldsymbol{H}^e(r_q)\right] w_q.$$

Evaluate this matrix for a two-node element with

$$u(r) = [(1-r)\ \ r]\begin{Bmatrix} \delta_1^e \\ \delta_2^e \end{Bmatrix} = \boldsymbol{H}^e(r)\,\boldsymbol{\delta^e},$$

$$\frac{du}{dr} = [-1\ \ +1]\begin{Bmatrix} \delta_1^e \\ \delta_2^e \end{Bmatrix} = \frac{d\boldsymbol{H}^e(r)}{dr}\boldsymbol{\delta^e},$$

$$[\boldsymbol{S^e}] = \sum_{q=1}^{q=n_q} \begin{Bmatrix} (1-r_q) \\ r_q \end{Bmatrix} [[-1\ 1] + AL^e[(1-r_q)\ \ r_q]]w_q.$$

The highest degree term is $\boldsymbol{H}^{e^T}\boldsymbol{H}^e$ which is degree $1 + 1 = 2 \leq (2n_q - 1)$, so the number of integration points must be 2 or higher. From Fig. 5.1-2, $r_1 = 0.2113, r_2 = 0.7887$ and $w_1 = w_2 = 0.5000$.

$$[\boldsymbol{S^e}] = \begin{Bmatrix} 0.7887 \\ 0.2113 \end{Bmatrix} [[-1\ 1] + AL^e[0.7887\ 0.2113]]0.5000$$

$$+ \begin{Bmatrix} 0.2113 \\ 0.7887 \end{Bmatrix} [[-1\ 1] + AL^e[0.2113\ 0.7887]]0.5000,$$

$$[\boldsymbol{S^e}] = \left[\begin{bmatrix} -0.5000 & 0.5000 \\ -0.5000 & 0.5000 \end{bmatrix} + AL^e \begin{bmatrix} 0.3333 & 0.1667 \\ 0.1667 & 0.3333 \end{bmatrix}\right],$$

which matches the prior analytical integration well:

$$[\boldsymbol{S^e}] = \left[\frac{1}{2}\begin{bmatrix} -1 & 1 \\ -1 & 1 \end{bmatrix} + \frac{AL^e}{6}\begin{bmatrix} 2 & 1 \\ 1 & 6 \end{bmatrix}\right],$$

and is easily extended to higher precision in extracting the tabulated data.

Example 6.2-7 Given: Prepare a Matlab script equivalent to the hand calculations in Examples 6.2-3, and 6.2-4 where the number of elements is optional.

Solution: Such a script is listed in Fig. 6.2-2.

```
function [] = ML_EX_62 ()          % created 2/8/21
% FEA solution of du/dx + A*u(x) = F, u(0) = 0
%           u_exact = F*(1-e^(-A*x))/A
% A, F, and L are given constants
% L   = length of the solution domain
% Le  = length of an element
% n_e = number of linear (two-noded) elements
% n_m = number of nodes in the mesh
% Ce  = element source column matrix
% C   = system column matrix, before Dirichlet BC
% Se  = element square matrix
% S   = system square matrix, before Dirichlet BC
% U   = solution values at mesh nodes
% Fix  = liist of nodes with Dirichlet BC
% Free = list of free nodes to solve for u
% Rows = list of equations for an element
A  = 2 ; F = 10 ; L = 0.5    ; % current input data
n_e = 4                      ; % number of elements
n_m = n_e + 1                   ; % number of nodes
Fix  = [1]                  ; % always for this ODE
Free = [2:n_m]              ; % always for this ODE
Le = L / n_e               ; % uniform element size
C = zeros (n_m,1) ; U = zeros (n_m,1) ; % allocate
S = zeros (n_m, n_m)              ; % allocate size
U (Fix) = 0                 ; % BC for this example
% define element matrices
Ce = [1 ; 1] * F*Le / 2         ; % constant source
Se = [2, 1; 1, 2]*A*Le/6 + [-1, 1; -1, 1]/2 ; % Sq
% assemble (scatter) into system matrices
for k = 1:n_e ; % loop over elements    --> --> -->
  Rows = [k, (k+1)]              ; % system eq numbers
  C (Rows)         = C (Rows)         + Ce; % assemble
  S (Rows, Rows) = S (Rows, Rows) + Se; % assemble
end ; % for each element k                <-- <-- <--

% Bring given Dirichlet BC to right hand side
C (Free) = C (Free) - S (Free, Fix) * U (Fix) ;
% Now, the Free rows and columns are unique
U(Free) = S(Free, Free) \ C(Free) ; % Solve free U
% n_e = 4 gives U'=[0 1.1187 1.9635 2.6501 3.1537]
% print results
x=L*[0:(n_m-1)]/(n_m-1)         ; % node coordinates
fprintf (' node    x      U  \n')  ; % results header
for k = 1:n_m                    ; % loop over nodes
  fprintf ('%i %9.2e  %10.4e \n',k, x(k), U(k))
end                                ; % for all nodes
```

Fig. 6.2-2: Matlab script equivalent to Example 6.2-3.

6.3 Methods of Weighted Residuals

There are several techniques known as the methods of weighted residuals (MWRs) which start with a PDE and create an equivalent integral form and are valid for nonlinear PDEs. The Galerkin process is a very popular weighted residual technique for several reasons. One reason is that by applying integration by parts (and Green's theorem in two- or three-dimensions) the finite element matrices are exactly the same form as those of the variational integral form. Another reason is that it has a strong mathematical foundation. By starting with the concept of making the solution error orthogonal to the solution, it can be shown that the Galerkin method gives the "best" approximation, as measured in a specific error norm.

For a 2 m even-order PDE, the highest derivative in either of the variational and Galerkin integral forms is order m. Since the PDE requires a solution with derivatives of order $2m$, it is called the *strong form*. That contrasts with the equivalent integral form which requires the solution to be a function with derivatives of order m, which is called a *weak solution*. The governing differential equation(s) and the boundary conditions of many physical problems can be written symbolically as

$$L_\Omega u^* - f^* = 0, \text{ in } \Omega, \quad \text{with EBC of } u = u_E \text{ on } \Gamma_E \tag{6.3-1}$$

sometimes with

$$L_N u^* - g^* = 0, \quad \text{on } \Gamma_N \text{ (the NBC)} \tag{6.3-2}$$

where $u^*(x, y, z)$ is the solution to be found, L_Ω is the governing differential operator in the domain Ω that is limited by its boundary, Γ, which consists of a portion with EBCs, Γ_E, combined with a non-overlapping portion with any secondary boundary conditions, Γ_N. That is, the boundary is the union of those two segments, $\Gamma = \Gamma_E \cup \Gamma_N$. On boundary region Γ_N the differential operator that defines the secondary boundary condition (if any) is L_N. The spatial source f^* is a known function inside the domain, Ω, and g^* is a known function of position on the boundary portion Γ_N.

If an approximate solution is assumed as $u(x, y, z) \neq u^*(x, y, z)$ and/or if the data are approximated by $f(x, y, z) \neq f^*(x, y, z)$ or $g(s) \neq g^*(s)$ then the above problems will not equal zero, but will define non-zero spatially dependent residual errors:

$$R_\Omega(x, y, z) = L_\Omega u - f \neq 0, \quad \text{in } \Omega, \tag{6.3-3}$$

plus the EBC, and

$$R_N(s) = L_N u - g \neq 0, \quad \text{on } \Gamma_N \tag{6.3-4}$$

where the last equation is the pointwise error in the NBC. Note that if EBCs are applied everywhere on the boundary, then operator L_N and operator R_N are not present. Before finite elements were invented, it was usually required that the assumed solution satisfy, in advance, all of the boundary conditions. When that was done there was no residual boundary error, $R_N \equiv 0$.

The residual error(s) will not vanish everywhere except in the unlikely case where the assumed approximation happens to be the exact solution. Thus, these methods do the next best thing and require that weighted integral(s) of the residual(s) vanish:

$$I = \int_{\Omega} w_k (x, y, z) R_{\Omega} (x, y, z) d\Omega + \alpha \int_{\Gamma_N} W_j (s) R_N (s) d\Gamma = 0 \tag{6.3-5}$$

for $1 \leq k \leq n$ and $1 \leq j \leq m$ where the total number of unknown constants in the approximate solution is $M = n + m$, and where α is an arbitrary scalar constant that scales the relative importance of any secondary boundary conditions. It also is used to achieve dimensional homogeneity since any valid equation must have the same dimensions in every term. Most analysts simply pick $\alpha = 1$, with the appropriate units. Others suggest that it be some ratio of some mathematical norm of the domain integral over the norm of the boundary integral, which has the proper units.

Note that the last term requires that only the integral of the error in the secondary boundary condition must vanish. That is why it is said that in the FEA the secondary boundary conditions are satisfied weakly. The numerical accuracy of such a condition depends on the mesh. Making the elements small in the direction normal to the boundary improves the accuracy of the gradient at the boundary (reduces the pointwise error in the NBC).

It should also be noted that the boundary operator is not needed ($m = 0$) when the domain integral can be simplified through integration by parts. That is because integration by parts automatically introduces the boundary operator into the domain residual, R_{Ω}. That situation often occurs in the Galerkin form of weighted residuals (defined in what follows), which is the main residual method utilized in this book.

6.4 Common Weighting Methods

The most common residual error methods used in finite element simulations are the Galerkin method and the least squares method. Two other common methods are the collocation method (which avoids the integrals) and the method of moments. To simplify this introduction, only the domain weights will be discussed (since R_N is often not present). The approximate solution is often taken as the sum of spatial functions, h_k, and constants, D_k, to be determined, as follows:

$$u(x, y, z) = \sum_{\mathrm{k=1}}^{\mathrm{M}} h_k(x, y, x) D_k. \tag{6.4-1}$$

Then, the residual depends on both choices, $R_\Omega(\mathrm{h_k}(x, y, z) D_k)$.

6.4.1 The least square method

The least square method defines the weights as

$$w_k(x, y, x) = \frac{\partial R_\Omega(x, y, z)}{\partial D_k}. \tag{6.4-2}$$

6.4.2 The method of moments

The method of moments defines the weights as

$$w_k(x, y, x) = x^{k-1} y^{k-1} z^{k-1}, \quad 1 \leq k \leq n. \tag{6.4-3}$$

6.4.3 The collocation methods

The collocation methods avoid the integration by defining the weights as the Dirac Distribution. Effectively that means that the residual error is set to zero at k arbitrary points since

$$w_k(x, y, x) = \delta(x - x_k)\, \delta(y - y_k)\, \delta(z - z_k), \tag{6.4-4}$$

where the distribution is defined as

$$\delta(x - x_k) = \begin{cases} 0 & \text{if } x \neq x_k \\ 1 & \text{if } x = x_k, \end{cases}$$

so its integral is simply the integrand evaluated at the point

$$\int_{-\infty}^{\infty} f(x, y, z) \delta(x - x_k)\, dx = f(x_k, y_k, z_k). \tag{6.4-5}$$

That property yields the simple relation that the differential equation is exactly satisfied at the arbitrary points as follows:

$$R_\Omega(x_k, y_k, z_k) \equiv 0.$$

While that is the fastest, cheapest way to generate a system of equations to solve for the unknown constants, there is no mathematical guidance as to how to pick the arbitrary locations so as to give some "best" solution. By way of comparison, the Galerkin method is proven to yield the "best" solution in a certain mathematical norm. It can also be proved that, in the limit as the number of elements increases, the Galerkin method exactly satisfies the original differential equation.

6.4.4 Galerkin weights

As shown above, the Galerkin weights are

$$w_k\left(x,y,x\right)=\frac{\partial u}{\partial D_k}=h_k\left(x,y,x\right) \tag{6.4-6}$$

Several finite element texts say that the Galerkin weight functions, $w_x(x)$, must be zero where the EBCs are applied. Making that requirement only makes it easy to mathematically prove that the solution of the integral form is also the solution of the original differential equation. Not making that assertion renders the mathematical proof very long and very difficult, but it is still true that the two formulations are equivalent.

Example 6.4-1 Given: The ODE $d^2u/dx^2+x^n=0$ with two Dirichlet BC of $u(0)=0=u(1)$ has an exact solution of

$$u(x)=\left(x-x^{n+2}\right)/\left(\left(n+1\right)\left(n+2\right)\right).$$

Use the historical Galerkin method (before FEA) and select an approximate solution with two constants that satisfies both boundary conditions in advance.

Solution: Let the approximation be split into the product of two functions where the first satisfies the Dirichlet BC and the second is a polynomial with two constants: $u\left(x\right)=g_{BC}(x)p_{\Delta}(x)$. There are several ways to do that; here pick

$$\begin{aligned}u\left(x\right)&=x\left(1-x\right)\left(\Delta_1+\Delta_2x\right)=\left(x-x^2\right)\Delta_1+\left(x^2-x^3\right)\Delta_2\\&\equiv w_1\left(x\right)\Delta_1+w_2\left(x\right)\Delta_2.\end{aligned}$$

The residual error in the ODE is

$$R\left(x\right)=x^n-2\Delta_1+\left(2-6x\right)\Delta_2\equiv R_0\left(x\right)+R_1\left(x\right)\Delta_1+R_2\left(x\right)\Delta_2.$$

To establish the two equations for the Δ_k, the weighted residual integrals are

$$I_k = \int_0^1 w_k(x)\, R(x)\, dx = 0 = \int_0^1 w_k(x)\, (R_0(x) + R_1(x)\,\Delta_1 + R_2(x)\,\Delta_2)\, dx.$$

Writing the two integrals in matrix form by factoring out the constants gives

$$\left\{\begin{matrix}\Delta_1\\ \Delta_2\end{matrix}\right\}^T \begin{bmatrix} \int_0^1 w_1(x)\, R_1(x)\, dx & \int_0^1 w_1(x)\, R_2(x)\, dx \\ \int_0^1 w_2(x)\, R_1(x)\, dx & \int_0^1 w_2(x)\, R_2(x)\, dx \end{bmatrix} \left\{\begin{matrix}\Delta_1\\ \Delta_2\end{matrix}\right\}$$

$$= \left\{\begin{matrix}\Delta_1\\ \Delta_2\end{matrix}\right\}^T \left\{\begin{matrix} \int_0^1 w_1(x)\, R_0(x)\, dx \\ \int_0^1 w_2(x)\, R_0(x)\, dx \end{matrix}\right\} \to \begin{bmatrix} \frac{1}{3} & \frac{1}{6} \\ \frac{1}{6} & \frac{2}{15} \end{bmatrix} \left\{\begin{matrix}\Delta_1\\ \Delta_2\end{matrix}\right\}$$

$$= \left\{\begin{matrix} \dfrac{1}{(n+2)(n+3)} \\ \dfrac{1}{(n+3)(n+4)} \end{matrix}\right\} \to \left\{\begin{matrix}\Delta_1\\ \Delta_2\end{matrix}\right\} = \left\{\begin{matrix} \dfrac{12-2n}{(n+2)(n+3)(n+4)} \\ \dfrac{10n}{(n+2)(n+3)(n+4)} \end{matrix}\right\}.$$

Checking the accuracy of the approximations: for $n = 0$, $\Delta_1 = 1/2$, $\Delta_2 = 0$, and $u(x) = x(1-x)/2$ which is exact. For $n = 1$, $\Delta_1 = 1/6$, $\Delta_2 = 1/6$, and $u(x) = x(1-x)(1+x)/6 = (x - x^3)/6$, which again is exact. However, for $n = 2$, $\Delta_1 = 1/15$, $\Delta_2 = 1/6$, and $u(x) = x(1-x)(1/15 + x/6)$ which is just a cubic while the exact solution is $(x - x^4)/12$. The last approximation is graphed in Fig. 6.4-1.

6.5 Euler's Theorem*

Euler (circa 1750) presented integral forms that yield their equivalent PDE when they are minimized. In other words, Euler's variational procedure starts with an integral and then establishes its corresponding PDE. Not all differential equations have a variational form, and nonlinear PDEs rarely have a variational form. The good news is that Euler gave the variational integral forms, and corresponding PDEs,

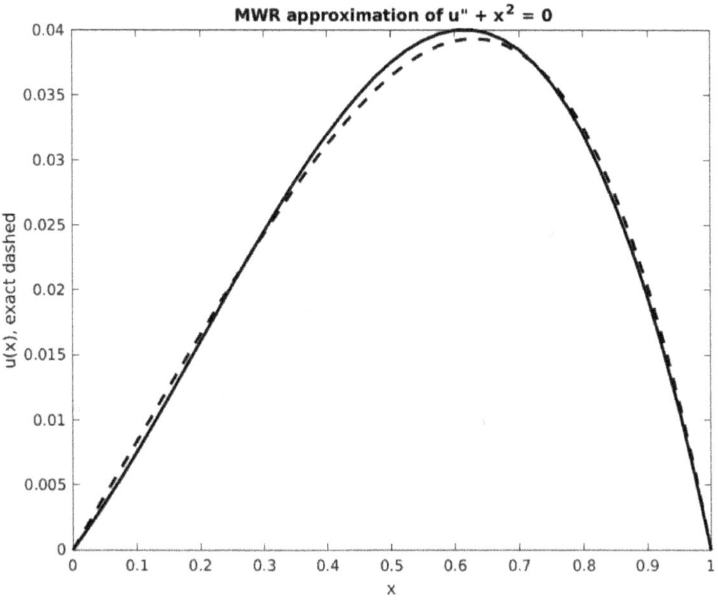

Fig. 6.4-1: Exact (dashed) and global MWR solutions.

for all the common linear even-order elliptic PDEs of importance in engineering and physics. Given the integral form, Euler gave a procedure whereby the differential equation and its NBCs are extracted from the functional. That contrasts with the weighted residual methods which start with the known differential equation.

The most common second-order PDEs in engineering are related to the functional

$$I = \int_{\Omega} f\left(x, y, z, \varphi, \frac{\partial \varphi}{\partial x}, \frac{\partial \varphi}{\partial y}, \frac{\partial \varphi}{\partial z}\right) d\Omega + \int_{\Gamma} (q\varphi + a\varphi^2) d\Gamma. \quad (6.5\text{-}1)$$

Euler's theorem states that the corresponding partial differential equation is

$$\frac{\partial f}{\partial \varphi} - \frac{\partial}{\partial x}\left(\frac{\partial f}{\partial(\partial \varphi / \partial x)}\right) - \frac{\partial}{\partial y}\left(\frac{\partial f}{\partial(\partial \varphi / \partial y)}\right) - \frac{\partial}{\partial z}\left(\frac{\partial f}{\partial(\partial \varphi / \partial z)}\right) = 0, \quad (6.5\text{-}2)$$

everywhere in Ω, and the differential equation normal to the boundary (the Neumann and/or Robin condition) is

$$n_x\left(\frac{\partial f}{\partial\left(\partial\varphi/\partial x\right)}\right)+n_y\left(\frac{\partial f}{\partial\left(\partial\varphi/\partial y\right)}\right)$$
$$+n_z\left(\frac{\partial f}{\partial\left(\partial\varphi/\partial z\right)}\right)+q+a\varphi=0, \qquad (6.5\text{-}3)$$

in terms of the direction cosines, n_x, n_y, n_z, of the unit normal vector on the boundary.

Example 6.5-1 Given: Poisson's two-dimensional PDE often occurs in fields of engineering. Determine if it is equivalent to the functional

$$I=\int_\Omega\left[\frac{1}{2}\left(K\frac{\partial\varphi}{\partial x}\right)^2+\frac{1}{2}\left(K\frac{\partial\varphi}{\partial y}\right)^2-C\varphi\right]d\Omega$$
$$+\int_\Gamma(q\varphi+a\varphi^2)d\Gamma=0$$

Solution: Apply Euler's process. The required terms are

$$\frac{\partial f}{\partial\left(\partial\varphi/\partial x\right)}=\frac{2}{2}\left(K\frac{\partial\varphi}{\partial x}\right),\quad \frac{\partial f}{\partial\left(\partial\varphi/\partial y\right)}=\frac{2}{2}\left(K\frac{\partial\varphi}{\partial y}\right),\quad \frac{\partial f}{\partial\varphi}=-C.$$

Then the corresponding PDE is

$$-C-\frac{\partial}{\partial x}\left(K\frac{\partial\varphi}{\partial x}\right)-\frac{\partial}{\partial y}\left(K\frac{\partial\varphi}{\partial y}\right)=0,$$

and the normal boundary gradient is

$$n_x\left(K\frac{\partial\varphi}{\partial x}\right)+n_y\left(K\frac{\partial\varphi}{\partial y}\right)+q+a\varphi=0=K\frac{\partial\varphi}{\partial n}+q+a\varphi,$$

and those are the Poisson PDE and its Robin condition (if any).

6.6 Summary

n_b	≡ Number of boundary segments	n_d	≡ Number of system unknowns
n_e	≡ Number of elements	n_g	≡ Number of generalized DOF per node
n_i	≡ Element independent DOF	n_m	≡ Number of mesh nodes
n_n	≡ Number of nodes per element	n_p	≡ Dimension of parametric space
n_s	≡ Dimension of physical space		
b	= boundary segment number	e	= element number

Galerkin weighted residuals

$$I = \int_{\Omega} \frac{\partial u}{\partial D_k} R_{\Omega}(x, y, z)\, d\Omega = 0_k, \text{ plus EBC.}$$

Least squares weighted residuals:

$$\begin{aligned} I = &\int_{\Omega} \frac{\partial R_{\Omega}(x,y,z)}{\partial D_k} R_{\Omega}(x,y,z) d\Omega \\ &+ \alpha \int_{\Gamma_N} \frac{\partial R_N(\mathrm{s})}{\partial D_k} R_N(s) d\Gamma = 0_k, \text{ plus EBC.} \end{aligned}$$

Finite element extension: $\Omega = \cup_e \Omega^e$ ≡ Solution domain, $\Gamma = \cup_b \Gamma^b$ ≡ Domain boundary, and

$$I = \sum_e I^e + \sum_b I^b,$$

$$u(x, y, z) = \sum_k H_k(x, y, x)\, D_k^e \text{ in } \Omega^e \text{ and on } \Gamma^b.$$

Chapter 7

Matrix Procedures for Finite Elements

7.1 Introduction

The extremely important assembly process (scattering) for combining element matrices to form the system matrices is independent of the physical application and the element type. The same process is used for fluid flow models and structural analysis, or any other fields of application. The topics covered in this chapter are automated and hidden within commercial finite element codes. The reader does not have to know this material if relying exclusively on such codes. However, if the reader plans to solve small problems by hand, then this information is critical.

The assembly process depends on how many unknowns are associated with each node in the mesh, and the element connection list which defines which nodes in the mesh are connected to each element. It is not necessary that every node have the same number of unknowns (degrees of freedom), but that common case is used here for simplicity. The assembly, the enforcement of boundary conditions and constraints, and the solution of the system matrices are easily automated and are hidden from the user of commercial software systems. However, to solve small problems by hand and to really understand the complete process, the reader should master these concepts.

Finite element applications all lead to a system of linear algebraic equations to be solved for the set of unknowns. Often, a confusing aspect of this is how are the small element matrices assembled (scattered) into the much larger algebraic equations of the system? Unlike most examples included in a linear algebra course, most of the system equations resulting from a finite element study will usually be singular until the essential boundary conditions (EBC) have been imposed on the algebraic system.

The scattering of the element matrices is mainly a problem in matrix algebra. Earlier, it was noted in passing that the assembly could technically be done by using Boolean matrices built from the element connection list. However, that process is grossly inefficient from the computational point of view. In this chapter, the critical process of assembling the system matrices is described in terms of a computationally efficient "direct assembly" that is equivalent to the theoretical Boolean matrix process. The concepts, necessary Matlab scripts, and examples are presented on how to build the large algebraic system that will eventually yield the degrees of freedom (DOF) at each node. Three methods for enforcing the EBCs on those matrices are given.

Also, it is not uncommon for the system matrix equations to be subjected to one or more algebraic constraint equations that reduce the number of unknowns in the original set of equations. A "multi-point constraints" (MPC) imposes a linear relationship between two or more of the unknowns. They occur often in real-world FEA and the process for including them is given and illustrated with simple examples. Both the EBC and any MPC must be imposed upon the system matrices before they can be solved for the unknown DOF, and any reactions of interest.

The system of equations is often very large and efficient ways for solving the linear equations must be used. A short discussion of factorization methods is also included here. Before any of these operations can be automated for all fields of application, it is necessary to define how the DOF are to be numbered at each node.

7.2 Equation Numbers for Gather and Scatter

The finite element mesh defines a small number of quantities at the nodes of an element as a subset of the huge number of the same quantities at all the nodes in the assembled mesh of elements. There are different choices for numbering the items in such a list. The most common approach, followed here, is to sequentially number all the same kinds of quantities at a node before going to the next node and repeating that process. Consider the common case where the same number of quantities, say n_g (for number of generalized items), occur at every node in the mesh. Then the local list of items at each node of any element can be defined as a subset of the same items at all the nodes in the mesh, say n_m, by a simple equation derived by deduction.

At any node denote the number of the jth item of interest as $j = 1 : n_g$, and let the ith local node number of an element be $i = 1 : n_n$. The element node connection list, say $e\_\text{nodes}(i)$ (input by the user or a mesh generator), identifies the system node number in the full mesh that corresponds to that local node number. The local element item number, $n(i, j)$, is

$$n(i,j) = n_g * (i-1) + j, \quad 1 \le i \le n_n, \quad 1 \le j \le n_g, \qquad (7.2\text{-}1)$$

and defining corresponding system node number in the mesh as I the corresponding system item number is

$$N(I,j) = n_g * (I-1) + j, \quad 1 \le I \le n_m, \quad 1 \le j \le n_g, \qquad (7.2\text{-}2)$$

but since the corresponding system node number in the mesh is $I = e\_\text{nodes}(i)$ the corresponding system item number is

$$N(i,j) = n_g * (e\_\text{nodes}(i) - 1) + j, \quad 1 \le i \le n_n, \quad 1 \le j \le n_g. \qquad (7.2\text{-}3)$$

Here, n_g is used to denote the number of unknowns at each node, also called the degrees of freedom (DOF) at each node. These local and system equation numberings are employed in gathering from the system unknowns to local unknowns and for scattering (adding) local known arrays into locations within the corresponding system arrays.

Equation (7.2-3) is the major key to automating the essential process of assembling (scattering) the element arrays into the system arrays. It creates a list of all of the system equation numbers associated with a specific element. Here, that list is given the name ***rows*** since it is initially used in examples to show how the rows of an element column matrix are scattered into the system column matrix. In other words, the list is used to convert the row subscript of an element array to the corresponding row in a system array. The same process is used to assemble square matrices which also each have a column subscript. The above list is also used to directly convert the column number of an element square matrix to the column number in the system square matrix where it is to be added. Since the list serves that dual purpose, it is sometimes also called the element *index* list.

Figure 7.2-1 shows how (7.2-3) is implemented as a Matlab script. The input arguments to the function *get_element_index.m* are the number of nodes connected to the element, $n\_n \longleftrightarrow n_n$, the number of generalized unknowns per node, $n\_g \longleftrightarrow n_g$, and the list of system node numbers connected to the element. The return from the function is the list of corresponding system equation numbers (which are used later as vector subscripts to achieve efficient programming). There is another aspect of the script that is related to the Matlab requirement that all lines in an input text file must have the same number of columns. The general finite element system provided herein allows the mesh to have a mixture (for example) of quadrilateral and triangular elements. In that case, the input line containing the connection list for the triangle must be appended (padded) with a zero so as to have the same number of columns as the quadrilaterals in the system connection list. Thus, the script has logic to skip zero node numbers due to a mesh containing different, but compatible, element types. The actual use of this script is shown later in Fig. 7.3-1.

The two concepts of gathering and scattering element data from and to the system, respectively, are illustrated in Fig. 7.2-2. The

```
function [rows] = get_element_index (n_g, n_n, e_nodes) % ====
% calculate system DOF numbers of element, for gather, scatter
% e_nodes = maximum connectivity list for any element type
% n_g     = number of DOF per node
% n_n     = maximum number of nodes per element
% rows    = vector subscript changing elem to system eq numbers
rows = zeros (1, n_g * n_n)          ; % allow for node = 0
for k = 1:n_n                        ; % loop over element nodes
 global_node = round (e_nodes (k)) ; % corresponding sys node
 for i = 1:n_g                       ; % loop over DOF at node
  eq_global  = i + n_g * (global_node - 1) ; % sys DOF, if any
  eq_element = i + n_g * (k           - 1) ; % el DOF number
  if ( eq_global > 0 )                     ; % check node=0 trick
    rows (1, eq_element) = eq_global       ; % valid DOF > 0
  end ; % if allow for omitted nodes
 end ; % for DOF i                           % end local DOF loop
end ; % for each element node                % end local node loop
% end get_element_index    % ==================================
```

Fig. 7.2-1: Calculation of system equation (DOF) numbers for an element.

Element	Nodes: 1	2
1	1	3
2	3	5
...	...	
5	6	4
6	4	2

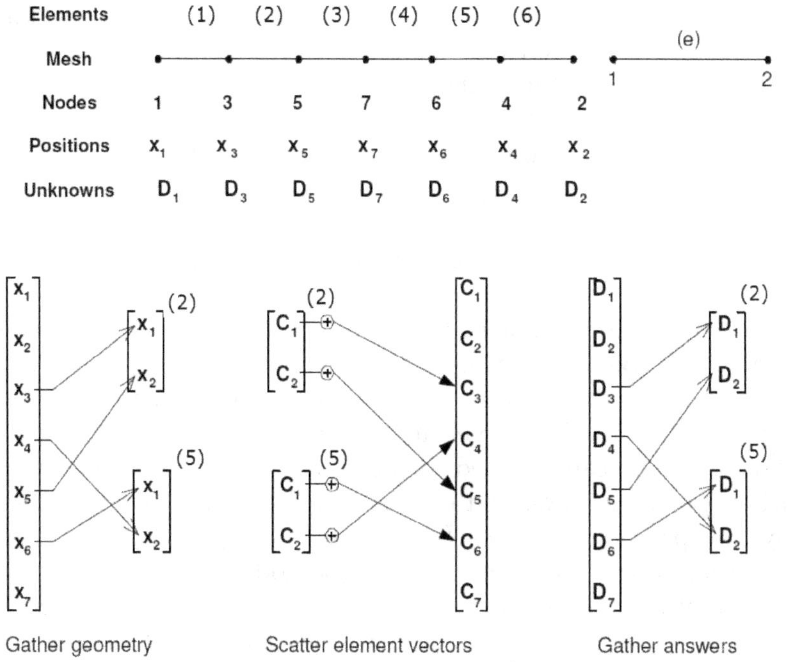

Fig. 7.2-2: Gathering and scattering data in a one-dimensional mesh ($n_g = 1$).

major differences between the two processes are that the gather operation retrieves known items from the system and brings them to the element without changing the item. In comparison, the scatter operation takes known (recently calculated) element coefficients and adds them to specific locations in the system arrays.

The example mesh in Fig. 7.2-2 has the system node numbers that are not in sequential order. While that is unusual in a one-dimensional mesh, it is common in two- and three-dimensional problems. Again, for simplicity that figure assumes just a single unknown per node. The script in Fig. 7.2-1 shows that scatter operations will work for any number of unknowns per node.

The mesh in Fig. 7.2-2 with a total of seven unknowns could be changed to three three-noded line elements (L3, $n_n = 3$) or two four-noded line elements (L4, $n_n = 4$) and the number of system nodes ($n_m = 7$) would be unchanged. Just the size of the typical element c^e matrices (and coordinate lists and connection lists) would increase from two rows to three or four rows, respectively. In other words, the element type (parametric space dimension) does not matter in the calculation of the element's system equation numbers; just the number of nodes in the connection list matters.

In practice, all of the element array coefficients must be added (scattered) to rows and columns of the square matrix, $\boldsymbol{S}$, and source vector, $\boldsymbol{c}$, of the system equilibrium matrices:

$$\boldsymbol{S}u = \boldsymbol{c} + \boldsymbol{c}_{\text{NBC}}. \tag{7.2-4}$$

The system column matrix $\boldsymbol{c}$ is built up, from zero, by scattering (adding) the column matrices $\boldsymbol{c}^e$ from all of the elements in the mesh. Likewise, the system square matrix, $\boldsymbol{S}$, is built up, from zero, by scattering into it all of the element square matrices, $\boldsymbol{S}^e$. The paired set of numbers can be used for other purposes also. For example, each node in the mesh and each local node on an element have n_s physical spatial coordinates. So, setting $n_g = n_s$ yields the equations for gathering the coordinates of a single node (where I is constant) or the physical coordinates of all the local nodes on an element (for $i = 1 : n_n$). Likewise, some applications have a list of properties assigned to every node. Then the above equations are easily converted to extract the nodal properties for an element.

This numbering system is illustrated in a one-dimensional case in Fig. 7.2-2 where the system has six nodes ($n_m = 6$) and each element has two nodes ($n_n = 2$) each with a single generalized degree of freedom ($n_g = 1$) and where the nodes are numbered randomly (as by automatic mesh generators). The connection lists in Fig. 7.2-2 are used to gather the one-dimensional spatial coordinates ($n_s = 1$) for each element. But the line element in the figure could just as easily have been a planar curve where both coordinates are gathered. For the two-node line elements, the gathered coordinates are used to calculate some 2×1 source column vector for each element, $\boldsymbol{c}^e$. Each of the element column vectors are assembled (scattered) into the resultant 6×1 system column, $\boldsymbol{c}$.

After the system square matrix has been assembled in a similar fashion (using real matrix values),and the system is modified to include the EBCs, the 6×1 system DOF, say $\boldsymbol{u}$, are computed. Most studies do not end there because the DOFs almost always must be post-processed at the element level to calculate other items of importance. In such post-processing loops over every element, the equation numbering system is used again to gather the now known 2×1 element DOF, say $\boldsymbol{u}^e$, from the appropriate system DOF for additional calculations in each element.

The scattering (assembly) process is the same for all finite element applications and needs to be clearly understood. Sometimes it is helpful to view the relationship between the equation numbers for the element's DOF and the equation numbers for the system's DOF in a tabular format. Table 7.2-1 gives such a table when the number of generalized DOF per node, n_g, is constant. The process is only slightly changed if every node in the system is allowed to have a different number of DOFs.

To provide a specific numerical example, consider a large planar truss having two DOFs per node: the horizontal and vertical displacement components (u and v). To be kinematically stable any truss mesh must be made up of triangular cells with three truss members pinned together at the vertices of the cell (sometimes the Earth serves as a third member of a cell). There must not be any quadrilateral cells enclosed by four truss members. Figure 7.2-3 shows a sample large truss with 400 nodes (800 DOF) along with segments of the system connectivity array (**nodes**) in which any row defines the connectivity of a single element (array **el_nodes**).

Each truss member has two nodes, and a planar truss has two displacements per node and thus contributes to four of the 800 system DOF. Consider truss element number 21 and how its element matrices would be scattered into the system matrices. The system equation numbers of the four truss DOFs are listed in Table 7.2-2. A planar truss member always has a 4×4 stiffness matrix, $\boldsymbol{S}^e$, and usually a 4×1 gravity and/or wind load resultant, $\boldsymbol{c}^e$. In order to add these element coefficients into the system equations, one must identify the relation between the local DOF numbers and the corresponding system DOF numbers. The array index provides this information for any specific element. In practice, the assembly procedure is as follows. First, the system matrices S and c are set equal to zero. Then a loop

Table 7.2-1: Relating local and system equation numbers.

Local numbers: Node	**DOF number**	**System node**	**Element degree of freedom (DOF)**	
			Local	**System**
$\boldsymbol{I_L}$	$\boldsymbol{J}$	$\boldsymbol{I_S = \text{el\_node}(I_L)}$	$\boldsymbol{n_g(I_L - 1) + J}$	$\boldsymbol{n_g(I_S - 1) + J}$
1	1	el_node(1)	1	$n_g(\text{el\_node}(1) - 1) + 1$
1	2	el_node(1)	2	$n_g(\text{el\_node}(1) - 1) + 2$
$\vdots$	$\vdots$	$\vdots$	$\vdots$	$\vdots$
1	n_g	el_node(1)	n_g	$n_g(\text{el\_node}(1) - 1) + n_g$
2	1	el_node(2)	$n_g + 1$	$n_g(\text{el\_node}(2) - 1) + 1$
2	2	el_node(2)	$n_g + 2$	$n_g(\text{el\_node}(2) - 1) + 2$
$\vdots$	$\vdots$	$\vdots$	$\vdots$	$\vdots$
k	j	el_node(k)	$n_g(k - 1) + j$	$n_g(\text{el\_node}(k) - 1) + j$
$\vdots$	$\vdots$	$\vdots$	$\vdots$	$\vdots$
n_n	1	el_node(n_n)	$n_g(n_n - 1) + 1$	$n_g(\text{el\_node}(n_n) - 1) + 1$
$\vdots$	$\vdots$	$\vdots$	$\vdots$	$\vdots$
n_n	n_g	el_node(n_n)	$n_n * n_g n_g(\text{el\_node}(n_n) - 1) + n_g$	

Note: n_g = number of DOF per node, n_n = number of nodes per element, el_node(k) = node connection list for element number k.

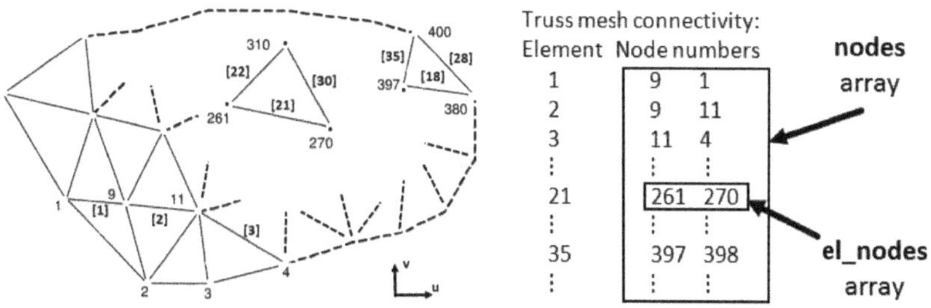

Fig. 7.2-3: Planar truss mesh, $n_g = 2$, $n_n = 2$, $n_s = 2$, $n_i = 4$.

Table 7.2-2: Equation numbers for truss element 21, $n_i \equiv n_g * n_n = 4$.

Node Local I_L	**Node System** I_S	**DOF Number** J	**Equation Local DOF**	**Equation System DOF**
1	261	1	1	521
1	261	2	2	522
2	270	1	3	539
2	270	2	4	540
$\leq n_n$	any	$\leq n_g$	$\leq n_i$	(index)

over all the elements is performed. For each element, the element matrices are generated in terms of the local DOF. Those coefficients of the element matrices are to be added to the corresponding coefficients in the system matrices. Before the addition is carried out, the element array index is used to directly convert the local subscripts of the coefficient to the system subscripts of the term in the system equations to which the coefficient is to be added.

Consider how all of the 20 element coefficients (4×4 and 4×1) for member 21 will be directly added into the system matrices. Here the symbol "$+ \longrightarrow$" is used to indicate directly converting an element equation number to a system equation number (row number and/or column number) and then adding the element term onto the system term at that location:

$$c_1^e + \longrightarrow c_{521}, \quad S_{1,1}^e + \longrightarrow S_{521,521}, \quad S_{1,2}^e + \longrightarrow S_{521,522}, \text{ etc.}$$

$$c_2^e + \longrightarrow c_{522}, \quad S_{2,2}^e + \longrightarrow S_{522,522}, \quad S_{2,3}^e + \longrightarrow S_{522,539}, \text{ etc.}$$

$$c_3^e + \longrightarrow c_{539}, \quad S_{3,3}^e + \longrightarrow S_{539,539}, \quad S_{3,4}^e + \longrightarrow S_{539,540}, \text{ etc.}$$

$$c_4^e + \longrightarrow c_{540}, \quad S_{4,1}^e + \longrightarrow S_{540,521}, \quad S_{4,4}^e + \longrightarrow S_{540,540}, \text{ etc.}$$

Example 7.2-1 Given: Using the line element data in Fig. 7.2-2, start with fictitious element column matrices where the two entries are simply the element number itself, $\boldsymbol{c}^{e^T} \equiv [e\ e]$, and then assemble the system column matrix, $\boldsymbol{c}$, starting with a null vector.

Solution: Adding each of the two numbers to the rows of $\boldsymbol{c}$ defined by the two numbers in the element connection list gives

$+e$	1	2	3	4	5	6	All
Eq	1, 3	3, 5	5, 7	7, 6	6, 4	4, 2	Total

$$\boldsymbol{c} = \begin{Bmatrix} 1 \\ 0 \\ 1 \\ 0 \\ 0 \\ 0 \\ 0 \end{Bmatrix} \rightarrow \begin{Bmatrix} 1 \\ 0 \\ (1+2) \\ 0 \\ (2) \\ 0 \\ 0 \end{Bmatrix} \rightarrow \begin{Bmatrix} 1 \\ 0 \\ 3 \\ 0 \\ (2+3) \\ 0 \\ (3) \end{Bmatrix} \rightarrow \begin{Bmatrix} 1 \\ 0 \\ 3 \\ 0 \\ 5 \\ (4) \\ (3+4) \end{Bmatrix}$$

$$\rightarrow \begin{Bmatrix} 1 \\ 0 \\ 3 \\ (5) \\ 5 \\ (4+5) \\ 7 \end{Bmatrix} \rightarrow \begin{Bmatrix} 1 \\ (6) \\ 3 \\ (5+6) \\ 5 \\ 9 \\ 7 \end{Bmatrix} = \begin{Bmatrix} 1 \\ 6 \\ 3 \\ 11 \\ 5 \\ 9 \\ 7 \end{Bmatrix}$$

Note: in this assembly the first two system nodes (1, 2) received only one number each. That is because those system nodes are only connected to one element. A general rule is that the system row in a column vector, like $\boldsymbol{c}$, will receive as many contributions to that row as there are elements connected to that system node. The entries in a real element column matrix are usually different and the first number goes to the row in $\boldsymbol{c}$ given by the first number in an element's connection list. Likewise, the second number goes to the row in $\boldsymbol{c}$ given by the second number in an element's connection list.

Example 7.2-2 Given: Assume that the *sequence* of nodes in Fig. 7.2-2 corresponds to three three-noded triangular elements each sharing one corner node with its neighbor, or two four-noded quadrilaterals sharing one corner. Develop the connection list for those two meshes.

Solution: Here the triangle and quadrilateral corners are numbered counter-clockwise. The lists can be created beginning at any corner without affecting the analysis. Thus, one set of triangle connection lists becomes

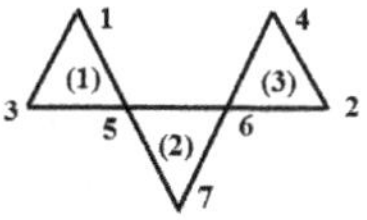

Element	Nodes: 1, 2, 3
1	1 3 5
2	7 6 5
3	2 4 6

and a set of quadrilateral connections becomes

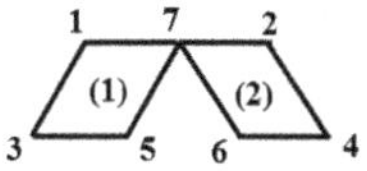

Element	Nodes: 1, 2, 3, 4
1	1 3 5 7
2	6 4 2 7

7.3 Vector Subscripts

A programming notation for arrays that is related to the use of vector subscripts is the colon, :, notation. In both Matlab and Fortran 90 using the colon as an array subscript means it refers to the full range of that subscript. For example, referring to Fig. 7.2-3 and citing $\boldsymbol{u}$ (:) means $\boldsymbol{u}(1)$ through $\boldsymbol{u}(6)$. An array subscript, and a loop, can also be ranged in an incremental fashion from a beginning integer, B, to an ending integer, E, with an integer increment of I. In Matlab that ranging is denoted by B:I:E; and in Fortran 90, as B:E:I. For example, $\boldsymbol{u}(1 : 2 : 6)$ above refers to the odd number of locations: $\boldsymbol{u}(1 : 2 : 6) \longleftrightarrow [u_1 \;\; u_3 \;\; u_5]$.

Vector subscripts are efficient programming tools in FEA. They are standard in the Fortran 90 language and in the Matlab environment. A *vector subscript* is a named integer vector (one-dimensional array) of values which do not have to be in sequential order and can contain duplicate values. When the named array is placed in the row and/or column locators of any other array, the software treats them as an implied "for loop" or "do loop" that uses each integer in the vector subscript, in sequential order, as the range values for that loop over the rows and/or columns of the second array.

For example, consider a 4×5 array, $\boldsymbol{A}$, from which four specific non-sequential coefficients, included in angle brackets, are to be copied:

$$\boldsymbol{A} = \begin{bmatrix} 1 & 2 & 3 & 4 & 5 \\ 6 & 7 & 8 & \langle 9 \rangle & \langle 10 \rangle \\ 11 & 12 & 13 & \langle 14 \rangle & \langle 15 \rangle \\ 16 & 17 & 18 & 19 & 20 \end{bmatrix}.$$

The row and column locations of those terms in matrix $\boldsymbol{A}$ can be identified with vector subscripts as $\boldsymbol{Row} = [23]$, $\boldsymbol{Col} = [45]$. In Fortran 90 and Matlab, a new array containing those four terms is

$$\boldsymbol{B} = \boldsymbol{A}(\boldsymbol{Row}, \boldsymbol{Col}) = \begin{bmatrix} 9 & 10 \\ 14 & 15 \end{bmatrix}.$$

Now assume those four terms are to be added (scattered) into the original matrix $\boldsymbol{A}$ in rows 3 and 4 and columns 1 and 3. A new set of vector subscripts are formed: $\boldsymbol{Row} = [34]$, $\boldsymbol{Col} = [13]$, and used to carry out the addition with a pair of implied loops:

$$\begin{aligned} \boldsymbol{A}(\boldsymbol{Row},\ \boldsymbol{Col}) &= \boldsymbol{A}(\boldsymbol{Row},\ \boldsymbol{Col}) + \boldsymbol{B}(:,:) \\ &= \begin{bmatrix} 1 & 2 & 3 & 4 & 5 \\ 6 & 7 & 8 & 9 & 10 \\ \langle 20 \rangle & 12 & \langle 23 \rangle & 14 & 15 \\ \langle 30 \rangle & 17 & \langle 33 \rangle & 19 & 20 \end{bmatrix}. \end{aligned}$$

As shown in the last section, the data needed for scattering the element arrays are in the connection lists for each element. Those numbers are the system mesh node numbers. Usually, the system node numbers are randomly assigned by an automatic mesh generator (and possibly re-ordered for more efficient storage and solution operations. That list of nodes defines were each local element row is to be added into a row in the system equations. For the special case of a single unknown per node ($n_g = 1$), such a direct equation subscript change defines the scatter destination row as

$$\text{Scatter\_row}(k) = \text{Element\_connection}(k), \quad k = 1, \ldots, n_n. \quad (7.3\text{-}1)$$

For example, to find where the single kth row term in an element source, $\boldsymbol{c}^e$, is to be added into the total system source vector, $\boldsymbol{c}$, the procedure is as follows. From the connection list for the system mesh extract the row of node connections for the current element. That row contains the list of integer node numbers that are attached to the element. From that list extract the kth system node number, say K. Then increase the system source sum by adding the kth of $\boldsymbol{c}^e$ to the Kth row of $\boldsymbol{c}$:

$$\boldsymbol{c}(K) = \boldsymbol{c}(K) + \boldsymbol{c}^e(k). \quad (7.3\text{-}2)$$

That would add the effect of a single DOF of that element into the system matrix. But, all of the element coefficients must be added into the system equations. As (7.3-1) shows, that is accomplished by looping over all of the node numbers for the current element. That would be done with a "for-loop" in Matlab or a "do-loop" in Fortran 90. However, the programming of a loop is not efficient; especially for parallel computers. Therefore, Fortran 90 and Matlab both offer a more efficient programming option known as a "vector subscript". The appearance of a vector subscript is an implied loop calculation to be executed in the most efficient way available in the computer being utilized.

Therefore, rather than write a loop over all the nodes in the element connection row, that row of integers is extracted from the input data and employed as a vector subscript. Here, that list is simply given the name in the array "row". For example, scattering (adding) the element column matrix, $\boldsymbol{c}^e$, to the system column matrix, $\boldsymbol{c}$, is written in code as

$$\boldsymbol{c}(\boldsymbol{row}) = \boldsymbol{c}(\boldsymbol{row}) + \boldsymbol{c}^e. \quad (7.3\text{-}3)$$

But this is actually executed as the implied loop:

```
% Scatter the element column matrix into the system column matrix
% Array "row" contains the system DOF numbers connected to this element
 n_DOF = size (row)                    % determine number of element equations
for k = 1:n_DOF                        % loop over all element DOF rows
   c (row (k)) = c (row (k)) + c_e (k)  % add element term to system term
end                                    % for k element column matrix terms
                                         (7.3-4)
```

(7.3-4)

In a similar fashion, the row subscripts and column subscripts are converted using the element connection lists. The column numbers are reordered exactly like the row numbers ($col \equiv row$). In vector subscript notation, the assembly (scattering) of the element square matrix into the system square matrix is

$$\boldsymbol{S}(\boldsymbol{row}, \boldsymbol{row}) = \boldsymbol{S}(\boldsymbol{row}, \boldsymbol{row}) + \boldsymbol{S}^e. \tag{7.3-5}$$

Again, this is executed as two implied loops:

```
% Scatter the element square matrix into the system square matrix
% Array "row" contains the system DOF numbers connected to this element
n_DOF = size (row)                        % determine number of element DOF
for m = 1:n_DOF                           % loop over all element DOF rows
    for n = 1:n_DOF                       % loop over all element DOF columns
        % add element term to the system term
        S (row (m), row (n)) = S (row (m), row (n)) + S_e (m, n)
    end                              % for n element square matrix column terms
end                                  % for m element square matrix row terms
                                        (7.3-6)
```

(7.3-6)

The above assembly process is very simple to program in the Fortran 90 language and in the Matlab environment by using vector subscripts. As illustrated in Fig. 7.3-1, the process is repeated for every element in the mesh.

```
for e = 1:n_e ; % Loop over every element ===> ===> ===> ====> ====>
...

% Generate the element arrays for the current application
...

%       SCATTER ELEMENT ARRAYS TO (ASSEMBLE INTO) SYSTEM ARRAYS
% Insert completed element matrices into system matrices
  [rows] = get_element_index (n_g, n_n, e_nodes) ; % sys eq numbers
  % rows = vector subscript converting element to system eq numbers
  S (rows, rows) = S (rows, rows) + S_e ;  % add to system sq array
  c (rows)       = c (rows)       + c_e ; % add to sys column array

  ...
end ; % for e elements <==== <==== <==== <==== <=== <==== <==== <====
```

Fig. 7.3-1: Assembling element square and column array into the system equations.

Example 7.3-1 Given: A single quadratic (three-noded) bar element has a load vector of

$$\boldsymbol{c}^e = \frac{w^e L^e}{6}\begin{Bmatrix} 1 \\ 4 \\ 1 \end{Bmatrix},$$

where L^e is the bar length and w^e is the axial load per unit length on the bar. Due to a non-sequential system node numbering, the connection list for that element is $[3\ \ 1\ \ 2] = \boldsymbol{row}$. Determine the system load vector resulting from scattering the coefficients to the system level.

Solution: For this single element, the scatter (assembly) of the element column matrix gives

$$\boldsymbol{c}^e(:) + \boldsymbol{c}(\boldsymbol{row}) \to \boldsymbol{c}(\boldsymbol{row}).$$

Looping through each of the three numbers in the vector subscripts gives

$$\boldsymbol{c}^e(1) + \boldsymbol{c}(3) \to \boldsymbol{c}(3) = \frac{w^e L^e}{6} + 0 = \frac{w^e L^e}{6};$$

$$\boldsymbol{c}^e(2) + \boldsymbol{c}(1) \to \boldsymbol{c}(1) = \frac{4 w^e L^e}{6} + 0 = 4\frac{w^e L^e}{6};$$

$$\boldsymbol{c}^e(3) + \boldsymbol{c}(2) \to \boldsymbol{c}(2) = \frac{w^e L^e}{6} + 0 = \frac{w^e L^e}{6}.$$

So, after the assembly the system source vector is

$$\boldsymbol{c} = \frac{w^e L^e}{6}\begin{Bmatrix} 4 \\ 1 \\ 1 \end{Bmatrix}.$$

7.4 Partitioning the System Equations

In most courses on matrix algebra the linear systems to be solved usually involve non-singular square matrices. That is because any constraints on the unknowns were satisfied in advance. In the finite element applications to be covered here, the constraints are satisfied last, which results in an initially singular square matrix because the reactions due to the constraints appear as unknowns on the column vector side of the equations. In other words, because the EBCs will be enforced last and there is no unique solution until that is done. A matrix partition can be used to allow for the solution constraints and to yield a smaller and non-singular system of equations to be solved. The algebraic system can be written in a general matrix form that more clearly defines what must be done to reduce the system to a solvable form by utilizing known EBC values. The system DOF, u, and the full equations could always be re-arranged in the following partitioned matrix form

$$\begin{bmatrix} \boldsymbol{S}_{uu} & \boldsymbol{S}_{uk} \\ \boldsymbol{S}_{ku} & \boldsymbol{S}_{kk} \end{bmatrix} \begin{Bmatrix} \boldsymbol{u}_{\boldsymbol{u}} \\ \boldsymbol{u}_{\boldsymbol{k}} \end{Bmatrix} = \begin{Bmatrix} \boldsymbol{c}_{\boldsymbol{u}} \\ \boldsymbol{c}_{\boldsymbol{k}} + \boldsymbol{r}_{\boldsymbol{k}} \end{Bmatrix}, \tag{7.4-1}$$

where u_u represents the unknown nodal parameters, and u_k represents the known essential boundary values of the other parameters. The r_k term represents that there are usually unknown generalized reactions associated with EBCs.

The only unknowns in this matrix system are the vectors $\boldsymbol{u}_{\boldsymbol{u}}$ and $\boldsymbol{r}_{\boldsymbol{k}}$. The net number of unknowns corresponds to the number of equations, but they must be re-arranged before all the remaining unknowns can be computed. Moving the unknown reactions, $\boldsymbol{r}_{\boldsymbol{k}}$, to the left side would destroy the very useful symmetry of the square matrix. So instead they are obtained as a post-solution calculation.

The sub-matrices $\boldsymbol{S}_{uu}$ and $\boldsymbol{S}_{kk}$ are square, whereas $\boldsymbol{S}_{uk}$ and $\boldsymbol{S}_{ku}$ are rectangular, in general. In a finite element formulation all of the coefficients in the $\boldsymbol{S}$ and $\mathbf{c}$ matrices are known. This means that in general after the EBCs ($\boldsymbol{u}_{\boldsymbol{k}}$) are prescribed, the remaining unknowns are $\boldsymbol{u}_{\boldsymbol{u}}$ and $\boldsymbol{r}_{\boldsymbol{k}}$. The unknown DOF are always calculated, but the calculation of the reaction unknowns is optional.

Here, for simplicity, it has been assumed that the equations have been numbered in a manner that places the prescribed parameters (EBCs) at the end of the system equations. The above matrix equations can be partitioned as

$$\begin{aligned} \boldsymbol{S}_{uu}\boldsymbol{u}_{\boldsymbol{u}} + \boldsymbol{S}_{uk}\boldsymbol{u}_{\boldsymbol{k}} &= \boldsymbol{c}_{\boldsymbol{u}} \\ \boldsymbol{S}_{ku}\boldsymbol{u}_{\boldsymbol{u}} + \boldsymbol{S}_{kk}\boldsymbol{u}_{\boldsymbol{k}} &= \boldsymbol{c}_{\boldsymbol{k}} + \boldsymbol{r}_{\boldsymbol{k}}, \end{aligned} \tag{7.4-2}$$

so that the unknown nodal parameters are obtained by inverting the non-singular square matrix $\boldsymbol{S}_{uu}$ in the top partitioned rows. That is,

$$\boldsymbol{u_u} = \boldsymbol{S}_{uu}^{-1}(\boldsymbol{c_u} - \boldsymbol{S}_{uk}\boldsymbol{u_k}). \tag{7.4-3}$$

Most books on numerical analysis assume that you have reduced the system to the above non-singular form where the essential conditions, $\boldsymbol{u_k}$, have already been moved to the right-hand side. Many authors use examples with null conditions $\boldsymbol{u_k} = \boldsymbol{0}$ so the solution is the simplest form, $\boldsymbol{u_u} = \boldsymbol{S}_{uu}^{-1}\boldsymbol{c_u}$. If desired, the values of the necessary reactions, $\boldsymbol{r_k}$, can now be determined from

$$\boldsymbol{r_k} = \boldsymbol{S}_{ku}\boldsymbol{u_u} + \boldsymbol{S}_{kk}\boldsymbol{u_k} - \boldsymbol{c_k}. \tag{7.4-4}$$

In structural applications using line elements like bars, beams, trusses, and frames, the reactions on each member is sometimes needed in the design of the member. They are the forces and/or moments that each member transmits at its interface nodes. For the individual element to be in equilibrium with its now known stiffness, $\boldsymbol{S}^e$, known displacement vector, $\boldsymbol{u}^e$, and known element source resultant vector, $\boldsymbol{c}^e$, as well as the unknown external reaction point forces and/or moments, $\boldsymbol{r}^e$, requires

$$\boldsymbol{S}^e\boldsymbol{u}^e = \boldsymbol{c}^e + \boldsymbol{r}^e \rightarrow \boldsymbol{r}^e = \boldsymbol{S}^e\boldsymbol{u}^e - \boldsymbol{c}^e. \tag{7.4-5}$$

That element level relation is probably easiest to envision for an element in the mesh that has no distributed external sources, $\boldsymbol{c}^e \equiv \boldsymbol{0}$, and then the member reactions are simply $\boldsymbol{r}^e = \boldsymbol{S}^e\boldsymbol{u}^e$ since, like with a linear spring, external forces are required to deform an elastic body.

In nonlinear and time-dependent applications, the reactions can be found from similar calculations. In most applications, the reaction data have physical meanings that are important in their own right, or useful in validating the solution. However, this part of the calculations is optional. If one formulates a finite element model that satisfies the EBCs in advance, then the second row of the partitioned system $\boldsymbol{S}$ matrix is usually not generated and one cannot recover the reaction data directly from the matrix system.

The above matrix partitioning can be accomplished easily with languages that allow vector subscripts. In several examples given later, the Matlab scripts will employ vector subscripts. Figure 7.4-1 illustrates how vector subscripts can extract the above partitions in

```
% Extraction of interlaced unknowns in
%   | S_uu   S_uk | {D_u} = {C_u}
%   | S_ku   S_kk | {D_k}   {C_k+R_k}
%     with unknowns {D_u} and (R_k}
%
% Example: n_d=5 eqs, n_f=3 unknowns
S = [55, -46,    0,    0,  0 ; ...
    -46, 140, -46,    0,  0 ; ...
      4, -46, 110, -46,  4 ; ...
      0,   0, -46, 142, -46 ; ...
      0,   0,   4, -46,  65 ]
C = [500, 2000, 1000, 2000, 900]'

Free = [2 3 4]   % Subscripts of unknowns
Fixed = [1  5]     % Subscripts of knowns
Total = [Free, Fixed]'      % List of all
n_d   = max(size(Total))       % Count all
D     = zeros (n_d, 1)  % Clear then all

D_k   = [150, 40]'   % Given known values
D(Fixed) = D_k       % Insert into answer

% Extract the non-singular partitions
S_uu = S (Free, Free)         % Square part
C_u  = C (Free)               % Column part
Det  = det(S_uu)              % Check not 0

S_uk = S (Free, Fixed)   % will go to RHS
C_uk = C_u - S_uk * D_k   % new RHS row 1

% Solve | S_uu   S_uk | {D_u} = {C_u}
%                      {D_k}
D_u  = inv(S_uu) * C_uk    % Get unknowns
C_k  = C (Fixed)          % Reactions data
S_ku = S (Fixed, Free)          % in row 2
S_kk = S (Fixed, Fixed)         % in row 2

% Solve |S_ku   S_kk| {D_u} = {C_k}+{R_k}
%                    {D_k}
R_k = S_ku*D_u + S_kk*D_k - C_k   % row 2
```

```
%    === Example Results ===
Total = 2 3 4 1 5
D_k = 150
       40

D = 150
     0
     0
     0
    40

S_uu = 140   -46     0
       -46   110   -46
         0   -46   142

C_u = 2000   Det = 1590088
      1000
      2000

S_uk = -46     0
         4     4
         0   -46

C_uk = 8900
        240
       3840

D_u = 81.6802 % Solution
      55.1137
      44.8960

C_k = 500
      900

S_ku = -46     0     0
         0     4   -46

S_kk = 55     0
        0    65

R_k = 1.0e+03 * [3.9927 -0.1448]
```

Fig. 7.4-1: Matrix partitions using vector subscripts (Free, Fixed).

a coupled matrix system and use them to solve for the unknowns and the reactions from the EBCs. In that example, the nodal DOF with EBCs occur at the first (1) and last (5) nodes, so those two numbers are defined as an integer vector subscript called ***Fixed***. All other DOF are unknown and are placed in the vector subscript ***Free***. The Matlab script is listed on the left side of that figure and the results of that script are on the right side.

7.5 Numerically Equivalent Process

The actual partitioning of the full matrix is not actually necessary and neither is the use of vector subscripts. Alternate ways to assign a known value to a single DOF, say $\boldsymbol{d}_j$, can be done with numerical manipulations. Since the number of EBCs are often a very small percentage of the number of unknowns, the enforcement of the EBCs can be completed by column and row operations that modify both the square matrix and the column vector for each assigned EBC for vector $\boldsymbol{d}$, say $\boldsymbol{d}_j = \boldsymbol{b}$.

The operation first subtracts the assigned value, b times the jth column of $\boldsymbol{S}$, and then zeros out that column in $\boldsymbol{S}$ along with the jth row of both $\boldsymbol{S}$ and $\boldsymbol{c}$. At this point, the system is singular (non-unique) because the EBC is still not included in the square matrix. To enforce the EBC, include the EBC as a scalar identity, $d_j = b$, in $\boldsymbol{S}$ and $\boldsymbol{c}$. That is, place a 1 in the matrix diagonal location S_{jj} and in the column vector set $d_j = b$ so the size of the equations remains the same, but the square matrix is rendered non-singular. For the final matrix form of the now non-singular matrix, see Fig. 7.5-1. This approach is stored in the function *enforce_essential_BC.m* and/or the related penalty method in the Matlab function *enforce_MPC_equations.m*. If the reaction data, r_j, need to be recovered in post-processing, then the original jth row of $\boldsymbol{S}$ and $\boldsymbol{c}$ must be saved for later use.

The above series of steps are repeated for each and every EBC in the problem. The prior matrix partition approach is correct for any size problem but is more commonly used on very small

$$
\begin{array}{c} 1 \\ \vdots \\ j \\ \vdots \\ k \\ \vdots \\ p \end{array}
\begin{bmatrix}
S_{11} & \cdots & 0 & \cdots & S_{1k} & \cdots & S_{1p} \\
\vdots & \vdots & \vdots & \vdots & \vdots & \vdots & \vdots \\
0 & \cdots & Big & \cdots & 0 & \cdots & 0 \\
\vdots & \vdots & \vdots & \vdots & \vdots & \vdots & \vdots \\
S_{k1} & \vdots & 0 & \vdots & S_{kk} & \vdots & S_{kp} \\
\vdots & & \vdots & & \vdots & & \vdots \\
S_{p1} & \cdots & 0 & \cdots & S_{pk} & \cdots & S_{pp}
\end{bmatrix}
\begin{Bmatrix} d_1 \\ \vdots \\ d_j \\ \vdots \\ d_k \\ \vdots \\ d_p \end{Bmatrix}
=
\begin{Bmatrix} c_1 - b\,S_{1j} \\ \vdots \\ Big\,b \\ \vdots \\ c_k - b\,S_{kj} \\ \vdots \\ c_p - b\,S_{pj} \end{Bmatrix}
$$

(column labels: $1 \;\cdots\; j \;\cdots\; k \;\cdots\; p$)

Fig. 7.5-1: Matrix modifications to enforce a Dirichlet boundary condition.

problems, while the identity manipulation (or the penalty method, below) is used when there are thousands or millions of equations in the problem.

7.6 EBC by a Penalty Method*

The EBCs can be satisfied, to a selected number of significant figures, by a penalty method that also leaves the original size and equation order unchanged (but which does change the column heights of a sparse storage approach). Let $\boldsymbol{d_j}$ be the DOF to be assigned an EBC, say $\boldsymbol{d_j} = \boldsymbol{b}$. A numerical trick to avoid partitions or zeroing out rows and columns is known as the penalty method. For an EBC it changes only two terms in the governing matrix system. The jth row of the resultant source vector is changed to

$$c_j = RbS_{j,j}$$

and its diagonal term is changed to

$$S_{j,j} = RS_{j,j}$$

where R is a really really big number. Then that row product of the system matrices becomes

$$S_{j,1}d_1 + \cdots + RS_{j,j}d_j + S_{j,k}d_k + \cdots + S_{j,n}d_n = RbS_{j,j}. \quad (7.6\text{-}1)$$

As the penalty term approaches infinity, $R \to \infty$, the numerical solution approaches $d_j = b$ to a certain number of significant figures. The actual value of R to be assigned depends on the hardware word length (which engineering programming languages can display). Values of R as high as $R = 10^{23}$ have been used while the author uses a scaling of the maximum diagonal element of the square matrix, say $R = 10^5 \times max\lceil \boldsymbol{S} \rfloor$.

7.7 Multiple Point Constraints* (MPC)

It is not uncommon for structures to be supported on rollers that move against a surface that is not parallel to any of the global axes. Then, what would normally be an EBC becomes a constraint involving the displacement vector and the normal vector at that surface. The above penalty approach is also the easiest way to treat cases where two or more DOFs are related by a linear constraint such as $Ad_j + Bd_k = C$ and $Ad_j + Bd_k + Cd_m = D$ coupling three DOFs, which occur frequently. Let the first DOF be the master and the following ones be dependent DOFs. Such a constraint equation between multiple rows (points) in the solution vector has long been called a "Multiple Point Constraint" (MPC). Clearly, the first coefficient is not zero, so the equation is divided through by it to store as many coefficients as there are DOFs in the constraint.

The constraint between two DOFs is

$$\begin{aligned} Ad_j + Bd_k &= C, \\ \frac{A}{A}d_j + \frac{B}{A}d_k &= \frac{C}{A}, \\ d_j + bd_k &= c, \end{aligned} \tag{7.7-1}$$

where $A \neq 0$ So, its input equations become $d_j + bd_k = c$, where the new coefficients are $b = B/A$, $c = C/A$. Likewise, for a linear constraint between three DOFs.

$Ad_j + Bd_k + Cd_m = D$ has an input form of $d_j + bd_k + cd_m = d$ where $b = B/A$, $c = C/A$ and $d = D/A$. To input such a constraint equation you would enter the constrained integer node number, its integer degree of freedom number for each DOF in the constraint, followed by the real values of the coefficients in the constraint.

Note that there is more than one DOF in each equation. That is, there are more unknowns than equations. An approximate solution can be obtained from a least-squares penalty model (or a singular-decomposition algorithm). Either of the example constraints can be written as a null matrix dot product for a Dirichlet boundary condition

$$[1 \ b]\begin{Bmatrix} d_j \\ d_k \end{Bmatrix} - c = 0.$$

For the Dirichlet form, the error is

$$[1 \ b]\begin{Bmatrix} d_j \\ d_k \end{Bmatrix} - c \neq 0 = Err.$$

The error squared is

$$Err^T Err = \left(\begin{Bmatrix} d_j \\ d_k \end{Bmatrix}^T [1\ b]^T - c^T \right) \left([1\ b] \begin{Bmatrix} d_j \\ d_k \end{Bmatrix} - c \right)$$

$$Err^2 = [d_j\ d_k] \begin{Bmatrix} 1 \\ b \end{Bmatrix} [1\ b] \begin{Bmatrix} d_j \\ d_k \end{Bmatrix} - [d_j\ d_k] \begin{Bmatrix} 1 \\ b \end{Bmatrix} c$$

$$- c^T [1\ b] \begin{Bmatrix} d_j \\ d_k \end{Bmatrix} + c^T c$$

$$Err^2 = [d_j\ d_k] \begin{bmatrix} 1 & b \\ b & b^2 \end{bmatrix} \begin{Bmatrix} d_j \\ d_k \end{Bmatrix} - 2[d_j\ d_k] \begin{Bmatrix} 1 \\ b \end{Bmatrix} c + c^T c$$

$$Err^2 = \frac{1}{2}[d_j\ d_k] \left(\begin{bmatrix} 1 & b \\ b & b^2 \end{bmatrix} \begin{Bmatrix} d_j \\ d_k \end{Bmatrix} - \begin{Bmatrix} c \\ bc \end{Bmatrix} \right) + \frac{1}{2} c^T c.$$

To find the constrained DOFs, $\boldsymbol{d^c}$, that minimize the error, solve for

$$\frac{\partial Err^2}{\partial \{\boldsymbol{d^c}\}} = \{0\}, \quad \frac{2}{2} \left(\begin{bmatrix} 1 & b \\ b & b^2 \end{bmatrix} \begin{Bmatrix} d_j \\ d_k \end{Bmatrix} - \begin{Bmatrix} c \\ bc \end{Bmatrix} \right) = \{0\},$$

when multiplied by a really big penalty number, R, these define a pseudo-element stiffness and load relation:

$$\boldsymbol{S^c d^c} = \boldsymbol{c^c}. \tag{7.7-2}$$

The matrices defined for the first form are

$$\boldsymbol{S^c} = R \begin{bmatrix} 1 & b \\ b & b^2 \end{bmatrix}, \quad \boldsymbol{c^c} = R \begin{Bmatrix} c \\ bc \end{Bmatrix}.$$

These matrix identities are treated as pseudo-element equations that are assembled into the system equations like actual elements. Sometimes you need two DOFs to be identical, then $d_j + (-1)d_k = 0$. Often that is called a rigid link and that constraint system is

$$\boldsymbol{S^c} = R \begin{bmatrix} 1 & -1 \\ -1 & 1 \end{bmatrix}, \quad \boldsymbol{c^c} = \begin{Bmatrix} 0 \\ 0 \end{Bmatrix}.$$

That square matrix is similar to that of a bar or linear spring:

$$\boldsymbol{S^e} = \frac{EA}{L} \begin{bmatrix} 1 & -1 \\ -1 & 1 \end{bmatrix},$$

where the term EA/L is known as the axial stiffness of a bar. Thus, the constraint equation is thought of as a pseudo-element which acts as a very stiff spring connecting the two equal DOFs. This is sometimes called a “rigid link”.

The elastic modulus of a material, E, is usually a very large number. Without the introduction of R, that almost always would lead to $\boldsymbol{S^e} \gg \boldsymbol{S^c}$ and the numerical constraint would not be accurately satisfied in the numerical solution of the assembled system matrix. The large penalty number scaling is needed such that the constraint equation pseudo-element has the proper units and is much larger than a physical element, $\boldsymbol{S^c} \gg \boldsymbol{S^e}$. That can be done by multiplying the constraint pseudo-element matrices by the huge number R, and by arbitrarily defining $R = 10^5 \times \max\lceil \boldsymbol{S} \rfloor$ it is assured that the constraints have the proper units. Likewise, the constraint equation for the three DOF example is

$$\boldsymbol{S^c} = R \begin{bmatrix} 1 & b & c \\ b & b^2 & bc \\ c & cb & c^2 \end{bmatrix}, \quad \boldsymbol{c^c} = R \begin{Bmatrix} d \\ bd \\ cd \end{Bmatrix}.$$

All MPC pseudo-element arrays have a connectivity list, and are scattered into the system arrays. That scatter is done last so that the maximum physical diagonal term, $max\lceil \boldsymbol{S} \rfloor$, is known. In the supplied library of finite element scripts, the MPC connectivity list (DOF numbers) and the list of user-defined coefficients are read by script *get_constraint_eqs.m*. Those data are supplied by the user in the text file *msh_mpc.txt*. After all constraint equation data are read, the system counts the number of each type of constraint so that memory can be allocated for the pseudo-elements of each type. Herein the constraint type is the number of coupled DOFs in the constraint equation. The script *count_MPC_eqs.m* counts the number of constraint equations of each type. The penalty method of enforcing the constraints (after complete assembly of all physical elements) on the system $\boldsymbol{S}$ and $\boldsymbol{c}$ arrays is carried out by the script *enforce_MPC_equations.m*.

The most common MPC occurs when a node in a structure is required to move tangent to an inclined support surface, as illustrated in Example. 7.7-1. For a surface in three dimensions, the components of its unit vector are simply the direction cosines of the line perpendicular to the surface.

Example 7.7-1 Given: the third node of a planar truss in Fig. 7.7-1 is supported by an inclined roller that makes an angle of α with respect to the positive x-axis and has a slope of three horizontal to four vertical. Determine the constraint equation between the components of the displacement vector at the support point.

Solution: A roller is defined as a support that allows motion tangent to its surface only. In other words, the displacement of a structure normal to the support surface is zero. The planar displacement vector is $\boldsymbol{\delta} = u\boldsymbol{i} + v\boldsymbol{j}$ and the surface normal vector is $\boldsymbol{n} = -\text{Sin}\,\alpha\boldsymbol{i} + \text{Cos}\,\alpha\boldsymbol{j}$. The constraint equation for zero normal displacement is $\boldsymbol{\delta} \cdot n \equiv$. From the definition of the dot product of two vectors, the constraint equation is

$$-u\,\text{Sin}\,\alpha + v\,\text{Cos}\,\alpha = 0.$$

For the given slope, $\text{Cos}\,\alpha = 3/5$ and $\text{Sin}\,\alpha = 4/5$. The system equation number for the x-displacement at node 3 is $2(3-1)+1 = 5$ while the equation number for the y-displacement is 6. Therefore, the constraint equation needed to enforce this support condition is $\delta_5(-4/5) + \delta_6(3/5) = 0$ which would be simplified for input as $\delta_5 - (3/4)\delta_6 = 0$. The data required in text file *msh_mpc.txt* to input that constraint equation is shown in Fig. 7.7-2.

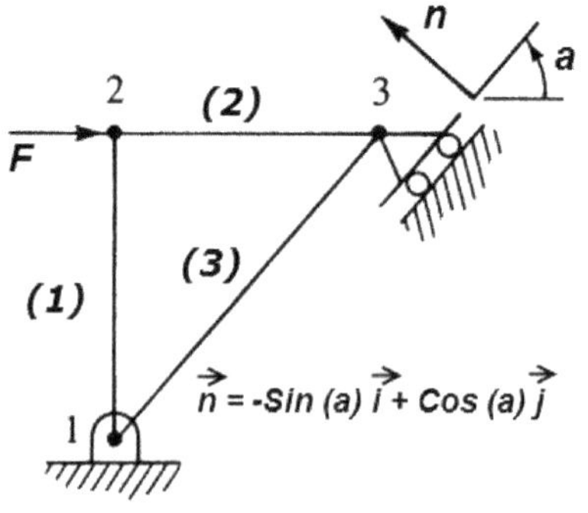

Fig. 7.7-1: A truss supported by an inclined roller.

```
% msh_remarks.txt: remarks about the application
A three bar planar truss with inclined support
Type 1 is a line truss element, n_n = 2
n_g = 2, n_e = 3, n_m = 3, n_d = 6
% msh_bc_xyz.txt:| n_g digit BC flag, x-coord, y-, z-coord
11  0.0     0.0
00  0.0     400.0
22  300.0   400.0
% msh_typ_nodes.txt: element-type, connection list
1    1, 2
1    2, 3
1    1, 3
% msh_load_pt.txt: node, direction, source_value
2   1   1e5
% msh_ebc.txt:  node-number, dof-number, assigned value
1   1   0.0
1   2   0.0
% msh_mpc.txt: one line per constraint equation
% group of node-dof pairs, group of coefficients
3  1  3  2  -0.75   0.0
% msh_properties.txt: one line per element OR element type
% for Type 1: Area, E_modulus, Spec_Wt, Alpha, Del_T
0.001  209e9  77e3  17e-6  0.
```

Fig. 7.7-2: Numerical text files to define the truss mesh and restraints.

Example 7.7-2 Given: For the supplied FEA Matlab library, prepare the user data files for the truss in Fig. 7.7-1 (except for the properties).

Solution: The only new operation for the truss is to note that it has a type 2 MPC. Thus, the digit 2 must appear in the boundary condition flag for each of the DOFs involved in the constraint (in line 8 of text file *msh_bc_xyz.txt*), and the new MPC data file must give the node number and degree of freedom number for each DOF in the constraint equation, and the corresponding constraint coefficients, like b, c, d above (see line 20). Those data go in text file *msh_mpc.txt*. The required user data are listed in Fig. 7.7-2. This truss is solved later in Example 8.5-4.

In the supplied library of finite element scripts, the nodal boundary condition flag also plays a part when any MPC is present in the data. Recall that the flag (present in file *msh_bc_xyz.txt*) is a packed integer consisting of n_g digits packed into a single integer. The first (leftmost) digit refers to any EBC or MPC that is active for the first

DOF at that node, and so on. If a digit value is 0, that means that there is no EBC or MPC active for that DOF at that node. If a digit value is 1, that means that there is a Dirichlet (a type 1 constraint equation) to be enforced for that DOF at that node. If a digit value is a number greater than one ($1 < m \leq 9$), that means that there is an MPC of type m to be enforced for that DOF at that node. Those integer flags are internally split back into their n_g individual integers for the purpose of allocating memory and for checking for consistency between the user input files for a single application. Those operations are completed in script *count_EBC_MPC_flags.m*.

There are exact matrix manipulation methods for enforcing MPC relations. The script library can handle full matrix systems having the common type 2 MPC with the matrix manipulator *apply_mpc_type_2.m*. It gives more accurate results than the penalty approach, but for sparse storage systems it tends to reduce the sparseness more than the penalty approach. That is not a problem when the system square matrix, **S**, is fully populated as in most of the examples herein.

Example 7.7-3 Given: The torsional shafts in Fig. 7.7-3 are coupled by two gears. The finite element unknowns are rotations at nodes 1 through 4. The shaft and gear rotation at node 2 is θ_2 and its gear has a radius of 5 inches. That gear engages a smaller gear with a 1 inch radius. The smaller gear and shaft node 3 have a rotation of θ_3. Determine the constraint equation between the shaft element rotations at nodes 2 and 3.

Solution: A point on the circumference of the large gear moves through an arc length of $L = \theta_2 R_2$. A point on the circumference of the smaller gear moves through the same arc length $L = \theta_3 R_3$, but with the rotation being in the opposite direction. Therefore, the constraint equation between the two rotations at the nodes coupled by those gears is

$$5\theta_2 + 1\theta_3 = 0.$$

(Shaft elements are derived in Section 8.2).

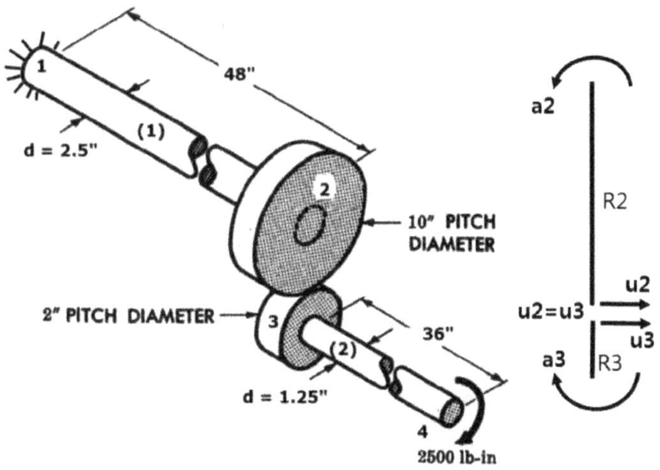

Fig. 7.7-3: Torsional rotations of coupled shafts.

7.8 Equation Factorization*

Most of the examples given herein imply that the solution of the equilibrium equations (after enforcing the boundary conditions), $Su = c$, will be obtained by inverting the system square matrix and multiplying that inverted matrix times the solution source vector, c, to obtain the system solution vector, $u = S^{-1}c$. While that is theoretically a correct matrix algebra procedure, it is not practical for more than three unknowns. A more efficient solution process is to factor the system square matrix into the product of a lower triangular matrix, L, and an upper triangular matrix, U, as

$$\boldsymbol{S} \equiv \boldsymbol{LU},$$

or as a triple matrix product using a diagonal matrix, $\boldsymbol{S} \equiv \boldsymbol{LDU}$, where usually $\boldsymbol{U} = \boldsymbol{L^T}$.

A factorization solution algorithm greatly reduces the operations count and the required storage. One important issue is that the finite element square matrix is sparse and diagonally dominate, but its inverse matrix is fully populated. That contrasts with a factorization process where the matrix factors of S have the same sparsity and can be stored within the original matrix and thus require no additional storage (when the factorizations are programmed efficiently, unlike the Matlab *lu* function).

Example 7.8-1 Given: Consider the sparse matrix $\boldsymbol{S}$ that follows. Use the Matlab function inv (S) to form the inverse and the function $lu(\boldsymbol{S})$, the two triangular factors, and compare the storage requirements. Verify that $\boldsymbol{S} \equiv \boldsymbol{LU}$.

$$\boldsymbol{S} = \begin{bmatrix} 2 & 1 & 0 & 0 & 0 \\ 1 & 2 & 1 & 0 & 0 \\ 0 & 1 & 2 & 1 & 0 \\ 0 & 0 & 1 & 2 & 1 \\ 0 & 0 & 0 & 1 & 2 \end{bmatrix}.$$

Solution: its inverse matrix is fully populated

$$\text{inv(S)} \rightarrow \boldsymbol{S}^{-1} = \frac{1}{6} \begin{bmatrix} 5 & -4 & 3 & -2 & 1 \\ -4 & 8 & -6 & 4 & -2 \\ 3 & -6 & 9 & -6 & 3 \\ -2 & 4 & -6 & 8 & -4 \\ 1 & -2 & 3 & -4 & 5 \end{bmatrix}.$$

but the two factors are sparse (banded), and in some cases can be stored in (overwrite) the original matrix:

$$\boldsymbol{L} = \begin{bmatrix} 1 & 0 & 0 & 0 & 0 \\ 1/2 & 1 & 0 & 0 & 0 \\ 0 & 2/3 & 1 & 0 & 0 \\ 0 & 0 & 3/4 & 1 & 0 \\ 0 & 0 & 0 & 4/5 & 1 \end{bmatrix},$$

$$\boldsymbol{U} = \begin{bmatrix} 2 & 1 & 0 & 0 & 0 \\ 0 & 3/2 & 1 & 0 & 0 \\ 0 & 0 & 4/3 & 1 & 0 \\ 0 & 0 & 0 & 5/4 & 1 \\ 0 & 0 & 0 & 0 & 6/5 \end{bmatrix}.$$

Evaluating the Matlab command $\boldsymbol{S} - \boldsymbol{LU}$ yields a null matrix as expected.

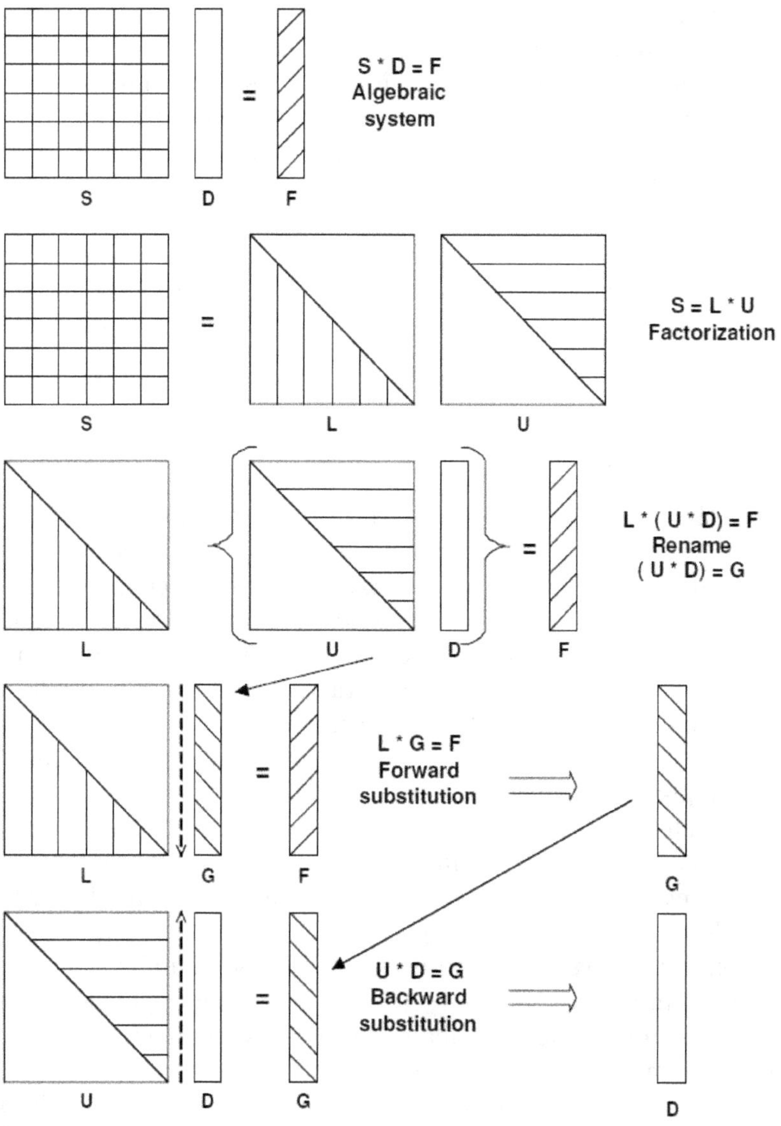

Fig. 7.8-1: Utilizing matrix factorization instead of matrix inversion.

In practical FEA the size of the equations is so large that a matrix inversion is not practical and a factorization of the equations or an iterative solution is used. Factorization is especially efficient when the square matrix is symmetric and positive definite. Then the Crout

Factorization, $\boldsymbol{S} \equiv \boldsymbol{L}\boldsymbol{D}\boldsymbol{U}$, is very popular for large finite element systems. The Crout factorization is used herein with the skyline sparse matrix storage method discussed in the next section. The process for factoring a square matrix into an upper and lower triangle product is sketched in Fig. 7.8-1. After the factorization, a forward-substitution loop and a backward-substitution loop are run. They each involve only one equation and one unknown when solving for the intermediate dummy unknown and the actual unknown in each row of the matrix system. When the matrix size gets extremely large, an iterative solver, like a pre-conditioned conjugant gradient method, is utilized.

7.9 Skyline Sparse Storage*

Up to this point, and in the majority of the supplied scripts, it has been assumed that the system square matrix will be assembled, stored, and factored as a full matrix. There are other more efficient sparse storage and solution techniques. A sparse storage technique for the system square matrix that has proved very efficient in finite element solutions is the "skyline storage mode". In that mode, the mainly non-zero terms in the full matrix are stored as one long vector. To use these procedures it is necessary to determine the top of the non-zero coefficients in every column of the system square matrix. The number of non-zero coefficients above, and including the diagonal coefficient, is called the height of the column. By using the element connection list, the DOF associated with the element are easily determined.

As shown in Fig. 7.9-1, those system equation numbers define the system column heights for that element. Retaining the highest height in each column defines how many coefficients will have to be stored in the system square matrix once the assembly of all elements is completed. If the system matrix is symmetric, then only the coefficients in the column heights need to be stored, as suggested by Fig. 7.9-2. If the application leads to a non-symmetric system matrix, then a second (lower triangle) skyline matrix of the same shape and size is used to store the other half of the coefficients (yes, that duplicates the storage of the diagonal terms).

Element: 1

DOF index $= (5 \quad 4 \quad 3)$
Minimum value $= 3$
Column height $= (3 \quad 2 \quad 1)$

Location in system

$$\Rightarrow \begin{bmatrix} 0 & 0 & 0 & 0 & 0 \\ 0 & 0 & 0 & 0 & 0 \\ 0 & 0 & \boxed{X} & \boxed{X} & \boxed{X} \\ 0 & 0 & X & \boxed{X} & \boxed{X} \\ 0 & 0 & X & X & \boxed{X} \end{bmatrix}$$

Element: 2

DOF index $= (3 \quad 2 \quad 5)$
Minimum value $= 2$
Column height $= (2 \quad 1 \quad 4)$

$$\Rightarrow \begin{bmatrix} 0 & 0 & 0 & 0 & 0 \\ 0 & \boxed{X} & \boxed{X} & 0 & \boxed{X} \\ 0 & X & \boxed{X} & 0 & \boxed{X} \\ 0 & 0 & 0 & 0 & 0 \\ 0 & X & X & 0 & \boxed{X} \end{bmatrix}$$

Element: 3

DOF index $= (1 \quad 3 \quad 4)$
Minimum value $= 1$
Column height $= (1 \quad 3 \quad 4)$

$$\Rightarrow \begin{bmatrix} \boxed{X} & 0 & \boxed{X} & \boxed{X} & 0 \\ 0 & 0 & 0 & 0 & 0 \\ X & 0 & \boxed{X} & \boxed{X} & 0 \\ X & 0 & X & \boxed{X} & 0 \\ 0 & 0 & 0 & 0 & 0 \end{bmatrix}$$

System equations
System DOF index $= (1 \quad 2 \quad 3 \quad 4 \quad 5)$
Maximum height $= (1 \quad 1 \quad 3 \quad 4 \quad 4)$

$$\begin{bmatrix} \boxed{X} & 0 & \boxed{X} & \boxed{X} & 0 \\ 0 & \boxed{X} & \boxed{X} & 0 & \boxed{X} \\ X & X & \boxed{X} & \boxed{X} & \boxed{X} \\ X & 0 & X & \boxed{X} & \boxed{X} \\ 0 & 0 & X & X & \boxed{X} \end{bmatrix}$$

Column 1 2 3 4 5

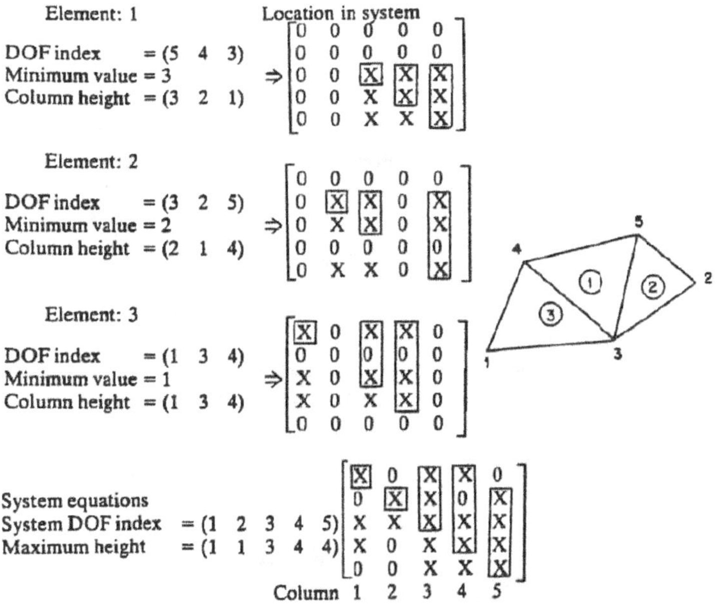

Fig. 7.9-1: Skyline storage for a five DOF mesh.

	1	2	2	4	2	4	2	4	Heights

$$S = \begin{bmatrix} \boxed{S_{11}} & \boxed{S_{12}} & 0 & \boxed{S_{14}} & 0 & 0 & 0 & 0 \\ & \boxed{S_{22}} & \boxed{S_{23}} & 0 & 0 & 0 & 0 & 0 \\ & & \boxed{S_{33}} & 0 & 0 & \boxed{S_{36}} & 0 & 0 \\ & & & S_{44} & \boxed{S_{45}} & S_{46} & 0 & 0 \\ & & & & \boxed{S_{55}} & S_{56} & 0 & \boxed{S_{58}} \\ & & & & & S_{66} & \boxed{S_{67}} & S_{68} \\ & \text{sym.} & & & & & S_{77} & 0 \\ & & & & & & & \boxed{S_{88}} \end{bmatrix}$$

Actual system square matrix

$$S \Leftrightarrow \begin{bmatrix} 1 & 2 & - & 6 & - & - & - & - \\ & 3 & 4 & 7 & - & - & - & - \\ & & 5 & 8 & - & 12 & - & - \\ & & & 9 & 10 & 13 & - & - \\ & & & & 11 & 14 & - & 18 \\ & & & & & 15 & 16 & 19 \\ & & & & & & 17 & 20 \\ & & & & & & & 21 \end{bmatrix} \quad \begin{matrix} 1 \\ 3 \\ 5 \\ 9 \\ 11 \\ 15 \\ 17 \\ 21 \end{matrix}$$

Corresponding vector locations   Diagonal location

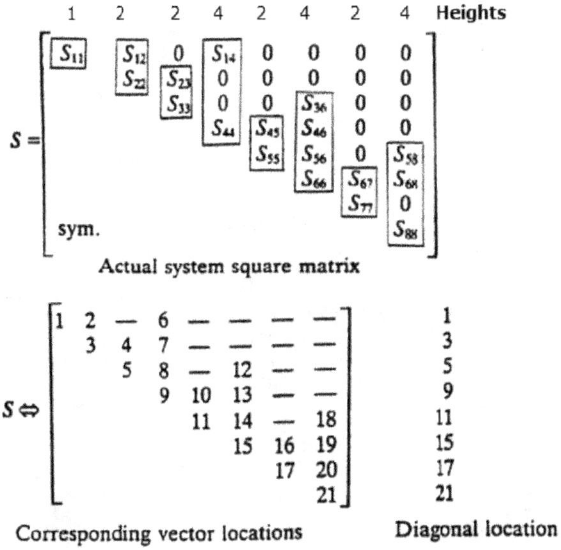

Fig. 7.9-2: System square matrix stored as a vector.

There are sparse storage modes that avoid storing and operating on any zero coefficients. They do that by storing the row and column number, and value, of every non-zero coefficient in the system square matrix. For finite element applications, the author has found that the skyline mode yields a much faster run time than the more general sparse storage and solver techniques. Figure 7.9-2 illustrates that the stored coefficients in each column are numbered from the top down from the first column to the last column. The script for finding column heights is given in Fig. 7.9-3. Note that the skyline storage mode can store some zero coefficients in the columns, like $S(2, 4)$ in Fig. 7.9-1, but their number is vastly smaller than the number of zeros stored, and operated upon, in a full matrix storage mode. There are re-sequencing algorithms (like the Cuthill-McGee algorithm) that can

```
function [i_dof_hi] = sky_hi (n_d, n_g, nodes) %=====
% * * * * * * * * * * * * * * * * * * * * * * * * * *
% find column heights of system equations in skyline
%    storage mode (zero height is inactive eq)
% * * * * * * * * * * * * * * * * * * * * * * * * * *
% i_dof_hi(i) = col height of sys dof i
% n_d         = total no of system dof
% n_g         = number of parameters per node
% nodes       = nodal incidences of all elements
n_e = size(nodes, 1) ; % number of elements
n_n = size(nodes, 2) ; % number of nodes per element
n_i = n_n * n_g      ; % max number of element dof

i_dof_hi = zeros (n_d, 1) ; % zero column heights
l_high   = zeros (n_i, 1) ; % zero work vector
lt_nodes = zeros (n_n, 1) ; % zero work vector
lt_index = zeros (n_i, 1) ; % zero work vector

%  loop over elements
for ie = 1:n_e ; % loop over elements ===> ===> ===> ===>
  lt_n = sum (nodes (ie, :) > 0)  ; % number of type nodes
  lt_nodes (1:lt_n) = nodes (ie, 1:lt_n); % get type nodes
  lt_free = lt_n*n_g ;   % get element types number of DOF
  lt_index (1:lt_free) = get_elem_index (lt_n, n_g, ...
                         lt_nodes); % get elem DOF numbers
  [l_high] = el_high (lt_free, lt_index);% this col height
  for j = 1: lt_free  ; % compare with current maximumb hi
    ndx = lt_index (j)         ; % get system column number
    if ( ndx > 0 )             ; % a valid column number ?
      if ( i_dof_hi (ndx) < l_high (j))  ; % exceeds max ?
        i_dof_hi (ndx) = l_high (j); % keep the new max hi
      end ; % if
    end ; % if
  end ; % for element type dof
end ; % for all elements <== <=== <=== <=== <=== <=== <===
% end function sky_hi ===================================
```

Fig. 7.9-3: Calculating the column height for each equation.

greatly reduce the column heights by renumbering the nodes in the mesh. That results in reduced memory requirements and drastically reduced solution times. Such algorithms are not utilized here.

Example 7.9-1 Given: In Example 12.14-1, the assembled sparse system conduction matrix is

$$\boldsymbol{S} = \begin{bmatrix} 4 & -4 & 0 & 0 & 0 & 0 \\ -4 & 16 & -8 & -4 & 0 & 0 \\ 0 & -8 & 16 & 0 & -8 & 0 \\ 0 & -4 & 0 & 8 & -4 & 0 \\ 0 & 0 & -8 & -4 & 16 & -4 \\ 0 & 0 & 0 & 0 & -4 & 4 \end{bmatrix},$$

which requires $6 \times 6 = 36$ storage locations. Develop the corresponding skyline storage matrix.

Solution: Since the system matrix is symmetric, it could have been stored and assembled as just an upper triangular matrix as

$$\boldsymbol{S} \leftrightarrow \boldsymbol{U} = \begin{bmatrix} 4 & -4 & 0 & 0 & 0 & 0 \\ 0 & 16 & -8 & -4 & 0 & 0 \\ 0 & 0 & 16 & 0 & -8 & 0 \\ 0 & 0 & 0 & 8 & -4 & 0 \\ 0 & 0 & 0 & 0 & 16 & -4 \\ 0 & 0 & 0 & 0 & 0 & 4 \end{bmatrix},$$

which requires only 21 storage locations, which is an 18% reduction in storage. But it still contains nine zeros with eight of those zeros in the uppermost columns portions. Those eight zeros would be filled with non-zeros during a factorization or inversion process. Thus, those (and any) zeros wastefully increase the number of operations needed to solve the system. The skyline mode stores only the columns from the first non-zero entry to the diagonal.

$$\rightarrow \boldsymbol{S_{sky}} = [4;\ -416;\ -816;\ -408;\ -8\ -416;\ -44]^T.$$

In this case, it is a 13×1 vector (which must be allocated before use) which corresponds to about a 64% reduction in the storage requirement. It also contains only one zero term and will reduce wasted operations on zeros by about 89%.

```
function [i_diag] = get_sky_diag (n_d, i_dof_hi)
% ===================================================
% use column heights to find diagonal locations for
% skyline storage mode. columns stored from top down
% ===================================================
% n_d          = total no of system equations
% i_dof_hi(i) = column height of eq i, with diag
% i_diag(i)   = locate diag of i-th eq in upper tri
% Total number of sq matrix terms = i_diag(n_d)

i_diag = zeros (n_d, 1) ; % allocate diagonal items

ipoint = 0      ; % initialize the diagonal location
for k = 1:n_d   ; % loop over all degrees of freedom
  ipoint      = ipoint + i_dof_hi (k) ; % add col hi
  i_diag (k) = ipoint ; % update diagonal locations
end                            ; % for k over all dof
% end get_sky_diag ==================================
```

Fig. 7.9-4: Extracting the system skyline from the element connection list.

Since a typical coefficient in the system square matrix can no longer be located by inspection if it is stored in skyline or any other sparse mode, all of the operations for gathering, scattering, applying EBCs, printing, or multiplying the coefficients by a vector must be programmed in a different way. All of those operations can be hidden from the user. An additional source library directory, called *Akin_Sky_Lib.m*, has been supplied for users that wish to extend the basic application library to solve practical problems with meshes introducing thousands of unknowns. Switching to the skyline mode can be quite simple by including the Matlab "*addpath*" command to automatically search that directory.

There are two important integer arrays that are required in skyline mode to: (1) Determine the amount of storage required, (2) Locate where a typical coefficient, $S(j,k)$, is stored in the *S_sky* vector. That information is required for any operation that is normally applied to the full mode $\boldsymbol{S}$ array, and is extracted from the element connection list. Those two vectors are named *i_dof_hi*, and *i_diag*, respectively, which are shown in Figs. 7.9-1 and 7.9-4.

7.10 Locate Full Locations in a Sparse Matrix*

While all sparse storage methods reduce the storage and operation counts for theoretical solutions, they complicate the gathering and/or scattering of any term in the original full matrix system, say

$S(j,k)$. The relation between the full storage row and column location $S(j,k)$, and the corresponding row, *j_k_v*, in *S_sky* is

$$S(j,k) \equiv S\_sky(j\_k\_v),$$

where

$$j\_k\_v = i\_\text{diag}(\max([j,k])) - abs(j-k), \tag{7.10-1}$$

if, and only if, the $S(j,k)$ coefficient falls within the skyline. Otherwise, using additional logic, the location is set to $j\_k\_v \equiv 0$ to flag that it is a zero coefficient outside the skyline and is not required for any operation on the square matrix. These operations are frequently needed and are executed in function *get_sky_subscript.m* given in Fig. 7.10-1.

The change to any sparse storage mode requires a complete library of other functions that do the many operations that are automatic in a full storage mode. For example, multiplying a square matrix by a vector is a common operation, but its sparse implementation requires locating the non-zero entries in each row and multiplying only them by the corresponding terms in the vector. The sequential changes that need to be made to the main program in order to use the sparse skyline storage mode to assemble and solve the system equations are stored at the *Akin_Sky_Lib* path. The main changes are to set a flag to use skyline storage, use the connection list to determine the number of terms in the sky vector, call alternate functions to: assemble the

```
function [i_j_v] = get_sky_subscript (n_d, i_diag, i, j)
% ====================================================
%   convert (i,j) full symmetric matrix subscripts to
%   (i_j_v) subscript of vector skyline storage mode.
%   i_j_v = 0 if outside skyline and thus has 0 value.
% ====================================================
% n_d       = total no of system equations
% i_diag(i) = location of diag of i-th column
% i, j      = row and column of full matrix item
% i_j_v     = corresponding location in the sky vector
%             or zero if not needed and not stored

id  = max ([i,j])           ; % biggest of row or column
i_j_v = i_diag (id) - abs(i-j)  ; % sky vector location

% Test for zero entry outside skyline
if ( id > 1 )            ; % is off-diagonal term required?
  if ( i_j_v <= i_diag (id - 1) ); % then is not needed
    i_j_v = 0  ; % flag full term not in vector storage
  end                    ; % if is location re-set needed
end                     ; % if full term is off the diagonal
% end get_sky_subscript ================================
```

Fig. 7.10-1: Locating a full matrix term in the skyline vector.

element square matrices; copy the data for calculating the reactions; to apply the EBCs; to solve the system equations; and recover the system reactions. Thereafter no changes are required.

Example 7.10-1 Given: Referring to Fig. 7.9-2, find where the full array coefficients $S(3,6)$ and $S(3,7)$are stored in the skyline vector.

Solution: For row 3 and column 6, Eq. (7.10-1) gives the corresponding possible single subscript location in the skyline vector as

$$\begin{aligned} j\_k\_v &= i\_\text{diag}(\max(3,6)) - \text{abs}(3-6) \\ &= i\_\text{diag}(6) - 3 = 15 - 3 = 12. \end{aligned}$$

But, is that a valid original location above the diagonal? Checking: is

$$12 > i\_\text{diag}(\max(3,6) - 1)?$$
$$12 > i\_\text{diag}(6-1)?$$

$12 > i_{\text{diag}}(5) = 11$? Yes.

Thus, $S(3,6) \equiv S\_sky(12)$ in Fig. 7.9-2. However, the term $S(3,7)$ has a possible location calculation of

$$\begin{aligned} j\_k\_v &= i\_\text{diag}(\max(3,7)) - \text{abs}(3-7) \\ &= i\_\text{diag}(7) - 4 = 17 - 4 = 13. \end{aligned}$$

But is $13 > i\_\text{diag}(\max(3,7) - 1)$?

$$13 > i\_\text{diag}(7-1)?$$
$$13 > i\_\text{diag}(6) = 15\text{? No!}$$

So term $S(3,7) = 0$ outside the skyline and was not stored in the skyline vector. Since it falls outside the skyline and is not stored, it is not needed for any future operation to be applied to the full S matrix. Therefore, set $j\_k\_v = 0$ to flag that coefficient $S(3,\ 7)$ is a zero term that is not stored in the skyline vector.

7.11 Summary

n_b	$\equiv$ Number of boundary segments	n_d	$\equiv$ Number of system unknowns
n_e	$\equiv$ Number of elements	n_g	$\equiv$ Number of unknowns per node
n_i	$\equiv$ Number of unknowns per element	n_m	$\equiv$ Number of mesh nodes
n_n	$\equiv$ Number of nodes per element	n_p	$\equiv$ Dimension of parametric space
n_q	$\equiv$ Number of total quadrature points	n_s	$\equiv$ Dimension of physical space
b	= boundary segment number	e	= element number
$\subset$	= subset of a larger set	$\cup$	= union of two sets

Boundary, element, and system unknowns: $\boldsymbol{\delta}^b \subset_b \boldsymbol{\delta}^e \subset_e \boldsymbol{\delta}$

Boolean extraction arrays: $\boldsymbol{\delta}^b \equiv \boldsymbol{\beta}_b \boldsymbol{\delta}, \boldsymbol{\delta}^e \equiv \boldsymbol{\beta}_e \boldsymbol{\delta}$

Geometry: $\Gamma^b \subset \Omega^e \equiv$ Boundary segment $\quad \Omega^e \equiv$ Element domain

$\Omega = \cup_e \Omega^e \equiv$ Solution domain $\quad \Gamma = \cup_b \Gamma^b \equiv$ Domain boundary

Local equation (degree of freedom) number at element node i for parameter j

$$n(i,j) = n_g * (i-1) + j, \quad 1 \le i \le n_n, \quad 1 \le j \le n_g.$$

System equation (degree of freedom) number at system node I for parameter j

$$N(I,j) = n_g * (I-1) + j, \quad 1 \le I \le n_m, \quad 1 \le j \le n_g.$$

System mesh node number, I, at local element node i : $I =$ e_nodes(i).

Matrix equilibrium equations (partitioned); $\boldsymbol{u_u}$ = remaining unknowns, $\boldsymbol{u_k}$ = set by EBCs, $\boldsymbol{r_k}$ = reactions needed to maintain EBCs, $\boldsymbol{S}$ = known stiffnesses, $\boldsymbol{c}$ = known sources:

$$\begin{bmatrix} \mathbf{S_{uu}} & \mathbf{S_{uk}} \\ \mathbf{S_{ku}} & \mathbf{S_{kk}} \end{bmatrix} \begin{Bmatrix} \mathbf{u_u} \\ \mathbf{u_k} \end{Bmatrix} = \begin{Bmatrix} \mathbf{c_u} \\ \mathbf{c_k} + \mathbf{r_k} \end{Bmatrix}.$$

$$\boldsymbol{u_u} = \boldsymbol{S_{uu}^{-1}}(\boldsymbol{c_u} - \boldsymbol{S_{uk}} \boldsymbol{u_k}), \boldsymbol{r_k} = \boldsymbol{S_{ku}} \boldsymbol{u_u} + \boldsymbol{u} - \boldsymbol{c_k}.$$

Multipoint constraints (MPC), Type 2: $Au_j + Bu_k = C \to u_j + bu_k = c$.

Numerical factorization of a symmetric, positive definite square matrix

$\boldsymbol{L}$ = lower triangle matrix, $\boldsymbol{U}$ = upper triangle matrix:

$$\boldsymbol{S}u = \boldsymbol{c}, \quad \boldsymbol{S} \Longrightarrow \boldsymbol{L}\times\boldsymbol{U}, \quad \boldsymbol{L}\times(\boldsymbol{U}\times\boldsymbol{u}) = \boldsymbol{c}, \quad \boldsymbol{U}\times\boldsymbol{u} \equiv \boldsymbol{g}, \quad \boldsymbol{L}\times\boldsymbol{g} = \boldsymbol{c}$$

Forward-substitution: $\rightarrow \boldsymbol{g}$, $\boldsymbol{U} \times \boldsymbol{u} = \boldsymbol{g}$, Backward-substitution: $\rightarrow \boldsymbol{u}$.

7.12 Review

1. A single element system has the equilibrium equation, before applying the Dirichlet BC, of

$$\frac{EA}{3L}\begin{bmatrix} 7 & -8 & 1 \\ -8 & 16 & -8 \\ 1 & -8 & 7 \end{bmatrix}\begin{Bmatrix} u_1 \\ u_2 \\ u_3 = d \end{Bmatrix} = \begin{Bmatrix} 0 \\ 0 \\ R_3 \end{Bmatrix} + \frac{\gamma AL}{6}\begin{Bmatrix} 1 \\ 4 \\ 1 \end{Bmatrix},$$

   where d is a known displacement value. Write the matrix equations for the two remaining unknowns. Do not solve for the remaining unknowns.
2. Briefly explain the operations of scatter and gather and the type of data upon which they operate.
3. A two-node space truss element (with three displacements per node) in a bridge is connected to nodes 27 and 32. What are the system DOF numbers (equation numbers) at node 32?
4. Convert the full matrix in the six spring assembly in (1.7-17) into a skyline vector and list its i diag values.

Chapter 8

Applications of One-Dimensional Lagrange Elements

8.1 Introduction

Most one-dimensional linear applications of second-order ODEs involve a scalar equation such as

$$-\frac{d}{dx}\left[K(x)\,\frac{du(x)}{dx}\right]+A(x)\,\frac{du(x)}{dx}+C(x)\,u(x)-Q(x)=0, \tag{8.1-1}$$

with two boundary conditions (BC). Typically, the coefficients in the equation represent so-called diffusion effects, K, advection effects, A, convection effects, C, and source or forcing terms, Q. The two potential BCs, as shown in Fig. 8.1-1, are either giving the function (Dirichlet) value and/or the slope (Neumann) value at one or more ends of the domain. After developing an equivalent integral form, the domain will be divided with a mesh of nodes and elements, and the solution will be approximated with an assumed polynomial within each element.

This is called the "strong form" because it requires any estimate of the solution to have a non-zero second derivative. Many finite element approximations use piecewise linear functions to approximate the solution, $u(x)$, and thus have a zero second derivative.

By applying the Galerkin weighted residual method the equivalent integral form is found by multiplying the residual by the approximate spatial form and setting their integral equal to zero (i.e., make the

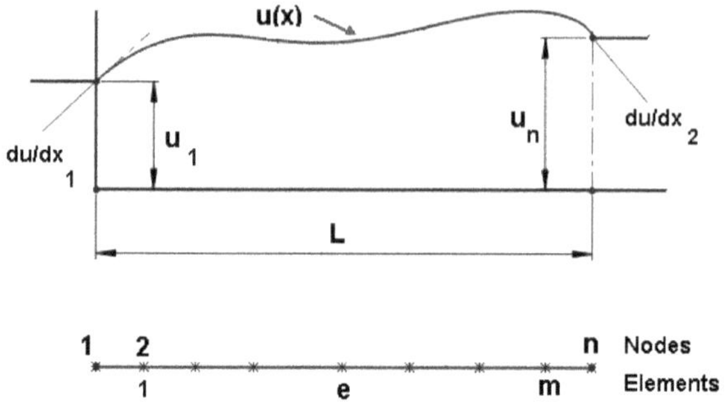

Fig. 8.1-1: An ODE domain with essential and secondary BC options.

residual orthogonal to the solution):

$$I = \int_{x_1}^{x_2} u(x)\left[-\frac{d}{dx}\left[K(x)\,\frac{du\,(x)}{dx}\right] + A\,(x)\,\frac{du\,(x)}{dx}\right.$$
$$\left. +C(x)\,u(x) - Q(x)\right]\,dx = 0.$$

This is called the "weak form" because any approximation now has to have only a non-vanishing first derivative. Thus, a piecewise linear approximation can be used with this equivalent form. The first term can be integrated by parts as

$$I = -\left[u\left(K(x)\frac{du}{dx}\right)\right]_{x_1}^{x_1+L} + \int_{x_1}^{x_1+L} \frac{du}{dx}K(x)\frac{du}{dx}dx$$
$$+\int_{x_1}^{x_1+L} u(x)\,A(x)\,\frac{du}{dx}\,dx \cdots + \int_{x_1}^{x_1+L} u(x)\,C(x)\,u(x)dx$$
$$-\int_{x_1}^{x_1+L} u(x)\,Q(x)dx = 0, \qquad (8.1\text{-}2)$$

where the first term introduces the products of the property K with the solution value on the boundary, and the non-essential BCs or reactions $du(L)/dx$ and $du(0)/dx$:

$$-\left[u\left(K(x)\frac{du}{dx}\right)\right]_{x_1}^{x_1+L=x_n} = -\left[u\,(x_n)\left(K(x_n)\frac{du(x_n)}{dx}\right)\right.$$
$$\left.-u\,(x_1)\left(K(x_1)\frac{du(x_1)}{dx}\right)\right]. \qquad (8.1\text{-}3)$$

In other words, at either end of the domain either the solution value or the flux value can be specified. If neither is specified, then that end defaults to an insulated end with zero gradient and zero flux. If $u(x_k)$ is given, then the corresponding flux value, $K(x_k)du\,(x_k)/dx$, will be recovered from (8.1-2) after all of the solution values, $\boldsymbol{u}$, have been computed. Conversely, if the solution value is unknown and the flux value, $K(x_k)du\,(x_k)/dx$, is specified, it simply becomes another source term that is used in computing all of the u values, including $u(x_k)$.

This equivalent integral form will be converted into matrix notation by assuming that the domain is divided with a finite element mesh with nodes and elements. Assume that the last node is at $x = L$ and that each node has a solution value that is to be determined. The list of all of the nodal solution values is denoted as $\boldsymbol{u}$ where $\boldsymbol{u^T} = \left[u_1\; u_2\; u_3\; \cdots\; u_{n-1}\; u_n\right]$. Then (8.1-3) can be padded with zeros to include all of the solution values so as to write it as a matrix product:

$$-\left[u\left(K(x)\frac{du}{dx}\right)\right]_{x_1}^{x_1+L=x_n} = -\left[u\,(L)\,K_L\frac{du\,(L)}{dx} - u\,(0)\,K_0\frac{du\,(0)}{dx}\right].$$

Assuming a sequential mesh with n nodes then this converts to a reference to the first and last nodes in the mesh:

$$-\left[u\left(K(x)\frac{du}{dx}\right)\right]_{x_1}^{x_1+L=x_n} = -\left[u_n\;K_L\tfrac{du(L)}{dx} - u_1 K_0\tfrac{du(0)}{dx}\right].$$

This can be expanded to include all other nodes multiplied by zero, which allows it to be written in matrix form as the matrix dot product of two arrays:

$$-\left[u\left(K(x)\frac{du}{dx}\right)\right]_{x_1}^{x_1+L=x_n}$$

$$-\left[-K_0\tfrac{du(0)}{dx}u_1\;(0)u_2\;(0)u_3\;\cdots\;(0)u_{n-1}\;K_n\tfrac{du(x_n)}{dx}u_n\right].$$

Or writing the scalar as a matrix dot product

$$-\left[u\left(K(x)\frac{du}{dx}\right)\right]_{x_1}^{x_1+L=x_n}$$

$$= -\left[u_1\ u_2\ u_3\ \cdots\ u_{n-1}\ u_n\right]\begin{Bmatrix} -K_1 du\left(x_1\right)/dx \\ 0 \\ 0 \\ \vdots \\ 0 \\ K_n du\left(x_n\right)/dx \end{Bmatrix}.$$

$$-\left[u\left(K(x)\frac{du}{dx}\right)\right]_{x_1}^{x_1+L=x_n} \equiv -\boldsymbol{u}^{\boldsymbol{T}}\boldsymbol{c}_{\mathrm{NBC}},\ \boldsymbol{c}_{\mathrm{NBC}} = \begin{Bmatrix} -K_1 du\left(x_1\right)/dx \\ 0 \\ 0 \\ \vdots \\ 0 \\ K_n du\left(x_n\right)/dx \end{Bmatrix}. \tag{8.1-4}$$

Here the system non-essential Neumann boundary condition (NBC) and/or reaction vector, $\boldsymbol{c}_{\mathrm{NBC}}$, is zero except for the two rows corresponding to the two end nodes of the mesh. Note that this process moves the NBCs into the integral form. The essential (Dirichlet) boundary conditions (EBCs) must still be explicitly enforced on the final matrix equations.

To continue inserting the matrix notation form into (8.1-2), begin with the special case where the approximation uses only a single element so the interpolation becomes $u(x) = \boldsymbol{H}(x)\boldsymbol{u} = \boldsymbol{u}^{\boldsymbol{T}}\boldsymbol{H}(x)^{\boldsymbol{T}}$ and $du/dx = d\boldsymbol{H}(x)/dx\boldsymbol{u} = \boldsymbol{u}^{\boldsymbol{T}}d\boldsymbol{H}(x)^{\boldsymbol{T}}/dx$:

$$\begin{aligned} I = -\boldsymbol{u}^{\boldsymbol{T}}\boldsymbol{c}_{\mathrm{NBC}} &+ \int_{\Omega}\left\{\boldsymbol{u}^{\boldsymbol{T}}\frac{d\boldsymbol{H}(x)}{dx}^{\boldsymbol{T}}\right\}\left[K(x)\frac{d\boldsymbol{H}(x)}{dx}\boldsymbol{u}\right]dx \\ &+ \int_{\Omega}\left\{\boldsymbol{u}^{\boldsymbol{T}}\boldsymbol{H}(x)^{\boldsymbol{T}}\right\}\left[A(x)\frac{d\boldsymbol{H}(x)}{dx}\boldsymbol{u}\right]dx \\ &+ \int_{\Omega}\left\{\boldsymbol{u}^{\boldsymbol{T}}\boldsymbol{H}(x)^{\boldsymbol{T}}\right\}\left[C(x)\boldsymbol{H}(x)\boldsymbol{u}\right]dx \\ &- \int_{\Omega}\left\{\boldsymbol{u}^{\boldsymbol{T}}\ \boldsymbol{H}(x)^{\boldsymbol{T}}\right\}Q(x)dx = 0, \end{aligned} \tag{8.1-5}$$

but the unknown solution constants, $\boldsymbol{u}$, factor out of the integrals so

$$\begin{aligned} I = -\boldsymbol{u}^{\boldsymbol{T}} \boldsymbol{c}_{NBC} + \boldsymbol{u}^{\boldsymbol{T}} \left[\int_{\Omega} \frac{d\boldsymbol{H}(x)^{\boldsymbol{T}}}{dx} K(x) \frac{d\boldsymbol{H}(x)}{dx}\, dx \right] \boldsymbol{u} \\ + \boldsymbol{u}^{\boldsymbol{T}} \left[\int_{\Omega} \boldsymbol{H}(x)^{\boldsymbol{T}} A(x) \frac{d\boldsymbol{H}(x)}{dx}\, dx \right] \boldsymbol{u} \\ + \boldsymbol{u}^{\boldsymbol{T}} \left[\int_{\Omega} \boldsymbol{H}(x)^{\boldsymbol{T}} C(x) \boldsymbol{H}(x) dx \right] \boldsymbol{u} \\ - \boldsymbol{u}^{\boldsymbol{T}} \left\{ \int_{\Omega} \boldsymbol{H}(x)^{\boldsymbol{T}} Q(x)\, dx \right\} = 0. \end{aligned}$$

Introducing the spatial interpolation matrix has introduced two square symmetric matrices, one square unsymmetric matrix, and another column vector:

$$\begin{aligned} I &= -\boldsymbol{u}^{\boldsymbol{T}} \boldsymbol{c}_{NBC} + \boldsymbol{u}^{\boldsymbol{T}} [\boldsymbol{S}_K] \boldsymbol{u} + \boldsymbol{u}^{\boldsymbol{T}} [\boldsymbol{U}_A] \boldsymbol{u} + \boldsymbol{u}^{\boldsymbol{T}} [\boldsymbol{M}_C] \boldsymbol{u} \\ &\quad - \boldsymbol{u}^{\boldsymbol{T}} \{\boldsymbol{c}_Q\} = 0 \\ I &= \boldsymbol{u}^{\boldsymbol{T}} [\boldsymbol{S}_K + \boldsymbol{U}_A + \boldsymbol{M}_C] \boldsymbol{u} - \boldsymbol{u}^{\boldsymbol{T}} \{\boldsymbol{c}_{\mathrm{NBC}} + \boldsymbol{c}_F\} = 0 \\ I &= \boldsymbol{u}^{\boldsymbol{T}} \langle [\boldsymbol{S}_K + \boldsymbol{U}_A + \boldsymbol{M}_C] \boldsymbol{u} - \{\boldsymbol{c}_{\mathrm{NBC}} + \boldsymbol{c}_Q\} \rangle = 0. \end{aligned}$$

To obtain a non-trivial solution ($\boldsymbol{u} \neq 0$) for arbitrary data (K, A, C, Q, and the NBC), the expression in the angled brackets must vanish. That gives the equivalent governing matrix form:

$$[\boldsymbol{S}_K + \boldsymbol{U}_A + \boldsymbol{M}_C] \boldsymbol{u} = \{\boldsymbol{c}_{\mathrm{NBC}} + \boldsymbol{c}_Q\}. \tag{8.1-6}$$

Such a system is singular until it is modified to include the EBCs, which are specified values of one or more terms in the solution vector, $\boldsymbol{u}$. The three square matrices are known as the diffusion (or conduction) matrix, the non-symmetric advection matrix, and the generalized mass matrix, respectively. The two-column vectors are the NBC and/or reaction vector and the source vector, respectively.

For a general finite element solution, more than one element is employed and the domain is split into the union of non-overlapping element domains, $\Omega^e : \Omega = \cup_e \Omega^e$. That in turn requires that any integral over the domain becomes the sum of the intervals over the element domains. Then the first integral in (8.1-2) becomes

$$\boldsymbol{u}^{\boldsymbol{T}}[\boldsymbol{S}_K]\boldsymbol{u} = \int_\Omega \frac{du}{dx} K(x) \frac{du}{dx} dx = \sum_{e=1}^{n_e} \int_\Omega^e \frac{du}{dx} K^e(x) \frac{du}{dx} dx,$$

and so forth for the other integrals. Substituting the solution interpolation approximation $u(x) = \boldsymbol{H}(r)\,\boldsymbol{u}^e$ within Ω^e into the above integral form leads to the scalar identity

$$\boldsymbol{u}^{\boldsymbol{T}}[\boldsymbol{S}_K]\boldsymbol{u} = \sum_{e=1}^{n_e} \boldsymbol{u}^{e^T} \left[\int_{\Omega^e} \frac{d\boldsymbol{H}(x)^{\boldsymbol{T}}}{dx} K^e(x) \frac{d\boldsymbol{H}(x)}{dx}\, dx \right] \boldsymbol{u}^e$$

$$= \sum_{e=1}^{n_e} \boldsymbol{u}^{e^T} [\boldsymbol{S}^e] \boldsymbol{u}^e.$$

Likewise, the element matrices for (8.1-1) are

$$\boldsymbol{S}^e = \int_{L^e} \frac{d\boldsymbol{H}(r)^T}{dx} K^e(x) \frac{d\boldsymbol{H}(r)}{dx} dx \quad \boldsymbol{U}^e = \int_{L^e} \frac{d\boldsymbol{H}(r)^T}{dx} A^e(x) \boldsymbol{H}(r) dx$$

$$\boldsymbol{M}^e = \int_{L^e} \boldsymbol{H}(r)^T C^e(x) \boldsymbol{H}(r) dx \quad \boldsymbol{c}^e = \int_{L^e} \boldsymbol{H}(r)^T Q^e(x) dx. \qquad (8.1\text{-}7)$$

For constant coefficients, these integrals were listed in closed form in Table 4.10-1.

The element degrees of freedom, $\boldsymbol{u}^e$, can be gathered from the system degrees of freedom, $\boldsymbol{u}$, by a Boolean matrix product, $\boldsymbol{u}^e = \boldsymbol{\beta}^e \boldsymbol{u}$, and/or by a vector subscript, $\boldsymbol{u}^e = \boldsymbol{u}(\boldsymbol{\beta}_e)$. For the former matrix algebra approach for scattering the small element arrays into the single large system, the array changes the prior scalar identity

$$\boldsymbol{u}^{\boldsymbol{T}}[\boldsymbol{S}_K]\boldsymbol{u} = \sum_{e=1}^{n_e} \boldsymbol{u}^{e^T} [\boldsymbol{S}^e] \boldsymbol{u}^e = \sum_{e=1}^{n_e} (\boldsymbol{\beta}^e \boldsymbol{u})^{\boldsymbol{T}} [\boldsymbol{S}^e] \boldsymbol{\beta}^e \boldsymbol{u}$$

$$= \boldsymbol{u}^{\boldsymbol{T}} \left[\sum_{e=1}^{n_e} (\boldsymbol{\beta}_e)^{\boldsymbol{T}} [\boldsymbol{S}^e] (\boldsymbol{\beta}_e) \right] \boldsymbol{u},$$

where $[\boldsymbol{S}_K] = [\sum_{e=1}^{n_e} (\boldsymbol{\beta}_e)^{\boldsymbol{T}} [\boldsymbol{S}^e] (\boldsymbol{\beta}_e)]$.

As discussed in Section 7.2 and illustrated in Fig. 7.2-2, this scattering operation adds the coefficients in each element matrix, $\boldsymbol{S}^e$, into only the rows and columns of the system matrix that correspond to those at nodes connected to the element.

Either use of the element connection list defines the assembly additions to the corresponding system matrices

$$[\boldsymbol{S} + \boldsymbol{U} + \boldsymbol{M}]\{\boldsymbol{u}\} = \{\boldsymbol{c}\} + \{\boldsymbol{c_{NBC}}\}, \tag{8.1-8}$$

where the system diffusion or conduction matrix, $\boldsymbol{S}$, is assembled from all of the element diffusion matrices, $\boldsymbol{S}^e$, etc. Any NBCs are weakly included in at least the system column matrix $\{\boldsymbol{c_{NBC}}\}$. Be warned that if the unsymmetric matrix $\boldsymbol{U}^e$ is present and if the advection term, $A(x)$, is large, then the ODE can change from being elliptic and the classical Galerkin MWR can give wildly oscillating results for certain data and it must be replaced by the Petrov–Galerkin MWR which is a theoretical process for high-speed advection solutions.

After the following related examples, the next two sections will introduce constant coefficient matrices and variable source terms, respectively.

Example 8.1-1 Given: For the ODE $K\,d^2u^*/dx^2 + Q(x) = 0$ for the domain $x_1 \leq x \leq (x_1 + L)$ let the NBC be $du(x_2)/dx = b$, and let the EBC be $u(x_1) = 0$. Beginning with the equivalent integral form (above) define all the matrix integrals for a single element approximation where the approximate solution is interpolated as $u^*(r) \cong u(r) = \boldsymbol{H}(r)\boldsymbol{u}^e$ along with the linear geometric mapping of $x(r) = x_1 + rL^e$.

Solution: The equivalent integral form is

$$I = \left[K\,u(x_2)\frac{du(x_2)}{dx} - K\,u(x_1)\frac{du(x_1)}{dx}\right] - \int_{x_1}^{x_2} \frac{du}{dx}K\frac{du}{dx}dx + \int_{x_1}^{x_2} u(x)\,Q(x)dx = 0,$$

where the NBC data are $du(x_2)/dx \equiv b$ and thus the system NBC/reaction vector is

$$\boldsymbol{c}_{NBC}^T = \left[-K du(x_1)/dx\; 0 \cdots Kb\right].$$

Another system vector is due to the source term, $Q(x)$, which is usually dependent on the physical location x. Let the source be input at the nodes and interpolated as $Q(x) = \boldsymbol{H}(r)\boldsymbol{q}^e$. Then the source integral contribution is

$$\int_{x_1}^{x_1+L} u(x)\, Q(x) dx = \int_{x_1}^{x_1+L} \boldsymbol{u}^{e^T} \boldsymbol{H}(r)^{\boldsymbol{T}}\, \boldsymbol{H}(r) \boldsymbol{q}^e\, dx$$
$$= \boldsymbol{u}^{e^T} (\boldsymbol{M}^e \boldsymbol{q}^e) \equiv \boldsymbol{u}^{e^T} \boldsymbol{c}^e.$$

The product with the square mass matrix $\boldsymbol{M}^e$ converts the nodal input sources, $\boldsymbol{q}^e$, to their nodal resultant $\boldsymbol{c}^e$. Likewise, the element diffusion square matrix defined by the integration by parts is

$$-\int_{x_1}^{x_1+L} \frac{du}{dx} K \frac{du}{dx} dx = -\int_{x_1^e}^{x_1+L} \left(\boldsymbol{u}^{e^T} \frac{d\boldsymbol{H}(r)}{dr}^{\boldsymbol{T}} \frac{dr}{dx} \right) K \left(\frac{d\boldsymbol{H}(r)}{dr} \frac{dr}{dx} \boldsymbol{u}^e \right) dx$$
$$= -\boldsymbol{u}^{e^T} \left[\int_0^1 \left(\frac{d\boldsymbol{H}(r)}{dr}^{\boldsymbol{T}} \frac{1}{L^e} \right) K \right.$$
$$\left. \left(\frac{d\boldsymbol{H}(r)}{dx} \frac{1}{L^e} \right) (L^e\, dr) \right] \boldsymbol{u}^e$$
$$\equiv -\boldsymbol{u}^{e^T} \boldsymbol{S}^e \boldsymbol{u}^e.$$

The combined governing integral form, in matrix notation, is

$$I = \boldsymbol{u}^{e^T} \mathbf{c}_{\mathrm{NBC}} - \boldsymbol{u}^{e^T} \boldsymbol{S}^e \boldsymbol{u}^e + \boldsymbol{u}^{e^T} \boldsymbol{c}^e = 0$$
$$= \boldsymbol{u}^{e^T} \{\boldsymbol{c}_{NBC} - \boldsymbol{S}^e \boldsymbol{u}^e + \boldsymbol{c}^e\}, \;\; u(0) = 0.$$

For arbitrary data the last term in brackets must be a null vector $\mathbf{c}_{\mathrm{NBC}} - \boldsymbol{S}^e \boldsymbol{u}^e + \boldsymbol{c}^e = 0$ and the governing matrix system is $\boldsymbol{S}^e \boldsymbol{u}^e = \mathbf{c}_{\mathrm{NBC}} + \boldsymbol{c}^e$ which is still subject to the Dirichlet BC $u(0) = 0 = u_1$.

Example 8.1-2 Given: For the ODE in Example 8.1-1, let the line source be constant, $Q(x) = c$. Beginning with the above integral form, evaluate the source matrix integral $\boldsymbol{c}^e$ for a single three-noded quadratic element approximation where the approximate solution is interpolated as $u^*(r) \cong \boldsymbol{H}(r)\boldsymbol{u}^e$ with $\boldsymbol{H}(r) = [(1-3r+2r^2)\ (4r-4r^2)\ (-r+2r^2)]$.

Solution: The integral contribution is

$$\int_{x_1}^{x_3} u(x)\, Q(x)\, dx = \boldsymbol{u}^{e^T} \left\{ \int_{x_1}^{x_3} \boldsymbol{H}(r)^{\boldsymbol{T}}\, Q(x)^e\, dx \right\} \equiv \boldsymbol{u}^{e^T} \boldsymbol{c}^e.$$

For a constant Jacobian element with a constant source, integration gives

$$\boldsymbol{c}^e = \int_{x_1}^{x_3} \boldsymbol{H}(r)^{\boldsymbol{T}}\, Q(x)^e\, dx = \int_0^1 \boldsymbol{H}(r)^{\boldsymbol{T}}\, c\, \frac{dx}{dr} dr$$

$$= c \int_0^1 \boldsymbol{H}(r)^{\boldsymbol{T}}\, (L^e\, dr)$$

$$= cL^e \int_0^1 \begin{Bmatrix} 1 - 3r + 2r^2 \\ 4r - 4r^2 \\ -r + 2r^2 \end{Bmatrix} dr = cL^e \begin{Bmatrix} r - 3r^2/2 + 2r^3/3 \\ 4r^2/2 - 4r^3/3 \\ -r^2/2 + 2r^3/3 \end{Bmatrix}_0^1$$

$$= cL^e \begin{Bmatrix} 1 - 3/2 + 2/3 \\ 4/2 - 4/3 \\ -1/2 + 2/3 \end{Bmatrix}$$

$$\boldsymbol{c}^e = \frac{cL^e}{6} \begin{Bmatrix} 1 \\ 4 \\ 1 \end{Bmatrix}.$$

Note that the sum of all the numerical coefficients in the generalized matrix is $6/6 = 1$ since the full integrated source, cL^e, must be accounted for in the matrix system. Two-thirds of the total constant source goes to the middle node and one-third is split equally to the two end nodes. (This agrees with Table 4.10-1.)

Example 8.1-3 Given: For the ODE in Example 8.1-1 with $u(0) = 0$, $du(L)/dx = b$, and a constant source, $Q(x) = c$, use one three-noded quadratic element approximation where the solution is interpolated as $u^*(r) \cong \boldsymbol{H}(r)\boldsymbol{u}^e$ with $\boldsymbol{H}(r) = [(1 - 3r + 2r^2)\ (4r - 4r^2)\ (-r + 2r^2)]$ to formulate the stiffness matrix and the equivalent matrix system before any EBC or NBC is applied.

Solution: Recall the integral form

$$I = \left[K\, u(x_2) \frac{du\,(x_2)}{dx} - K\, u(x_1) \frac{du(x_1)}{dx}\right]$$

$$- \int_{x_1}^{x_2} \frac{du}{dx} K \frac{du}{dx} dx + \int_{x_1}^{x_2} u(x)\, Q(x) dx = 0$$

converts to the matrix form $\boldsymbol{S}^e \boldsymbol{u}^e = \boldsymbol{c}_{\rm NBC} + \boldsymbol{c}^e$ subject to enforcing the EBC and NBC. The scalar first term with the NBC is converted to the dot product of two vectors

$$\left[K\, u(x_2)\frac{du(x_2)}{dx} - K\, u(x_1)\frac{du(x_1)}{dx}\right] \equiv \boldsymbol{u}^T \boldsymbol{c}_{NBC}.$$

For the single element model $u(x_1) = u_1$ and $u(x_3) = u_3$, so the NBC/reaction matrix identity is padded only with one interior zero:

$$\boldsymbol{c}_{\rm NBC}^T = \left\{\begin{matrix} -K\, du(x_1)/dx \\ 0 \\ K\, b \end{matrix}\right\}, \quad \boldsymbol{u} = \left\{\begin{matrix} u_1 \\ u_2 \\ u_3 \end{matrix}\right\}.$$

Likewise, the element square (stiffness) matrix was defined by the integration by parts:

$$-\int_{x_1^e}^{x_3} \frac{du}{dx} K \frac{du}{dx} dx = -\boldsymbol{u}^{e^T} \int_0^1 \left(\frac{d\boldsymbol{H}(r)}{dr}^{\boldsymbol{T}} \frac{1}{L^e}\right) K \left(\frac{d\boldsymbol{H}(r)}{dr}\frac{1}{L^e}\right)$$

$$(L^e\, dr)\, \boldsymbol{u}^e = -\boldsymbol{u}^{e^T} \boldsymbol{S}^e \boldsymbol{u}^e$$

$$= -\boldsymbol{u}^{e^T} \int_0^1 \frac{1}{L^e} \left\{\begin{matrix} (-3+4r) \\ (4-8r) \\ (-1+4r) \end{matrix}\right\} \frac{K}{L^e}$$

$$\big[(-3+4rt)\ (4-8r)\ (-1+4r)\big]\, (L^e\, dr)\, \boldsymbol{u}^e.$$

The inner matrix product is

$$\begin{bmatrix} (-3+4r)^2 & (4-8r)(-3+4r) & (-1+4r)(-3+4r) \\ (-3+4r)(4-8r) & (4-8r)^2 & (-1+4r)(4-8r) \\ (-3+4r)(-1+4r) & (4-8r)(-1+4r) & (-1+4r)^2 \end{bmatrix}.$$

Integrating

$$-\int_{x_1^e}^{x_3} \frac{du}{dx} K \frac{du}{dx} dx = -\boldsymbol{u}^{e^T} \frac{K}{3L^e} \begin{bmatrix} 7 & -8 & 1 \\ -8 & 16 & -8 \\ 1 & -8 & 7 \end{bmatrix} \boldsymbol{u}^e \equiv -\boldsymbol{u}^{e^T} \boldsymbol{S}^e \boldsymbol{u}^e.$$

Note that the sum of the numerical coefficients of the square stiffness matrix is zero. The singular governing matrix system before imposing any BCs is $\boldsymbol{S}^e \boldsymbol{u}^e = \boldsymbol{c}_{\text{NBC}} + \boldsymbol{c}^e$, which expands to

$$\frac{K}{3L^e}\begin{bmatrix} 7 & -8 & 1 \\ -8 & 16 & -8 \\ 1 & -8 & 7 \end{bmatrix}\begin{Bmatrix} u_1 \\ u_2 \\ u_3 \end{Bmatrix} = \begin{Bmatrix} -K\,du(0)/dx \\ 0 \\ K\,b \end{Bmatrix} + \frac{c\,L^e}{6}\begin{Bmatrix} 1 \\ 4 \\ 1 \end{Bmatrix}.$$

Here, the Neumann BC is included in the third row of $\boldsymbol{c}_{\text{NBC}}$, and the first row contains the reaction needed when u_1 is assigned its Dirichlet BC value. That reaction becomes the third unknown in these three equations.

Example 8.1-4 Given: the governing matrix system from Example 8.1-3 imposes the EBC that $u_1 = 0$ and the symmetry NBC that $du(L)/dx = 0$. Solve for u_2 and u_3 and for the reaction value $(-du(0)/dx)$ needed to maintain that EBC.

Solution: Substitute the BCs into the previously singular three equations:

$$\frac{K}{3L^e}\begin{bmatrix} 7 & -8 & 1 \\ -8 & 16 & -8 \\ 1 & -8 & 7 \end{bmatrix}\begin{Bmatrix} u_1 = 0 \\ u_2 \\ u_3 \end{Bmatrix} = \begin{Bmatrix} -Kdu(0)/dx \\ 0 \\ K\,du(L)/dx = 0 \end{Bmatrix} + \frac{c\,L^e}{6}\begin{Bmatrix} 1 \\ 4 \\ 1 \end{Bmatrix}.$$

The three unknowns are $u_2, u_3, -du(0)/dx$, but the reaction must be recovered after all of the primary unknowns, $\boldsymbol{u}^e$, are known. Carry the effect of the EBC to the right-hand side and use the last two rows to find those primary unknowns

$$\frac{K}{3L^e}\begin{bmatrix} 16 & -8 \\ -8 & 7 \end{bmatrix}\begin{Bmatrix} u_2 \\ u_3 \end{Bmatrix} = \begin{Bmatrix} 0 \\ 0 \end{Bmatrix} + \frac{c\,L^e}{6}\begin{Bmatrix} 4 \\ 1 \end{Bmatrix} - (u_1 = 0)\,\frac{K}{3L^e}\begin{Bmatrix} -8 \\ 1 \end{Bmatrix}$$
$$= \frac{c\,L^e}{6}\begin{Bmatrix} 4 \\ 1 \end{Bmatrix}.$$

Inverting the 2×2 matrix yields the exact analytic values for the primary unknowns

$$\begin{Bmatrix} u_2 \\ u_3 \end{Bmatrix} = \frac{3L^e}{K}\frac{1}{48}\begin{bmatrix} 7 & 8 \\ 8 & 16 \end{bmatrix}\frac{c\,L^e}{6}\begin{Bmatrix} 4 \\ 1 \end{Bmatrix} = \frac{c\,{L^e}^2}{8K}\begin{Bmatrix} 3 \\ 4 \end{Bmatrix}.$$

Now the first row gives the necessary reaction, which is also exact:

$$\frac{K}{3L^e}\begin{bmatrix}7 & -8 & 1\end{bmatrix}\frac{c\,L^{e^2}}{8K}\begin{Bmatrix}0\\3\\4\end{Bmatrix} = \{-K\,du(0)/dx\} + \left\{\frac{c\,L^e}{6}\right\}.$$

$$\left\{\frac{-20\,c\,L^e}{24}\right\} - \left\{\frac{4\,c\,L^e}{24}\right\} = c\,L^e = \{-K\,du(0)/dx\}.$$

8.2 Constant Coefficient Matrices

Very often the coefficients in the ODE, and the source term, are treated as constants. Then the constant-coefficient matrices of (8.2-2)–(8.2-4) can be used directly and can be assembled (scattered) into the governing system matrices by directly adding every coefficient in the element matrices into the proper row and column (defined by the element connection list) of the corresponding system matrix:

$$\boldsymbol{S} \Longleftarrow \sum_e \boldsymbol{S}^e, \quad \boldsymbol{M} \Longleftarrow \sum_e \boldsymbol{M}^e, \quad \boldsymbol{U} \Longleftarrow \sum_e \boldsymbol{U}^e, \quad \boldsymbol{c} \longleftarrow \sum_e \boldsymbol{c}^e$$

where a single line arrow means that only rows are added into the system matrix and a double line arrow means that both rows and columns are added into the system matrix. It will be shown by means of several examples that for constant-coefficient applications, with linear geometry mapping, the above matrices can be written in closed form for the linear ($L2$), quadratic ($L3$), and cubic ($L4$) line elements. The integrals, in Table 4.10-1, become the above element matrices when multiplied by the corresponding constant-coefficient in (8.1-1).

A common subset of 8.1-1 is the ODE

$$-\frac{d}{dx}\left[K(x)A(x)\frac{du(x)}{dx}\right] + p(x)\,h(x)[u(x) - u_\infty(x)] + Q(x) = 0. \tag{8.2-1}$$

In mechanical engineering, this represents one-dimensional heat transfer in a bar with an internal rate of heat generation per unit length, $Q(x)$, a convection transfer from the surface area defined by the perimeter of the cross-section, $p(x)$, the surface's convection coefficient, $h(x)$, and the temperature of the surrounding fluid, $u_\infty(x)$. For ODEs with constant coefficients the element matrices for the terms in (8.1-1) can be written in closed form and become simply the constant scalar coefficient times the corresponding integrated matrices summarized in Tables 4.10-1 and 4.10-2.

The temperature distribution, $u(x)$, depends on the cross-sectional area, $A(x)$, and the material thermal conductivity of the bar, $K(x)$. In structural engineering, this represents one-dimensional load transfer in a vertical pile with an internal gravity load per unit length, $Q(x)$, a transfer to an elastic foundation (soil) from the surface area defined by the perimeter of the cross-section, $p(x)$, the surface's foundation stiffness, $h(x)$, and the far-field foundation settlement, $u_\infty(x)$, which is almost always zero. The axial (vertical) displacement, $u(x)$, depends on the cross-sectional area, $A(x)$, and the material elastic modulus the bar, $K(x)$. In both cases, a point source of heat or load can be obtained by using the Dirac Delta Distribution, $\delta(x - x_p)$, to define the location, x_p, of the point source. Figure 8.2-1 shows a Matlab script to automate the calculation of the matrices defined by (8.2-5), with constant coefficients.

To build the element matrices, the main program must read the problem description to establish an array, say **x**, for the system node coordinates, a rectangular array to hold the connection list, say **nodes**, that lists the nodes connected to each element, and an array containing the ODE coefficients (properties) of every element (or every element type). From that array, the coefficients (properties) for each element, say **el_prop**, are extracted. Then there is a loop over all elements where the constant element matrices are calculated, and then the connection list is used to assemble the system matrices from the sums of the element matrices. The generation and assembly loop for those calculations are given in detail in Fig. 8.2-1. After assembly and enforcement of the EBCs, the unknown values at each mesh node would be computed and be available for other uses in a post-processing stage. In general, the properties and/or sources can vary with position and it is necessary to employ numerical integration to evaluate each element matrix. That procedure (presented in Section 8.6) requires an additional loop over all of the numerical integration points needed to integrate the arrays of a specific polynomial degree. To illustrate the procedure outlined by the script in

```
% Element matrices for [d/dx (K*A du/dx)] - h*P (u - u_inf) + Q = 0
%     with properties 1=K, 2=A, 3=h, 4=P, 5=u_inf, 6=Q1 ...
for j = 1:n_e     ; % loop over elements ====>> ====>> ====>> ====>>
  e_nodes = nodes (j, 1:n_n)                 ; % element connectivity

% Gather nodal coordinates and element properties
  xy_e (1:n_n, 1) = x(e_nodes(1:n_n))         ; % x coord at el nodes
  L_e = abs (xy_e (n_n, 1) - xy_e (1, 1))          ; % element length
  K   = el_prop (1) ; % . . .                 % gather all properties
  Q_v = el_prop (6:5+n_n)                      ; % line load at nodes
  KA = K * A ; hP = h * P                      ; % combine properties

% Closed form matrices for constant element properties
  if (n_n == 2)                              ; % linear element L2_C0
    S_e =  KA*[1  -1; -1  1]/L_e                   ; % stiffness L2_C0
    M_g = L_e*[2   1;  1  2]/6            ; % generalized mass L2_C0
    c_inf = L_e*hP*u_inf*[1; 1]/2     ; % surroundings source L2_C0
  elseif (n_n == 3)                       ; % quadratic element L3_C0
    S_e =  KA*[7 -8  1; -8 16 -8; ...
                 1 -8  7]/(3*L_e)                  ; % stiffness L3_C0
    M_g = L_e*[4  2 -1; 2 16 2; ...
               -1  2  4]/30               ; % generalized mass L3_C0
    c_inf = L_e*hP*u_inf*[1; 4; 1]/6  ; % surroundings source L3_C0
  elseif (n_n == 4)                           ; % cubic element L4_C0
    S_e =  KA*[148 -189   54  -13 ;
              -189  432 -297   54 ;
                54 -297  432 -189 ;
               -13   54 -189  148]/(40*L_e)      ; % stiffness L4_C0
    M_g = L_e*[128   99  -36   19 ;
                99  648  -81  -36 ;
               -36  -81  648   99 ;
                19  -36   99  128]/1680   ; % generalized mass L4_C0
    c_inf = L_e*hP*u_inf*[1; 3; 3; 1]/8        ; % surroundings L4_C0
  end % if number of nodes on this element
  c_e = c_inf + M_g * Q_v          ; % u_inf and line source resultants
  S_e = S_e + hP * M_g                  ; % add surroundings sq matrix

% Insert completed element matrices into system matrices
  [rows] = get_element_index (n_g, n_n, e_nodes)       ; % eq numbers
  % rows = vector subscript converting element to system eq numbers
  c (rows)       = c (rows)         + c_e    ; % add to system sources
  S (rows, rows) = S (rows, rows) + S_e ; % add to system stiffness
end % for each j element in mesh <<==== <<==== <<==== <<==== <<====
```

Fig. 8.2-1: Analytic element matrices for linear, quadratic, or cubic line elements.

Fig. 8.2-1, the torsion of a cylindrical shaft is considered. The differential equation for the equilibrium of the angular rotational displacement of a circular torsional shaft of radius R is a subset of (8.1-1):

$$\frac{d}{dx}\left(G\,J\frac{d\theta}{dx}\right)+t(x)=0, \qquad (8.2\text{-}2)$$

where the constant coefficients are G, which is the shear modulus of the material, $G = E/2\,(1+\nu)$, the polar moment of inertia of the cross-section, $J = \pi R^4/2$. The unknown θ is the small angle of twist per unit length, and $t(x)$ is the torque per unit length, which includes point torques. The shear stress is $\tau = T\,R/J$.

A point torque at a node point x_A is defined by the Dirac Delta as $t(x) = T_A\,\delta(x - x_A)$. When integrated to define the element source resultant it reduces simply to the point torque T_A being inserted into the system column vector in the row that corresponds to rotation θ_A. A shaft having only point torques applied will have a linear variation of the angle of twist along the length between the point sources. Such problems can be solved exactly using two-noded linear shaft elements:

$$\frac{G^e J^e}{L^e}\begin{bmatrix} 1 & -1 \\ -1 & 1 \end{bmatrix}\begin{Bmatrix} \theta_1 \\ \theta_2 \end{Bmatrix} = \begin{Bmatrix} T_1 \\ T_2 \end{Bmatrix}.$$

The next most common torque applied to a shaft is a constant torque per unit length, t^e. That can be caused, for example, by an oil well drill string rotating in the viscous drilling mud. For a constant torque per unit length and a constant cross-section, the angle of twist can be exactly modeled by a three-noded quadratic shaft element whose element equilibrium equation is

$$\frac{G^e J^e}{3L^e}\begin{bmatrix} 7 & -8 & 1 \\ -8 & 16 & -8 \\ 1 & -8 & 7 \end{bmatrix}\begin{Bmatrix} \theta_1 \\ \theta_2 \\ \theta_3 \end{Bmatrix} = \frac{t^e L^e}{6}\begin{Bmatrix} 1 \\ 4 \\ 1 \end{Bmatrix} + \begin{Bmatrix} T_1 \\ T_2 \\ T_3 \end{Bmatrix}.$$

Consider the steel statically indeterminate cylindrical shaft in Fig. 8.2-2 which has ends fixed against rotation and point torques applied at its third point. The unknowns are the two interior rotations and the two end reaction (point) torques.

These unknowns will be found from the four matrix equations of equilibrium. The three torsional stiffness matrices for linear elements will be the same since they have the same length, $L^e = L/3$, and the same constant GJ product:

$$\boldsymbol{S}^e = \frac{G^e J^e}{L^e}\begin{bmatrix} 1 & -1 \\ -1 & 1 \end{bmatrix} = \frac{3GJ}{L}\begin{bmatrix} 1 & -1 \\ -1 & 1 \end{bmatrix}.$$

The four-point torque values insert into the rows of the source vector: $c^T = \begin{bmatrix} T_L & -T_A & T_B & T_R \end{bmatrix}$. The element connection lists are $\begin{bmatrix} 1 & 2 \\ 2 & 3 \\ 3 & 4 \end{bmatrix}$.

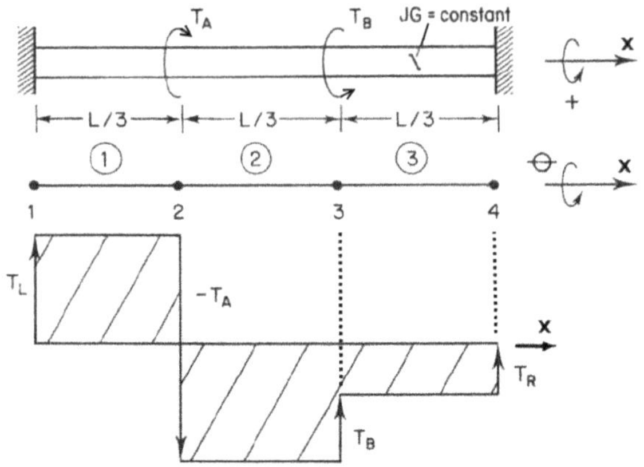

Fig. 8.2-2: Point torques on an indeterminate torsional shaft.

That shows that nodes 1 and 4 will receive only one stiffness connection because those nodes are connected to only one element each, and the two interior nodes (2 and 3) will each receive two-element stiffness terms. Scattering the first element stiffness matrices into first and second rows and columns into the 4×4 matrix equation of equilibrium gives:

$$\frac{3GJ}{L}\begin{bmatrix} 1 & -1 & 0 & 0 \\ -1 & 1 & 0 & 0 \\ 0 & 0 & 0 & 0 \\ 0 & 0 & 0 & 0 \end{bmatrix}\begin{Bmatrix} \theta_1 = 0 \\ \theta_2 \\ \theta_3 \\ \theta_4 = 0 \end{Bmatrix} = \begin{Bmatrix} T_L \\ -T_A \\ T_B \\ T_R \end{Bmatrix}.$$

Scattering the second stiffness matrix to the second and third rows gives

$$\frac{3GJ}{L}\begin{bmatrix} 1 & -1 & 0 & 0 \\ -1 & (1+1) & -1 & 0 \\ 0 & -1 & 1 & 0 \\ 0 & 0 & 0 & 0 \end{bmatrix}\begin{Bmatrix} \theta_1 = 0 \\ \theta_2 \\ \theta_3 \\ \theta_4 = 0 \end{Bmatrix} = \begin{Bmatrix} T_L \\ -T_A \\ T_B \\ T_R \end{Bmatrix}.$$

Finally, the third element scatters to complete the assembly:

$$\frac{3GJ}{L}\begin{bmatrix} 1 & -1 & 0 & 0 \\ -1 & (2) & -1 & 0 \\ 0 & -1 & (1+1) & -1 \\ 0 & 0 & -1 & 1 \end{bmatrix}\begin{Bmatrix} \theta_1 = 0 \\ \theta_2 \\ \theta_3 \\ \theta_4 = 0 \end{Bmatrix} = \begin{Bmatrix} T_L \\ -T_A \\ T_B \\ T_R \end{Bmatrix}.$$

This torsional system is singular until the displacement BCs are included. Rows 2 and 3 are the independent equations for the unknown displacements and they contain the two known point torques, T_A and T_B. They also include the two known displacements times their respective columns (1 and 4). Those known products are subtracted from the equations:

$$\frac{3GJ}{L}\begin{bmatrix} 2 & -1 \\ -1 & 2 \end{bmatrix}\begin{Bmatrix} \theta_2 \\ \theta_3 \end{Bmatrix} = \begin{Bmatrix} -T_A \\ T_B \end{Bmatrix} - (\theta_1 = 0)\frac{3GJ}{L}\begin{Bmatrix} -1 \\ 0 \end{Bmatrix}$$

$$-(\theta_4 = 0)\frac{3GJ}{L}\begin{Bmatrix} 0 \\ -1 \end{Bmatrix} = \begin{Bmatrix} -T_A \\ T_B \end{Bmatrix}.$$

Inverting the non-singular partition gives the desired rotations

$$\begin{Bmatrix} \theta_2 \\ \theta_3 \end{Bmatrix} = \frac{L}{3GJ}\frac{1}{3}\begin{bmatrix} 2 & 1 \\ 1 & 2 \end{bmatrix}\begin{Bmatrix} -T_A \\ T_B \end{Bmatrix} = \frac{L}{9GJ}\begin{Bmatrix} T_B - 2T_A \\ 2T_B - T_A \end{Bmatrix}.$$

Substituting all of the known displacements into the first row of the matrix equilibrium relation gives the torque, T_L, necessary to maintain the essential (Dirichlet) BC of $\theta_1 = 0$:

$$\frac{3GJ}{L}[1 \ \ -1 \ \ 0 \ \ 0]\frac{L}{9GJ}\begin{Bmatrix} 0 \\ T_B - 2T_A \\ 2T_B - T_A \\ 0 \end{Bmatrix} = -(T_B - 2T_A)/3 = \{T_L\}.$$

and the last row gives the right reaction as $T_R = -(2T_B - T_A)/3$. The finite element method is not based on Newton's laws, but it enforces equilibrium so the applied torques must sum to zero:

$$T_L - T_A + T_B + T_R = -(T_B - 2T_A)/3 - T_A + T_B - (2T_B - T_A)/3 \equiv 0.$$

Example 8.2-1 Given: Consider the steady-state heat transfer through the wall of a chimney made of three materials. The wall is large enough that as a first approximation (except in the corners) a one-dimensional model gives a very good model of the temperature through a unit area of the wall. The chimney has an internal temperature of $1,500°$F with 9 inches of firebrick with a thermal conductivity of $k_f = 0.72\text{BTU}/(\text{hr ft °F})$ against 5 inches of insulation with $k_i = 0.08\text{BTU}/(\text{hr ft}\,^\circ\text{F})$ against 7.5 inches of redbrick with $k_r = 0.50\text{BTU}/(\text{hr ft}\,^\circ\text{F})$ which has an exterior surface temperature of 150°F. Find the temperatures at the material interfaces, and the heat flow through each layer of material, A $q(x)$, where the heat flux per unit area at any point defined by Fourier's law is $q(x) = -k du/dx$.

Solution: The differential equation is

$$k\,A\,\frac{d^2u}{dx^2} = 0, \qquad (8.2\text{-}3)$$

where k is the thermal conductivity, A is the area normal to x, and u is the temperature. The three material layers are internal firebrick, insulation, and external redbrick. Both the interior and exterior temperatures have been measured and are known as EBCs. There are no internal heat sources, $Q = 0$. Find the internal temperature distribution. This example is used to remind analysts that all the data must be input in a single set of consistent units. Today, commercial codes allow the users to input different data in different units while hidden from the user they are all converted to the single SI units for storage. The software illustrated here requires the user to assure that all data are in a single units system. As an extreme example, let the x-coordinates be input in "fence posts" (about 1.5 m long). That defines the length units so that the area has to be input in "fence posts" squared. If it were a structures problem, the displacement answers would be in the same length units of "fence posts" used to input the geometry; and if force was measured in "cow weight" (about 5,000 N), then the stress (force per unit area) would be output as "cow weight per fence posts squared" and the material elastic modulus and pressure loads would have to have been input in those units also.

The length units are not consistent. Either the thermal conductivities must be converted to inches or the thicknesses must be converted to feet. The latter is easier. Use a three-element model (the minimum for three materials) with L2 linear line elements. The consistent input data are as follows:

e	$A(ft^2)$	L (ft)	K(BTU/ hr ft°F)	Connections
1	1	$9/12 = 0.75$	0.72	1, 2
2	1	$5/12 = 0.41667$	0.08	2, 3
3	1	$7.5/12 = 0.625$	0.50	3, 4

This means the x-coordinates are 0, 0.75, 1.16667, and 1.79167 *ft*. Recall that the conduction matrix for one-dimensional problems is

$$\boldsymbol{S}^e = \frac{k^e A^e}{L^e}\begin{bmatrix} 1 & -1 \\ -1 & 1 \end{bmatrix},$$

and there is no heat source so there is no element column matrix. Assembling the three conduction elements gives:

$$A^e\begin{bmatrix} k_1/L_1 & -k_1/L_1 & 0 & 0 \\ -k_1/L_1 & (k_1/L_1 + k_2/L_2) & -k_2/L_2 & 0 \\ 0 & -k_2/L_2 & (k_2/L_2 + k_3/L_3) & -k_3/L_3 \\ 0 & 0 & -k_3/L_3 & k_3/L_3 \end{bmatrix}\begin{Bmatrix} \mathrm{u}_1 \\ \mathrm{u}_2 \\ \mathrm{u}_3 \\ \mathrm{u}_4 \end{Bmatrix}$$

$$= \mathrm{A^e}\begin{Bmatrix} -k_1\,\mathrm{du/dx(0)} \\ 0 \\ 0 \\ k_3\,\mathrm{du/dx(L)} \end{Bmatrix}.$$

Inserting the numerical data

$$1\begin{bmatrix} \frac{0.72}{0.75} & \frac{-0.72}{0.75} & 0 & 0 \\ \frac{-0.72}{0.75} & \left(\frac{0.72}{0.75} + \frac{0.08}{0.41667}\right) & \frac{-0.08}{0.41667} & 0 \\ 0 & \frac{-0.08}{0.41667} & \left(\frac{0.08}{0.41667} + \frac{0.50}{0.625}\right) & \frac{-0.50}{0.625} \\ 0 & 0 & \frac{-0.50}{0.625} & \frac{0.50}{0.625} \end{bmatrix}\begin{Bmatrix} u_1 \\ u_2 \\ u_3 \\ u_4 \end{Bmatrix}$$

$$= 1\begin{Bmatrix} -0.72\ du/dx(0) \\ 0 \\ 0 \\ 0.50\ du/dx(L) \end{Bmatrix}$$

$$1\begin{bmatrix} 0.96 & -0.96 & 0 & 0 \\ -0.96 & (1.152) & -0.1920 & 0 \\ 0 & -0.1920 & (0.9920) & -0.8 \\ 0 & 0 & -0.8 & 0.8 \end{bmatrix}\begin{Bmatrix} u_1 = 1500 \\ u_2 \\ u_3 \\ u_4 = 150 \end{Bmatrix}$$

$$= 1\begin{Bmatrix} -0.72\ du/dx(0) \\ 0 \\ 0 \\ 0.50\ du/dx(L) \end{Bmatrix}.$$

Retaining the middle two rows of the matrix system and moving the two EBCs to the right-hand side:

$$\begin{bmatrix} 1.152 & -0.1920 \\ -0.1920 & 0.9920 \end{bmatrix}\begin{Bmatrix} u_2 \\ u_3 \end{Bmatrix} = \begin{Bmatrix} 0 \\ 0 \end{Bmatrix} - 1{,}500\begin{Bmatrix} -0.96 \\ 0 \end{Bmatrix} - 150\begin{Bmatrix} 0 \\ -0.8 \end{Bmatrix}$$

$$(\text{BTU/hr} - \text{ft}^\circ\text{F})\mathbf{u} = {}^\circ\text{F}^*(\text{BTU/hr} - \text{ft}^\circ\text{F})$$

$$\begin{Bmatrix} u_2 \\ u_3 \end{Bmatrix} = \begin{Bmatrix} 1{,}312.5 \\ 375 \end{Bmatrix}{}^\circ\text{F}.$$

The first row of the matrix equilibrium equations gives the reaction heat flow from the hot internal gases:

$$0.96(1{,}500) - 0.96(1{,}312.5) + 0 + 0$$
$$= -0.72\, du/dx(0) = 180\ \text{BTU/hrft}^2,$$

which is the heat flow, f, into the wall area from the chimney gas that keeps the interior wall at 1,500°F. The other reaction from row 4 gives the exiting heat flow

$$0 + 0 - 0.8(375) + 0.8(150) = 0.50\, du/dx(L) = -180\ \text{BTU/hrft}^2.$$

Post-processing gives the gradient and heat flux in each element. For a linear element, the gradient is

$$\frac{\partial u}{\partial x} = \frac{\partial \boldsymbol{H(r)}}{\partial x} \boldsymbol{u}^e \equiv \boldsymbol{B}^e \boldsymbol{u}^e = \frac{1}{L^e}[-1 \ 1]\boldsymbol{u}^e, \text{here } {}^\circ\text{F}/ft,$$

and Fourier's Law defines the heat flux as $q = -kdu/dx$. For the first element, gather the solution

$$\boldsymbol{u}^e = \begin{Bmatrix} 1{,}500 \\ 1{,}312.5 \end{Bmatrix} {}^\circ\text{F},$$

so

$$q^e = -\frac{k^e}{L^e}[-1 \ 1]u^e = -\frac{0.72}{0.75}[-1 \ 1]\begin{Bmatrix} 1{,}500 \\ 1{,}312.5 \end{Bmatrix} = 180\,\text{BTU/hr ft}^2,$$

and the heat flux in the fire brick is $f = A\ q = (1ft^2)(180\ \text{BTU}/\text{hr ft}^2)$. The heat flux through the second element made of insulation is

$$f = -(1)\frac{0.08}{0.41667}[-1 \ 1]\begin{Bmatrix} 1{,}312.5 \\ 375 \end{Bmatrix} = 180\ BTU/hr,$$

and the third element made of redbrick has a heat flux of

$$q^e = -\frac{0.50}{0.625}[-1 \ 1]\begin{Bmatrix} 375 \\ 150 \end{Bmatrix} = 180\ \text{BTU/hr}.$$

As expected, the heat flux entering at the chimney wall is conserved as it flows through each area and exits the inside wall. In other words, in a one-dimensional model different materials have different temperature gradients but the same heat flow (if no convection is present).

Example 8.2-2 Given: An axial bar has an axial point load, P, at its center. As shown in Fig. 8.2-1, the bar is fixed at its left end, $x = 0$, and has a settlement displacement of Δ at the right end, $x = \text{L}$. Determine the deflections, reactions, and stresses in the bar with constant properties.

Solution: The governing ODE, for constant material modulus, E, and cross-sectional area, A, is

$$E\,A\,\frac{d^2u}{dx^2} + w(x) = 0, \tag{8.2-4}$$

and where $w(x)$ is the load per unit length, which includes any point load, P, as a special case. An element interface must occur at any discontinuity in the data or the loading. Thus, at least two elements are required.

With only point loads acting on a bar the exact displacements will be linear between load points. Select two linear elements, so $L^e = L/2$, and a sequential numbering of the mesh nodes. For this ODE and element, the stiffness matrix was shown earlier to be

$$\boldsymbol{S}^e = \frac{E^e A^e}{L^e}\begin{bmatrix} 1 & -1 \\ -1 & 1 \end{bmatrix}.$$

Of course, the point load and point reaction forces are added directly to their respective rows of the system load vector. Scattering the two stiffness gives the following system matrices:

$$\frac{2EA}{L}\begin{bmatrix} 1 & -1 & 0 \\ -1 & (1+1) & -1 \\ 0 & -1 & 1 \end{bmatrix}\begin{Bmatrix} u_1 = 0 \\ u_2 \\ u_3 = \Delta \end{Bmatrix} = \begin{Bmatrix} 0 \\ P \\ 0 \end{Bmatrix} + \begin{Bmatrix} r_1 \\ 0 \\ r_3 \end{Bmatrix}.$$

Enforcing that $u_1 = 0$ and $u_3 = \Delta$ leaves only the second row as an independent equation for the displacement:

$$\frac{2EA}{L}[2]\{u_2\} = \{P\} + \{0\} - (u_1 = 0)\frac{2\,EA}{L}\{-1\}$$
$$-(u_3 = \Delta)\frac{2\,EA}{L}\{-1\}$$
$$\{u_2\} = \left\{\frac{PL}{4EA} + \frac{\Delta}{2}\right\},$$

which is the exact center displacement. The first row of the matrix equilibrium equations now gives the left reaction force needed to maintain the displacement there as zero:

$$\frac{2EA}{L}[1 \quad -1 \quad 0]\begin{Bmatrix} 0 \\ \frac{PL}{4EA}+\frac{\Delta}{2} \\ \Delta \end{Bmatrix} = 0 + r_1, \quad r_1 = -\frac{P}{2} - \frac{\Delta EA}{L},$$

and the third row gives the right reaction:

$$\frac{2EA}{L}[0 \quad -1 \quad 1]\begin{Bmatrix} 0 \\ \frac{PL}{4EA}+\frac{\Delta}{2} \\ \Delta \end{Bmatrix} = 0 + r_3, \quad r_3 = -\frac{P}{2} + \frac{\Delta EA}{L}.$$

As a logical check, note that if there is no settlement, $\Delta = 0$, then the force P along the length is balanced by half its value at each end, acting in the opposite direction. Similarly, if there is just a positive settlement, $P = 0$, the bar is in tension with the end forces acting in opposite directions. Also, the sum of the reactions is $-P$ which is opposite to the total externally applied loads. At the right end $\Delta/L = \varepsilon$ is the axial strain and $E\Delta/L = \sigma$ is the axial stress (force per unit area) and $AE\Delta/L = F$ is the force needed to impose the specified displacement. To post-process for the stresses, the known element displacements must be gathered from $\{\boldsymbol{u}\}$. For the first element:

$$\{\boldsymbol{u}\}^e = \begin{Bmatrix} 0 \\ \frac{PL}{4EA}+\frac{\Delta}{2} \end{Bmatrix},$$

$$\varepsilon^e = \frac{dH(r)}{dx}\{\boldsymbol{u}\}^e = \frac{1}{L^e}[-1 \quad 1]\,\{\boldsymbol{u}\}^e$$

$$= \frac{2}{L}[-1 \quad 1]\begin{Bmatrix} 0 \\ \frac{PL}{4EA}+\frac{\Delta}{2} \end{Bmatrix} = \frac{2}{L}\left(\frac{PL}{4EA}+\frac{\Delta}{2}\right),$$

$$\sigma^e = E^e\varepsilon^e = \frac{P}{2A} + \frac{E\Delta}{L}.$$

For the second element, gathering the element DOFs from the known solution,

$$\{\boldsymbol{u}\}^e = \begin{Bmatrix} PL/4EA + \Delta/2 \\ \Delta \end{Bmatrix}, \quad \varepsilon^e = \frac{2}{L}[-1 \quad 1]\begin{Bmatrix} PL/4EA + \Delta/2 \\ \Delta \end{Bmatrix},$$

$$\sigma^e = \frac{-P}{2A} + \frac{E\Delta}{L}.$$

As a logical check, if there is no settlement ($\Delta = 0$, both ends fixed), then the first element is in tension and the second element is in compression. If there is no load, but the settlement stretches the bar, then both halves are in tension.

Example 8.2-3 Given: A bar hangs vertically under its own weight and is supported by its topmost point. The bottom point is stress-free. Find the displacement of the bar, and the top reaction force.

Solution: The ODE for the axial displacement, $u(x)$, for material modulus, E, and cross-sectional area, A, is

$$E\,A\,\frac{d^2u}{dx^2} + w(x) = 0, \tag{8.2-5}$$

and where $w(x)$ is the load per unit length which is the weight per unit length of the bar given by the specific weight times the cross-sectional area: $w^e = f_x^e A^e = \gamma^e A^e = \rho^e g\, A^e$, for mass density ρ^e. Here, the axial strain is $\varepsilon_x = du/dx$, the axial stress is $\sigma_x = E\varepsilon_x$, and the axial force is $F_x = A\,\sigma_x$.

The axial stress in the bar is not constant since the axial displacement varies over the entire length. Thus, the two-node linear element used above is not a good choice because it gives a constant stress. Use a three-noded quadratic element with the system nodes numbered sequentially from the top to bottom of the bar. The top end $x = 0$ has a zero displacement, $u(0) = 0$, which is an EBC. The bottom end $x = L$ is force-free (and stress-free) which is the natural Neumann condition, $E(L)\,A(L)\,du(L)/dx = 0$. The weight per unit length of the bar is the specific weight times the cross-sectional area: $w^e = f_x^e A^e = \gamma^e A^e$. The matrix equilibrium equations are

$$\frac{E^e A^e}{3L^e}\begin{bmatrix} 7 & -8 & 1 \\ -8 & 16 & -8 \\ 1 & -8 & 7 \end{bmatrix}\begin{Bmatrix} u_1 = 0 \\ u_2 \\ u_3 \end{Bmatrix} = \begin{Bmatrix} R_1 \\ 0 du(L)/dx = 0 \end{Bmatrix} + \frac{w^e L^e}{6}\begin{Bmatrix} 1 \\ 4 \\ 1 \end{Bmatrix}.$$

Impose the EBC by multiplying the first column by u_1, carry it to the right and keep the bottom two rows:

$$\frac{E^e A^e}{3L^e}\begin{bmatrix} 16 & -8 \\ -8 & 7 \end{bmatrix}\begin{Bmatrix} u_2 \\ u_3 \end{Bmatrix} = \begin{Bmatrix} 0 \\ 0 \end{Bmatrix} + \frac{w^e L^e}{6}\begin{Bmatrix} 4 \\ 1 \end{Bmatrix} - \frac{u_1 E^e A^e}{3L^e}\begin{Bmatrix} -8 \\ 1 \end{Bmatrix}$$
$$= \frac{w^e L^e}{6}\begin{Bmatrix} 4 \\ 1 \end{Bmatrix}.$$

Inverting the square matrix gives the displacement of the mid-point and end as

$$\begin{Bmatrix} u_2 \\ u_3 \end{Bmatrix} = \frac{3L^e}{E^e A^e}\frac{1}{48}\begin{bmatrix} 7 & 8 \\ 8 & 16 \end{bmatrix}\frac{w^e L^e}{6}\begin{Bmatrix} 4 \\ 1 \end{Bmatrix} = \frac{w^e L^{e^2}}{96 E^e A^e}\begin{bmatrix} 7 & 8 \\ 8 & 16 \end{bmatrix}\begin{Bmatrix} 4 \\ 1 \end{Bmatrix}$$
$$= \frac{w^e L^{e^2}}{96 E^e A^e}\begin{Bmatrix} 36 \\ 48 \end{Bmatrix} = \frac{w^e L^{e^2}}{8 E^e A^e}\begin{Bmatrix} 3 \\ 4 \end{Bmatrix}.$$

These values are analytically exact at the nodes. This shows that the mid-point of the bar displaces 3/4 as much as the free end. Now, the original first row of the matrix equilibrium system can be used to determine the reaction force, R_1, necessary to maintain the $u_1 = 0$ displacement at $x = 0$:

$$\frac{E^e A^e}{3L^e}[7 \quad -8 \quad 1]\begin{Bmatrix} u_1 \\ u_2 \\ u_3 \end{Bmatrix} = \{R_1\} + \frac{w^e L^e}{6}\{1\},$$

$$\frac{E^e A^e}{3L^e}\frac{w^e L^{e^2}}{8 E^e A^e}[7 \quad -8 \quad 1]\begin{Bmatrix} 0 \\ 3 \\ 4 \end{Bmatrix} = \frac{w^e L^e}{24}\{-20\} = \{R_1\} + \frac{w^e L^e}{6}\{1\}$$
$$\rightarrow R_1 = -w^e L^e.$$

Example 8.2-4 Given: For the above hanging bar single element solution in **Example 8.2-3,** post-process the displacements to determine the axial strain, $\varepsilon_x = du/dx$, the axial stress is $\sigma_x = E\varepsilon_x$, and the axial force is $F_x = A\,\sigma_x$ along its length.

Solution: The system and element displacements are the same for a single element model. They are

$$\begin{Bmatrix} u_1 \\ u_2 \\ u_3 \end{Bmatrix} = \frac{w^e L^{e^2}}{8E^e A^e} \begin{Bmatrix} 0 \\ 3 \\ 4 \end{Bmatrix} = \frac{W^e L^e}{8E^e A^e} \begin{Bmatrix} 0 \\ 3 \\ 4 \end{Bmatrix}, \quad W^e = w^e L^e.$$

For any element $\varepsilon_x = du/dx = du/dr\, dr/dx$ and for equally spaced nodes $dr/dx = 1/L^e$. Here the strain is

$$\varepsilon_x = \frac{1}{L^e}\frac{d\boldsymbol{H}(r)}{dr}\boldsymbol{u} = \frac{1}{L^e}[(-3+4r)\ (4-8r)\ (-1+4r)]\frac{W^e L^e}{8E^e A^e}\begin{Bmatrix} 0 \\ 3 \\ 4 \end{Bmatrix},$$

where a positive value denotes tension. The strain clearly varies linearly over the length of the bar. At the top support point, $r = 0$,

$$\varepsilon_x = \frac{1}{L^e}[-3(0) + 4(3) - 1(4)]\frac{W^e L^e}{8E^e A^e} = \frac{W^e}{E^e A^e}.$$

At the bottom end, $r = 1, \varepsilon_x = \frac{1}{L^e}[1(0) - 4(3) + 3(4)]\frac{W^e L^e}{8E^e A^e} = 0$, as expected.

The axial stress at the top is $\sigma_x = E\varepsilon_x = E^e \frac{W^e}{E^e A^e} = \frac{W^e}{A^e}$, and the axial force at the top is the weight of the bar. Since, the chosen element polynomial just happened to include the exact displacement function, this is one of the few examples where the finite element solution is analytically exact everywhere, as plotted in Fig. 8.2-2.

Example 8.2-5 Given: A bar hangs vertically under its own weight and is supported by its topmost point. The bottom point also supports a point force of three times the weight of the bar. Find the displacement of the bar and the top reaction force.

Solution: The governing ODE for the axial displacement, $u(x)$, for material modulus, E, and cross-sectional area, A, is

$$E\,A\,\frac{d^2u}{dx^2} + w(x) = 0,$$

and where $w(x)$ is the load per unit length which is the weight per unit length of the bar given by the specific weight times the cross-sectional area: $w^e = \rho^e g\,A^e$, for mass density ρ^e. Thus, the total weight of the bar is $W = \rho^e g\,A^e L$. Here, the axial strain is $\varepsilon_x = du/dx$, the axial stress is $\sigma_x = E\varepsilon_x$, and the axial force is $F_x = A\,\sigma_x$.

The axial stress in the bar is not constant since the axial displacement varies over the entire length. Thus, the two-node linear element used above is not a good choice because it gives a constant stress. Use a three-noded quadratic element with the system nodes numbered sequentially from the top to bottom of the bar. The top end $x = 0$ has a zero displacement, $u(0) = 0$, which is an EBC. The bottom end $x = L$ supports the external force of 3W, which is the Neumann condition, $E(L)\,A(L)\,du(L)/dx = 3W$. The matrix equilibrium equations are only changed by the addition of the point load at the third node

$$\frac{E^e A^e}{3L^e}\begin{bmatrix} 7 & -8 & 1 \\ -8 & 16 & -8 \\ 1 & -8 & 7 \end{bmatrix}\begin{Bmatrix} u_1 = 0 \\ u_2 \\ u_3 \end{Bmatrix} = \begin{Bmatrix} R_1 \\ 0 \\ EA\,du(L)/dx = 3W \end{Bmatrix} + \frac{w^e L^e}{6}\begin{Bmatrix} 1 \\ 4 \\ 1 \end{Bmatrix}.$$

Impose the EBC by multiplying the first column by u_1, carry it to the right and keep the bottom two rows:

$$\frac{E^e A^e}{3L^e}\begin{bmatrix} 16 & -8 \\ -8 & 7 \end{bmatrix}\begin{Bmatrix} u_2 \\ u_3 \end{Bmatrix} = \begin{Bmatrix} 0 \\ 3W \end{Bmatrix} + \frac{w^e L^e}{6}\begin{Bmatrix} 4 \\ 1 \end{Bmatrix} - \frac{u_1\,E^e A^e}{3L^e}\begin{Bmatrix} -8 \\ 1 \end{Bmatrix}$$

$$= \frac{W}{6}\begin{Bmatrix} 4 \\ 19 \end{Bmatrix} - \begin{Bmatrix} 0 \\ 0 \end{Bmatrix}.$$

Inverting the square matrix gives the displacement of the mid-point and end as

$$\begin{Bmatrix} u_2 \\ u_3 \end{Bmatrix} = \frac{3L^e}{E^e A^e}\frac{1}{48}\begin{bmatrix} 7 & 8 \\ 8 & 16 \end{bmatrix}\frac{W}{6}\begin{Bmatrix} 4 \\ 19 \end{Bmatrix} = \frac{WL}{96E^e A^e}\begin{bmatrix} 7 & 8 \\ 8 & 16 \end{bmatrix}\begin{Bmatrix} 4 \\ 19 \end{Bmatrix}$$

$$= \frac{WL}{8E^e A^e}\begin{Bmatrix} 15 \\ 28 \end{Bmatrix}.$$

These values are analytically exact at the nodes. This shows that the mid-point of the bar displaces 3/4 as much as the free end. Now, the original first row of the matrix equilibrium system can be used to determine the reaction force, R_1, necessary to maintain the $u_1 = 0$ displacement at $x = 0$:

$$\frac{E^e A^e}{3L^e}[7\ -8\ 1]\begin{Bmatrix} u_1 \\ u_2 \\ u_3 \end{Bmatrix} = \{R_1\} + \frac{w^e\,L^e}{6}\{1\},$$

$$\frac{E^e A^e}{3L^e}\frac{WL}{8E^e A^e}[7\ -8\ 1]\begin{Bmatrix} 0 \\ 15 \\ 28 \end{Bmatrix} = \frac{W}{24}\{-92\} = \frac{W}{6}\{-23\}$$

$$= \{R_1\} + \frac{W}{6}\{1\} \rightarrow R_1 = -\frac{W}{6}\{24\}.$$

In other words, as expected (from Newton's Laws) the top reaction of 4W is equal and opposite to the total weight, W^e, of the hanging bar and the end force of 3W.

Example 8.2-6 Given: A bar hangs vertically under its own weight and is supported by its topmost point. The bottom point is stress-free. Find the displacement of the bar and the top reaction force.

Solution: The governing ODE for the axial displacement, $u(x)$, for material modulus, E, and cross-sectional area, A, is

$$E\,A\,\frac{d^2u}{dx^2} + w(x) = 0,$$

and where $w(x)$ is the load per unit length which is the weight per unit length of the bar given by the specific weight times the cross-sectional area: $w^e = f_x^e A^e = \gamma^e A^e = \rho^e g\,A^e$, for mass density ρ^e.

Here, the axial strain is $\varepsilon_x = du/dx$, the axial stress is $\sigma_x = E\varepsilon_x$, and the axial force is $F_x = A\,\sigma_x$. The top end $x = 0$ has a zero displacement, $u(0) = 0$, which is an EBC. The bottom end $x = L$ is force-free (and stress-free) which is the natural Neumann condition, $E(L)\,A(L)\,du(L)/dx = 0$.

The axial stress in the bar is not constant since the axial force varies over the entire length. The two-node linear element is a poor choice for a single element approximation because it gives a constant stress. Thus, try a two linear element model, and a four linear element model, where the element equilibrium equations are

$$\frac{E^e A^e}{L^e}\begin{bmatrix} 1 & -1 \\ -1 & 1 \end{bmatrix}\begin{Bmatrix} u_1 \\ u_2 \end{Bmatrix}^e = \frac{w^e\,L^e}{2}\begin{Bmatrix} 1 \\ 1 \end{Bmatrix}.$$

For a two-element model with equal length elements, $L^e = L/2$, and a sequential numbering of nodes, the matrix equilibrium equations are

$$\frac{E^e A^e}{(L/2)}\begin{bmatrix} 1 & -1 & 0 \\ -1 & (1+1) & -1 \\ 0 & -1 & 1 \end{bmatrix}\begin{Bmatrix} u_1 = 0 \\ u_2 \\ u_3 \end{Bmatrix} = \begin{Bmatrix} R_1 \\ 0 \\ E\,A\,du(L)/dx = 0 \end{Bmatrix} + \frac{w^e(L/2)}{2}\begin{Bmatrix} 1 \\ (1+1) \\ 1 \end{Bmatrix}.$$

Impose the EBC by multiplying the first column by u_1, carry it to the right and keep the bottom two rows:

$$\frac{2E^e A^e}{L}\begin{bmatrix} 2 & -1 \\ -1 & 1 \end{bmatrix}\begin{Bmatrix} u_2 \\ u_3 \end{Bmatrix} = \begin{Bmatrix} 0 \\ 0 \end{Bmatrix} + \frac{w^e L}{4}\begin{Bmatrix} 2 \\ 1 \end{Bmatrix} - \begin{Bmatrix} 0 \\ 0 \end{Bmatrix} = \frac{w^e\,L}{4}\begin{Bmatrix} 2 \\ 1 \end{Bmatrix}.$$

Inverting the square matrix gives the displacement of the mid-point and end as

$$\begin{Bmatrix} u_2 \\ u_3 \end{Bmatrix} = \frac{L}{2E^e A^e}\frac{1}{1}\begin{bmatrix} 1 & 1 \\ 1 & 2 \end{bmatrix}\frac{w^e L}{4}\begin{Bmatrix} 2 \\ 1 \end{Bmatrix} = \frac{w^e L^2}{8E^e A^e}\begin{bmatrix} 1 & 1 \\ 1 & 2 \end{bmatrix}\begin{Bmatrix} 2 \\ 1 \end{Bmatrix}$$
$$= \frac{w^e L^2}{8E^e A^e}\begin{Bmatrix} 3 \\ 4 \end{Bmatrix}.$$

These values are analytically exact at the nodes. This shows that the mid-point of the bar displaces 3/4 as much as the free end. Now, the original first row of the matrix equilibrium system can be used to determine the reaction force, R_1, necessary to maintain the $u_1 = 0$ displacement at $x = 0$:

$$\frac{2E^e A^e}{L}\begin{bmatrix}1 & -1 & 0\end{bmatrix}\begin{Bmatrix}u_1\\u_2\\u_3\end{Bmatrix} = \{R_1\} + \frac{w^e\,L}{4}\{1\},$$

$$\frac{2E^e A^e}{L}\frac{w^e L^2}{8E^e A^e}\begin{bmatrix}1 & -1 & 0\end{bmatrix}\begin{Bmatrix}0\\3\\4\end{Bmatrix} = \frac{w^e L}{4}\{-3\} = \{R_1\} + \frac{w^e\,L}{4}\{1\}$$

$$\rightarrow \quad R_1 = -w^e\,L.$$

In other words, as expected (from Newton's Laws) the top reaction is equal and opposite to the total weight, W^e, of the hanging bar.

For the above hanging bar solution, post-process the displacements to determine the axial strain, $\varepsilon_x = du/dx$, the axial stress $\sigma_x = E\varepsilon_x$, and the axial force $F_x = A\,\sigma_x$ along its length. The system displacements are

$$\begin{Bmatrix}u_1\\u_2\\u_3\end{Bmatrix} = \frac{W^e L}{8E^e A^e}\begin{Bmatrix}0\\3\\4\end{Bmatrix}, \quad W^e = w^e L^e.$$

So, for the first element, its displacements are $\begin{Bmatrix}u_1\\u_2\end{Bmatrix}^e = \begin{Bmatrix}u_1\\u_2\end{Bmatrix} = \frac{W^e L}{8E^e A^e}\begin{Bmatrix}0\\3\end{Bmatrix}$. For any element the axial strain at $\varepsilon_x = du/dr = (1/L^e)$ is

$$\varepsilon_x = \frac{1}{L^e}\frac{d\boldsymbol{H}(r)}{dr}\boldsymbol{u} = \frac{2}{L}\begin{bmatrix}-1 & 1\end{bmatrix}\frac{W^e L}{8E^e A^e}\begin{Bmatrix}0\\3\end{Bmatrix} = \frac{6W^e}{8E^e A^e} = \frac{3W^e}{4E^e A^e},$$

everywhere in the element; where a positive value denotes tension. The strain clearly is constant over the length of the bar. The constant axial stress is $\sigma_x = E\varepsilon_x = 3W^e/4A^e$. Likewise, the displacements at the second element are

$$\begin{Bmatrix} u_1 \\ u_2 \end{Bmatrix}^e = \frac{W^e L}{8E^e A^e} \begin{Bmatrix} 3 \\ 4 \end{Bmatrix},$$

and the stress is $\sigma_x = 1W^e/4A^e$. Since the chosen element polynomial was a solution to the homogeneous ODE, this is one of the few examples where the finite element solution is analytically exact at the nodes, as plotted in Fig. 8.2-2. From that figure it is noted that the finite element displacements are most accurate at the nodes, are least accurate inside the two elements; and the Neumann BC is only approximately satisfied. (A shorter element at the bottom makes the Neumann BC error smaller.) Furthermore, the finite element stresses are least accurate at the nodes and are more accurate inside the element. Indeed, there is one interior point (the element center) where the stress is exact.

Likewise, for a four-element model with equal length elements, $L^e = L/4$, and a sequential numbering of nodes, the matrix equilibrium equations are

$$\frac{E^e A^e}{(L/4)} \begin{bmatrix} 1 & -1 & 0 & 0 & 0 \\ -1 & 2 & -1 & 0 & 0 \\ 0 & -1 & 2 & -1 & 0 \\ 0 & 0 & -1 & 2 & -1 \\ 0 & 0 & 0 & -1 & 1 \end{bmatrix} \begin{Bmatrix} u_1 = 0 \\ u_2 \\ u_3 \\ u_4 \\ u_5 \end{Bmatrix} = \begin{Bmatrix} R_1 \\ 0 \\ 0 \\ 0 \\ E\,A\,du(L)/dx = 0 \end{Bmatrix} + \frac{w^e(L/4)}{2} \begin{Bmatrix} 1 \\ 2 \\ 2 \\ 2 \\ 1 \end{Bmatrix}.$$

Solving, the displacements are found to be exact at each node. Post-processing for the stresses gives constant step changes; with the element stresses exact at their centers. In other words, the stresses are discontinuous at the element interfaces; while the displacements are continuous at element interfaces, as seen in Fig. 8.2-3.

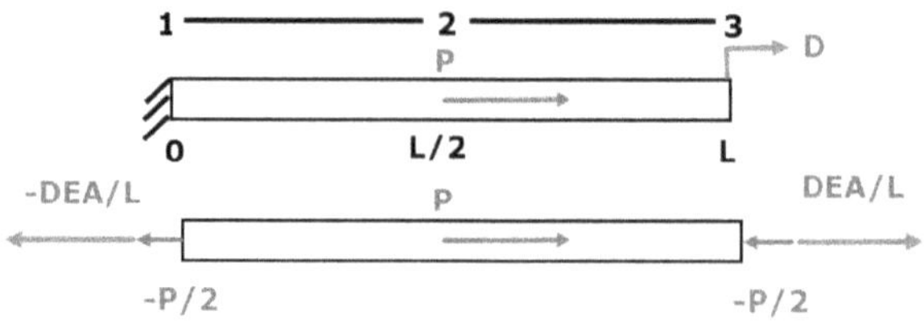

Fig. 8.2-3: Reactions from settlement, D, and center load.

Example 8.2-7 Given: An axial bar is fixed at both ends and undergoes a temperature increase, ΔT. Find the deflection of the bar, the end reactions, and the bar strain and stress.

Solution: This should be a constant stress case, so a linear element would give exact results everywhere. To be sure, use a three-noded quadratic bar that can exactly model a linear stress distribution. The exact solution and boundary conditions are shown in Fig. 8.2-4. The results for two, and four, linear elements are superimposed in Fig. 8.2-5, and 8.2-6, respectively. There is no external distributed axial force (gravity) per unit length, and only the thermal load (initial strain) is active. It will be shown later that a constant temperature change over the bar causes a new load term:

$$\boldsymbol{c}_{\boldsymbol{0}}^{e} = E^e A^e \alpha^e \Delta T^e \int_{L^e} \frac{d\boldsymbol{H}^T}{dx}\, dx = E^e A^e \alpha^e \Delta T^e \int_0^1 \frac{d\boldsymbol{H}^T}{dr} \frac{1}{L^e} (L^e dr).$$

For the quadratic line element, (2.2-2) gives $d\boldsymbol{H}/dr = [(-3 + 4r)(4 - 8r)(-1 + 4r)]$, which gives the thermal load as $\boldsymbol{c}_{\boldsymbol{0}}^{e} = E^e A^e \alpha^e \Delta T^e \left[-1\ 0\ 1\right]^T$ so the matrix equilibrium system is modeled by a single element:

$$\frac{E^e A^e}{3L^e} \begin{bmatrix} 7 & -8 & 1 \\ -8 & 16 & -8 \\ 1 & -8 & 7 \end{bmatrix} \begin{Bmatrix} u_1 = 0 \\ u_2 \\ u_3 = 0 \end{Bmatrix} = E^e A^e \alpha^e \Delta T^e \begin{Bmatrix} -1 \\ 0 \\ 1 \end{Bmatrix} + \begin{Bmatrix} r_1 \\ 0 \\ r_3 \end{Bmatrix}.$$

The two end displacements, u_1 and u_3, are known (zero), so multiply them times their columns in the square stiffness matrix and subtract those values from the right side. Retain the second row to calculate

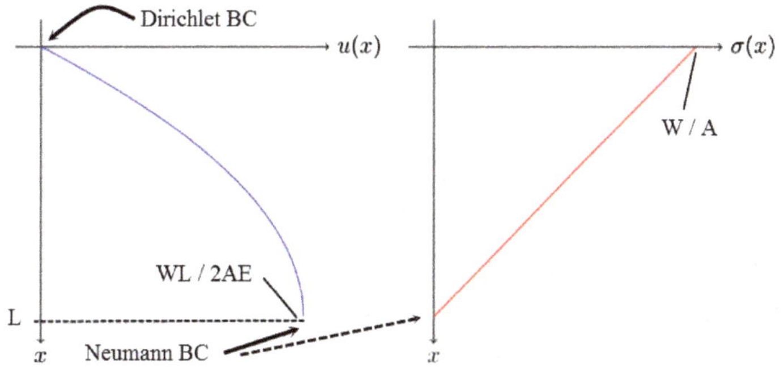

Fig. 8.2-4: Exact displacement and axial stress in a hanging bar.

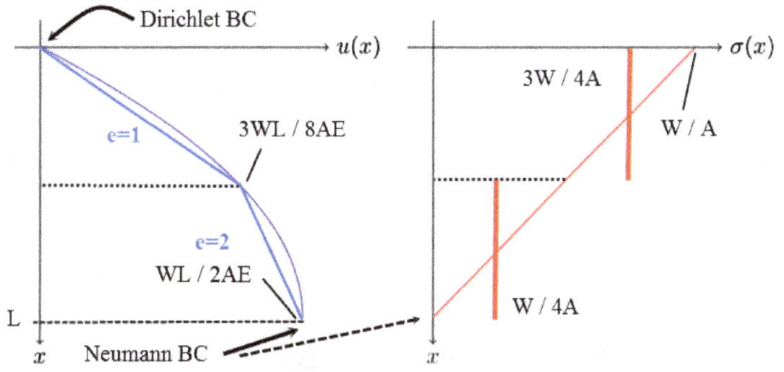

Fig. 8.2-5: Displacement and axial stress in a hanging bar for two linear elements.

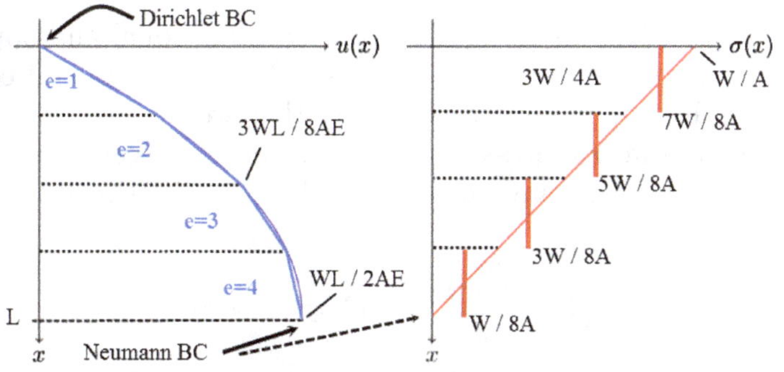

Fig. 8.2-6: Displacement and axial stress in a hanging bar for four linear elements.

the independent displacement of the mid-point node:

$$\frac{E^eA^e}{3L^e}[16]\{u_2\} = E^eA^e\alpha^e\Delta T^e\{0\} + \{0\} - u_1\frac{E^eA^e}{3L^e}[-8] - u_3\frac{E^eA^e}{3L^e}[-8] = \{0\}.$$

So $\{u_2\} = \{0\}$ and there are no displacements in the bar (but there is a stress). Use the first row of the matrix equilibrium system to recover the left reaction force:

$$\frac{E^eA^e}{3L^e}\begin{bmatrix}7 & -8 & 1\end{bmatrix}\begin{Bmatrix}0\\0\\0\end{Bmatrix} = E^eA^e\alpha^e\Delta T^e\{-1\} + \{r_1\} + \{0\},$$

$$r_1 = A^eE^e(\alpha^e\Delta T^e) = A^eE^e(\varepsilon_o^e) = A^e\sigma^e.$$

This reaction is a positive force. That is, it acts in the positive x-direction, and puts the bar in compression. Use the third row of the matrix system to recover the right reaction force:

$$\frac{E^eA^e}{3L^e}\begin{bmatrix}1 & -8 & 7\end{bmatrix}\begin{Bmatrix}0\\0\\0\end{Bmatrix} = E^eA^e\alpha^e\Delta T^e\{1\} + \{r_3\} + \{0\},$$

$$r_3 = -A^eE^e(\alpha^e\Delta T^e) = -A^eE^e(\varepsilon_o^e) = -A^e\sigma^e.$$

That reaction force is a negative force which is equal and opposite to the first reaction. That is, it acts in the negative x-direction, and puts the bar in compression. In other words, the bar is in a state of uniform compression. There are no displacements, so the mechanical strain at any point should be zero. Post-processing for the mechanical strain:

$$\varepsilon_x^e = \frac{\partial u}{\partial x} = \frac{d\boldsymbol{H}(r)}{dr}\frac{\partial r}{\partial x}\boldsymbol{u}^e \equiv \boldsymbol{B}(x)^e\boldsymbol{u}^e,$$

$$\varepsilon_x^e(r) = \frac{1}{L^e}[(4r-3)\ (4-8r)\ (4r-1)]\begin{Bmatrix}0\\0\\0\end{Bmatrix} = 0.$$

However, the stress depends on the net strain which is the mechanical strain less the initial (thermal) strain: $\varepsilon^e(r) = \varepsilon^e_x(r) - \varepsilon^e_o(r) = 0 - \alpha^e \Delta T^e$. Therefore, the stress in the bar becomes

$$\sigma^e_x(r) = E^e \varepsilon^e(r) = -E^e \alpha^e \Delta T^e,$$

so the axial stress is not zero, and is in a state of constant compression (the local position r has dropped out). This is because the fixed walls have prevented the bar from expanding with the increase in temperature. Note that if the temperature change was negative, all the signs would change and the bar would be in uniform tension because the fixed walls would prevent it from getting shorter.

Example 8.2-8 Given: For the chimney wall of Example 8.2-1 let the two temperatures quoted be the temperatures of the gas adjacent to the interior and exterior walls, instead of EBCs. The convection coefficients interior and exterior to the chimney are $h(0) = 110$ BTU/(hr ft^2 °F) and $h(L) = 50$ BTU/hr ft^2 °F), respectively. Determine the revised heat flux in each wall material.

Solution: There are no longer any EBCs. Both walls are subjected to convection BCs, which are mathematically mixed boundary conditions (MBCs). The new MBCs from the integration by parts of the Galerkin method are

$$\left[u(x)\, A(x)\, k(x) \frac{du}{dx} \right]_0^L = [u\, A\, h\{u - u_\infty\}]_0^L$$

$$\left[u(x)\, A(x)\, k(x) \frac{du}{dx} \right]_0^L = u_4 A_4 h_r \left\{ u_4 - u_{\infty_r} \right\} + u_1 A_1 h_f \left\{ u_1 - u_{\infty_f} \right\}.$$

Therefore, the two endpoint MBCs contribute a total of two terms to the system column vector and two terms to the diagonal of the system square matrix. Converting these scalar equations to matrix products, the MBCs for both ends are

$$\left[u(x)\, A(x)\, k(x) \frac{du}{dx} \right]_0^L \equiv \boldsymbol{u}^T \boldsymbol{S}_{\mathbf{MBC}} \boldsymbol{u} - \boldsymbol{u}^T \boldsymbol{c}_{\mathrm{MBC}}.$$

That places two non-zero terms on the diagonal of the square matrix and the column matrix:

$$\left[u(x)\,A(x)\,k(x)\frac{du}{dx}\right]_0^L = [u_1\ u_2\ u_3\ u_4]\begin{bmatrix} A_f h_f & 0 & 0 & 0 \\ 0 & 0 & 0 & 0 \\ 0 & 0 & 0 & 0 \\ 0 & 0 & 0 & A_r h_r \end{bmatrix}\begin{Bmatrix} u_1 \\ u_2 \\ u_3 \\ u_4 \end{Bmatrix} \cdots$$

$$-[u_1\ u_2\ u_3\ u_4]\begin{Bmatrix} A_f h_f u_{\infty_f} \\ 0 \\ 0 \\ A_r h_r u_{\infty_r} \end{Bmatrix}.$$

The line element matrices from the material layers and the point element matrices from the MBC must be assembled (scattered) into the system matrices (here $A_f = A_r = A^e$):

$$A^e \begin{bmatrix} (k_1/L_1 + h_f) & -k_1/L_1 & 0 & 0 \\ -k_1/L_1 & (k_1/L_1 + k_2/L_2) & -k_2/L_2 & 0 \\ 0 & -k_2/L_2 & (k_2/L_2 + k_3/L_3) & -k_3/L_3 \\ 0 & 0 & -k_3/L_3 & (k_3/L_3 + h_r) \end{bmatrix}$$

$$\begin{Bmatrix} u_1 \\ u_2 \\ u_3 \\ u_4 \end{Bmatrix} = A^e \begin{Bmatrix} h_f u_{\infty_f} \\ 0 \\ 0 \\ h_r u_{\infty_r} \end{Bmatrix},$$

$$1 \begin{bmatrix} (0.96 + 110) & -0.96 & 0 & 0 \\ -0.96 & (1.152) & -0.1920 & 0 \\ 0 & -0.1920 & (0.9920) & -0.8 \\ 0 & 0 & -0.8 & (0.8 + 50) \end{bmatrix}\begin{Bmatrix} u_1 \\ u_2 \\ u_3 \\ u_4 \end{Bmatrix}$$

$$= 1 \begin{Bmatrix} 110(1{,}500) \\ 0 \\ 0 \\ 50(375) \end{Bmatrix},$$

giving

$$[u_1\ u_2\ u_3\ u_4]^T = [1{,}498.4\ \ 1{,}311.6\ \ 378.0\ \ 153.9]^\circ\text{F}.$$

For the first element, gather the temperature solution at its nodes,

$$\boldsymbol{u}^{e^T} = [1{,}498.4\ \ 1{,}311.6]^\circ\text{F},$$

so the heat flux through the first wall is

$$q^e = -\frac{k^e}{L^e}[-1\ \ 1]u^e = -\frac{0.72}{0.75}[-1\ \ 1]\begin{Bmatrix}1,498.4\\1,311.6\end{Bmatrix} = 179.3\,\text{BTU/hrft}^2.$$

The second element gives $q^e = -\frac{0.08}{0.41667}[-1\ \ 1]\begin{Bmatrix}1{,}311.6\\378.0\end{Bmatrix} = 179.3$ BTU/hrft^2 and the third gives $q^e = 179.3$ BTU/hr ft^2. The heat flux is the same through all layers.

Example 8.2-9 Given: Consider a wall, of thickness L, with a known inside wall temperature with convection to air on the outside surface. The outside temperature is $u_\infty = 200^\circ$C, the thermal conductivity of the wall is $k = 2.5\,\text{W/m}^\circ\text{C}$, the inside air temperature is $u_1 = 35^\circ$C, and the outside convection coefficient is h. Determine the inside wall temperature.

Solution: With no internal heat generation the temperature change through the wall is linear, so a linear two-node ($L2$) conduction element will be exact. The convection on the surface, for a one-dimensional model, will be a point element. For pure conduction, the element square matrix (and system matrix) is

$$\boldsymbol{S_k} = \frac{k\,A}{L}\begin{bmatrix}1 & -1\\-1 & 1\end{bmatrix}.$$

The point convection square and column matrices at the second node are

$$\boldsymbol{S_h} = A\,h\begin{bmatrix}0 & 0\\0 & 1\end{bmatrix}, \quad \text{and} \quad \boldsymbol{C_h} = A\,h\,u_\infty\begin{Bmatrix}0\\1\end{Bmatrix}.$$

Assembling the convection matrices into the conduction matrices gives the system matrix

$$\begin{bmatrix} k\,A/L & -k\,A/L \\ -k\,A/L & (k\,A/L + A\,h) \end{bmatrix} \begin{Bmatrix} u_1 \\ u_2 \end{Bmatrix} = \begin{Bmatrix} -k\,A\partial u/\partial x(0) \\ A\,h\,u_\infty \end{Bmatrix}.$$

This can be used to obtain the analytically exact $_{\text{surface}}$ temperature and then to recover the heat flow through the wall. Note that the area cancels out. Applying the EBC that u_1 is known, the second row gives the inside wall surface temperature:

$$[(k\,A/L + A\,h)]\{u_2\} = \{A\,h\,u_\infty\} - u_1\{-k\,A/L\},$$

so

$$\{u_2\} = (L\,h\,u_\infty + u_1 k)/(L\,h + k).$$

Substituting the given numerical values gives $u_2 = 110°\mathrm{C}$. The heat flow reaction needed to maintain the specified inner temperature is $k\,A/L[u_1 - u_2] = -k\,A\partial u/\partial x(0)$:

$$\frac{k\,A}{L}\left[\frac{u_1(L\,h + k) - (L\,h\,u_\infty + u_1 k)}{L\,h + k}\right] = -k\,A\partial u/\partial x(0)$$

$$k\,A\left[\frac{h(u_1 - u_\infty)}{L\,h + k}\right] = -k\,A\partial u/\partial x(0) = 4,125\,W.$$

8.3 Variable Source Terms

In a physical one-dimensional application the source term, $Q(x)$, represents a force per unit length, or a heat generation rate per unit length, etc. Therefore, the total force or heat generation is the area under the $Q(x)$ versus x curve:

$$\int_0^L Q(x)dx = \text{Total source} = \text{Area under } Q(x) \text{ versus } x \text{ curve.} \tag{8.3-1}$$

This creates a source vector which is usually dependent on the physical location x. Its integral contribution is

$$\int_{x_1}^{x_1+L} u(x)Q(x)dx = \int_{x_1}^{x_1+L} \boldsymbol{u}^{e^T} \boldsymbol{H}(r)^T Q(x)^e$$

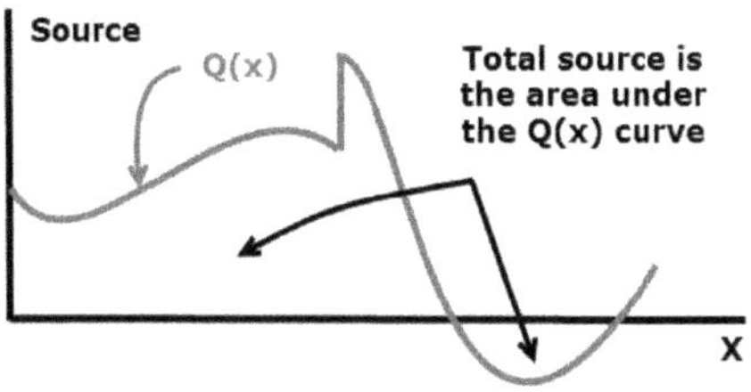

Fig. 8.3-1: Variable sources determine the ODE solution.

$$dx = \boldsymbol{u}^{e^T} \left\{ \int_{x_1}^{x_1+L} \boldsymbol{H}(r)^T Q(x)^e dx \right\},$$

$$\int_{x_1}^{x_1+L} u(x)Q(x)dx \equiv \boldsymbol{u}^{e^T} \boldsymbol{c}^e. \tag{8.3-2}$$

If the line source is discontinuous, as in Fig. 8.3-1, then the analytic solution must be split between the regions on either side of the source discontinuity. In the context of FEA, this means that an element interface must be placed at any location where a known discontinuity in the source occurs. Clearly, completion of the source integral in (8.1-7) depends on the application-dependent source, $Q(x)$. Those data could be supplied by a user function. However, that requires programming knowledge and introduces potential error not due to FEA theory.

Spatially dependent sources are very common, so a reliable way to define (input) application dependent sources is desirable. While every element can have different properties, it should be clear that every node could have associated data that are required in an analysis. In other words, a variable coefficient model that depends on the nodal coordinates could be input alongside the node coordinates and viewed as fake coordinates or just a nodal property. That is, a common practice is to input those data at the nodes in the mesh, so they can be gathered to the element and interpolated in the "isoparametric" way

That is, the sources are interpolated using the same (iso) parametric interpolation matrix, $\boldsymbol{H}(r)$, which is used to interpolate the solution:

$$Q(r) = \boldsymbol{H}(r)\boldsymbol{q}^e = \boldsymbol{H}(r) \begin{Bmatrix} q_1 \\ q_2 \\ q_3 \end{Bmatrix}^e . \tag{8.3-3}$$

Here, this integral will be exact for constant, linear, or quadratic source terms. It would be approximate for any other variation, like sin(x) or x^4. Then, the error in this assumption will depend on the size of the element used. For this assumption, the resultant source vector, $\boldsymbol{c}^e$, is

$$\int_{x_1}^{x_1+L} u(x)\, Q(x) dx = \int_{x_1}^{x_1+L} \boldsymbol{u}^{e^T} \boldsymbol{H}(r)^T \boldsymbol{H}(r)\, \boldsymbol{q}^e\, dx$$
$$= \boldsymbol{u}^{e^T} (\boldsymbol{M}^e \boldsymbol{q}^e) \equiv \boldsymbol{u}^{e^T} \boldsymbol{c}^e.$$

The product with the square generalized mass matrix $\boldsymbol{M}^e$ converts the nodal input sources, $\boldsymbol{q}^e$, to their nodal resultant $\boldsymbol{c}^e$.

$$\boldsymbol{c}^e = \left[\int_{x_1}^{x_1+L} \boldsymbol{H}(r)^T \boldsymbol{H}(r) dx \right] \boldsymbol{q}^e = \boldsymbol{M}^e \boldsymbol{q}^e. \tag{8.3-4}$$

The new square matrix is called the generalized mass matrix because it becomes a true mass matrix (later) when the mass density per unit length is included. The generalized mass matrix for any line element integrates to

$$\boldsymbol{M}^e = \int_{x_1}^{x_1+L} \boldsymbol{H}(r)^T \boldsymbol{H}(r)\, dx.$$

When a source term is spatially dependent, like Fig. 8.3-2, the resultant of the element, $\boldsymbol{c}^e$, will depend on the location of the element and its size.

To illustrate that, substitute an assumed $Q(x) = cx$ into the resultant of the element of a constant Jacobian quadratic line element with

$$\boldsymbol{H}(r) = [(1 - 3r + 2r^2)\ (4r - 4r^2)\ (-r + 2r^2)],$$

which gives

$$\boldsymbol{c}^e = \frac{L^e}{30} \begin{bmatrix} 4 & 2 & -1 \\ 2 & 16 & 2 \\ -1 & 2 & 4 \end{bmatrix} \begin{Bmatrix} q_1 \\ q_2 \\ q_3 \end{Bmatrix}^e = \frac{L^e}{30} \begin{bmatrix} 4 & 2 & -1 \\ 2 & 16 & 2 \\ -1 & 2 & 4 \end{bmatrix} \begin{Bmatrix} cx_1 \\ cx_2 \\ cx_3 \end{Bmatrix}^e,$$

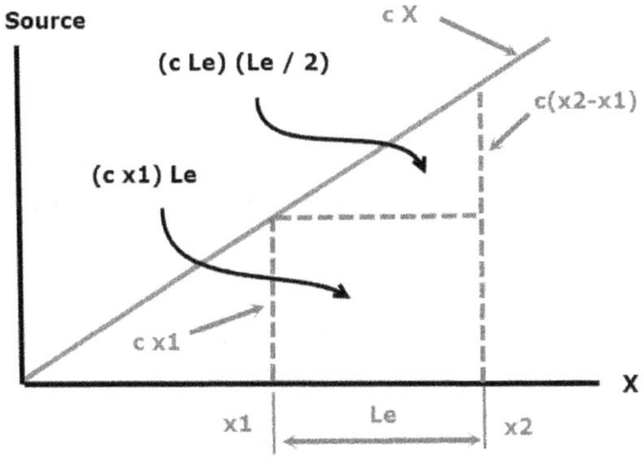

Fig. 8.3-2: Element source total is the area under the curve.

$$\boldsymbol{c}^e = \frac{c\,L^e}{30}\begin{bmatrix} 4 & 2 & -1 \\ 2 & 16 & 2 \\ -1 & 2 & 4 \end{bmatrix}\begin{Bmatrix} x_1 \\ x_1 + L^e/2 \\ x_1 + L^e \end{Bmatrix}^e . \qquad (8.3\text{-}5)$$

This resultant depends on where the element begins, x_1, and how large it is, L^e.

Another common source of variable source terms occurs in a solid with a variable temperature distribution. Recall from physics that if a solid is completely free, a temperature increase just results in a change of length of $\Delta L = \alpha\,\Delta T\,L$, where α is the material's coefficient of thermal expansion (CTE), and ΔT temperature increase from its stress-free configuration. When an axial bar is subjected to a temperature change, that induces an initial thermal strain (change in length per unit length) of $\varepsilon_o = \alpha\,\Delta T$. Any such "initial strain" introduces an addition possible internal load state and an additional term in the differential equation of equilibrium. The previously considered ODE, with the addition of any initial strain effect, becomes

$$\frac{d}{dx}\left(E(x)A(x)\frac{du}{dx}\right) + w(x)\ \frac{d}{dx}\left([E(x)\,A(x)\alpha\,\Delta T(x)]u\right) = 0.$$

The presence of any initial strain defines a new element variable source load vector:

$$\boldsymbol{c}_0^e = \int_{L^e} \frac{d\boldsymbol{H}^T}{dx}\,E(x)\,A(x)\,\alpha\,\Delta T(x)dx. \qquad (8.3\text{-}6)$$

Generally, the temperature change data is not constant and is the output of a proceeding finite element thermal study. In that case, the temperature would be input to the stress calculation as nodal data to be gathered to the element, $\boldsymbol{T}^e$. Then, using that element's stress-free temperature $\boldsymbol{T}^e_{\text{Free}}$ (which would be a material property) the local nodal values of the temperature change $\boldsymbol{\Delta T}^e = \{\boldsymbol{T}^e - \boldsymbol{T}^e_{\text{Free}}\}$ would be interpolated within the element as $\Delta T(r) = \boldsymbol{H}(r)\,\boldsymbol{\Delta T}^e$. The more general form of the initial strain results is

$$\boldsymbol{c}_0^e = \int_{L^e} \frac{d\boldsymbol{H}^T}{dx} E^e A^e \alpha^e\, \boldsymbol{H}(r) dx\, \boldsymbol{\Delta T}^e.$$

For constant properties, the exact integral (from the chapter summary) for the linear line element and the quadratic line element are

$$\boldsymbol{c}_0^e = \frac{E^e A^e \alpha^e}{2} \begin{bmatrix} -1 & -1 \\ 1 & 1 \end{bmatrix} \begin{Bmatrix} \Delta T_1 \\ \Delta T_2 \end{Bmatrix}^e,$$

$$\boldsymbol{c}_0^e = \frac{E^e A^e \alpha^e}{6} \begin{bmatrix} -3 & -4 & 1 \\ 4 & 0 & -4 \\ -1 & 4 & 3 \end{bmatrix} \begin{Bmatrix} \Delta T_1 \\ \Delta T_2 \\ \Delta T_3 \end{Bmatrix}^e,$$

and for the cubic line element it is

$$\boldsymbol{c}_0^e = \frac{E^e A^e \alpha^e}{80} \begin{bmatrix} -40 & -57 & 24 & -7 \\ 57 & 0 & -81 & 24 \\ -24 & 81 & 0 & -57 \\ 7 & -24 & 57 & 40 \end{bmatrix} \begin{Bmatrix} \Delta T_1 \\ \Delta T_2 \\ \Delta T_3 \\ \Delta T_4 \end{Bmatrix}^e.$$

When the temperature change is constant throughout the element, the thermal load effects for linear, quadratic, or cubic line elements become, respectively,

$$\boldsymbol{c}_0^e = E^e A^e \alpha^e \Delta T^e \begin{Bmatrix} -1 \\ 1 \end{Bmatrix}, \boldsymbol{c}_0^e = E^e A^e \alpha^e \Delta T^e \begin{Bmatrix} -1 \\ 0 \\ 1 \end{Bmatrix},$$

$$\boldsymbol{c}_0^e = E^e A^e \alpha^e \Delta T^e \begin{Bmatrix} -1 \\ 0 \\ 0 \\ 1 \end{Bmatrix}. \tag{8.3-7}$$

Since thermal loads are common, these arrays can be useful in obtaining simple analytic results and to include in numerical scripts using many elements. Initial strains can arise from other causes. The second most common cause of an initial strain is a change in moisture content in wood or advanced composite materials. Then, the material property is the coefficient of moisture expansion (CME) which is defined as the fractional increase in strain per unit mass variation due to the moisture content change. Multiplying that property by the percent change in moisture content defined the initial strain. After the following related examples, the next two sections will introduce MBCs and automate Lagrange element solutions with numerical integration, respectively.

Example 8.3-1 Given: For the ODE $d^2u^*/dx^2 + Q(x) = 0$ for the domain $x_1 \le x \le (x_1 + L)$, evaluate the source term, $Q(x) = cx$, in a "sub-parametric" way. That is, use a linear interpolation for the geometry and a quadratic to interpolate the solution. Split that source vector into two parts; one dependent on its position and the other dependent only on its length. Compare that split to the area under the source curve at the element's location as illustrated in Fig. 8.3-2.

Solution: For equally spaced nodes in physical space the interpolated location becomes linear. Then the geometry interpolation is

$$x(r) = (1-r)x_1^e + rx_3^e = x_1^e + r(x_3^e - x_1^e) = x_1^e + r\,L^e \text{ so } dx/dr = L^e.$$

Denote the different geometry interpolations as $x(r) = (1-r)x_1^e + rx_3^e = \boldsymbol{G}(r)\boldsymbol{x}^e$. Here, the spatial source is also "sub-parametric" so interpolate it in the same way:

$$Q(r) = (1-r)q_1^e + rq_3^e = \boldsymbol{G}(r)\boldsymbol{q}^e = [(1-r)r]\begin{Bmatrix} q_1 = cx_1^e \\ q_3 = cx_3^e \end{Bmatrix}^e.$$

The source integral in terms of the spatial source values now involves a rectangular instead of the square generalized mass matrix:

$$\int_{x_1}^{x_3} u(x)\,Q(x)dx = \int_{x_1}^{x_3} \boldsymbol{u}^{e^T}\boldsymbol{H}(r)^T\,\boldsymbol{G}(r)\boldsymbol{q}^e\,dx = \boldsymbol{u}^{e^T}(\boldsymbol{R}^e\boldsymbol{q}^e)$$
$$\equiv \boldsymbol{u}^{e^T}\boldsymbol{c}^e.$$

The product with the rectangular matrix $\boldsymbol{R}^e$ transforms the nodal input sources, $\boldsymbol{q}^e$, to their resultant source vector, $\boldsymbol{c}^e$.

In practice, this matrix form is always utilized to create the resultant, $\boldsymbol{c}^e$, as a single numerical vector. As an educational tool here, however, that rule will be violated to create two terms that show where the contributions are coming from in this special linear source distribution. The source term is $Q(x) = c\,x = c\,\boldsymbol{G}(r)\boldsymbol{x}^e = Q(r)$. Drop the matrix notation by preforming the product $x = \boldsymbol{G}(r)\boldsymbol{x}^e$ and keep $Q(r)$ in its scalar form:

$$\int_{x_1}^{x_3} u(x)\,Q(x)dx = c\int_{x_1}^{x_3} \boldsymbol{u}^{e^T}\boldsymbol{H}(r)^{\boldsymbol{T}}(x_1 + rL)dx,$$

$$\int_{x_1}^{x_3} u(x)\,Q(x)dx = \boldsymbol{u}^{e^T}\left\{cx_1\int_0^1 \boldsymbol{H}(r)^{\boldsymbol{T}}(Ldr)\right.$$

$$\left. +cL\int_0^1 \boldsymbol{H}(r)^{\boldsymbol{T}}r\,(Ldr)\right\} \equiv \boldsymbol{u}^{e^T}\boldsymbol{c}^e,$$

where

$$\boldsymbol{c}^e = cx_1^eL^e\int_0^1 \begin{Bmatrix} (1-3r+2r^2) \\ (4r-4r^2) \\ (-r+2r^2) \end{Bmatrix} dr$$

$$+cL^{e^2}\int_0^1 \begin{Bmatrix} (r-3r^2+2r^3) \\ (4r^2-4r^3) \\ (-r^2+2r^3) \end{Bmatrix} dr$$

$$= \frac{cx_1^eL^e}{6}\begin{Bmatrix} 1 \\ 4 \\ 1 \end{Bmatrix} + \frac{cL^{e^2}}{6}\begin{Bmatrix} 0 \\ 2 \\ 1 \end{Bmatrix}.$$

The presence of the x_1^e term shows that the resultant source at the element's nodes depends on where the element starts in space, as well as how much of that space it occupies, L^e. Note that for an element not beginning at the origin, the total source contribution is $cx_1^eL^e + cL^{e^2}/2$ which is the area under the *source* versus x curve. From Fig. 8.3-2 the first source term is the lower rectangular area and the second source term is the upper triangular area. A special case occurs if the element begins at the origin, $x_1 = 0$, and the source simplifies to: $\boldsymbol{c}^{e^T} = cL^{e^2}[0\ 2\ 1]/6$.

Example 8.3-2 Given: Solve the problem $d^2u^*/dx^2 + cx = 0$, $x =]0, L[$ with the EBCs: $u_1 = u(0) = 0$, and $u(L) = 0$ with a single quadratic element and compare the result to the exact answer $u^*(x) = cL^2x/6 - cx^3/6$.

Solution: From the previous example and Example 8.2-4, the equivalent matrix equilibrium system from a single quadratic line element, before enforcing the EBC(s), is

$$\frac{1}{3L}\begin{bmatrix} 7 & -8 & 1 \\ -8 & 16 & -8 \\ 1 & -8 & 7 \end{bmatrix}\begin{Bmatrix} u_1 = 0 \\ u_2 \\ u_3 = 0 \end{Bmatrix} = \begin{Bmatrix} -du(0)/dx \\ 0 \\ du(L)/dx \end{Bmatrix} + \frac{cL^2}{6}\begin{Bmatrix} 0 \\ 2 \\ 1 \end{Bmatrix},$$

where now the two EBCs make u_1 and u_3 known. The three unknowns in this system are the internal value, u_2, and the two end reactions $-du(0)/dx$ and $du(L)/dx$.

The matrix system can be partitioned, and the second row is the only independent equation for u_2, and once it is known, the first and third rows will give the reactions associated with the EBC at nodes 1 and 3. Multiply the first column by the known value of u_1 and move its second row over to the right-hand side, and likewise multiply the third column by the known value of u_3 and move its second row over to the right-hand side:

$$\begin{aligned}\frac{1}{3L}[16]\{u_2\} &= \{0\} + \frac{cL^2}{6}\{2\} - (u_1 = 0)\frac{1}{3L}\{-8\} - (u_3 = 0)\frac{1}{3L}\{-8\} \\ &= \frac{cL^2}{6}\{2\}.\end{aligned}$$

Note that the EBCs could have assigned any value to u_1 and u_3 and this process automatically allows for that. Solving by inverting the

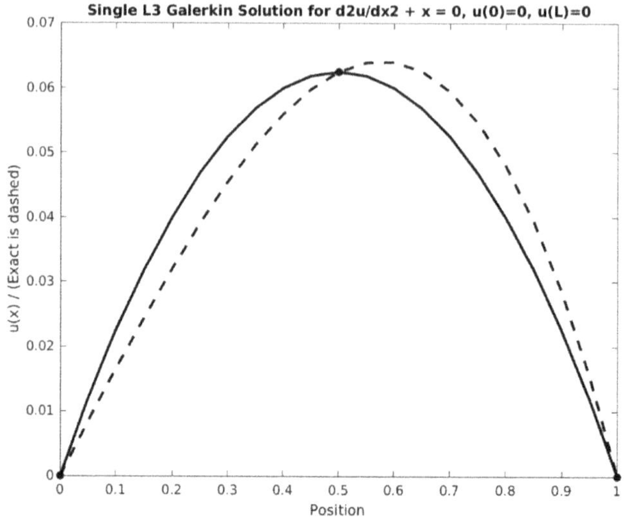

Fig. 8.3-3: Exact (dashed) and FEA solutions for EBCs $u(0)=u(L)=0$.

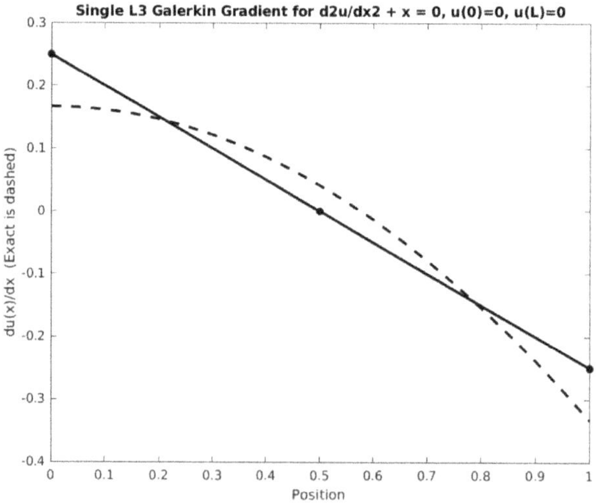

Fig. 8.3-4: Exact (dashed) and FEA gradient for EBCs $u(0)=u(L)=0$.

square partitioned matrix gives the solution (in the prior notation)

$$\boldsymbol{u_u} = \boldsymbol{S_{uu}^{-1}}(\boldsymbol{c_u} - \boldsymbol{S_{uk}}\boldsymbol{u_k}),$$

$$\{u_2\} = 3L\left[\frac{1}{16}\right]\left(\frac{cL^2}{6}\{2\} - 0\right) = \frac{cL^3}{16},$$

which is the exact value at the center node. Substituting u_2 and the two EBCs into the first row of the governing matrix system gives the reaction slope at node 1:

$$\boldsymbol{r}_k = \boldsymbol{S}_{ku}\boldsymbol{u}_u + \boldsymbol{S}_{kk}\boldsymbol{u}_k - \boldsymbol{c}_k,$$

$$r_1 = -\frac{du(0)}{dx} = \frac{1}{3L}\begin{bmatrix}7 & -8 & 1\end{bmatrix}\begin{Bmatrix}0\\ cL^3/16\\ 0\end{Bmatrix} - \frac{cL^2}{6}\{0\} = -\frac{cL^2}{3},$$

and the third row gives the reaction (solution slope) at the right end:

$$r_3 = du(L)/dx = \frac{1}{3L}\begin{bmatrix}1 & -8 & 7\end{bmatrix}\begin{Bmatrix}0\\ cL^3/16\\ 0\end{Bmatrix} - \frac{cL^2}{6}\{1\} = -\frac{cL^2}{3}.$$

Thus, the node value and two reactions recovered from the matrix form are analytically exact. The solution and gradient are in Figs. 8.3-3 and 8.3-4. Note again that the quadratic element is exact at its nodes and inexact in its interior. Also, the finite element gradient is least accurate at the three nodes but exact at two interior points (which happen to be Gauss integration points).

Example 8.3-3 Given: Solve the problem $\frac{d^2u^*}{dx^2} + cx = 0$, $x =]0, L[$ with the EBCs: $u_1 = u(0) = 0$, and the secondary condition $du(L)/dx = b$ with a single quadratic element and compare the result to the exact answer

$$u^*(x) = bx + cL^2x/2 - cx^3/6.$$

Sketch the solution and gradient values when b =0.

Solution: From the previous Example 8.2-2, $L^e = L$. The equivalent matrix system, before enforcing the EBC(s), is

$$\frac{1}{3L^e}\begin{bmatrix}7 & -8 & 1\\ -8 & 16 & -8\\ 1 & -8 & 7\end{bmatrix}\begin{Bmatrix}u_1 = 0\\ u_2\\ u_3\end{Bmatrix} = \begin{Bmatrix}-du(0)/dx\\ 0\\ du(L)/dx = b\end{Bmatrix} + \frac{cL^{e^2}}{6}\begin{Bmatrix}0\\ 2\\ 1\end{Bmatrix},$$

where now the EBC makes u_1 known. The three unknowns in this system are u_2, u_3, and the reaction $du(0)/dx$. Rewriting the equations to move $du(0)/dx$ to the left-hand side would have the undesirable effect of destroying the symmetry of the equations. The matrix system can be partitioned, and the last two rows are independent equations for u_2 and u_3; and once they are known, the first row will give the reaction associated with the EBC at node 1. Multiply the first column by the known value of u_1 and move its last two rows over to the right-hand side:

$$\frac{1}{3L^e}\begin{bmatrix}16 & -8\\ -8 & 7\end{bmatrix}\begin{Bmatrix}u_2\\ u_3\end{Bmatrix} = \begin{Bmatrix}0\\ b\end{Bmatrix} + \frac{cL^{e^2}}{6}\begin{Bmatrix}2\\ 1\end{Bmatrix} - (u_1 = 0)\frac{1}{3L^e}\begin{Bmatrix}-8\\ 1\end{Bmatrix}.$$

Note that the EBC could have assigned any value to u_1 and this process automatically allows for that. Solving by inverting the square matrix gives (in the prior notation)

$$\boldsymbol{u_u} = \boldsymbol{S}_{\boldsymbol{uu}}^{-1}\left(\boldsymbol{c_u} - \boldsymbol{S_{uk}}\boldsymbol{u_k}\right)$$

$$\begin{Bmatrix}u_2\\ u_3\end{Bmatrix} = 3L^e\left(\frac{1}{48}\right)\begin{bmatrix}7 & 8\\ 8 & 16\end{bmatrix}\left(\begin{Bmatrix}0\\ b\end{Bmatrix} + \frac{cL^{e^2}}{6}\begin{Bmatrix}2\\ 1\end{Bmatrix} - \begin{Bmatrix}0\\ 0\end{Bmatrix}\right)$$
$$= \frac{L^e}{48}\begin{Bmatrix}11\,cL^2 + 24b\\ 16\,cL^2 + 48b\end{Bmatrix},$$

which are the exact analytical values at the nodes. Substituting these and the EBC into the first row gives the associated reaction at node 1: $\boldsymbol{r_k} = \boldsymbol{S_{ku}}\boldsymbol{u_u} + \boldsymbol{S_{kk}}\boldsymbol{u_k} - \boldsymbol{c_k}$, or

$$\boldsymbol{r_k} = -du(0)/dx = \frac{1}{3L^e}\begin{bmatrix}7 & -8 & 1\end{bmatrix}\frac{L^e}{48}\begin{Bmatrix}0\\ 11\,cL^2 + 24b\\ 16\,cL^2 + 48b\end{Bmatrix} - \frac{cL^{e^2}}{6}\{0\}$$
$$= -b - cL^2/2,$$

which is also exact. This value recovered from the matrix system arising from the integral form is always more accurate than the gradient in the element evaluated at the element node on the boundary! The quadratic finite element approximation has given exact values at the nodes, and the exact reaction, but is only approximate at any interior non-node location.

The error in the approximate solution cannot be plotted without assigning numerical values to b, c, and L. Here assume $c = L = 1$. Generally, the smaller the b, the larger is the error in the approximation. Plots for $u(x)$ with $b = 0$ are given in Fig. 8.3-5. In that figure, note the illustration of the general result that solution values are always most accurate at the nodes, while gradient values *calculated at the element level*, in Fig. 8.3-6, are least accurate at the nodes (for C^0 continuity elements). However, the left slope (reaction) had the exact value when recovered from the governing matrix system of equations.

It can be proven that the most accurate spatial derivatives appear interior to the element. Usually, those accurate derivative locations are at or near the quadrature points. In Fig. 8.3-4, the slope is most accurate at the Gauss points $a = \mp 0.577$, or $r = 0.211$, and $r = 0.789$.

Example 8.3-4 Given: Use two quadratic elements to solve Example 8.3-3, and selectively refine the mesh so the element adjacent to the right node NBC is a quarter of the size of the other element.

Solution: The error in the element recovered normal boundary flux is always mesh dependent. Look at the right node approximate slope in Figs. 8.3-5 and 8.3-6. Making the (second) element that is adjacent to the boundary smaller will make the NBC error smaller.

As expected, the results are exact at the nodes but are in error between the nodes because the exact solution is a cubic polynomial in x. A plot of this result for two different length constant Jacobian elements is given in Fig. 8.3-7, with $L_2 = L_1/4$. Compared to Fig. 8.3-5, that plot illustrates that refining a mesh in the direction normal to a boundary having a natural BC does improve the slope accuracy in the element adjacent to that boundary.

Example 8.3-5 Given: Solve the problem $d^2u^*/dx^2 + cx = 0,\ x =]0, L[$ with the EBCs: $u_1 = u(0) = 0$, and $u(L) = 0$ with a single two-noded linear element and compare the result to the exact answer $u^*(x) = cL^2x/6 - cx^3/6$.

Solution: Why bother? Clearly, the finite element solution value will be a very poor interpolated zero value everywhere, but still

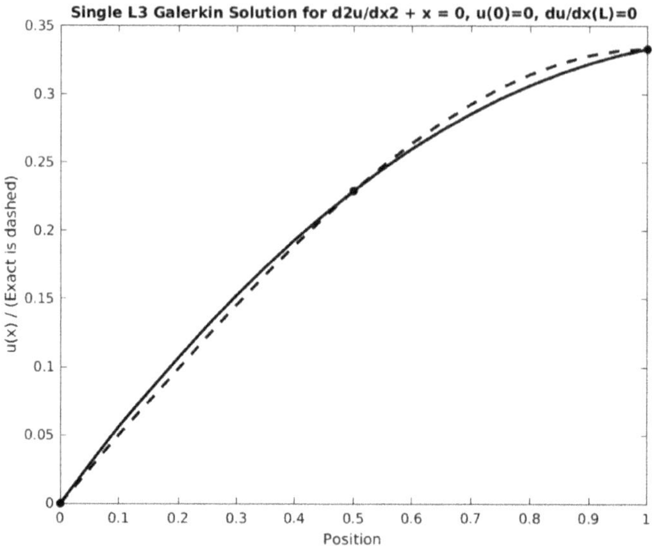

Fig. 8.3-5: Single element nodally exact approximation and exact (dashed) solution.

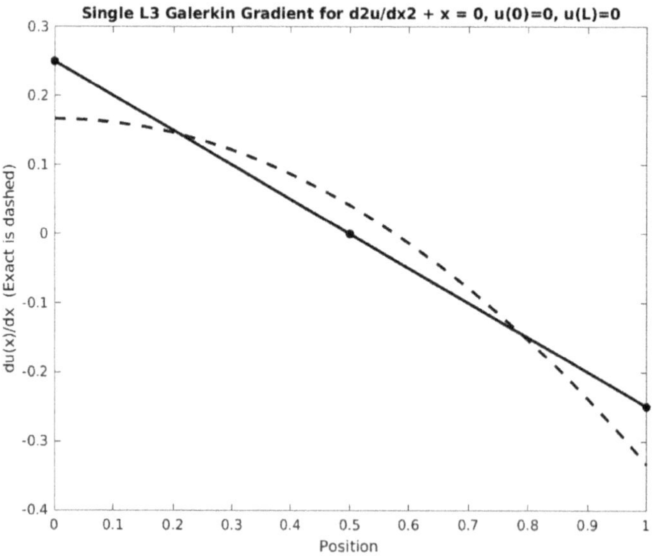

Fig. 8.3-6: Single element gradient and exact gradient (dashed).

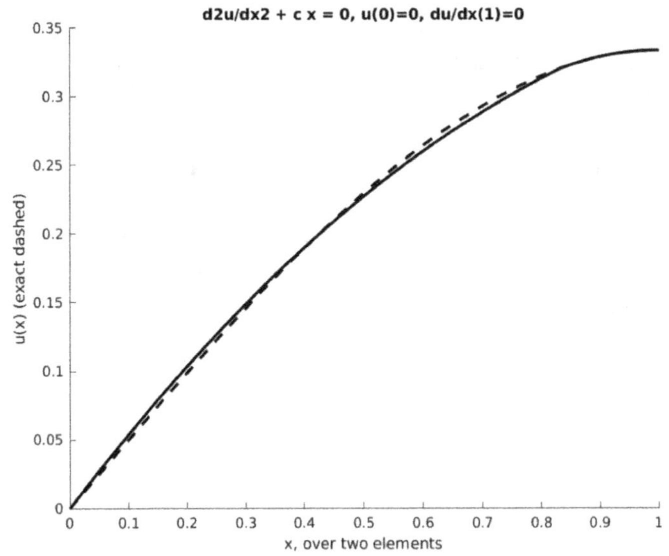

Fig. 8.3-7: Refining the mesh near non-essential BCs is desirable.

exact at the two EBC. Might there be any useful reaction data contained in the matrix system? For a single linear element, the matrix system, before EBCs, is

$$\frac{1}{L^e}\begin{bmatrix} 1 & -1 \\ -1 & 1 \end{bmatrix}\begin{Bmatrix} u_1 = 0 \\ u_2 = 0 \end{Bmatrix}^e = \frac{c\,x_1^e L^e}{2}\begin{Bmatrix} 1 \\ 1 \end{Bmatrix} + \frac{c\,L^{e^2}}{6}\begin{Bmatrix} 1 \\ 2 \end{Bmatrix} + \begin{Bmatrix} -r_1 \\ r_2 \end{Bmatrix},$$

where r_1 and r_2 are the left and right system node reactions, respectively. Here, the EBCs give $u_1 = 0 = u_2$, so the left-hand side becomes a null vector. Having satisfied the EBCs with $x_1^e = 0$, the reactions become

$$\begin{Bmatrix} 0 \\ 0 \end{Bmatrix} = \begin{Bmatrix} 0 \\ 0 \end{Bmatrix} + \frac{c\,L^{e^2}}{6}\begin{Bmatrix} 1 \\ 2 \end{Bmatrix} + \begin{Bmatrix} -r_1 \\ r_2 \end{Bmatrix} \rightarrow \begin{Bmatrix} r_1 \\ r_2 \end{Bmatrix} = \frac{c\,L^{e^2}}{6}\begin{Bmatrix} 1 \\ -2 \end{Bmatrix},$$

which are again the exact solution end slopes. However, post-processing for the end element's fluxes would give non-exact values. Again, the emphasis here is that *if the flux values (reactions) on the boundary at an EBC are important, they should always be recovered from the governing matrix equations!*

Example 8.3-6 Given: the equation $k(x)d^2u^*/dx^2 + g(x)u^* + Q(x) = 0,\ \ x \,\text{in}\,]0, L[$ with properties of $k(x) = 1$, $g(x) = 1$, $Q(x) = x$ with two EBC of $u(0) = 0 = u(1) = 0$, and $L = 1$. The exact solution is $u^*(x) = \sin(x)/\sin(1) - x$. Use a single quadratic line element to approximate the solution.

Solution: Again, use a Galerkin weighted residual formulation. The appearance of the term $g(x)u^*$ in the ODE will introduce a new matrix while the rest of the formulation is the same as previous examples. The presence of that term also changes the homogeneous solution of the ODE so that it is no longer a polynomial. Therefore, the finite element solution will no longer be exact at the nodes. Here the Galerkin method requires

$$I = \int_0^L u(x)\left[k(x)\frac{d^2u}{dx^2} + g(x)u + Q(x)\right]dx = 0.$$

Integrating only the first integral by parts gives

$$I = \left[u\,k(x)\frac{du}{dx}\right]_0^L - \int_0^L \frac{du}{dx}k(x)\frac{du}{dx}dx + \int_0^L u\,g(x)u\,dx$$
$$+ \int_0^L u(x)\,Q(x)dx = 0.$$

For a single quadratic element, recall that the column matrix of NBC and/or reactions arising from the first term is a scalar that can be written as the dot product of two arrays:

$$\left[u\,k(x)\frac{du}{dx}\right]_0^L = [u_1 \quad u_2 \quad u_3]\begin{Bmatrix} -kdu(0)/dx \\ 0 \\ k\,du(L)/dx \end{Bmatrix} \equiv \boldsymbol{u}^T\,\boldsymbol{c}_{\text{NBC}}.$$

From prior examples, the first square matrix (stiffness or conduction), for a constant k is

$$\boldsymbol{S}^e = \frac{k^e}{3L^e}\begin{bmatrix} 7 & -8 & 1 \\ -8 & 16 & -8 \\ 1 & -8 & 7 \end{bmatrix}.$$

The new additional (foundation or convection) square matrix, from the third term in I, is

$$\int_0^L u\,g(x) u\,dx = -\boldsymbol{u}^{e^T}\left[\int_0^L \boldsymbol{H}(r)^T g(x)\,\boldsymbol{H}(r)\,dx\right]\boldsymbol{u}^e \equiv -\boldsymbol{u}^{e^T}\boldsymbol{M}^e\boldsymbol{u}^e$$

and for a constant Jacobian element and a constant property g becomes

$$\boldsymbol{M}^e = \frac{g^e\,L^e}{30}\begin{bmatrix} 4 & 2 & -1 \\ 2 & 16 & 2 \\ -1 & 2 & 4 \end{bmatrix}.$$

Again, for a linear source term, $Q(x) = x$, the last integral (only when $x_1 = 0$) is

$$\boldsymbol{c}_Q^e = \frac{L^2}{6}\begin{Bmatrix} 0 \\ 2 \\ 1 \end{Bmatrix}.$$

Before enforcing the EBC, the matrix system is $\boldsymbol{c}_{\text{NBC}} - \boldsymbol{S}^e\boldsymbol{u}^e + \boldsymbol{m}^e\boldsymbol{u}^e + \boldsymbol{c}_{\boldsymbol{Q}}^e = \boldsymbol{0}$. Moving the column arrays to the right-hand side gives the following governing matrix formulation:

$$\frac{k}{3L}\begin{bmatrix} 7 & -8 & 1 \\ -8 & 16 & -8 \\ 1 & -8 & 7 \end{bmatrix}\begin{Bmatrix} u_1 \\ u_2 \\ u_3 \end{Bmatrix} - \frac{g\,L}{30}\begin{bmatrix} 4 & 2 & -1 \\ 2 & 16 & 2 \\ -1 & 2 & 4 \end{bmatrix}\begin{Bmatrix} u_1 \\ u_2 \\ u_3 \end{Bmatrix}$$

$$= \begin{Bmatrix} \frac{-k\,du(0)}{dx} \\ 0 \\ k\,\frac{du(L)}{dx} \end{Bmatrix} + \frac{L^2}{6}\begin{Bmatrix} 0 \\ 2 \\ 1 \end{Bmatrix}.$$

Combining the two square matrices:

$$\begin{bmatrix} \left(\frac{7k}{3L} - \frac{4gL}{30}\right) & \left(\frac{-8k}{3L} - \frac{2gL}{30}\right) & \left(\frac{k}{3L} + \frac{gL}{30}\right) \\ \left(\frac{-8k}{3L} - \frac{2gL}{30}\right) & \left(\frac{16k}{3L} - \frac{16gL}{30}\right) & \left(\frac{-8k}{3L} - \frac{2gL}{30}\right) \\ \left(\frac{k}{3L} + \frac{gL}{30}\right) & \left(\frac{-8k}{3L} - \frac{2gL}{30}\right) & \left(\frac{7k}{3L} - \frac{4gL}{30}\right) \end{bmatrix} \begin{Bmatrix} u_1 = 0 \\ u_2 \\ u_3 = 0 \end{Bmatrix}$$

$$= \begin{Bmatrix} \frac{-k\, du(0)}{dx} \\ 0 \\ k\,\frac{du(L)}{dx} \end{Bmatrix} + \frac{L^2}{6} \begin{Bmatrix} 0 \\ 2 \\ 1 \end{Bmatrix}.$$

Again, this matrix equation is not unique until the EBC is enforced. Since the EBCs require that $u(0) = 0 = u(1) = 0$, the three unknowns are u_2, $-k\,du(0)/dx$, and $k\,du(L)/dx$. Only the second row is an independent equation for u_2. Multiply column 1 by u_1 and subtract it from the right-hand side, and similarly, multiply column 3 by u_3 and subtract it from the right-hand side. The independent second row is

$$\left[\frac{k}{3L}[16] - \frac{g\,L}{30}[16]\right]\{u_2\} = \{0\} + \frac{L^2}{6}\{2\} - (0)\left\{\frac{k}{3L}[-8] - \frac{g\,L}{30}[2]\right\}$$
$$-(0)\left\{\frac{k}{3L}[-8] - \frac{g\,L}{30}[2]\right\}.$$

This gives the approximate value $\{u_2\} = 5L^3/8\left(10k - gL^2\right)$, which for $k = g = L = 1$ becomes $u_2 = 5/72 = 0.06944$ compared to the exact value of 0.06975, and error of less than 1%. Use the first row to solve for the left reaction using the known $\boldsymbol{u}^e$:

$$0 + \left(\frac{k}{3L}[-8] - \frac{g\,L}{30}[2]\right)u_2 + 0 = \frac{-k\,du(0)}{dx} + 0$$

$$\rightarrow \quad \frac{du(0)}{dx} = \frac{L^2(40k + gL^2)}{24k(10k - gL^2)},$$

which for the above data is $du(0)/dx = +0.1898$ compared to the exact value of $+0.1884$. Finally, using the third row to recover the reaction at the right node:

$$0 + \left[\frac{k}{3L}[-8] - \frac{gL}{30}[2]\right] u_2 + 0 = \frac{L^2}{6}\{1\} + \left\{k\frac{\partial u(L)}{\partial x}\right\} \to \frac{\partial u(L)}{\partial x}$$

$$= \frac{L^2(-80k + 3gL^2)}{24(10k - gL^2)}.$$

For the constant values, the approximate reaction is $\partial u(L)/\partial x = -77/216 = -0.3565$ compared to the exact value of -0.3565, with only a 0.4% error. Using the matrix equations derived from the integral form is always the most accurate way to recover the reactions at the EBCs.

Example 8.3-7 Given: Replace the right end EBC in the previous Example 8.3-6 with the NBC $\partial u(L)/\partial x = 0$ (which is also a natural BC since it is the default at a node without an EBC).

Solution: The matrix form with three equations still applies. Now u_1 and $\partial u(L)/\partial x$ have known values, so the three unknowns are u_2, u_3, and $-k\, du(0)/dx$. Just the NBC column vector has changed, so before enforcing the EBC, the system matrix is

$$\begin{bmatrix} \left(\frac{7k}{3L} - \frac{4gL}{30}\right) & \left(\frac{-8k}{3L} - \frac{2gL}{30}\right) & \left(\frac{k}{3L} + \frac{gL}{30}\right) \\ \left(\frac{-8k}{3L} - \frac{2gL}{30}\right) & \left(\frac{16k}{3L} - \frac{16gL}{30}\right) & \left(\frac{-8k}{3L} - \frac{2gL}{30}\right) \\ \left(\frac{k}{3L} + \frac{gL}{30}\right) & \left(\frac{-8k}{3L} - \frac{2gL}{30}\right) & \left(\frac{7k}{3L} - \frac{4gL}{30}\right) \end{bmatrix} \begin{Bmatrix} u_1 = 0 \\ u_2 \\ u_3 \end{Bmatrix}$$

$$= \begin{Bmatrix} \frac{-k\, du(0)}{dx} \\ 0 \\ k\,\frac{du(L)}{dx} = 0 \end{Bmatrix} + \frac{L^2}{6}\begin{Bmatrix} 0 \\ 2 \\ 1 \end{Bmatrix}.$$

These can be partitioned between known and unknown, with the known first:

$$\begin{bmatrix} \boldsymbol{S}_{kk} & \boldsymbol{S}_{ku} \\ \boldsymbol{S}_{uk} & \boldsymbol{S}_{uu} \end{bmatrix} \begin{Bmatrix} \boldsymbol{u}_k \\ \boldsymbol{u}_u \end{Bmatrix} = \begin{Bmatrix} \boldsymbol{c}_k + \boldsymbol{r}_k \\ \boldsymbol{c}_u \end{Bmatrix}.$$

Then the square matrix partitions as

$$\begin{bmatrix} \boldsymbol{S}_{kk} & \boldsymbol{S}_{ku} \\ \boldsymbol{S}_{uk} & \boldsymbol{S}_{uu} \end{bmatrix} = \begin{bmatrix} \left(\frac{7k}{3L} - \frac{4gL}{30}\right) & \vdots & \left(\frac{-8k}{3L} - \frac{2gL}{30}\right) & \left(\frac{k}{3L} + \frac{gL}{30}\right) \\ \cdots & \cdots & \cdots & \cdots \\ \left(\frac{-8k}{3L} - \frac{2gL}{30}\right) & \vdots & \left(\frac{16k}{3L} - \frac{16gL}{30}\right) & \left(\frac{-8k}{3L} - \frac{2gL}{30}\right) \\ \left(\frac{k}{3L} + \frac{gL}{30}\right) & \vdots & \left(\frac{-8k}{3L} - \frac{2gL}{30}\right) & \left(\frac{7k}{3L} - \frac{4gL}{30}\right) \end{bmatrix}.$$

Enforcing that u_1 is known; retain the lower partition of two rows that are the independent equations for the nodal values:

$$\begin{bmatrix} \left(\frac{16k}{3L} - \frac{16gL}{30}\right) & \left(\frac{-8k}{3L} - \frac{2gL}{30}\right) \\ \left(\frac{-8k}{3L} - \frac{2gL}{30}\right) & \left(\frac{7k}{3L} - \frac{4gL}{30}\right) \end{bmatrix} \begin{Bmatrix} u_2 \\ u_3 \end{Bmatrix} = \begin{Bmatrix} 0 \\ 0 \end{Bmatrix} + \frac{L^2}{6} \begin{Bmatrix} 2 \\ 1 \end{Bmatrix}$$

$$-u_1 \begin{Bmatrix} \left(\frac{-8k}{3L} - \frac{2gL}{30}\right) \\ \left(\frac{k}{3L} + \frac{gL}{30}\right) \end{Bmatrix} = \frac{L^2}{6} \begin{Bmatrix} 2 \\ 1 \end{Bmatrix}.$$

For numerical values of $k = g = L = 1$ and $u_1 = 0$

$$\frac{1}{30} \begin{bmatrix} 144 & -82 \\ -82 & 66 \end{bmatrix} \begin{Bmatrix} u_2 \\ u_3 \end{Bmatrix} = \begin{Bmatrix} 0 \\ 0 \end{Bmatrix} + \frac{1}{6} \begin{Bmatrix} 2 \\ 1 \end{Bmatrix} - (0) \frac{1}{30} \begin{Bmatrix} -82 \\ 11 \end{Bmatrix} = \frac{1}{6} \begin{Bmatrix} 2 \\ 1 \end{Bmatrix}.$$

The numerical inversion gives

$$\begin{Bmatrix} u_2 \\ u_3 \end{Bmatrix} = \frac{1}{2780} \begin{bmatrix} 66 & 82 \\ 82 & 144 \end{bmatrix} \begin{Bmatrix} 10 \\ 5 \end{Bmatrix}$$

$$= \begin{Bmatrix} 0.3849 \\ 0.5540 \end{Bmatrix}, \quad \text{with} \begin{Bmatrix} u_2 \\ u_3 \end{Bmatrix}_{\text{exact}} = \begin{Bmatrix} 0.3873 \\ 0.5574 \end{Bmatrix}.$$

Substituting these numerical values into the first row to recover the left end reaction:

$$0 + \left(\frac{k}{3L}[-8] - \frac{gL}{30}[2]\right) u_2 + \left(\frac{k}{3L}[1] - \frac{g\,L}{30}[-1]\right) u_3 = \frac{-k\, du(0)}{dx} + 0$$

$$0 - 2.7333\, u_2 + 0.3666\, u_3 = 0 - 1\partial u(0)/\partial x,$$

so the approximate left reaction is $\partial u(0)/\partial x = +0.8489$ and the exact reaction is $+0.8508$. Recall that for this example the NBC was only enforced weakly. The end slope of the computed approximate solution is not zero. The slope error on the right can be reduced by introducing additional elements. In contrast, the inaccurate gradient of the interpolated solution at the endpoint is found from the interpolated solution:

$$\frac{\partial u(r)}{\partial x} = \frac{\partial \boldsymbol{H}(r)}{\partial x}\boldsymbol{u}^e = \frac{1}{L}\frac{\partial \boldsymbol{H}(r)}{\partial r}\boldsymbol{u}^e$$

$$\frac{\partial u(r)}{\partial x} = \frac{1}{L}\left[(4r-3)\ (4-8r)\ (4r-1)\right]\begin{Bmatrix} u_1 \\ u_2 \\ u_3 \end{Bmatrix}.$$

For the endpoint at $x = L$, the parametric coordinate is $r = 1$ and the physical gradient in the adjacent element is

$$\frac{\partial u(1)}{\partial x} = \frac{1}{1}[1 \quad -4 \quad 3]\begin{Bmatrix} 0 \\ 0.3849 \\ 0.5540 \end{Bmatrix} = +0.1224,$$

instead of the natural BC value of zero. It was noted previously NBCs are invoked "weakly" through the integral form and that mesh control adjacent to an NBC region can reduce the difference between the NCB specified value and the gradient found in the adjacent element.

Example 8.3-8 Given: Replace the natural BC at the right end of the Example 8.3-7 with a non-zero NBC at the right end that corresponds to the slope that the exact solution should have. That is, set $\partial u(1)/\partial x = du^*(1)/dx = \cos(1)/\sin(1) - 1 = -0.3579$.

Solution: The system matrix NBC/reaction vector is

$$\boldsymbol{c}_{\text{NBC}} = \begin{Bmatrix} -k\,du(0)/dx \\ 0 \\ k(-0.3579) \end{Bmatrix}.$$

Enforcing that u_1 is known; again retain the lower partition of two rows:

$$\begin{bmatrix} \left(\frac{16k}{3L} - \frac{16gL}{30}\right) & \left(\frac{-8k}{3L} - \frac{2gL}{30}\right) \\ \left(\frac{-8k}{3L} - \frac{2gL}{30}\right) & \left(\frac{7k}{3L} - \frac{4gL}{30}\right) \end{bmatrix} \begin{Bmatrix} u_2 \\ u_3 \end{Bmatrix} = \begin{Bmatrix} 0 \\ -0.3579\,k \end{Bmatrix}$$

$$+\frac{L^2}{6}\begin{Bmatrix} 2 \\ 1 \end{Bmatrix} - u_1 \begin{Bmatrix} \left(\frac{-8k}{3L} - \frac{2gL}{30}\right) \\ \left(\frac{k}{3L} + \frac{gL}{30}\right) \end{Bmatrix}.$$

Substituting the current numerical values of $k = g = L = 1$ and $u_1 = 0$ gives

$$\begin{Bmatrix} u_2 \\ u_3 \end{Bmatrix} = \begin{Bmatrix} 0.0682 \\ -0.0022 \end{Bmatrix}, \quad \text{with} \quad \begin{Bmatrix} u_2 \\ u_3 \end{Bmatrix}_{\text{exact}} = \begin{Bmatrix} 0.0697 \\ 0 \end{Bmatrix},$$

and the left reaction is recovered from the first row, as above, as $\partial u(0)/\partial x = +0.1872$, which compares well to the exact value of $+0.1884$.

8.4 Mixed Boundary Conditions

Any ODE can be subject to a natural BC of the mixed type:

$$K_n \partial u/\partial n + c\,u = b. \tag{8.4-1}$$

These are generally known as Robin conditions (RBC) or Cauchy conditions. This RBC type of non-essential BC introduces both a boundary square matrix and a column matrix. It will be shown later that their general forms on a surface Γ^b are

$$\boldsymbol{S}^b = \int_\Gamma^b \boldsymbol{H}^b(r)^T c(r) \boldsymbol{H}^b(r) d\Gamma^b, \quad \mathbf{c}^b = \int_\Gamma^b \boldsymbol{H}^b(r)^T b(r) d\Gamma^b. \tag{8.4-2}$$

In this chapter, the focus is on the form of the degenerate one-dimensional case where the boundary domain, Γ^b, is the element cross-sectional area at an endpoint. Then the domain end surface, Γ^b, is just the cross-sectional area at the endpoint of the one-dimensional line element, say A_n^b. Usually, that area is included in the ODE as a coefficient. If not, it defaults to unity. Also, recall that all Lagrangian interpolations take on the value of unity when evaluated at a node (and are zero at all other nodes). Let r_n be the parametric coordinate of any node where the mixed RBC is specified at the end of a one-dimensional mesh. Then, these two boundary matrices degenerate to 1×1 arrays (scalars) because at either end node $\boldsymbol{H}^b(r_n) \equiv 1$:

$$\boldsymbol{S}^b = \int_{\Gamma_n{}^b} \boldsymbol{H}^b(r_n)^T c(r_n) \boldsymbol{H}^b(r_n)\, d\Gamma^b, \quad \boldsymbol{c}^b = \int_{\Gamma_n{}^b} \boldsymbol{H}^b(r_n)^T b(r_n) d\Gamma^b,$$

$$\boldsymbol{S}^b = \int_{\Gamma_n{}^b} 1 \times c(r_n) \times 1\; d\Gamma^b = c(r_n) \int_{\Gamma_n{}^b} d\Gamma^b, \tag{8.4-3}$$

$$\boldsymbol{c}^b = \int_{\Gamma_n{}^b} 1 \times b(r_n) d\Gamma^b = b(r_n) \int_{\Gamma_n{}^b} d\Gamma^b,$$

$$\boldsymbol{S}^b = c(r_n) A_n^b, \quad \boldsymbol{c}^b = b(r_n) A_n^b. \tag{8.4-4}$$

Therefore, in one-dimensional applications both of the RBC square and column matrices contain only a single term. The $\boldsymbol{S}^b$ matrix is scattered (added to) the nth diagonal term in the system matrix, $\boldsymbol{S}$, and $\boldsymbol{c}^b$ is scattered to the nth row of system array $\boldsymbol{c}$, where n is the endpoint degree of freedom number. Note that if the boundary data term $c(r)$, like a heat convection coefficient, is zero, then only the source resultant, $\boldsymbol{c}^b$, is present. Likewise, if the boundary source data term $b(r)$ is also zero, like for an insulated surface, then neither boundary matrix exists. In FEA, this common special case is called a "natural boundary condition" (NatBC) because it requires no action on the part of the analysts because the integral is identically zero and it is the default BC in many applications.

A common NBC is a convection BC over the area, A, at one or both ends of a one-dimensional model: $-K_n \partial u/\partial n = h(u - u_\infty)$, Then $c = -Ah$, and $b = -Ahu_\infty$ in (8.4-1). One of the simplest examples of (8.1-1) subject to a Robin BC is the common thermal analysis involving heat transfer through a wall with fluid convection of temperature u_∞ on the exterior and interior sides. If the wall is homogeneous, then its temperature change is linear and a single two-node conduction element, $\boldsymbol{S}^e$, gives the exact conduction solution. On each pair of the convecting faces, the RBC gives a pair of point boundary matrices, $\boldsymbol{S}^b$ and $\boldsymbol{c}^b$. Assembling the single conduction element and the two pairs of RBC elements with

$$\boldsymbol{S}^e = \frac{k\,A}{L}\begin{bmatrix} 1 & -1 \\ -1 & 1 \end{bmatrix}, \; \boldsymbol{S}_1^b = [A\,h_1], \; \boldsymbol{c}_1^b = \{A\,h_1\,u_{\infty 1}\},$$

etc. gives the exact system matrices:

$$\begin{bmatrix} (k\,A/L + A\,h_1) & -k\,A/L \\ -k\,A/L & (k\,A/L + A\,h_2) \end{bmatrix} \begin{Bmatrix} u_1 \\ u_2 \end{Bmatrix} = \begin{Bmatrix} A\,h_1\,u_{\infty 1} \\ A\,h_2\,u_{\infty 2} \end{Bmatrix}.$$

Each of the two convection relations acts as an indirect EBC with the fluid temperature, u_∞, which causes the square matrix to be non-singular. Inverting gives the two exact surface temperatures in terms of the two surrounding air temperatures.

After the following related examples, the next two sections will introduce automating temperatures:

$$\begin{Bmatrix} u_1 \\ u_2 \end{Bmatrix} = \frac{1}{k(h_1 + h_2) + Lh_1h_2} \begin{Bmatrix} k\,(h_1u_{\infty_1} + h_2u_{\infty 2}) + Lh_1h_2u_{\infty_1} \\ k\,(h_1u_{\infty_1} + h_2u_{\infty_2}) + Lh_1h_2u_{\infty_2} \end{Bmatrix}.$$

Lagrange element solutions, respectively.

A similar NBC is that of heat transfer by radiation. Then the Kelvin (absolute) temperatures, $^\circ K$, must be used in the model and the normal heat flux at the surface is

$$-K_n\partial u/\partial n = \varepsilon\sigma(u^4 - u_\infty^4),$$

where ε is the emissivity of the surface, σ is the Stefan–Boltzmann constant, and u_∞ is the known absolute temperature of the irradiating body. The presence of radiation makes the problem nonlinear and requires other solution methods not considered here. Radiation can be recast into an iterative linear convection solution by rewriting the source as

$$-K_n\partial u/\partial n = \varepsilon\sigma(u^4 - u_\infty^4) = \varepsilon\sigma[t(u^2 - u_\infty^2)(u + u_\infty)](u - u_\infty)$$
$$-K_n\partial u/\partial n = h_r(u - u_\infty), \; h_r \equiv \varepsilon\sigma[(u_-^2 - u_\infty^2)(u_- + u_\infty)],$$

where h_r is the fake convection coefficient for the next iteration, and u_- is the approximate surface temperature calculated in the previous iteration.

Example 8.4-1 Given: A fin extends from a hot wall and convects heat away through its perimeter and end surfaces. Use four two-noded linear elements to approximate the temperature, $u(x)$, in the axial direction. The governing one-dimensional ODE is

$$k\,A\,\frac{d^2u}{dx^2} - h\,P\,u + h\,P\,u_\infty = 0,$$

where $k = 3\,W/\text{cm}\,^\circ\text{C}$ is the thermal conductivity of the material, $A = 4\,\text{cm}^2$ is the fin cross-sectional area (and free end area), which has a perimeter of $P = 10\,\text{cm}$, and the temperature of the surrounding fluid is $u_\infty = 20^\circ\text{C}$. The convection coefficient along the length and on the end area is $h = 0.1\ W/\text{cm}^{2\,\circ}\text{C}$. The EBC is the wall temperature at $u(x = 0) = 80^\circ\text{C}$. The convection loss at the free end area at $x = L = 8\,\text{cm}$ is given by an NBC of the mixed kind $-\,k\,Adu/dx = h\,A(u - u_\infty)$.

Solution: From the previous ODE, and the chapter summary, the conduction matrix and convection matrix in each element, for a uniform mesh, are

$$\boldsymbol{K}^e = \frac{k^e A^e}{L^e}\begin{bmatrix} 1 & -1 \\ -1 & 1 \end{bmatrix} W/^\circ\text{C}, \quad \text{and} \quad \boldsymbol{M}^e = \frac{h^e P^e L^e}{6}\begin{bmatrix} 2 & 1 \\ 1 & 2 \end{bmatrix} W/^\circ\text{C},$$

and they combine to form the net element square matrix $\boldsymbol{S}^e = [\boldsymbol{K}^e + \boldsymbol{M}^e]$. The element source vector gives the resultant of the heat flow into or out of the perimeter surface of the line elements

$$\boldsymbol{C}^e = \frac{h^e P^e L^e u_\infty^e}{2}\begin{Bmatrix} 1 \\ 1 \end{Bmatrix}\text{W}.$$

The MBC (element) at the end leads to a point boundary square matrix and point column matrix of: $\boldsymbol{S}^b = h^b A^b\ W/^\circ\text{C}$, and $\boldsymbol{C}^b = h^b A^b u_\infty^b$ W. The line elements all have the same size and properties, with $L^e = L/4$ so:

$$\boldsymbol{K}^e = 6\begin{bmatrix} 1 & -1 \\ -1 & 1 \end{bmatrix} W/^\circ\text{C}, \quad \boldsymbol{M}^e = \frac{2}{6}\begin{bmatrix} 2 & 1 \\ 1 & 2 \end{bmatrix} W/^\circ\text{C},$$

$$\boldsymbol{S}^e = \boldsymbol{K}^e + \boldsymbol{M}^e = \frac{1}{6}\begin{bmatrix} 40 & -34 \\ -34 & 40 \end{bmatrix} W/^\circ\text{C},$$

$$\boldsymbol{C}^e = 20\begin{Bmatrix} 1 \\ 1 \end{Bmatrix}\text{W},$$

and for the last point element at node 5 $\boldsymbol{S}^b = 0.4\ W/^\circ\text{C}$, $\boldsymbol{C}^b = 8$ W. The mesh connection and properties data for four line elements and one point element are

El °C	**Type**	**Node 1**	**Node 2**	$\boldsymbol{k}$ **(W/cm°C)**	$\boldsymbol{A}$ **(cm^2)**	$\boldsymbol{h}$ **(W/cm^2 °C)**	$\boldsymbol{P}$ **(cm)**	u_∞
1	1	1	2	3	4	0.1	10	20
2	1	2	3	3	4	0.1	10	20
3	1	3	4	3	4	0.1	10	20
4	1	4	5	3	4	0.1	10	20
5	2	5	**0**	0	4	0.1	0	20

For the above connection list, the assembled system matrix (with the reaction from the EBC) becomes

$$\frac{1}{6}\begin{bmatrix} 40 & -34 & 0 & 0 & 0 \\ -34 & (40+40) & -34 & 0 & 0 \\ 0 & -34 & (40+40) & -34 & 0 \\ 0 & 0 & -34 & (40+40) & -34 \\ 0 & 0 & 0 & -34 & (40+0.4) \end{bmatrix} \begin{Bmatrix} u_1 = 80 \\ u_2 \\ u_3 \\ u_4 \\ u_5 \end{Bmatrix} =$$

$$\begin{Bmatrix} 20 \\ (20+20) \\ (20+20) \\ (20+20) \\ (20+8) \end{Bmatrix} + \begin{Bmatrix} -kAdu/dx(0) \\ 0 \\ 0 \\ 0 \\ 0 \end{Bmatrix}.$$

Enforcing the EBC, the independent equations for the temperature are the bottom four rows:

$$\frac{1}{6}\begin{bmatrix} 80 & -34 & 0 & 0 \\ -34 & 80 & -34 & 0 \\ 0 & -34 & 80 & -34 \\ 0 & 0 & -34 & 42.4 \end{bmatrix} \begin{Bmatrix} u_2 \\ u_3 \\ u_4 \\ u_5 \end{Bmatrix} = \begin{Bmatrix} 40 \\ 40 \\ 40 \\ 28 \end{Bmatrix} + \begin{Bmatrix} 0 \\ 0 \\ 0 \\ 0 \end{Bmatrix} - \frac{80}{6}\begin{Bmatrix} -34 \\ 0 \\ 0 \\ 0 \end{Bmatrix}$$

$$= \frac{1}{6}\begin{Bmatrix} 2960 \\ 240 \\ 240 \\ 168 \end{Bmatrix}.$$

The finite element values and the reported exact hyperbolic cosine solution values are

$$\begin{Bmatrix} u_2 \\ u_3 \\ u_4 \\ u_5 \end{Bmatrix} = \begin{Bmatrix} 53.95 \\ 39.87 \\ 32.81 \\ 30.27 \end{Bmatrix} {}^\circ\text{C}, \quad \begin{Bmatrix} u_2 \\ u_3 \\ u_4 \\ u_5 \end{Bmatrix}_{\text{exact}} = \begin{Bmatrix} 54.3 \\ 40.2 \\ 33.2 \\ 30.6 \end{Bmatrix} {}^\circ\text{C}.$$

The pricewise linear finite element approximation is graphed in Fig. 8.4-1. The reaction at the wall (heat flow into the fin) is obtained from the first row of the matrix system:

$$\frac{1}{6}\begin{bmatrix} 40 & -34 & 0 & 0 & 0 \end{bmatrix} \boldsymbol{u}^T = \{20\} - \{k(0)A(0)du/dx(0)\},$$

$$\frac{1}{6}[40(80)-34(53.95)+0+0+0]-20) = 207.64\,\text{W} = \frac{k(0)A(0)du}{dx(0)} \equiv Q_0.$$

The heat flow needed to maintain the required wall EBC of 80°C is about 207.6 W.

Example 8.4-2 Given: Post-process Example 8.4-1 to verify the conservation of the heat flow in the convecting fin solution.

Solution: The prior reaction shows that $207.64\,\text{W} \equiv Q_0$ of heat flow entered into the fin. An equal total amount must flow out from the convection surfaces. Along the length of a line element, the amount of heat flow per unit length due to convection is the temperature difference times the surface area times the convection coefficient $dQ = h^e P^e (u(x) - u_\infty) dx$. Integrating over the length of the element, the increment of heat loss (or gain) is

$$\Delta Q^e = \int_{L^e} h^e P^e (u(x) - u_\infty) dx.$$

The temperature difference is $u(x) - u_\infty = \boldsymbol{H}(r)\boldsymbol{u^e} - u_\infty = \boldsymbol{H}(r)\{\boldsymbol{u^e} - \boldsymbol{u_\infty}\}$. For a typical line element, the resulting heat flow through the surface is

$$\Delta Q^e = \int_{L^e} h^e P^e \boldsymbol{H}(r) dx \{\boldsymbol{u}^e - \boldsymbol{u}_\infty\}$$
$$= \int_0^1 h^e P^e \boldsymbol{H}(r) L^e dr \{\boldsymbol{u}^e - \boldsymbol{u}_\infty\}.$$

This defines a rectangular post-processing array that gives the heat flow through the surface of a line element as a matrix dot product:

$$\Delta Q^e = h^e P^e L^e \, \boldsymbol{R}^e \{\boldsymbol{u}^e - \boldsymbol{u}_\infty\}, \quad \boldsymbol{R}^e \equiv \int_0^1 \boldsymbol{H}(r) dr,$$

for any type of line element. For the linear element used in the prior example, $\boldsymbol{R}^e = \begin{bmatrix} 1 & 1 \end{bmatrix} / 2$. Substitute the numerical values from the prior example, at element 1: Gather the element DOFs,

$$\boldsymbol{u}^e = \begin{Bmatrix} 80 \\ 53.95 \end{Bmatrix} {}^\circ\mathrm{C}, \text{ thus } \{\boldsymbol{u}^e - \boldsymbol{u}_\infty\} = \begin{Bmatrix} 60 \\ 33.95 \end{Bmatrix} {}^\circ\mathrm{C},$$

$$\Delta Q^{e=1} = (0.1\mathrm{W/cm^{2\circ}})(10\,\mathrm{cm})(2\,\mathrm{cm})\frac{1}{2}[1\ 1] \begin{Bmatrix} 60 \\ 33.95 \end{Bmatrix} {}^\circ\mathrm{C} = 93.95\,\mathrm{W}.$$

Likewise, for the other elements: $\Delta Q^{e=2} = 53.82\,\mathrm{W}$, $\Delta Q^{e=3} = 32.68\,\mathrm{W}$, $\Delta Q^{e=4} = 23.09\,\mathrm{W}$. For the end surface (point element 5), the increment in heat flow is $\Delta Q^b = h^b A^b \{u^b - u_\infty\}$. For that point element the connection list gives $u^b = u_5 = 30.27^\circ\mathrm{C}$ and the

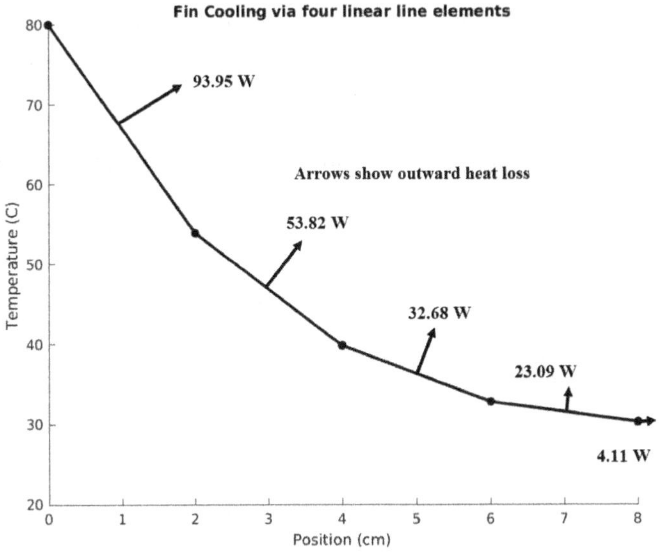

Fig. 8.4-1: Heat flow conservation in a cooling fin.

incremental heat flow contribution is

$$\Delta Q^b = (0.1\text{W/cm}^{2\,\circ}\text{C})(4\,\text{cm}^2)(30.27 - 20)^\circ\text{C} = 4.110\,\text{W}.$$

Summing all of the convection heat flows gives an outflow of $\Delta Q = 207.64\,\text{W}$. That exactly matches the amount of heat flowing into the fin at the EBC. Therefore, conservation of the heat flow is verified. These approximate outward heat flows are shown as arrows in Fig. 8.4-1.

Example 8.4-3 Given: A fin, with the same thermal properties and geometry as in Example 8.4-1, is one of many attached to a large diameter pipeline. Knowing the total heat flow ejected by the pipe and dividing that value by the number of identical fins it is determined that the heat flow into each fin is 207.6418 W. Solve for the temperature along the typical fin and verify conservation of heat flow.

Solution: In other words, the NBC $-kA\,du/dx(0) = 207.6418\,\text{W}$ has replaced the given temperature EBC at the left end of the fin. The right end surface still has the mixed NBC of $-k\,Adu(L)/dx =$

$h\,A(u - u_\infty)$. At first glance, since u_1 is now unknown, it appears that this problem has no EBC. However, all the elements are dependent on the given value of the surrounding fluid (air) temperature, u_∞. Specifying the value of the temperature u_∞ supplies an indirect EBC. Therefore, the previous full set of five equations, with the addition of one 207.6418 W term, is solved:

$$\frac{1}{6}\begin{bmatrix} 40 & -34 & 0 & 0 & 0 \\ -34 & 80 & -34 & 0 & 0 \\ 0 & -34 & 80 & -34 & 0 \\ 0 & 0 & -34 & 80 & -34 \\ 0 & 0 & 0 & -34 & 40.4 \end{bmatrix} \begin{Bmatrix} u_1 \\ u_2 \\ u_3 \\ u_4 \\ u_5 \end{Bmatrix} = \begin{Bmatrix} 20 \\ 40 \\ 40 \\ 40 \\ 28 \end{Bmatrix} + \begin{Bmatrix} 207.6418 \\ 0 \\ 0 \\ 0 \\ 0 \end{Bmatrix}$$

$$\rightarrow \begin{Bmatrix} u_1 \\ u_2 \\ u_3 \\ u_4 \\ u_5 \end{Bmatrix} = \begin{Bmatrix} 80.0000 \\ 53.9456 \\ 39.8719 \\ 32.8119 \\ 30.2737 \end{Bmatrix},$$

and the temperatures and outflowing heat values are still the same as in Fig. 8.4-1.

Example 8.4-4 Given: The ODE for a vertical pile in soil for partially supporting a structure is

$$-\frac{d}{dz}\left[E(z)A(z)\frac{du(z)}{dz}\right] + p(z)\,k(x)[u(z) - u_\infty] + w(z) = -0.$$

where all the data can vary with the vertical location, z. Those data are: u_∞ = a known settlement (almost always zero) measured at a radial location considered to be at infinity [m], E = casing elastic modulus [N/m^2], γ = casing weight per unit volume [N/m^3], A = cross-sectional area of the casing [m^2], p = outer perimeter of the casing [m], k = the foundation modulus of the soil [N/m^2/m] (zero if not in contact with p), and w = the vertical line load per unit length on the pile; usually $w = \gamma A$ [N/m]. Point forces [N] are a special case of the axial line load $w(z)$ and can also be applied at any point along the pile (but that requires an element interface there). The bottom end of the pile ($z = L$) is subject to the mixed NBC: $EAdu/dz = k\,A(u - u_\infty)$. Determine the vertical displacement, $u(z)$, along the pile for a specified top load. Also post-process each element to determine how much of the axial load is taken out (through shear stress around the perimeter) and transferred to the soil.

Solution: The top end of the pile ($z = 0$) is subject to a specified vertical force (NBC) of $-EAdu/dz = P(0)$. This structural problem is just like the fin thermal Example 8.4-1, since the two ODEs are the same. Just the physical meanings of the data and the computed solution differ. Therefore, the solution, for constant properties, is going to be analogous to the fin results plotted in Fig. 8.4-1. The solid line temperature becomes the vertical displacement of the pile. The leftmost heat inflow corresponds to the applied vertical load. That load must be equal and opposite to the tangential shear forces the soil applies to the elements. In the fin figure, the heat-out arrows perpendicular to the fin line elements are replaced by resisting shear forces tangent to the vertical line elements. Finally, at the right end of the mesh, the last pile node has a vertical displacement that is resisted by the end surface vertical force indicated by the smallest arrow.

8.5 Automating Lagrange Element Solutions

At this point, the automation of this type of solution and its generalization to higher-dimensional applications is anticipated by beginning a general Matlab script for the solution of linear finite element simulations. The solution employs matrix notation and several different arrays are required. The sizes of all of those arrays can be defined by a few control integers. Establishing a script using those few control integers allows this implementation to be valid for one-, two-, and three-dimensional domains as well as allowing for analytically or numerically integrated element arrays. To provide the reader with a general-purpose finite element system, a library of modular functions was developed around a set of application control integers. This allows for efficient allocation of the required memory and useful logic branches in the modules. The primary control integers are:

$n\_b \longleftrightarrow n_b \equiv$ Number of boundary segments
$n\_d \longleftrightarrow n_d \equiv$ Number of system unknowns $= n\_g \times n\_m$
$n\_e \longleftrightarrow n_e \equiv$ Number of elements
$n\_g \longleftrightarrow n_g \equiv$ Number of generalized DOF per node
$n\_i \longleftrightarrow n_i \equiv$ Number of unknowns per element $= n\_g \times n\_n$
$n\_m \longleftrightarrow n_m \equiv$ Number of mesh nodes
$n\_n \longleftrightarrow n_n \equiv$ Number of nodes per element
$n\_p \longleftrightarrow n_p \equiv$ Dimension of parametric space
$n\_q \longleftrightarrow n_q \equiv$ Number of total quadrature points
$n\_r \longleftrightarrow n_r \equiv$ Number of rows in the $\boldsymbol{B}^e$ matrix (and material matrix)
$n\_s \longleftrightarrow n_s \equiv$ Dimension of physical space.

This is a good point to introduce the first bare-bones Matlab FEA system. As time goes on, some of the manual coding, like hard coding the physical coordinates, will be replaced with scripts that do such tasks in a general and more automated way. In time, a completely automated system will be provided that can be utilized to solve a wide range of applications. Here, the first example of automating an ODE with a Matlab script will be computing the displacement and stress in an elastic bar which is rotating about one end at a constant angular velocity, ω. From physics it is known that the angular velocity causes a radial acceleration component of $a_r = r\omega^2$ which acts on the mass per unit length, $A\rho$, of the bar to cause a radial force per unit length that increases with the radial position, R. The governing differential equation:

$$\frac{d}{dx}\left(E\,A\frac{du}{dx}\right) + A\,\rho\,x\omega^2 = 0, \tag{8.5-1}$$

is subject to the EBC of $u(0) = 0$, and the natural BC that the free end of the bar is stress-free and thus force-free: $EA\,du(L)/dx = 0$. In this example, the material elastic modulus, E, the bar area, A, the mass density, ρ, and the angular velocity, ω, are taken as constants. Thus, the axial load per unit length is proportional to the position $x \equiv r$ and increases linearly from the center of rotation: $f_x = (A\,\rho\omega^2)x \equiv cx$. The ODE is easily integrated to give the exact solution: $u(x) = (L^2x - x^3/3)A\rho\omega^2/2EA$. A single quadratic element will be used to solve for the displacements and stresses which will be compared to the exact values at selected locations. The bar

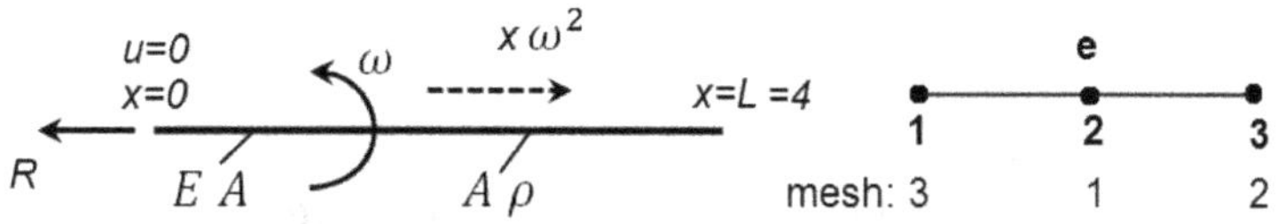

Fig. 8.5-1: Spinning bar and a quadratic element.

```
% The 1D solution of [d/dx (E*A du/dx)] + c*x = 0
% w(x)=c*x Rotating about x=0: c = A*rho*omega^2
% with EBC u(x=0)=0, & Natural BC du(L)/dx=0
% For type 1 stress element with nodes 1---2---3 -->r

%  Set controls and logics
n_e  = 1        ; % number of elements in the mesh
n_g  = 1        ; % number of DOF per node
n_m  = 3        ; % number of nodal points in mesh
n_n  = 3        ; % number of nodes per element
n_p  = 1        ; % dimension of parametric space
n_r  = 1        ; % number of rows in element B_e matrix
n_s  = 1        ; % dimensions of physical space
p_n  = 5        ; % number of post-process points in element
post = 1        ; % turn on(1)/off(0) post-processing option

% Compute derived controls
n_d = n_g * n_m             ; % system degrees of freedom (DOF)
n_i = n_g * n_n             ; % number of DOF per element

% Allocate (main) system memory
Ans    = zeros (n_d, 1)         ; % system results
c      = zeros (n_d, 1)         ; % system force or source
S      = zeros (n_d, n_d)       ; % system stiffness
nodes  = zeros (n_e, n_n)       ; % element node numbers
x      = zeros (n_m, n_s)       ; % system coordinates

% Input coordinates, properties, EBC
nodes = [3, 1, 2]                   ; % mesh connections
x     = [2.0, 4.0, 0.0]             ; % coords, (m)
E_e = 10 ; A_e = 2 ; e_c = 3        ; % (N/m^2) (m^2) (N/m)
EBC_n = 3                           ; % node at EBC
EBC_v = 0                           ; % EBC value (m)
```

Fig. 8.5-2: Assign general control numbers and logic flags, allocate arrays.

is sketched in Fig. 8.5-1 along with a quadratic line element which is used for the cubic solution.

An initial control phase of a script is given in Fig. 8.5-2. Many of the above control integers are manually set, as are the coordinates, the connection list, and the coefficients in the differential equation.

The script is set to run with a single element, but more elements could be run by expanding the coordinates list and adding additional rows to the element connections list. The last data to be manually set in that figure is the node number and value assigned as the essential BC. After the control integers are finalized, the sizes of several arrays can be set in a general way, and that set of arrays can have their memory requirements allocated. That is required in efficient languages, like Fortran 2008, and it is very important in the Matlab scripting environment. Failure to allocate arrays in Matlab scripts drastically reduces the efficiency and increases the run times of the scripts!

Figures 8.5-1 and 8.5-2 contain an example of the fact that an automatic mesh generator assigns node numbers to the created points in a random order. That means when the mesh generator next builds the element connection lists, the nodes assigned to an element usually do not appear as sequential numbers, which contrasts with the element local node numbers. Thus, a beginner in FEA may be confused by the two script lines reading:

$$\text{nodes} = [3, 1, 2]; \quad \%\ \text{mesh connections}$$

$$x = [2.0, 4.0, 0.0]; \quad \%\ \text{coordinates, (m)}.$$

Looking at Fig. 8.5-1, the first node on the element is the first mesh node in the connection list, 3, and the coordinate of the third mesh node is $x = 0.0$. Similarly, the second (mid-point) node on the element is the second mesh node in the connection list, 1, and the coordinate of the first mesh node is $x = 2.0$, and the third local node is at $x = 4.0$. If the connections are manually inserted in a sequential fashion, they could look as follows:

$$\text{nodes} = [1, 2, 3]; \quad \%\ \text{mesh connections}$$

$$x = [0.0, 2.0, 4.0]; \quad \%\ \text{coordinates (m)}.$$

In the next segment of the script, in Fig. 8.5-3, a loop over all the elements (here just one) begins in order to calculate the element arrays and to scatter (assemble) them into the system arrays. The element array memory allocations can be done before that loop if all entries are calculated within the loop. In Fig. 8.5-3, the analytic matrix expressions are used for the stiffness matrix and the resultant load vector from the angular velocity. Those four lines, in the future, can be replaced by a numerical integration loop. Vector subscripts are used to efficiently scatter the element arrays into the system arrays.

In Fig. 8.5-4, the system matrices are modified to enforce the EBCs. The solution is computed, compared to the known exact solution, and printed. The last action in that figure is to recover the

```
%     Allocate and clear element type arrays
c_e   = zeros (n_i,   1)          ; % clear array el sources
S_e   = zeros (n_i, n_i)          ; % clear array el stiffness
x_e   = zeros (n_n, n_s)          ; % element coordinates

for k = 1:n_e  ; % loop over elements ====>> ====>> ====>>
% Gather coordinates, properties, form element arrays
  rows = nodes (k, 1:n_n)         ; % this element connections
  x_e = x (rows)                           ; % gather x-coords
  L_e = max (x_e) - min (x_e)               ; % element length
  S_e = [ 7, -8,  1, ; ...                % stiffness L3_C0 (N/m)
         -8, 16, -8, ; ...
          1, -8,  7 ] * E_e * A_e / (3*L_e) ;
  c_e = e_c * L_e^2 * [0; 2; 1] / 6       ; % spin load force (N)

% Scatter element arrays into system arrays
  % rows = vector subscript converts el to system eq numbers
  S (rows, rows) = S (rows, rows) + S_e (:, :)  ; % add stiff
  c (rows)       = c (rows)       + c_e (:)     ; % add forces
end % for each k element in mesh   <<==== <<==== <<==== <<====
fprintf ('Total spin load = %g \n', sum(c))  % Resultant force
```

Fig. 8.5-3: Set the coefficient data, build element arrays, assemble into system arrays.

```
% Enforce EBC and NBC (natural here), Solve equations
% by trick to avoid partitions, save reaction row first
R_S = S (EBC_n, 1:n_d) ; R_c = c(EBC_n)        ; % for later use
Diag = max ( max (S) )            ; % for better condition number

% Carry known columns*EBC to RHS. Zero that column and row
c (1:n_d) = c (1:n_d) - EBC_v * S (1:n_d, EBC_n)   ; % new RHS
S (1:n_d, EBC_n) = 0 ; S (EBC_n, 1:n_d) = 0        ; % new LHS
%   Insert EBC identity, Diag * EBC_dof = Diag * EBC_value
c (EBC_n)        = Diag * EBC_v                    ; % new RHS
S (EBC_n, EBC_n) = Diag                            ; % new LHS

% Solve the modified system
Ans = S \ c                                        ; % Results
fprintf ('Node, x,      solution    exact \n')       % title
for k = 1:n_m  % for all nodes                       % pretty
  x_p   = x(k)                                     ; % check
  exact = e_c*x_p*(L_e^2-x_p^2 / 3)/2/(E_e*A_e)    ; % check
  fprintf ('%i,  %7.2e,  %8.3e   %8.3e \n', ...
           k, x(k), Ans(k), exact)                   % print
end % for all k system nodes (and 1 DOF)

% Get reaction (NBC) at EBC node (via trick method)
React = R_S * Ans - R_c                           ; % NBC value
fprintf ('\n')
fprintf ('Reaction at node %i = %8.3e \n', EBC_n, React)
```

Fig. 8.5-4: Enforce EBC, solve the system, and recover the reaction.

reaction force required to enforce the zero displacement at the EBC node. That reaction should be equal and opposite to the total axial load imposed on the bar by the centripetal loading. In other words, the reaction will be the opposite of the sum of all of the terms in the assembled load vector, $\boldsymbol{c}$. That sum was created in the last line in Fig. 8.5-3.

In most applications, additional auxiliary variables remain to be computed after the solution and its reactions have been calculated. In this case, the gradient of the displacement solution defines the mechanical strain which is multiplied by the material modulus to obtain the axial stress. Then the stress is multiplied by the geometric area to obtain the axial force.

The optional post-processing is carried out in Fig. 8.5-5. Even though numerical integration was not used to form the system matrices, this script evaluates the solution gradient at quadrature locations since they can be shown to be more accurate. The post-processing steps in Fig. 8.5-5 always require a loop over the elements to gather the element coordinates and the element unknowns. Inside the loop over the elements there is another loop over points interior to the element where the output of the post-processing calculations are desired. Within that loop the script calculates the parametric derivative of the solution, the element Jacobian, the physical derivative of the solution (the mechanical strain), multiplies by the material property, E, to get the stress (force per unit area), and then multiplies by the area, A, to get the axial force in the bar.

In Fig. 8.5-6, the solution, reaction, and post-processing results are printed. The purpose of selecting five interior locations for the stress is to emphasize again that the stress is least accurate at nodes and most accurate on the interior, usually at the Gauss points. In that figure, the Gauss point stress is essentially exact and the nodal stress estimates are about 12% off.

The following examples will show that there are several actions that must be taken to fully automate a FEA. Almost all studies require the input of the location and value of all EBCs. The library of scripts includes *get_ point_sources.m* for that purpose. It reads the text file *msh_load_pt.txt*, which has three columns: the node number where the EBC occurs ($\leq n_m$), the degree of freedom direction ($\leq n_g$), and the value assigned to that generalized force. The user must always specify the coordinates of all of the nodes. Those node

```
if ( post == 1 ) % use computed solution
  p_n = 5                          ; % fake #: 2 interior, 3 nodes
  r_q (5) = 1.0000000000000000000000          ; % right node
  r_q (4) = 0.5000000000000000000000          ; % mid node
  r_q (3) = 0                                 ; % left node
  r_q (2) = 7.8867513459481288225457e-01       ; % from tables
  r_q (1) = 2.1132486540518711774543e-01       ; % from tables

  fprintf ('Post-processing Results (at 2 qp & 3 nodes) \n')
  fprintf ('Elem  x        strain     stress     force  \n')
  fprintf ('Exact x        strain     stress     force  \n')

% Allocate element coordinates and element answers
  x_e   = zeros (n_n, n_s) ; Ans_e = zeros (n_i, 1) ;

  for k = 1:n_e   ; % loop over elements ====>> ====>> ====>>
%   Gather coordinates, properties, form element arrays
    rows  = nodes (k, 1:n_n)        ; % this element connections
    x_e   = x (rows)                ; % gather x-coords
    L_e = max (x_e) - min (x_e)     ; % element length
    Ans_e = Ans (rows)              ; % gather element solution

%   Loop over most accurate points (quadrature) & node points
    for q = 1:p_n ; % loop over points ---> ---> ---> ---> --->
      r = r_q(q)                          ; % non-dimensional pt

      % Find interpolations, local derivatives, and location
      H_q   = [(1-3*r+2*r^2),(4*r-4*r^2),(2*r^2-r)]   ; % L3 C0
      DLH_q = [(-3+4*r), (4-8*r), (4*r-1)]            ; % L3 C0
      x_q   = H_q * x_e'                        ; % physical x (m)

      % Get exact axial strain, stress, and stress
      dudx_e    = e_c*(L_e^2 - x_q^2)/2 /(E_e*A_e)    ; % exact
      stress_e = dudx_e*E_e; force_e = stress_e*A_e   ; % exact

      % Find Jacobian, inverse, physical derivative, stress
      Jac = DLH_q * x_e'                ; % Jacobian
      inv_J = 1 / Jac                   ; % inverse Jacobian
      dudx_q = inv_J * DLH_q * Ans_e    ; % gradient (strain m/m)
      stress_q = E_e * dudx_q           ; % flux (stress N/m^2)
      force_q  = A_e * stress_q         ; % flow (force N)
      fprintf ('%i,    %7.2e  %8.3e  %8.3e  %8.3e \n', ...
            k, x_q, dudx_q, stress_q, force_q)      % FEA values
      fprintf ('%i,    %7.2e  %8.3e  %8.3e  %8.3e \n', ...
            k, x_q, dudx_e, stress_e, force_e)    % exact values
    end % for q selected points  <--- <--- <--- <--- <--- <---
  end % for each k element in mesh   <<==== <<==== <<==== <<====
end % if  use computed solution
```

Fig. 8.5-5: Post-processing the results at selected points.

location inputs are read by script *get_mesh_nodes.m*, which reads those data from the sequential text file *msh_bc_xyz.txt*. The number of lines in that file defines the total number of nodes in the mesh, n_m.

```
% Running gives
Total spin load = 24

Node,   x,          solution     exact
1,   2.00e+00,   2.200e+00    2.200e+00
2,   4.00e+00,   3.200e+00    3.200e+00
3,   0.00e+00,   0.000e+00    0.000e+00

Reaction at node 3 = -2.400e+01

Post-processing Results (at 2 qp & 3 nodes)
Elem   x          strain       stress       force
Exact x           strain       stress       force
1,    8.45e-01   1.146e+00    1.146e+01    2.293e+01 % qp
1,    8.45e-01   1.146e+00    1.146e+01    2.293e+01 % qp
1,    3.15e+00   4.536e-01    4.536e+00    9.072e+00 % qp
1,    3.15e+00   4.536e-01    4.536e+00    9.072e+00 % qp

1,    0.00e+00   1.400e+00    1.400e+01    2.800e+01 % node
1,    0.00e+00   1.200e+00    1.200e+01    2.400e+01 % node
1,    2.00e+00   8.000e-01    8.000e+00    1.600e+01 % node
1,    2.00e+00   9.000e-01    9.000e+00    1.800e+01 % node
1,    4.00e+00   2.000e-01    2.000e+00    4.000e+00 % node
1,    4.00e+00   0.000e+00    0.000e+00    0.000e+00 % node
```

Fig. 8.5-6: Comparison of internal quadrature and node location gradients.

Every application must also specify the node connection lists of all element types (volumes, areas, lines, and/or points). They are read by script *get_mesh_elements.m* from the user-supplied sequential text file *msh_typ_nodes.txt*. The number of lines in that file defines the total number of elements in the mesh, n_e and the number of different types of elements, n_t. The provided general finite element software system allows a mixture of compatible element types to be input. For example, it may contain a mixture of element types; say quadrilaterals and triangles and/or line elements. For a mixed mesh, the connection list must be padded with zeros to assure that the input text file has a constant number of columns (in Matlab, but not in Fortran).

Most problems also have specified properties, or coefficients in the ODE, which are application dependent. Their order of input depends on the person that writes the application script. The script *get_mesh_properties.m* reads the element or type properties from the text file *msh_properties.txt* and counts the number of properties *n_vals* (columns of data) and it counts the number of rows of data, *n_mats*. The number of rows of properties must equal either the number of elements or the number of different types of elements. A mixed mesh can also have different properties for each element type. When needed, the properties list for an element type must be padded with zeros to assure that the input text file has a constant number of columns.

8.6 Numerically Integrated Elements

The discussions in Section 8.2 assumed that the data allowed the closed-form version of the element matrices based on constant properties and a constant geometric Jacobian. When those conditions are not true, then the element matrices must be numerically integrated. Example 8.4-4 illustrated a Matlab script to formulate the constant property version of the more general ODE

$$-\frac{d}{dx}\left[K(x)\,A(x)\frac{du(x)}{dx}\right] + P(x)\,h(x)[u(x) - u_\infty(x)] + Q(x) = -0. \tag{8.6-1}$$

Here, the closed-form element matrices are replaced with a numerical integration loop that forms the element matrices by integrating the element type interpolation functions, their derivatives, and various products thereof. Figure 8.6-1 illustrates the details of that process and should be compared to Fig. 8.2-1.

The preliminary steps include extracting the locations and weights of the integration points. They also open a sequential binary file to store much of the data needed at the integration points to build the element matrices because it so happens that those data are almost always needed again to post-process the solution results.

Within the integration loop the specific quadrature point parametric location and weight are recovered, the interpolation function and its local derivative are numerically evaluated at the point, the physical coordinate of the point is interpolated from the node coordinates (for graphing and post-processing use), the Jacobian matrix is formed numerically as the product of the interpolation derivative at the point times the element's nodal coordinates. The determinant

```
% Element matrices for [d/dx (K*A du/dx)] - h*P (u - u_inf) + Q = 0
%     with properties 1=K, 2=A, 3=h, 4=P, 5=u_inf, 6=Q1 ...

qp_unit = fopen('qp_store.bin','w'); % open file for post-processing
[r_q, s_q, t_q, w_q]=get_quadrature_rule (n_n, n_p, n_q); % get data

for j = 1:n_e    ; % loop over elements ====>> ====>> ====>> ====>>
  e_nodes = nodes (j, 1:n_n)                ; % element connectivity
  xy_e (1:n_n, 1) = x(e_nodes(1:n_n))        ; % x coord at el nodes
  K    = el_prop (1) ; % . . .               % gather all properties
  Q_v = el_prop (6:5+n_n)                     ; % line load at nodes
  KA = K * A ; hP = h * P                     ; % combine properties

%      Numerical Integration of S_e, c_e , in 1D parametric
  for q = 1:n_q  ; % begin quadrature loop ---> ---> ---> ---> --->
    r = r_q (q) ; w = w_q (q)             ; % recover integration data
%       Element scalar interpolation, H and local derivatives DLH
    [H_q, DLH_q] = Lagrange_1D_library (n_n, r)      ; % interpolate
%       Interpolate global position of quadrature point
    xy_q = H_q * xy_e (1:n_n, :)              ; % interpolate global x
%       Compute the geometry mapping data, d_parm to d_physical
    Jacobian = DLH_q * xy_e (1:n_n, 1)           ; % local to physical
    J_det = det (Jacobian); J_Inv = inv (Jacobian); % det & inverse
%       Physical global derivatives of interpolations H are DGH
    DGH_q = J_Inv * DLH_q                          ; % derivatives dH/dx
%              Update element square matrices
    S_e = S_e + (DGH_q'*KA*DGH_q) * J_det * w_q (q)   ; % conduction
%         Generalized mass matrix update (and for variable Q)
    M_g = M_g + (H_q' * H_q) * J_det * w_q (q)        ; % convection
    c_inf = c_inf + hP * u_inf * J_det * w_q (q)    ; % u_inf source
%         save data needed for post-processing stresses
    if ( post == 1 ) % save post-processing data for this point
      fwrite (qp_unit, xy_q,  'double')         ; % save coordinates
      fwrite (qp_unit, KA,    'double')            ; % save material
      fwrite (qp_unit, DGH_q, 'double')            ; % save gradient
    end % if save integration point data for post-processing
  end ; % for q quadratures <--- <--- <--- <--- <--- <--- <--- <---
  c_e = c_inf + M_g * Q_v      ; % u_inf plus line source resultants
  S_e = S_e + hP * M_g      ; % conduction plus convection sq matrix
%   Insert completed element matrices into system matrices . . .
end % for each j element in mesh <<==== <<==== <<==== <<==== <<====
```

Fig. 8.6-1: Loop to automate the integration of the element matrices (see Fig 8.2-1).

and inverse of that Jacobian matrix are also evaluated numerically. Then the physical derivative of the interpolation functions at that point are evaluated by multiplying the numerical value of the Jacobian with the element's nodal coordinates. Then the required element matrix products are multiplied together and post multiplied by the scalar determinant and the scalar integration weight. When the integration loop is completed, the element matrices are complete, in numerical form, and ready to be scattered into the system arrays, as illustrated previously. At the end of the calculations in that figure, the system equations would have to be modified to include the EBCs of the problem to render the system non-singular.

8.6.1 Bars

ODEs with variable coefficients and/or sources usually require numerical integration. Two common applications of second-order ODEs with variable coefficients, which are subsets of (8.2-5), are tapered axial bars and tapered torsional shafts such as that in Fig. 8.6-2. A tapered shape causes their areas, volume, and moments of inertia to vary with the axial location. The bar equation for the axial displacement, $u(x)$ is

$$\frac{d}{dx}\left(E(x)A(x)\frac{du}{dx}\right) + w(x) = 0. \tag{8.6-2}$$

For a circular bar, the cross-sectional area is $A = \pi R^2$, and the force per unit length often includes the member weight, $w(x) = \gamma\, A(x)$ where γ is the specific weight of the material. This describes the elongation, $u(x)$, along a straight line through the centroid of the cross-sectional area of the bar. The post-processing of the displacements is often more important. The gradient of the solution defines the axial strain $\varepsilon(x) = du/dx$, which is constant over the cross-sectional area. The normal stress (force per unit area) which depends on the material's elastic modulus, E, is defined as $\sigma = E\,\varepsilon(x)$ and is also constant over the cross-sectional area. The axial stress is compared to the material's failure stress to verify a reliable bar.

In the common case where there is a constant axial load of P at one end (and the weight is neglected), it is clear from direct physical arguments that the stress can also be written as $\sigma = P/A(x)$, but

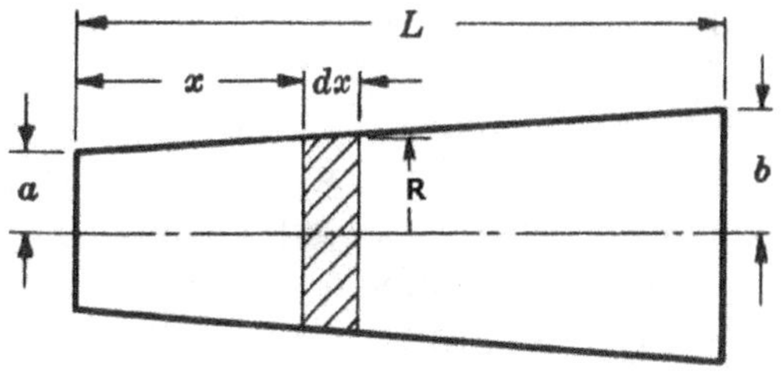

Fig. 8.6-2: Tapered axial bar or torsional shaft.

the displacements would remain unknown. In a finite element model, the gradient is usually only an approximation of the exact gradient.

The generally tapered bar was implemented by using numerical integration and including the variable cross-sectional area. The Matlab script for the numerically integrated variable is similar to the process for constant coefficients in the ODE. The changes in the current Matlab script use a numerical integration loop and interpolate the radius, $R(r)$, from the nodal values to calculate the area at each quadrature point, to optionally include the gravity load, and to determine the system weight and volume as related useful information. The condensed element loop and numerical integration loop to determine those items are given in Fig. 8.6-3.

When all of the calculations in Fig. 8.6-3 have been completed and the full system matrix equations have been assembled, then their EBCs are enforced and the system is finally solved for the value of the axial displacement at each node. The task is not complete since the stress in the bar needs to be compared to the material failure relation. Therefore, the results must be post-processed to find the stress. That requires another loop over every element. In every element, there are an infinite number of axial locations where the stress could be computed. For a fine mesh, the stress in each element should have only a small variation, but the stress must be calculated at least at one location (usually the element centroid) in the element. Much of the data needed to calculate the stress was previously utilized to form the element stiffness matrix for the tapered element. Those data include the elastic modulus of the material, E, the physical derivative of the interpolation function, $d\boldsymbol{H}/dx$, at a small number of integration points within each element. Therefore, most finite element stress models save such data as they are created in the formulation of the stiffness matrix.

In a practical post-processing stress recovery, the script must loop over every element and loop over every numerical integration point of that element. The element loop starts by gathering the node numbers of the element connections and the material properties of that element. The node numbers are used to gather the element coordinates, $\boldsymbol{x}^e$, and to get the equation numbers associated with that element. They in turn are used to gather the now known displacement answers for that element from all of the system displacements, $\boldsymbol{u}^e \subset_e \boldsymbol{u}$. The element displacements, $\boldsymbol{u}^e$, are needed to obtain the element stress

```
%  Tapered Axial Bar: -[E A(x) u']' + w(x) = 0, w(x) = Gamma*A(x)
%    Element properties are: E, Gamma, and the n_n nodal radii
 . . .
%   Get quadrature rule for current element type
[r_q, w_q] = qp_rule_unit_Gauss (n_q)              ; % integration data
volume = 0 ; weight = 0         ; % initialize system volume and weight
for k = 1:n_e; % loop over elements ===>> ====>> ====>> ====>> ====>>
  e_nodes = nodes (k, 1:n_n)                            ; % connectivity
  xy_e (1:n_n, 1) = x(e_nodes(1:n_n))            ; % x coord at el nodes
%   Allocate and clear element type arrays   . . .
% Shorthand el property names              Modulus, Specific Wt, Radii
  E_e          = el_prop (1)                       ; % material modulus
  G_e          = el_prop (2)                 ; % weight per unit volume
  R_e(1:n_n) = el_prop (3:2+n_n)             ; % radius at element nodes
%   Numerical Intergation of S_e, C_e , in 1D parametric space
  e_vol = 0                                ; % initialize element volume
  for q = 1:n_q ; % begin quadrature loop ---> ---> ----> ---> --->
    r = r_q (q) ; w = w_q (q)                ; % recover quadrature data
%   Element scalar interpolation, H, & local derivatives, DLH
    [H_q, DLH_q] = Lagrange_1D_library (n_n, r)           ; % H libary
    xy_q = H_q * xy_e (1:n_n, :)                           ; % global x
    R_q  = H_q * R_e'                                    ; % radius at q
    A_q  = pi() * R_q^2                         ; % cross-sectional area

    Jacobian = DLH_q * xy_e (1:n_n, 1)           ; % geometric Jacobian
    J_det = det (Jacobian)                            ; % J determinant
    J_Inv = inv (Jacobian)                                ; % J inverse
    DGH_q = J_Inv * DLH_q ; [B_q] = DGH_q                   ; % dH / dx

    S_e = S_e + (B_q' * E_e * A_q * B_q)* J_det * w_q (q)    ; % stiff
    C_e = C_e - H_q' * G_e * A_q * J_det * w_q (q)           ; % weight
    e_vol = e_vol + A_q * J_det * w_q (q)          ; % update el volume
%      Save data needed for post-processing . . .
   end % for quadratures point q <--- <--- <--- <--- <--- <--- <---
   volume = volume + e_vol                  ; % update system volume
   weight = weight + e_vol * G_e            ; % update system weight
% Insert completed element matrices into system matrices
   [rows] = get_element_index (n_g, n_n, e_nodes)  ; % eq dof numbers
   S (rows, rows) = S (rows, rows) + S_e ;  % add to system stiffness
   C (rows)        = C (rows)       + C_e     ; % add to system forces
end % for each k element in mesh    <<==== <<==== <<==== <<==== <<====
fprintf ('Total system volume = %g \n', volume)
fprintf ('Total system weight = %g \n', weight)
```

Fig. 8.6-3: Numerical integration of matrices for tapered bar line elements.

and/or the reaction forces at the nodes of the element. Specifically, in the loop over the numerical integration points the axial strain is calculated from $\varepsilon = d\boldsymbol{H}/dx\boldsymbol{u}^e$, using the matrix $d\boldsymbol{H}/dx$ that was saved at that point when forming the stiffness matrix. The physical location of that strain calculation is needed for printing, graphing, or contouring the strain. The axial location is found by interpolation: $x = \boldsymbol{H}(r)\,\boldsymbol{x}^e$. That interpolation $\boldsymbol{H}(r)$ matrix was formed at the same point when it was used to calculate the source vector and to calculate the radius and area of the cross-section; so it too was saved for later post-processing uses. Once the strain is known at the integration point, it is multiplied by the elastic material modulus (matrix) to obtain the stress $\sigma = E\,\varepsilon(x)$, which can likewise be graphed for easier interpretation. The maximum stress found in the bar would be compared to the material yield stress. Those major portions of the post-processing steps are shown in Fig. 8.6-3 and were taken from the application script *Tapered_Axial_Bar.m* that is provided in the application library. Some structural designers would like to optionally obtain the reaction forces, at the nodes of the element, that are required to keep the individual element in equilibrium. Those optional calculations are also shown near the end of Fig. 8.6-3.

8.6.2 Shafts

A related, but slightly more complicated, analysis is that of a tapered torsional shaft. The differential equation for the equilibrium of the angular rotational displacement of a variable radius circular torsional shaft is very similar to that of the variable area bar:

$$\frac{d}{dx}\left(G(x)\,J(x)\frac{d\theta}{dx}\right) + t(x) = 0, \tag{8.6-3}$$

where G is the shear modulus of the material, $G = E/2(1+\nu)$, J is the polar moment of inertia of the cross-section, θ is the small angle of twist per unit length, and $t(x)$ is the torque per unit length. For non-circular cross-section shafts, a two-dimensional PDE is required to solve the torsion problem. Unlike the cylindrical axial bar which has a constant axial strain and stress, the shear strain in a circular shaft is zero at the center and increases to a maximum at the outer radius surface.

The torsional shear strain, γ, is the gradient of the twist angle multiplied by the radius, ρ, to a point: $\gamma = \rho\, d\theta/dx$. The shear stress, τ, acting tangent to the cross-sectional area is the product of the material shear modulus with the shear strain: $\tau = G\gamma = G\,\rho\, d\theta/dx$. So, the torsional shear stress of a circular bar is maximum at its outer surface where $\rho = R$. (Surprisingly, for a non-circular shaft, covered later, the maximum shear stress generally occurs on the exterior surface point that is closest to the centroid of the cross-sectional area.) The maximum shear stress in a shaft element,

$\tau_{\max} = G\,R\,d\theta/dx$, is obtained by post-processing the angular rotations. From the above equations, the shear stress at the radial point is just a fraction of the maximum value, $\tau = \tau_{\max}\,\rho/R$. Another related item is the total torque acting on the cross-section about the center of the circular bar. That torque is the integral over the area of the differential force $dF = \tau(\rho)\,dA$ times its radial lever arm, ρ:

$$T(x) = \int_A \rho\, dF = \int_A \rho\tau(\rho) dA = \int_A \rho^2 (G d\theta/dx)\, dA \equiv G\,J\,d\theta/dx. \tag{8.6-4}$$

The polar inertia of a circular section is $J \equiv \int_A \rho^2\, dA = \int_0^{2\pi}\int_0^R \rho^2\, d\rho(\rho\, d\beta) = \pi R^4/2$ and $d\theta/dx = d\boldsymbol{H}/dx\boldsymbol{\theta}^e$ so the element torque at the section is $T(x) = G\,J\,d\boldsymbol{H}(r)/dx\boldsymbol{\theta}^e$.

The analysis of a tapered torsional shaft shown in Fig. 8.6-1 is best implemented using numerically integrated elements. The Matlab script will be very similar to that for the tapered bar given in Figs. 8.6-2 and 8.6-3. The main difference is that in addition to calculating the area (for optionally finding the shaft volume), the stiffness matrix includes integrating the polar moment of inertia along with the gradient of the interpolation functions. Thus, the tapered shaft element requires more numerical integration points than the tapered bar element. The shaft stiffness matrix for a circular cross-section is

$$\begin{aligned}\boldsymbol{S}^e &= \int_{L^e} \left[\frac{d\boldsymbol{H}(r)}{dx}^T G J(r) \frac{d\boldsymbol{H}(r)}{dx}\right] dx\\ &= \frac{\pi G}{2}\int_{L^e}\left[\frac{d\boldsymbol{H}(r)}{dx}^T R(r)^4 \frac{d\boldsymbol{H}(r)}{dx}\right] dx.\end{aligned} \tag{8.6-5}$$

If the element used to interpolate the twist angle is of degree D and the same polynomial is used to interpolate the radius from the element's node radii, then the polynomial degree of the stiffness matrix integrand is $(D-1)+4D+(D-1) = 6D-2 \le (2n_q - 1)$. That relationship determines the number of quadrature points, n_q, required in the integration loop for each element. For the cubic line element,

$D = 3$, so it requires nine integration points. The Matlab script for the FEA of a tapered bar is easily extended to study a tapered shaft. Relative to Fig. 8.6-2, the changes for the shaft stiffness operations are minor. In the element loop, the first two properties are changed to be the shear modulus and the constant torque per unit length. In the numerical integration loop, the area calculation is followed by the evaluation of the polar inertia moment. In the stiffness matrix product, the $E^e A^e$ term is replaced with $G^e J^e$, and in the source product $\gamma^e A^e$ is simply replaced by any line torque per unit length, t^e. Actually, the varying area calculation is not needed now, but when torsional shaft vibrations are considered later, it will be needed to form the physical mass matrix:

$$\boldsymbol{M}^e = \int_{\mathrm{L}}^{\mathrm{e}} \boldsymbol{H}(r)^{\mathrm{T}} \rho\, A(\mathrm{r}) \;\; \boldsymbol{H}(r) dx,$$

where ρ is the mass density of the material.

The post-processing changes for the shaft compared to Fig. 8.6-3 are only slightly more complicated than for the bar because the strain and stress vary with radial position in the shaft. Therefore, the previously saved maximum radius at the integration point is also recovered. The gradient of the angle of twist is found in the usual way, and it is then multiplied by the radius to obtain the maximum strain. As usual, the stress is obtained by multiplying the material modulus times the strain. Those post-processing changes for a shaft are summarized in Fig. 8.6-4.

There are only a few analytical solutions for tapered shafts. However, the endpoint rotation of a truncated conical shaft, like Fig. 8.6-1, with constant end torques and small radius R_1 and large radius R_2, has been shown to be

$$\theta_1 = \frac{TL}{G\,J_1}\left[\frac{\beta^2 + \beta + 1}{3\beta^3}\right], \;\; \beta = R_2/R_1,$$

where the polar inertia of the small end is $J_1 = \pi R_1^4/2$. Of course, for a cylindrical shaft, these reduce to $\beta = 1$ and $\theta_1 = TL/GJ$. Both analytic solutions can give useful validation checks for a finite element solution. Numerical values must be assigned to the data in order to compare this analytic deflection to a finite element result.

```
fprintf ('Element Post-processing: \n')
for k = 1:n_e ; % loop over elements ====>> ====>> ====>> ====>>
  E_e      = el_prop (1)                          ; material modulus
  e_nodes = nodes (k, 1:n_n)                      ; % connectivity
  [rows]  = get_element_index (n_g, n_n, e_nodes) ; % eq numbers
  Ans_e (1:n_i) = Ans(rows)      ; % gather element displacements

% Recover previously calculated arrays for this element
  for q = 1:n_q ; % begin quadrature loop --> ---> ---> ---> --->
%  Recover previous calculations at this point
    [xy_q] = fread (qp_unit, [1, n_s],    'double'); % get x coord
    [B_q]  = fread (qp_unit, [n_r, n_i], 'double');% get operator

%  Compute the strain (gradient) and stress at this point
    Grad = B_q * Ans_e(1:n_i)'                ;  % gradient (strain)
    Flux = E_e * Grad                            ;  % axial stress

%   List quadrature point results
    if ( show_qp > 0 ) % then list the location, strain, stress
     fprintf ('\n')
     fprintf ('El, Pt, Coordinate    %i, %i, %g \n', k, q, xy_q)
     fprintf ('El, Pt, Gradient      %i, %i, %g \n', k, q, Grad)
     fprintf ('El, Pt, Axial stress  %i, %i, %g \n', k, q, Flux)
    end % if optional print

%  save location and stress for plot programs . . .
  end % for q quadrature points    <--- <--- <--- <--- <--- <---

% Optional output of nodal reaction force on every element
  if ( el_react ) % list the end forces for this element
    C_m = S_e * Ans_e' - C_e  ;
    fprintf ('Reactions at element nodes %i \n', k); disp (C_m')
  end % if el_react list
end % for each k element in mesh      <<==== <<==== <<==== <<====
```

Fig. 8.6-4: Post-processing numerically integrated tapered axial bar.

Example 8.6-1 Given: A tapered steel conical shaft 18 inches long, fixed at one end with radii of 1 and 2 inches, is loaded with an end torque, $T = 10{,}000$ in-lb. Create a Matlab script to model Eq. (8.6-4) with numerically integrated elements. Compare the free end rotation to the analytic value in (8.6-5) and the maximum shear stress from mechanics theory, $\tau = T\,r/J$.

Solution: Two four-noded cubic line elements, formulated with nine integration points each, were chosen. The Matlab script is a minor extension of the tapered axial bar script in Fig. 8.6-2. Line 23, for determining the area, was retained to obtain the volume of the shaft but was supplemented with the polar moment of inertia

```
  for k = 1:n_e ; % loop over elements ====>> ====>> ====>> ====>>
    G_e = el_prop (1)                          ; % get material modulus
    . . .
%   Recover previously calculated arrays for this element . . .
    for q = 1:n_q ; % begin quadrature loop --> --> ---> ---> --->
%     Recover previous calculations at this point  . . .
      [xy_q] = fread (qp_unit, [1, n_s], 'double')  ; % get x coord
      [B_q]  = fread (qp_unit, [n_r, n_i],'double'); % get operator
      [R_q]  = fread (qp_unit, [1, 1], 'double')     ; % get radius
      . . .
%     Compute the gradient, max strain, and max stress
      Grad   = B_q * Ans_e(1:n_i)'                     ;  % gradient
      Strain = R_q * Grad                        ; % maximun shear strain
      Stress = G_e * Strain                      ; % maximun shear stress
      if ( show_qp > 0 ) % then list the gradient and flux
       fprintf ('\n')
       fprintf ('El, Pt, Coordinate   %i, %i, %g \n', k, q, xy_q)
       fprintf ('El, Pt, Shear strain %i, %i, %g \n', k, q, Strain)
       fprintf ('El, Pt, Max stress   %i, %i, %g \n', k, q, Stress)
    end % if optional print
%     Save flux for plot programs . . .
    end ; % for q quadrature points  <--- <--- <--- <--- <--- <---
    . . .
  end % for each k element <<=== <<=== <<==== <<==== <<==== <<====
```

Fig. 8.6-5: Post-processing a tapered torsional shaft.

value:

A_q = pi()*R_q^2;   % area at q

J_q = pi()*R_q^4/2;   % polar moment of inertia.

The stiffness matrix integration simply replaced the elastic modulus, E, with the shear modulus, G, and the cross-sectional area, A_q, with inertia of the cross-section, J_q:

S_e = S_e + **(B_q'*G_e*J_q*B_q)*J_det*w_q(q); % stiffness**.

The post-processing for the shear stresses is a minor modification of the tapered axial bar post-processing quadrature loop in Fig. 8.6-3. The operations are the same; just the variable names have changed since they now have a different physical meaning. The innermost segment of that quadrature point loop is in Fig. 8.6-5.

The numerically integrated elements gave an end twist angle that was accurate to four significant figures. The maximum shear stress from two four-noded cubic elements is shown in Fig. 8.6-6 and is compared to the exact stress (dashed line). The maximum stress error at any integration point differs from the exact value by less than 2%. The graph shows that the element near the small end has the largest stress error and the largest rate of change with position. Clearly

```
%     Compute the generalized gradient and shear stress
      Grad    = B_q * Ans_e(1:n_i)'         ; % twist angle gradient
      strain = R_q * Grad                  ; % shear strain at radius
      shear   = G_e * Grad                  ; % shear stress at radius

%       List quadrature point results
      if ( show_qp > 0 )          ; % then list the gradient and flux
       fprintf ('\n')                                      ; % line feed
       fprintf ('El, Pt, Coordinate     %i, %i, %g \n', k, q, xy_q)
       fprintf ('El, Pt, Shear strain  %i, %i, %g \n', k, q, strain)
       fprintf ('El, Pt, Shear stress  %i, %i, %g \n', k, q, shear)
       stress_T = Tend*R_q/J_q           ; % mechanics Tau = T*radius/J
       fprintf ('            True stress             %g \n', stress_T)
      end                                                   ; % if print
```

Fig. 8.6-6: Partial post-processing for a tapered shaft in torsion.

smaller elements should be used in that region where the mechanics of materials theory shows that the stresses vary most rapidly. (The element shear stress plots in Fig. 8.6-6 do not extend to the ends of the elements because that graph actually shows only straight lines connecting the element shear stress at the nine integration points in each element.)

8.6.3 Hydrodynamic lubrication

Another common mechanical engineering problem with variable coefficients in the differential equation is that of hydrodynamic lubrication by a fluid between two solid surfaces having relative velocities. This simplification of the Navier–Stokes equation to study distributions on the bearing surfaces is Reynolds' Equation in one-dimensional:

$$\frac{d}{dx}\left(\frac{h(x)^3 dP}{6\nu\ dx}\right) - \frac{d(U\ h\,(x))}{dx} = 0, \tag{8.6-6}$$

where Fig. 8.6-8 shows two machine bearing where one component moves near the second component with a relative velocity of U. The gap contains a lubrication fluid of viscosity ν. The gap space, $h(x)$, varies with location and its geometry determines the pressure distribution in the fluid, $P(x)$, relative to the inlet and outlet pressures, which serve as the EBCs. The supported force applied to the top bearing, F, and its location is determined by post-processing integrals of the pressure.

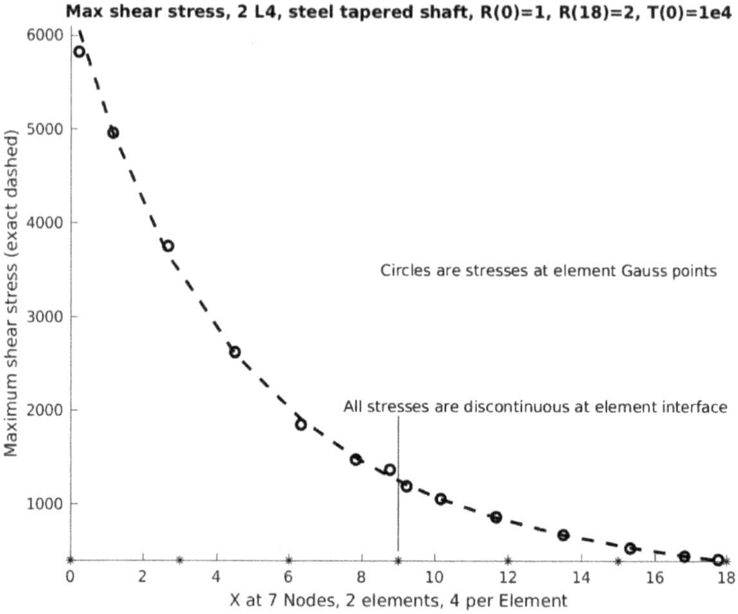

Fig. 8.6-7: Maximum exact (dash) and element shear stress in a tapered shaft.

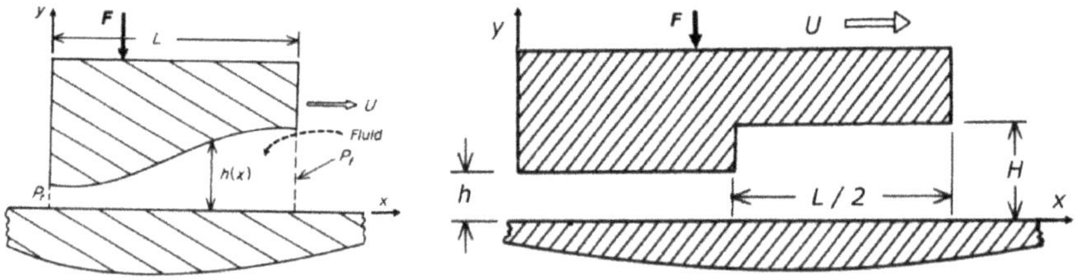

Fig. 8.6-8: General and stepped hydrodynamic bearings.

The gap space can change smoothly and can have discontinuous changes. This is a case where the smooth part of the gap space $h(x)$ can be put in as a fake y-coordinate along with the x-coordinate. Jumps in the gap space can be specified as element data and can be discontinuous between elements. Note that for a one-dimensional-model a smooth region could be modeled with a four-noded cubic element which would interpolate the geometry exactly. Any simpler type of element can still work with reasonable mesh refinement. These elements are almost always numerically integrated. For gap spaces made of constant steps, the two-node linear elements will give the exact solution.

A fairly flexible hydrodynamic lubrication script, *Reynolds_1D_Lub.m*, has been prepared in the Application Library. It allows the film thickness to be specified by the ways mentioned above and contains a fair amount of input data checking features. It accepts any of the Lagrangian line elements given previously, but the cubic is recommended. Of course, it is still necessary to have an element interface at any point where there is a discontinuity in the lubricant film thickness. This application is one where the main interest, after getting an accurate pressure, is integrating the pressure to find what force the bearing resists and where is that force located.

The bearing analysis is one of the rare cases where more than one integral of the computed solution is need in addition to the usual gradient calculation. The supported force components are determined by integrating the pressure over the bearing surface in the direction of the surface unit normal vector, $\vec{\mathbf{n}} = [n_x \; n_y]$. Here, the vertical supported force is

$$F_y = \int_{L^e} n_y(x)p(r)dx = \int_{L^e} n_y(x)\mathbf{H}(r)\{\mathbf{p}\}^e \, dx, \quad F_y = [\boldsymbol{H\_i}]\{\boldsymbol{p}\}^e, \tag{8.6-7}$$

$$[\boldsymbol{H\_i}] \equiv \sum_{q=1}^{n_q} n_y(r_q)\boldsymbol{H}(r_q) \mid J(r_q) \mid \, w_q.$$

In order to locate the supported force, it should be in equilibrium with the moment of the pressure with respect to the coordinate origin. In one dimension, the pressure moment magnitude is

$$M_z = \int_{L^e} x(r)n_y(r)p(r)dx = \int_{L^e} x(r)n_y(r)\mathbf{H}(r)\{\mathbf{p}\}^e \, dx, \tag{8.6-8}$$

$$M_z = [\boldsymbol{H\_ix}]\{\boldsymbol{p}\}^e \quad [\boldsymbol{H\_ix}] \equiv \sum_{q=1}^{n_q} x(r_q)n_y(r_q)\boldsymbol{H}(r_q) \mid J(r_q) \mid \, w_q.$$

Equating the two moments gives the location of the force: $\overline{x} = M_z/F$. For two-dimensional bearings, the y-location would be found in a similar way.

The script was applied here to a bearing with a known analytic solution: the linear slope slider bearing. It will serve to give some insight to this subject that is so important to most lubricated dynamic joints. Since the film thickness is cubed in the ODE coefficient, the spatial distribution of the pressure is expected to also change rapidly. Therefore, four-noded cubic line elements were employed to model the pressure distribution. Once the pressure approximation has been computed, a new post-processing sequence is required. The force supported by the bearing and its location are important features of the bearing and they are found by including the integral of the pressure and its moment in the post-processing loop along the full length of the bearing. The first model used only four equal-length elements. Their pressure distribution and pressure gradient are shown at the top of Fig. 8.6-9. Clearly there are kinks in the

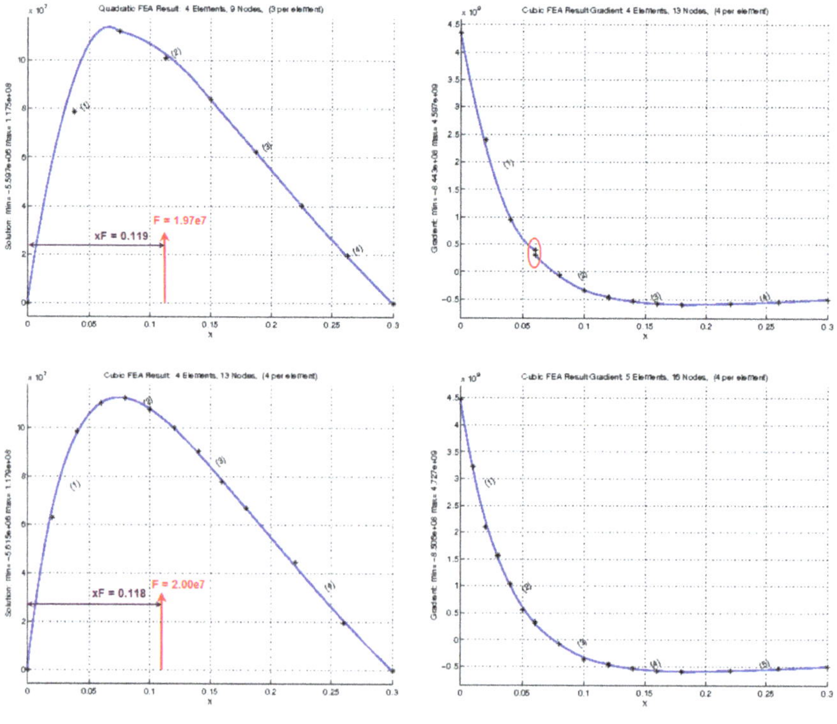

Fig. 8.6-9: Bearing pressure, force, and pressure gradient for 4 (top) and 6 L4.

pressure curve that imply that the mesh was too crude. That problem was clearer in the pressure gradient plot where there appears an obvious jump between elements. There are always such jumps, but with a good mesh they should be small enough not to be detectable by the eye. The next mesh used six equal-length cubic elements and their corresponding results are shown in the lower portion of Fig. 8.6-8. The pressure kinks and the pressure gradient jumps are no longer visible to the eye and the supported force and its location changed by less than 2%. Aspects of the bearing post-processing are given in Fig. 8.6-7.

8.6.4 Variable coefficients

There are some applications where the variable coefficient, $K(x)$, in (8.1-1) moves before the first derivative term. Some examples of that type of model are as follows.

Example 8.6-2 Given: The system $-(1+x^2)\frac{d^2u(x)}{dx^2}+12u+12x(x-1)=0$, subject to the EBCs $u(0)=0$ and $u(1)=2$, has the solution $u(x)=x^4+x$. This form does not match model (8.1-1). It is similar to the form

$$-\kappa(x)\frac{d^2u(x)}{dx^2}+A(x)\frac{du(x)}{dx}+C(x)\ u(x)+Q(x)=0,$$

where the coefficients are $\kappa(x)=(1+x^2), A(x)=0, C(x)=12$, and $Q(x)=12x(x-1)$. Obtain a Galerkin method formulation of this form and compare it to the solution based on the original formulation written as

$$-\frac{d}{dx}\left(1\frac{du(x)}{dx}\right)+\frac{12}{(1+x^2)}u+\frac{12\ x(x-1)}{(1+x^2)}=0.$$

Solution: The finite element model must have a means to receive the spatially varying coefficients. That is most easily done by having each of the variable coefficients input at the nodes of each element as element properties. In a Galerkin method, the difference occurs in the integration-by-parts of the first product:

$$I_{K\kappa} = -\int_0^L [u(x)\kappa(x)] \left[\frac{d^2u(x)}{dx^2}\right] dx$$
$$= -\left[u(x)\kappa(x)\frac{du(x)}{dx}\right]_0^L + \int_0^L \frac{d[u(x)\kappa(x)]}{dx}\left[\frac{du(x)}{dx}\right] dx.$$

The secondary BCs are the same as before, but the remaining integral splits into two integrals;

$$I_\kappa = -\left[u(x)\kappa(x)\frac{du(x)}{dx}\right]_0^L + \int_0^L \frac{du(x)}{dx}\kappa(x)\left[\frac{du(x)}{dx}\right] dx$$
$$+ \int_0^L u(x)\frac{d\kappa(x)}{dx}\left[\frac{du(x)}{dx}\right] dx.$$

The last term is a new non-symmetric matrix containing the gradient of the leading variable coefficient. Its element level contribution is

$$\boldsymbol{G}^e = \int_{L^e} \boldsymbol{H}^{eT} \frac{d\kappa(x)}{dx}\frac{\boldsymbol{dH}^e}{dx} dx,$$

which has the undesirable features of being non-symmetric and needing the derivative of a variable coefficient which might not be known in an analytic form. Of course, if a coefficient is input as nodal data in an element, its derivative can be approximated by the derivative of the interpolated property. The new matrix is like the transpose of matrix $\boldsymbol{U}^e$ of (8.1-2). In other words, referring to (8.1-6), the presence of a non-constant coefficient multiplying the highest derivative will introduce a second non-symmetric element into the system matrix. The assembled system matrix for this less desirable form is $[\boldsymbol{S} + \boldsymbol{G} + \boldsymbol{U} + \boldsymbol{M}]\{\boldsymbol{u}\} = \{\boldsymbol{c}\} + \{\boldsymbol{c}_{NBC}\}$.

Both matrix forms where implemented for variable coefficients input as element nodal properties. The interpolation of the material properties and their use in the numerical integration of the matrices is shown in Fig. 8.6-10. The solutions obtained from the two different approaches, for six quadratic elements, are plotted in Fig. 8.6-11 along with the exact solution. The open circles are from the symmetric solution. The triangles are from the non-symmetric form that is less accurate due mainly to having to approximate the derivative of the $\kappa(x)$ coefficient. When repeated with four cubic elements, the three curves fall on top of each other to three significant figures. Not shown are the two system reaction flux values of -0.9921 and 10.01 units at nodes 1 and 13, respectively.

```
if ( post == 1 )          ; % then post-process all element pressures
 Length     = 0                     ; % initialize total bearing length
 F_integral = 0                     ; % initialize total bearing  force
 M_integral = 0                     ; % initialize total bearing moment

 for k = 1:n_e ; % loop over elements ====>> ====>> ====>> ====>>
   e_nodes = nodes (k, 1:n_n)                     ; % get connectivity
   [rows]  = get_element_index (n_g, n_n, e_nodes) ; % eq numbers
   Ans_e (1:n_i) = Ans(rows)              ; % gather element pressures

 % Recover previously calculated interpolation integrals
   [H_i]  = fread (el_unit, [n_i, 1], 'double')     ; % H integral
   [H_ix] = fread (el_unit, [n_i, 1], 'double')   ; % x*H integral

   for q = 1:n_q ; % begin quadrature loop -> ---> ---> ---> --->
 %   Recover previous calculations at this point  (or re-compute)
     [xy_q] = fread(qp_unit, [1, n_s],    'double'); % get x value
     [B_q]  = fread(qp_unit, [n_r, n_i], 'double')   ; % get dH/dx

     gradient = B_q * Ans_e                     ;  % pressure gradient
     fprintf (q_id, '%g %g \n',  xy_q (1), gradient)   ; % to plot
   end ; % for q quadrature points  <--- <--- <--- <--- <--- <---

   if ( integral == 1 )          ; % add element integrals to system
     F_integral = F_integral + dot (Ans_e, H_i)   ; % add el force
     M_integral = M_integral + dot (Ans_e, H_ix); % add el moment
     Length     = Length + L_e   ; % add element length to bearing
   end                         ; % if pressure integrals are required
 end ; % for each k element in mesh   <<==== <<==== <<==== <<====

 if ( integral == 1 ) ; % report system pressure integral results
   fprintf ('Total vertical force = %g \n', F_integral) % print F
   x_F = M_integral / F_integral            ; % locate F x-coordinate
   fprintf ('Force located at x = %g \n', x_F);% print F location
   fprintf ('Total moment about z = %g \n', M_integral) % print M
   fprintf ('Total bearing length = %g \n', Length)% print length
 end                                ; % if pressure integrals required
end                                   ; % if post-processing required
```

Fig. 8.6-10: Post-processing integrals for a hydrodynamic bearing.

```
for k = 1:n_e ; % loop over elements ====>> ====>> ====>> ====>>
% Allocate and zero element arrays before summations . . .
  e_nodes = nodes (k, 1:n_n)                    ; % get connectivity
  xy_e (1:n_n, 1) = x(e_nodes(1:n_n))      ; % x coord at el nodes
% Get element properties . . .
% Shorthand property names K(x) or k(x), A(x), C(x), Q(x) values
%     class = 0:  -(K(x) u')' + A(x) u' + C(x) u + Q(x) = 0
%     class = 1:    -k(x) u'' + A(x) u' + C(x) u + Q(x) = 0
  Kx (1:n_n) = el_prop (1:n_n)     ; % K or k at each element node
  Ax (1:n_n) = el_prop (n_n+1:2*n_n)      ; % one A value per node
  Cx (1:n_n) = el_prop (2*n_n+1:3*n_n)   ; % one C value per node
  Qx (1:n_n) = el_prop (3*n_n+1:4*n_n)   ; % one Q value per node

% Numerical Intergation of S_e, C_e , in 1D parametric space
  for q = 1:n_q       ; % begin quadrature loop --> ---> ---> --->
    r = r_q (q) ; w = w_q (q)          ; % recover integration data

%   Element scalar interpolation, H, & local derivatives, DLH
    [H_q, DLH_q] = Lagrange_1D_library (n_n, r)      ; % evaluate
    xy_q = H_q * xy_e (1:n_n, :)        ; % quadrature pt location
%   Interpolate four material properties at quadrature point
    Kx_q = H_q * Kx ; Ax_q = H_q * Ax ; % interpolate prop 1 & 2
    Cx_q = H_q * Cx ; Qx_q = H_q * Qx ; % interpolate prop 3 & 4

%   Compute geometry mapping, physical derivative, and operator
    Jacobian = DLH_q * xy_e (1:n_n, 1)     ; % geometric Jacobian
    J_det = det (Jacobian) ; J_Inv = inv (Jacobian); % det & inv
    DGH_q = J_Inv * DLH_q ; [B_q] = DGH_q  ; % for scalars dH/dx

%   Update element diffusion square matrix, from K(x) or k(x)
    S_e = S_e + (B_q' * Kx_q * B_q) * J_det * w_q (q); % conduct
%   Update new element square matrix, if dk(x)/dx terms needed
    if ( class == 1 )    ; % then variable k(x) derivative needed
      dk_q = DGH_q * Kx        ; % approximate derivative of k(x)
      G_e = G_e + (H_q' * dk_q * B_q) * J_det * w_q (q);% varies
    end                        ; % if derivative of k(x) needed

%   Update advection and mass matrices, and source vector
    A_e = A_e + (B_q' * Ax_q * H_q) * J_det * w_q (q) ; % advect
    M_e = M_e + (H_q' * Cx_q * H_q) * J_det * w_q (q); % convect
    C_e = C_e - H_q' * Qx_q * J_det * w_q (q)          ; % source
  end ; % for quadratures <--- <-- <--- <--- <--- <--- <--- <---

% Insert completed element matrices into system matrices
   S_e     = S_e + G_e + A_e + M_e           ; % net square matrix
   [rows] = get_element_index (n_g, n_n, e_nodes) ; % eq numbers
  % rows = vector subscript to convert elem to system eq numbers
   S (rows, rows) = S (rows, rows) + S_e    ; % add to stiffness
   C (rows)        = C (rows)       + C_e   ; % add to sys source
end ; % for each k element in mesh    <<==== <<==== <<==== <<====
```

Fig. 8.6-11: Interpolating variable coefficients for numerical integration.

Example 8.6-3 Given: Use the numerical integration solution of Example 8.6-2

$$-(1+x^2)\frac{d^2u(x)}{dx^2} + 12\,u + 12\,x(x-1) = 0$$

to determine the approximate flux $q(x) = \kappa(x)du(x)/dx = (1+x^2)du(x)/dx$ at each of the integration points of each element. Also, the presence of the convection-like term $C(x)u(x) = 12u$ means that some flux will enter or exit along the length of each element. Determine the flux crossing both ends of each element and estimate each element's external flux gain or loss.

Solution: During the integration loop in Fig. 8.6-13, the value of $\kappa(x)$ at each quadrature point in each element, Kx_q, and its physical location, xy_q, are saved to a binary sequential file along with the physical derivatives of the interpolation matrix, B_q. The graphs of those numerical results are given in Fig. 8.6-14. After completing the element loop, the combined element square matrix, say $\boldsymbol{S}_t^e \equiv \boldsymbol{S}^e+\boldsymbol{G}^e+\boldsymbol{A}^e+\boldsymbol{M}^e$, is saved to another sequential file. After the assembled system equations have been solved, the optional post-processing begins. It repeats the element loop and each quadrature loop. At each point in the quadrature loop the approximate solution gradient, $du/dx_q = \boldsymbol{B}_q^e\boldsymbol{u}^e$, is computed using the previously stored B_q array. Then, the previously stored $Kx\_\,q$ and xy_q values are read from the quadrature loop sequential file and the approximate flux is calculated as $q = Kx\_q\,du/dx_q$ and that value is printed (and saved for plotting) along with its location.

A partial list of those quadrature point flux values are at the top of Fig. 8.6-13. From a portion of that list for the third element, the approximate flux at the first quadrature point is about 1.29 units and increased at the next point. The first quadrature point is the closest to the first node, thus the flux entering the third element should be about that value. The flux leaving the third element will be near the last quadrature point approximate flux value. Their difference will approximate the convective (or elastic foundation) loss or gain along the length.

The most accurate element flux values can be obtained as optional element reactions. Assuming each element is also in equilibrium, its flux reactions are obtained by analogy to the system reactions: $[\boldsymbol{S}^e+\boldsymbol{G}^e+\boldsymbol{A}^e+\boldsymbol{M}^e]\boldsymbol{u}^e=\boldsymbol{c}^e + \boldsymbol{c}_{NBC}^e$ where now every

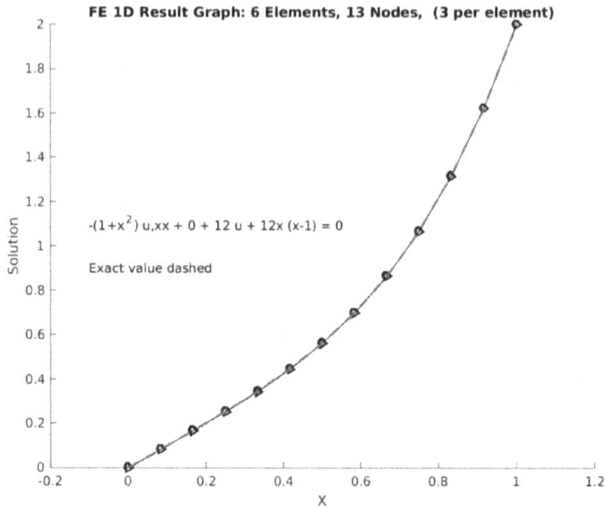

Fig. 8.6-12: Exact, symmetric (o), and non-symmetric FEA solutions.

```
Element Post-processing:
Point location, approximate flux
. . .
El, Pt, Coordinates . 3, 1, 0.34113
El, Pt, Gradient .... 3, 1, 1.15217
Exact Gradient ...... 3, 1, 1.15879
El, Pt, Flux ........ 3, 1, 1.28625

El, Pt, Coordinates . 3, 2, 0.37180
El, Pt, Gradient .... 3, 2, 1.21592
Exact Gradient ...... 3, 2, 1.20559
El, Pt, Flux ........ 3, 2, 1.38398
. . .

Element end reactions and flux loss
NOTE: - enters element, + leaves element
El, Left         Right        Loss or Gain
1   -9.921e-01   1.037e+00    4.521e-02
2   -1.037e+00   1.288e+00    2.506e-01
3   -1.288e+00   1.883e+00    5.953e-01
4   -1.883e+00   3.163e+00    1.280e+00
5   -3.163e+00   5.622e+00    2.459e+00
6   -5.622e+00   1.001e+01    4.384e+00
```

Fig. 8.6-13: Quadrature flux and more accurate element reaction flux values.

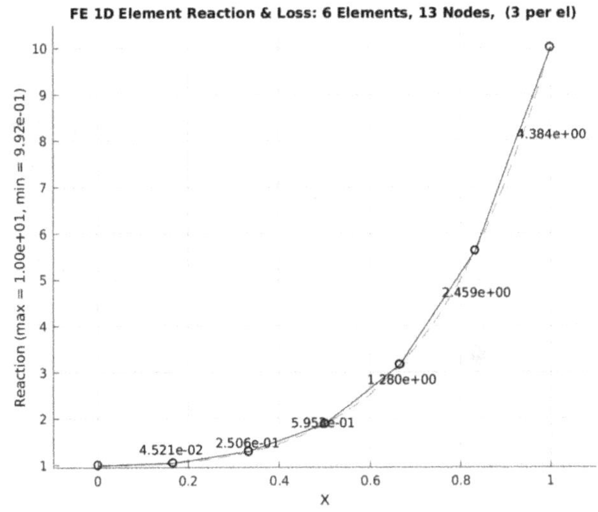

Fig. 8.6-14: Exact flux (dashed), element reaction flux (circled), and flux gain.

element array is known except for the element end flux values, $\boldsymbol{c}^e_{NBC}$. At the end of the post-processing element loop, the fully integrated total square matrix, $\boldsymbol{S}^e_t$, is recovered. The element flux reactions are computed as

$$\boldsymbol{c}^e_{NBC} = \boldsymbol{S}^e_t \boldsymbol{u}^e - \boldsymbol{c}^e.$$

The values in $\boldsymbol{c}^e_{NBC}$ are zero at any node not connected to another element. Thus, it contains only the entering and exiting flux values for any line element, and their difference is flux entering and/or leaving along the length of the element. The values of the optional element reaction fluxes are listed at the bottom of Fig. 8.6-12. As expected, the reaction flux leaving one element is the same as that entering the adjacent element (with a different sign convention).

For comparison to the quadrature point list, the value leaving the second element and entering the third is 1.288 units. The optional reaction flux values are graphed with straight-line connections between the circled point values in Fig. 8.6-14 along with the element loss or gain printed near the element centroid. Note that the first and last element reaction flux values match the system end reaction flux values of -0.9921 and 10.01 units, respectively. The exact flux is shown as a dashed line in that figure.

8.7 Symbolic Solutions*

A number of single-element solutions have been presented in detail to yield more insight into an application than a straight numerical solution can provide. It is logical to expect that such small problems can also be exactly solved in closed form using the Matlab symbolic features. To illustrate this, return to the spinning bar example; add an axial force on the distal end and a non-zero EBC at the proximal end. The governing differential equation is

$$\frac{d}{dx}\left(E\,A\frac{du}{dx}\right) + A\,\rho\,x\omega^2 = 0, \tag{8.7-1}$$

which is subject to the arbitrary EBC of $u(0) = 2$, and the non-essential (force) BC that the distal end of the bar has an imposed strain (gradient) of $du(L)/dx = b$. From the governing integral form that NBC also implies the existence of the end force of $F_L = EA\,du(L)/dx = EA\,b$. Such a force would be caused by a small endpoint mass, m, and the centrifugal acceleration, $a_r = L\,\omega^2$ giving $F_L = m\,L\,\omega^2$. The symbolic Matlab script for solving this approximation analytically with a single quadratic line element is given in Fig. 8.7-1. It begins by essentially allocating various arrays. For example, the nodal displacement vector is filled with three yet unknown symbolic variables. Then the element interpolation functions, $\boldsymbol{H}(r)$, are written in closed form. Their analytical physical derivative matrix is obtained from the Matlab *diff* function. The point sources vector, here NBC, holds the unknown reaction at node 1, $-du(0)/dx$, the zero center point load, and the given NBC value, $du(L)/dx = b$. The three DOF are split into a **Fixed** set and a **Free** set. The only **Fixed** DOF is set equal to zero. The variable source element vector is

$$\mathbf{c}^e = \int_L^e c\,x\boldsymbol{H}(r)\,dx = \int_{r=0}^{r=1} c\,(r\,L)\boldsymbol{H}(r)\,(L\,dr),$$

```
%  Symbolic solution for one L3 element for
%   u'' + cx = 0, u(0)=2, u'(L)=b, L=1, x=rL
% Exact u(x) = 2 + bx + cL^3*[3x/L-(x/L)^3]/6
% The L3 quadratic is exact only at the nodes
syms r c L          real       % symbolic variables
syms u_e u1 u2 u3   real                 % solution
syms b NBC u_dx_0   real    % end slopes, pt source
syms S_e c_e        real         % system matrices
u_e = [u1, u2, u3]'              % open the solution
% define interpolation functions, H
H(r) = [2*r^2 - 3*r + 1, -4*r^2 + 4*r, 2*r^2 - r]

% define their physical derivative,        x = L*r
dH_dx = diff (H(r), r) / L

% set unknown reaction & known end slopes, as NBC
NBC = [-u_dx_0 0 b]'

% locate and set essential boundary condition, EBC
Fixed = [1]                            % EBC location
u_e(Fixed) = 0                            % EBC value
Free=[2,3]                % all other dof are free

% Prepare the matrix system to be solved
% S_e*u_e = c_e + NBC         % matrix equilibrium

% integrate c*L*r*H(r) for source vector
c_e = c*L * int((r*H'),r,0,1)*L % resultant vector
% integrate the square matrix
S_e = int ( dH_dx'*dH_dx, r, 0,1) * L  % stiffness

% solve the matrix for the exact node displacements
u_e(Free)= S_e(Free,Free) \ (c_e(Free) + NBC(Free))
% interpolate the approximate interior solution
u(r) = H(r) * u_e ; u(r) = simplify(u(r)) % inexact

% optionally find the reaction
NBC(Fixed) = S_e(Fixed, Free) * u_e(Free) ...
           + S_e(Fixed, Fixed)* u_e(Fixed) ...
           - c_e(Fixed)           % reaction at EBC
% restate the right reaction slope
u_dx_0 = -NBC(1)              % echo reaction. Done.
```

Fig. 8.7-1: Symbolic solution of ODE with non-zero EBC and NBC.

which is integrated in parametric coordinates from 0 to 1 by the Matlab function *int*. That same function is used to integrate the stiffness matrix in parametric coordinates (with EA =1)

$$\boldsymbol{S}^e = \int_L^e \frac{d\boldsymbol{H}(r)}{dx}^T EA \frac{d\boldsymbol{H}(r)}{dx}\, dx = \int_{r=0}^{r=1} \frac{d\boldsymbol{H}(r)}{dx}^T \frac{d\boldsymbol{H}(r)}{dx} (L\, dr)$$

to complete the equilibrium equation, $\boldsymbol{S}^e \boldsymbol{u}^e = \boldsymbol{c}^e + \text{NBC}$. Then the analytic solution for the **Free** rows of the displacements is obtained using the **Free** rows of the right-hand side and inverse of the **Free** rows and columns of the stiffness matrix. That makes all of the element node displacements known. Then the dot product of the analytic interpolation functions with the analytic node displacements gives the expression for the displacements everywhere. The last action is to use the remaining **Fixed** rows of the matrix equilibrium equation to obtain the analytic expression for the reaction at the one **Fixed** node.

The actual screen output (*diary*) from the analytic script is given in Fig. 8.7-2. It is clear that the exact solution is cubic over the length of the domain so that this single quadratic element cannot give that result. However, it does give the analytically exact displacements at the nodes and gives the exact analytic reaction at the EBC.

Example 8.7-1 Given: An axial bar in Fig. 8.6-2 has a linear taper of its radius. It is fixed at one end and has an axial load of P at the other end. For a single quadratic element, use symbolic processing to find an analytic stiffness matrix. For a constant diameter bar, compare that stiffness to previously derived quadratic stiffness matrix.

Solution: This is a case of a variable coefficient, $A(x)$, in the ODE. The symbolic integration approach is given in Fig. 8.7-3. The stiffness is most simply written in terms of contributions from each of the three interpolation functions:

$$\boldsymbol{S}^e = \frac{\pi a^2 E}{15\, L} \begin{bmatrix} 23 & -26 & 3 \\ -26 & 32 & -6 \\ 3 & -6 & 3 \end{bmatrix} + \frac{\pi a b\, E}{15\, L} \begin{bmatrix} 9 & -8 & -1 \\ -8 & 16 & -8 \\ -1 & -8 & 9 \end{bmatrix}$$

```
%   Symbolic results for one L3 element for
%   u'' + cx = 0, u(0)=2, u'(L)=b, L=1, x=rL
% Exact u(x) = 2 + bx + cL^3*[3x/L-(x/L)^3]/6
u_e = [u1  u2  u3]'                % initialize name
RHS = [R1  R2  R3]'                % initialize name

H(r) = [2*r^2 - 3*r + 1, -4*r^2 + 4*r, 2*r^2 - r]
dH_dx = [(4*r - 3)/L, -(8*r - 4)/L, (4*r - 1)/L]

NBC = -u_dx_0     % the reaction to be found at BC
            0                      % no point source
            b                         % NBC at x = L
Fixed = 1       % locate where BC will be enforced
u_e =   2            % assigned essential BC value
       u2                     % unknown displacement
       u3                     % unknown displacement
Free = 2   3   % the unknown displacement numbers

C_e =      0   % variable source resultant, node 1
  (L^2*c)/3    % variable source resultant, node 2
  (L^2*c)/6       % resultant, node 2. sum is cL/2
S_e = [ 7/(3*L), -8/(3*L),  1/(3*L)]  % stiffness
      [-8/(3*L), 16/(3*L), -8/(3*L)]  % stiffness
      [ 1/(3*L), -8/(3*L),  7/(3*L)]  % stiffness

RHS =   R1 % before EBC, reaction plus source (0)
     (L^2*c)/3                  % system load, node 2
 (c*L^2)/6 + b                  % system load, node 3
RHS =                    R1     % update with BC u1=2
    (L^2*c)/3 + 16/(3*L)        % update with BC u1=2
 b + (L^2*c)/6 - 2/(3*L)        % update with BC u1=2

u_e =                          2  % node value and BC
 (11*c*L^3)/48 + (b*L)/2 + 2              % u2 exact
          (c*L^3)/3 + b*L + 2             % u3 exact
            % inexact interpolation between nodes
u(r) = L*b*r - (L^3*c*r^2)/4 + (7*L^3*c*r)/12 + 2

NBC = - b - (L^2*c)/2           % reaction at node 1
                        0    % old point load, node 2
                        b          % old NBC, node 3
u_dx_0 = (c*L^2)/2 + b       % restate the reaction
```

Fig. 8.7-2: Symbolic result for ODE with non-zero EBC NBC.

```
% stiffness of an axial bar with a linear tapered section
syms r L E a b real               ; % r = x / L  % math limits
R_e = [a ; b]                           ; % radii at each end
h(r) = [(1-r) r]                      ; % geometry interpolation
R(r) = h(r) * R_e                   ; % radius vs axial position
A(r) = pi() * R^2                     ; % area vs axial position

% interpolate quadratic axial displacements
H(r) = [2*r^2 - 3*r + 1, -4*r^2 + 4*r, 2*r^2 - r]     ; % L3

% their physical axial derivatives, x = L*r
dH_dx = diff (H(r), r) / L                          ; % dH(r)/dx

% form the matrix prpducts to be integrated
prod = dH_dx' * A(r) * dH_dx ; % stiffness matrix intergand
prod = simplify (prod)         ; % stiffness matrix intergand

% analytic integration
S_e = int (prod, r, 0, 1) * L ; % symbolic stiffness matrix
S_e = E * simplify (S_e)        % symbolic stiffness matrix
```

Fig. 8.7-3: Symbolic stiffness matrix for a quadratic tapered axial bar.

$$+\frac{\pi b^2 E}{15\, L}\begin{bmatrix} 3 & -6 & 3 \\ -6 & 32 & -26 \\ 3 & -26 & 23 \end{bmatrix}.$$

Checking the result for a constant radius bar with $b = a$ gives the matrix derived earlier for a constant area:

$$S^e = \frac{\pi a^2 E}{15\, L}\begin{bmatrix} 35 & -40 & 5 \\ -40 & 80 & -40 \\ 5 & -40 & 35 \end{bmatrix} = \frac{A\, E}{3\, L}\begin{bmatrix} 7 & -8 & 1 \\ -8 & 16 & -8 \\ 1 & -8 & 7 \end{bmatrix}.$$

Example 8.7-2 Given: A cylindrical steel tapered bar with small radius of 2 in., a large radius of 4 in., and a length of 36 in. undergoes a uniform temperature increase of $\Delta T = 40°$F. Both ends are restrained against axial movement but are free to expand radially. Find the end reaction forces and the maximum axial stress in the bar.

Solution: Recall that the "initial strain" at a point due to an increase in temperature from the stress-free temperature is $\varepsilon_o = \alpha\Delta T$, which is constant here. Also, (8.3-4) gives the resultant nodal loads for an "initial strain" distribution as

$$c_0^e = \int_{L^e} \frac{d\boldsymbol{H}^T}{dx} E(x)\, A(x)\, \varepsilon_o(x)\, dx = E\alpha\Delta T \int_{L^e} \frac{d\boldsymbol{H}^T}{dx} A(x)\, dx.$$

This will normally be integrated numerically. The end forces will be equal and opposite, say P, and mechanics gives the axial stress as $\sigma = P/A(x)$ where $A(x) = \pi[a + (b-a)x/L]^2$, which suggests at least a cubic element should be used in a numerical study. However, the previous symbolically integrated quadratic element can be used to give an approximate answer to validate (within a few percent) any numerical study. First, the stiffness matrix in Example 8.7-1 needs to be supplemented with the symbolic integration of the above thermal load resultant:

$$c_0^e = \frac{E^e \alpha^e \Delta T^e \pi}{3} \begin{Bmatrix} -a(2a+b) \\ a^2 - b^2 \\ b(a+2b) \end{Bmatrix}.$$

For $b = a$, this agrees with (8.3-5). Here, $b = 2a$ so

$$c_0^e = E^e \alpha^e \Delta T^e \pi a^2 [-4 \quad -6 \quad 10]^T/3,$$

and for a single element equilibrium

$$\boldsymbol{S}^e \boldsymbol{\theta}^e = \boldsymbol{c}_0^e + \boldsymbol{c}_P^e:$$

$$\left[\frac{\pi a^2 E}{15\,L} \begin{bmatrix} 23 & -26 & 3 \\ -26 & 32 & -6 \\ 3 & -6 & 3 \end{bmatrix} + \frac{\pi a(2a)\,E}{15\,L} \begin{bmatrix} 9 & -8 & -1 \\ -8 & 16 & -8 \\ -1 & -8 & 9 \end{bmatrix} \cdots \right.$$

$$\left. + \frac{\pi (2a)^2 E}{15\,L} \begin{bmatrix} 3 & -6 & 3 \\ -6 & 32 & -26 \\ 3 & -26 & 23 \end{bmatrix} \right] \begin{Bmatrix} u_1 = 0 \\ u_2 \\ u_3 = 0 \end{Bmatrix} = \frac{E\alpha\Delta T \pi a^2}{3} \begin{Bmatrix} -4 \\ -6 \\ 10 \end{Bmatrix} + \begin{Bmatrix} P_1 \\ 0 \\ P_3 \end{Bmatrix}.$$

Applying the EBC that $u_1 = 0 = u_3$, the second row gives the mid-node displacement equation

$$\frac{\pi a^2 E}{15\,L}[32 + 2(16) + 4(32)]u_2 = \frac{-6\,E\alpha\Delta T \pi a^2}{3} \text{ so } u_2 = -5\alpha\Delta T L/32,$$

while the first row gives the left reaction force

$$\frac{\pi a^2 E}{15\,L}\left[0+(-26-16-24)\left(-\frac{5\alpha\Delta TL}{32}\right)+0\right]$$

$$=\frac{-4\,E\alpha\Delta T\,\pi a^2}{3}+P_1 \text{ so } P_1=\frac{97E\alpha\Delta T\,\pi a^2}{48},$$

and row 3 gives $P_3 = -P_1$, as expected. For steel, $E = 30\text{e}6$ psi and $\alpha = 6.5\text{e}-6/°\text{F}$. Using the other data gives $u_2 = 1.463\text{e}3$ in. and $P_1 = 1.981\text{e}5$ lb. At node 1, mechanics gives the approximate axial stress as $\sigma = P/A = -1.577\text{e}4$ psi. The exact stress is $-1.560\text{e}4$ psi.

8.8 Symmetry and Anti-Symmetry

Often a problem has a symmetry or anti-symmetry condition that allows half of the domain to be modeled. For two- and three-dimensional problems it is often a necessity. Using either a symmetry or anti-symmetry condition reduces the memory requirements by two and the number of solution operations (and thus solution time) by a factor of about eight. Your computer will at some point become too small to solve real problems without using one or both of these conditions. When applying either condition the edge or face of the omitted domain must be replaced by a new BC. Figure 8.8-1 introduces the concepts of one-dimensional symmetry and anti-symmetry. A symmetry (mirror) plane is one where the domain and its material (coefficients in the ODE) are mirror images, as are the EBCs. Then only half of the domain is meshed and at the point (or edge or face) falling on the plane of symmetry has a natural BC of zero normal slope, $\partial T/\partial n \equiv 0$, which is applied to replace the removed material. The solution to that problem gives the actual solution on both sides of the mirror plane.

For an anti-symmetry plane, the domain and its material are mirror images, but the EBCs have equal and opposite changes in value, relative to the value at the mirror plane. The domain is cut in half, and the removed material is replaced with an EBC at the point (or edge or face) in the plane: $T_p = (T_{\text{left}} + T_{\text{right}})/2$. Thus, an anti-symmetry solution over half of the line gives the change in

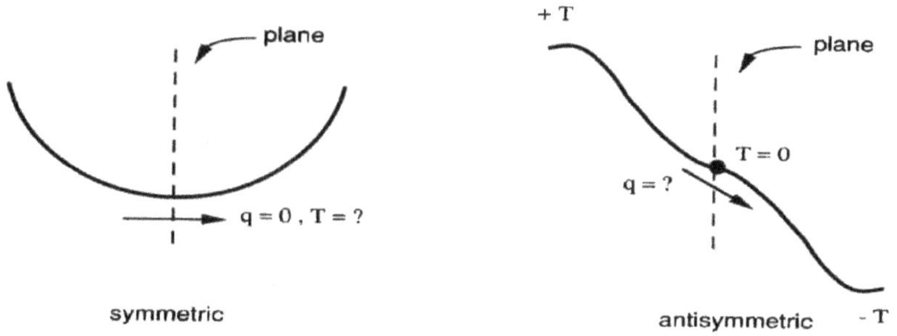

Fig. 8.8-1: Symmetric and anti-symmetric solutions along a line.

the solution value $\Delta T(x)$, with respect to T_p, so the actual solution is $T(x) = T_p + \Delta T(x)$. On the other (omitted) half of the line, the change is the solution has its sign reversed and the actual solution is $T(x) = T_p - \Delta T(x)$.

After the following related examples, the next two sections will cover the topics the patch test and methods for creating exact solutions for validating software implementations.

8.9 Patch Test*

The patch test can be used to verify that an element analytically and/or numerically satisfies the necessary and sufficient convergence criterion that an element must be able to exactly model the state of constant derivatives to the order found in the governing integral form. The numerical process also verifies that the entire finite element procedures have been implemented correctly. The procedure is to produce an arbitrary mesh containing at least one interior node. A constant derivative function of the spatial coordinates is assumed, like $u_p(x, y, z) = c_1 + c_2 x + c_3 y + c_3 z$, if a linear constant derivative is required. Then an EBC is set for every node on the outer boundary by substituting the nodal coordinates into the assumed form of u_p. That leaves only the internal nodes with unknown solution values. For a given differential equation, its equivalent matrix form is solved for the internal node values of u. The first requirement of the patch test is that the computed solution must be exactly equal to the u_p value obtained by substituting the coordinates of the internal node into the assumed form. The second requirement of the test is that when the element is post-processed for its gradient, at any and all points the gradient components must exactly match the c_k constants in the assumed form.

For second-order ODEs in one dimension, the patch test is quite simple to execute. The heat transfer ODE without internal sources is $K\,Ad^2u/dx^2 = 0$ and the equivalent matrix form is

$$I = -\boldsymbol{u}^T\ \boldsymbol{c}_{\text{NBC}} + \int_\Omega \boldsymbol{u}^T \frac{d\boldsymbol{H}(x)}{dx}^{\boldsymbol{T}} A(x)K(x)\frac{d\boldsymbol{H}(x)}{dx}\ \boldsymbol{u}\,dx.$$

Since the highest derivative in the integral is the first, any patch text will require a constant first derivative everywhere after the matrix system, $\boldsymbol{S}^{\boldsymbol{u}} = \boldsymbol{c}_{\text{NBC}}$, is solved. In one dimension, a patch test can be constructed with two linear elements or a single quadratic or cubic element. A quadratic element yields a linear gradient and has the equivalent matrix form of

$$\frac{A\,K}{3\,L}\begin{bmatrix} 7 & -8 & 1 \\ -8 & 16 & -8 \\ 1 & -8 & 7 \end{bmatrix}\begin{Bmatrix} u_1 \\ u_2 \\ u_3 \end{Bmatrix} = \begin{Bmatrix} -du(0)/dx \\ 0 \\ du(L)/dx \end{Bmatrix}.$$

Form a single element patch test, assuming that $u_p(x) = c_1 + c_2 x$, let patch boundaries be $x_1 = 0$ and $x_3 = L$. The boundary EBCs become $u_1 = c_1$ and $u_3 = (c_1 + c_2 L)$. Only the center node value remains to be computed from the second row of the system matrix:

$$\frac{A\,K}{3\,L}[16]\{u_2\} = \{0\} - (c_1)\frac{A\,K}{3\,L}\{-8\} - (c_1 + c_2 L)\frac{A\,K}{3\,L}\{-8\},\ \text{so}\ u_2$$
$$= c_1 + c_2 L/2.$$

Does that satisfy the first patch test requirement? Substitute the coordinate of the middle node into the assumed patch form: $u_p(L/2) = c_1 + c_2 L/2 \equiv u_2$, as required. Evaluate the gradient inside the element:

$$du(x)/dx = d\boldsymbol{H}(x)/dx\,\boldsymbol{u}^e = d\boldsymbol{H}(r)/dr(1/L)\boldsymbol{u}^e$$
$$du(x)/dx = [(-3 + 4r)(c_1) + (4 - 8r)(c_1 + c_2 L/2)$$
$$+(-1 + 4r)(c_1 + c_2 L)]/L$$
$$du(x)/dx = c_2.$$

For all values of x that is the required constant derivative; so the second and final stage of the patch test is satisfied. That means that the element matrix derived for the given differential equation will converge to the exact solution as the element size goes to zero.

8.10 Summary

$n\_b \longleftrightarrow n_b \equiv$ Number of boundary segments
$n\_d \longleftrightarrow n_d \equiv$ Number of system unknowns $= n\_g \times n\_m$
$n\_e \longleftrightarrow n_e \equiv$ Number of elements
$n\_g \longleftrightarrow n_g \equiv$ Number of generalized DOF per node
$n\_i \longleftrightarrow n_i \equiv$ Number of unknowns per element $= n\_g \times n\_n$
$n\_m \longleftrightarrow n_m \equiv$ Number of mesh nodes
$n\_n \longleftrightarrow n_n \equiv$ Number of nodes per element
$n\_p \longleftrightarrow n_p \equiv$ Dimension of parametric space
$n\_q \longleftrightarrow n_q \equiv$ Number of total quadrature points
$n\_r \longleftrightarrow n_r \equiv$ Number of rows in the $\boldsymbol{B}^e$ matrix (and material matrix)
$n\_s \longleftrightarrow n_s \equiv$ Dimension of physical space

b = boundary segment number | e = element number
$\subset$= subset | $\cup$ = union of sets
Boundary, element, and system unknowns: $\boldsymbol{\delta}^b \subset_b \boldsymbol{\delta}^e \subset_e \boldsymbol{\delta}$
Boolean extraction arrays: $\boldsymbol{\delta}^b \equiv \boldsymbol{\beta}_b\boldsymbol{\delta}, \quad \boldsymbol{\delta}^e \equiv \boldsymbol{\beta}_e\boldsymbol{\delta}$
Geometry: $\Omega = \cup_e \Omega^e \equiv$ Solution domain | $\Omega^e \equiv$ Element domain
$\Gamma = \cup_b \Gamma^b \equiv$ Domain boundary | $\Gamma^b \subset \Omega^e \equiv$ Boundary segment

Geometry Mapping: $\boldsymbol{x}(r) = \boldsymbol{G}(r)\boldsymbol{x}^e, \boldsymbol{H}(r) \leq \boldsymbol{G}(r) \geq \boldsymbol{H}(r)$
$\partial x(r)/\partial r = (\partial \boldsymbol{G}(r)/\partial r)\boldsymbol{x}^e.$

Interpolation: $u(\boldsymbol{x}) = \boldsymbol{H}(r)\boldsymbol{\delta}^e = u(\boldsymbol{x})^T = \boldsymbol{\delta}^{e^T}\boldsymbol{H}(r)^T.$

Local gradient: $\partial u(r)/\partial r = (\partial \boldsymbol{H}(r)/\partial r)\,\boldsymbol{\delta}^e.$

Physical gradient: $\partial u(x)/\partial x = (\partial u(r)/\partial r)(\partial r/\partial x)$
$= (\partial u(r)/\partial r)\,(\partial x/\partial r)^{-1}$
$\partial u(x)/\partial x = [(\partial \boldsymbol{G}(r)/\partial r)\,\boldsymbol{x}^e]^{-1}$
$(\partial \boldsymbol{H}(r)/\partial r)\,\boldsymbol{\delta}^e \equiv \boldsymbol{B}(r)\boldsymbol{\delta}^e.$

Typical Model ODE: $-\frac{d}{dx}\left[K(x)\,\frac{du(x)}{dx}\right] + A(x)\frac{du(x)}{dx} + C(x)\,u(x) + F(x) = 0.$

Conduction line element matrix (see Table 4.10-1 for constant properties):

$$\boldsymbol{S}_{\boldsymbol{k}}^{e} = \int_{L^e} \frac{d\boldsymbol{H}(r)}{dx}^{T} K(x)\, A(x) \frac{d\boldsymbol{H}(r)}{dx}\, dx.$$

Convection line element matrices (see Table 4.10-1 for constant properties):

$$\boldsymbol{S}_{\boldsymbol{h}}^{e} = \int_{L}^{e} \boldsymbol{H}(r)^T p(x)\, h(x)\, \boldsymbol{H}(r)\, dx,\ \boldsymbol{c}_{\boldsymbol{h}}^{e} = \int_{L}^{e} \boldsymbol{H}(r)^T p(x)\, h(x)\, u_\infty\, dx.$$

Convection point element "matrices": $K_n \partial u/\partial n + c\,u = b$,

$$\boldsymbol{S}_{\boldsymbol{h}}^{b} = hA_n^b, \quad \boldsymbol{c}_{\boldsymbol{h}}^{b} = h\, u_\infty A_n^b.$$

A symmetry plane gives a natural BC: $\partial u/\partial x = 0$.

An anti-symmetry plane gives an averaged EBC: $u_p = (u_{\text{left}} + u_{\text{right}})/2$.

For constant properties but varying temperatures, the thermal strain resultant load matrices for the linear line element and the quadratic line element are

$$\boldsymbol{c}_{\boldsymbol{0}}^{e} = \frac{E^e A^e \alpha^e}{2} \begin{bmatrix} -1 & -1 \\ 1 & 1 \end{bmatrix} \begin{Bmatrix} \Delta T_1 \\ \Delta T_2 \end{Bmatrix}^e,$$

$$\boldsymbol{c}_{\boldsymbol{0}}^{e} = \frac{E^e A^e \alpha^e}{6} \begin{bmatrix} -3 & -4 & 1 \\ 4 & 0 & -4 \\ -1 & 4 & 3 \end{bmatrix} \begin{Bmatrix} \Delta T_1 \\ \Delta T_2 \\ \Delta T_3 \end{Bmatrix}^e,$$

and for the cubic line element, it is

$$\boldsymbol{c}_{\boldsymbol{0}}^{e} = \frac{E^e A^e \alpha^e}{80} \begin{bmatrix} -40 & -57 & 24 & -7 \\ 57 & 0 & -81 & 24 \\ -24 & 81 & 0 & -57 \\ 7 & -24 & 57 & 40 \end{bmatrix} \begin{Bmatrix} \Delta T_1 \\ \Delta T_2 \\ \Delta T_3 \\ \Delta T_4 \end{Bmatrix}^e.$$

For constant temperature, change the thermal loads for linear, quadratic, and cubic bars:

$$\boldsymbol{c}_{\boldsymbol{\alpha}}^{e} = E^e A^e \alpha^e \Delta T^e \begin{Bmatrix} -1 \\ 1 \end{Bmatrix}, \quad \boldsymbol{c}_{\boldsymbol{\alpha}}^{e} = E^e A^e \alpha^e \Delta T^e \begin{Bmatrix} -1 \\ 0 \\ 1 \end{Bmatrix},$$

$$\boldsymbol{c}^e_{\boldsymbol{\alpha}} = E^e A^e \alpha^e \Delta T^e \begin{Bmatrix} -1 \\ 0 \\ 0 \\ 1 \end{Bmatrix}.$$

Equilibrium equations for a linear (L2) bar element:

$$\frac{E^e A^e}{L^e}\begin{bmatrix} 1 & -1 \\ -1 & 1 \end{bmatrix}\begin{Bmatrix} u_1 \\ u_2 \end{Bmatrix} = \begin{Bmatrix} P_1 \\ P_2 \end{Bmatrix} + \frac{1}{6L^e}\begin{bmatrix} 2 & 1 \\ 1 & 2 \end{bmatrix}\begin{Bmatrix} q_1 \\ q_2 \end{Bmatrix} + E^e A^e \alpha^e \Delta T^e \begin{Bmatrix} -1 \\ 1 \end{Bmatrix}.$$

Linear element (L2) convection along length and end area:

$$\boldsymbol{S}^e_{\boldsymbol{p}} = \frac{h\,p\,L}{6}\begin{bmatrix} 2 & 1 \\ 1 & 2 \end{bmatrix},\ \boldsymbol{c}^e_{\boldsymbol{p}} = \frac{h\,u_\infty\,p\,L}{2}\begin{Bmatrix} 1 \\ 1 \end{Bmatrix},\ \boldsymbol{S}^{\boldsymbol{A}}_{\boldsymbol{h}} = [A\,h],\ \boldsymbol{c}^{\boldsymbol{A}}_{\boldsymbol{h}} = \{A\,h\,u_\infty\}.$$

Equilibrium equations for a quadratic (L3) bar element are

$$\frac{E^e A^e}{3L^e}\begin{bmatrix} 7 & -8 & 1 \\ -8 & 16 & -8 \\ 1 & -8 & 7 \end{bmatrix}\begin{Bmatrix} u_1 \\ u_2 \\ u_3 \end{Bmatrix} = \begin{Bmatrix} P_1 \\ P_2 \\ P_3 \end{Bmatrix} + \frac{L^e}{30}\begin{bmatrix} 4 & 2 & -1 \\ 2 & 16 & 2 \\ -1 & 2 & 4 \end{bmatrix}\begin{Bmatrix} q_1 \\ q_2 \\ q_3 \end{Bmatrix}^e$$
$$+ E^e A^e \alpha^e \Delta T^e \begin{Bmatrix} -1 \\ 0 \\ 1 \end{Bmatrix}.$$

Quadratic (L3) element convection along length and end area:

$$\boldsymbol{S}^e_{\boldsymbol{p}} = \frac{h^e L^e}{30}\begin{bmatrix} 4 & 2 & -1 \\ 2 & 16 & 2 \\ -1 & 2 & 4 \end{bmatrix},\ \boldsymbol{c}^e_{\boldsymbol{p}} = \frac{h^e u_{\infty^e} L^e}{6}\begin{Bmatrix} 1 \\ 4 \\ 1 \end{Bmatrix},$$
$$\boldsymbol{S}^{\boldsymbol{A}}_{\boldsymbol{h}} = [A\,h],\ \boldsymbol{c}^{\boldsymbol{A}}_{\boldsymbol{h}} = \{A\,h\,u_\infty\}.$$

Equilibrium equations for a cubic (L4) bar element are

$$\frac{E^e A^e}{40L^e}\begin{bmatrix} 148 & -189 & 54 & -13 \\ -189 & 432 & -297 & 54 \\ 54 & -297 & 432 & -189 \\ -13 & 54 & -189 & 148 \end{bmatrix}\begin{Bmatrix} u_1 \\ u_2 \\ u_3 \\ u_4 \end{Bmatrix}$$

$$= \begin{Bmatrix} P_1 \\ P_2 \\ P_3 \\ P_4 \end{Bmatrix} + \frac{L^e}{1680} \begin{bmatrix} 128 & 99 & -36 & 19 \\ 99 & 648 & -81 & -36 \\ -36 & -81 & 648 & 99 \\ 19 & -36 & 99 & 128 \end{bmatrix} \begin{Bmatrix} q_1 \\ q_2 \\ q_3 \\ q_4 \end{Bmatrix}^e$$

$$+ E^e A^e \alpha^e \Delta T^e \begin{Bmatrix} -1 \\ 0 \\ 0 \\ 1 \end{Bmatrix}.$$

Cubic element (L4) convection along length and end area:

$$\boldsymbol{S}_{\boldsymbol{p}}^{\boldsymbol{e}} = \frac{h^e L^e}{1680} \begin{bmatrix} 128 & 99 & -36 & 19 \\ 99 & 648 & -81 & -36 \\ -36 & -81 & 648 & 99 \\ 19 & -36 & 99 & 128 \end{bmatrix}, \quad \boldsymbol{c}_{\boldsymbol{p}}^{\boldsymbol{e}} = \frac{h^e u_{\infty^e} L^e}{8} \begin{Bmatrix} 1 \\ 3 \\ 3 \\ 1 \end{Bmatrix},$$

$$\boldsymbol{S}_{\boldsymbol{h}}^{\boldsymbol{A}} = [A\,h], \ \boldsymbol{c}_{\boldsymbol{h}}^{\boldsymbol{A}} = \{A\,h\,u_\infty\}.$$

Thermal equilibrium equations of a wall with a known temperature and a convecting face,

$$\begin{bmatrix} k\,A/L & -k\,A/L \\ -k\,A/L & (k\,A/L + A\,h) \end{bmatrix} \begin{Bmatrix} u_1 \\ u_2 \end{Bmatrix} = \begin{Bmatrix} A\,q_1 \\ A\,h\,u_\infty \end{Bmatrix},$$

give the second wall face temperature $\{u_2\} = (L\,h\,u_\infty + u_1 k)/(L\,h + k)$.

Thermal equilibrium equations of a wall with two convecting faces,

$$\begin{bmatrix} (k\,A/L + A\,h_1) & -k\,A/L \\ -k\,A/L & (k\,A/L + A\,h_2) \end{bmatrix} \begin{Bmatrix} u_1 \\ u_2 \end{Bmatrix} = \begin{Bmatrix} A\,h_1\,u_{\infty_1} \\ A\,h_2\,u_{\infty_2} \end{Bmatrix},$$

give the wall face temperatures

$$\begin{Bmatrix} u_1 \\ u_2 \end{Bmatrix} = \frac{1}{k(h_1 + h_2) + Lh_1 h_2} \begin{Bmatrix} k(h_1 u_{\infty_1} + h_2 u_{\infty_2}) + Lh_1 h_2 u_{\infty_1} \\ k(h_1 u_{\infty_1} + h_2 u_{\infty_2}) + Lh_1 h_2 u_{\infty_2} \end{Bmatrix}.$$

8.11 Review

1. Solve the equations in Example 8.6-1 when only the self-weight load acts on the truss to verify the results shown in Fig. 8.6-2.
2. Follow the process in Example 8.6-2 to find the displacements and force in each truss member when the truss is loaded only by gravity.
3. A symmetry plane divides mirror images of the ____.

   (a) Geometric shape
   (b) Distribution of material properties
   (c) Essential boundary conditions
   (d) External loadings
   (e) All of the above
   (f) None of the above

4. Beginning with knowledge of the governing differential equation, list the major steps or phases of a finite element analysis (in order of occurrence).
5. In a bar structural analysis, what is the sum of the terms in the resultant element force vector due to only the body weight?
6. A material that is the same at all points is _____.

   (a) Homogeneous
   (b) Non-homogeneous
   (c) Isotropic
   (d) Anisotropic
   (e) Orthotropic

7. The magnitude of a heat flux vector always depends on the _____.

   (a) Temperature
   (b) Temperature gradient
   (c) Thermal conductivity
   (d) Specific heat
   (e) Convection coefficient
   (f) Both (b) and (c)

8. In heat transfer the heat flow is _____.

   (a) Area integral of the normal flux
   (b) The area integral of the temperature
   (c) The volume integral of the heat flux
   (d) Zero across insulated surfaces
   (e) Zero at specified temperatures
   (f) Both (a) and (d)

9. In a bar structural analysis, what is the sum of the terms in the element stiffness matrix?

10. In a bar thermal analysis, what is the sum of the terms in the element convection square matrix?
11. In stress analysis, the default Neumann BC at a point on the exterior surface is: ______.

(a) Zero heat flux (b) Zero displacement (c) Zero stresses
(d) Zero temperature (e) None of these (f) All of these

12. In thermal analysis, the default Neumann BC at a point on an exterior surface is: _____.

(a) Zero heat flux (b) Zero displacement (c) Zero stresses
(d) Zero temperature (e) None of these (f) All of these

13. Which boundary conditions are satisfied weakly in a finite element formulation? _____.

(a) Dirichlet (b) Neumann (c) Both

14. A singular single element system has the equilibrium equation, before applying the Dirichlet BC, of

$$\frac{EA}{3L}\begin{bmatrix} 7 & -8 & 1 \\ -8 & 16 & -8 \\ 1 & -8 & 7 \end{bmatrix}\begin{Bmatrix} u_1 \\ u_2 \\ u_3 = d \end{Bmatrix} = \begin{Bmatrix} 0 \\ 0 \\ R_3 \end{Bmatrix} + \frac{\gamma AL}{6}\begin{Bmatrix} 1 \\ 4 \\ 1 \end{Bmatrix},$$

where d is a known displacement value. Write the non-singular matrix equations for the two remaining unknowns. Do not solve for the remaining unknowns.
15. Where must element interfaces be introduced when creating the mesh?
16. Briefly explain the operations of scatter and gather and the type of data upon which they operate.
17. At a point on a plane of structural symmetry, which items are zero? ______.

(a) Tangential displacements	(b) Normal displacement	(c) Tangential heat flux
(d) Temperature	(e) Normal rotations	(f) Tangential rotations
(g) Both (b) and (f)	(h) All of the above	(i) None of the above

18. At a point on a plane of thermal symmetry, which items are zero? -----.

(a) Tangential displacements	(b) Normal displacement	(c) Tangential heat flux
(d) Temperature	(e) Normal heat flux	(f) Tangential rotations
(g) Normal rotations	(h) All of the above	(i) None of the above

19. A two-node space truss element (with three displacements per node) in a bridge is connected to nodes 27 and 32. What are the system degree of freedom numbers (equation numbers) at node 32?
20. What happens to a finite element solution if you fail to apply the EBCs to the matrix form?
21. In a thermal analysis, what is the sum of the terms in the element conduction matrix?

Chapter 9

Truss Analysis

9.1 Planar Truss

The differential equation for the equilibrium of an elastic bar (above) showed that it has only axial forces and axial displacements due to applied forces and/or temperature changes. A truss is a structural system composed of straight "two force members" defined as having only two equal and opposite end forces acting along the axis of the member and thereby causing only axial displacement of the member. These members are joined (in theory) only at their ends to span the space between concurrent support points. Clearly, the "two force members" are the axial bars governed by the element matrices developed from the differential equation of equilibrium. A truss is just multiple axial bars joined together, but they are not all aligned in the same direction and usually more than two bars are connected at a joint. A planar truss requires all of the joints and external loads lie in the same plane.

The design of a truss usually requires a series of analyses. Historically, the first is usually just based on the assumed geometry (truss mesh), a constant assumed area for each member, and neglects the weight of the truss. Today, the FEA easily allows the inclusion of the member weights in the first analysis. Multiple vertical and horizontal load cases are considered to determine the maximum tension force and maximum compression force in each member. Then, each member is assigned a new area (and weight) consistent with material stress limits in tension and compression, and each load case is re-run. In the final iteration, the compression members are checked for buckling and additional braces may be attached at the center of long compression members to reduce their effective buckling length. An application script to carry out automated planar truss studies is supplied with the name *Planar_Truss.m*.

Modern trusses continue to have the centroidal axes of the truss members intersect at a single point. However, the members are often joined to plates that lie in the plane of the truss. Such joints can actually transmit bending moments (from distributed weight or wind loads), so the final step in a design is to re-check the truss by modeling it as a planar frame which includes its bending moments of inertia.

The question here is how can the bar matrices developed in the prior chapter be used to analyze a truss structure? The key to the process is to recall that the displacement of the bar is a vector quantity. Previously, when two or more bars were joined together, all of the displacement vectors at the joints were collinear. Consider a planar truss where all of the bars lie in the x–y plane. Some of the bars must be inclined relative to the x-axis, as in Fig. 9.1-1. That means that the bar displacement vectors, which previously were all directed along the x-axis, now have components in both the x- and y-directions. In other words, the bar matrices need to be revised to account for being inclined in the x–y plane.

The position vector defining the length, L, between the two ends of the truss member now includes horizontal and vertical components, Δx and Δy, that combine to form a right triangle that defines that total length: $L^2 = \Delta x^2 + \Delta y^2$ and the direction cosines with respect to the x- and y-axes: $\cos\theta_x = \Delta x/L$ and $\cos\theta_y = \Delta y/L$. Of course, those length components depend on the differences in the x- and y-coordinates of the two end nodes. Let the axial displacement of the bar now be denoted as u_b. It is collinear with the length of the bar. Therefore, the displacement vector at either end of the member

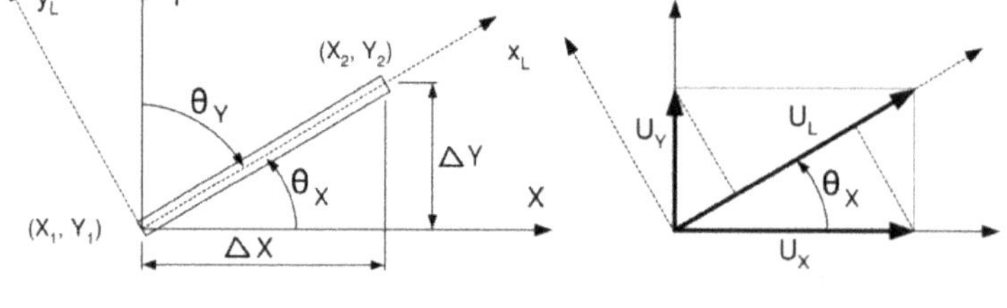

Fig. 9.1-1: Direction cosines for an inclined truss member.

also now has two components, u_x and u_y, when viewed in the $x - y$ plane containing the truss. From similar triangles, the two system (global) displacement components are $u_x = u_b \cos\theta_x = u_b \Delta x/L$ and $u_y = u_b \cos\theta_y = u_b \Delta y/L$.

Before extending the bar stiffness matrix to a truss stiffness matrix, consider what the above observations require as changes to a computer model of the structure. Now, both the x- and y-coordinates of each node will be required. That means that the physical space dimension control integer has increased to two, $n_s = 2$. Each truss node now has two generalized displacements, $n_g = 2$, and the number of unknowns has basically doubled at both the element and system levels. There are still only two nodes on the element, $n_n = 2$, but the number of independent degrees of freedom on the element has increased to four, $n_i = n_g \times n_n = 2 \times 2 = 4$. Likewise, if the truss system has a total of n_m nodes, then the total number of displacement equations for the truss, $n_d = n_g \times n_m$, has doubled. Also, vector subscripts for gathering and scattering element data double because their number is directly proportional to n_g. Furthermore, when specifying an essential boundary condition (EBC) (known displacement) at a node, there has to be a way to distinguish between horizontal or vertical components.

For each truss element, the connecting nodes are gathered and used to get the nodal x-coordinates in order to compute the element length. The connections are used again with the control integers to generate the system degree of freedom numbers for the element. That is done with the *get_element_index.m* script given in Fig. 7.2-1. That script is always used for each element being assembled. Here, because $n_g = 2$ the system equation number for degree of freedom j at system node number N is

$$\text{row}(j) = n_g (N - 1) + j, \quad 1 \le j \le n_g.$$

For a planar truss, the degree of freedom $j = 1$ corresponds to a horizontal displacement and $j = 2$ corresponds to the vertical displacement.

The truss equilibrium analysis requires solving for all of the horizontal and vertical displacements. Since the node displacement components, u_x and u_y, are now the primary unknowns, they need to be related to the bar displacement, u_b, by using the orientation (direction cosines) of the bar element. From geometry, at any node the local bar axial displacement is related to the global x- and y-components by: $u_b = u_x \cos\theta_x + u_y \cos\theta_y$. This identity can be written in matrix form

$$\{u_b\}_L = [\cos\theta_x \ \ \cos\theta_y] \begin{Bmatrix} u_x \\ u_y \end{Bmatrix}_G \quad \text{or} \quad \boldsymbol{u_L} = \boldsymbol{t}(\theta)\,\boldsymbol{u_G} \tag{9.1-1}$$

$$(1 \times 1) = (1 \times 2)\,(2 \times 1).$$

Since the direction cosines are actually calculated from the length components of the truss, it is practical to re-write the direction cosines and the member length components and the node displacement transformation as $\cos\theta_x \equiv C_x = \Delta x/L$, $\cos\theta_y \equiv C_y = \sin\theta_x = \Delta y/L$

$$\{u_b\}_L = [C_x \ C_y] \begin{Bmatrix} u_x \\ u_y \end{Bmatrix}_G = \frac{1}{L}[\Delta x \ \Delta y] \begin{Bmatrix} u_x \\ u_y \end{Bmatrix}_G \quad \text{or} \quad \boldsymbol{u_L} = \boldsymbol{t}(\theta)\,\boldsymbol{u_G}.$$

In Example 8.3-1, the structural stiffness matrix of the two-noded bar was shown to be

$$\boldsymbol{S}^e = \frac{E^e A^e}{L^e} \begin{bmatrix} 1 & -1 \\ -1 & 1 \end{bmatrix}.$$

That stiffness was obtained from the element's scalar contribution to the integral equilibrium form

$$I_S = \boldsymbol{u_L^T} \boldsymbol{S}^e \boldsymbol{u_L} = \begin{Bmatrix} u_1 \\ u_2 \end{Bmatrix}_b^{\boldsymbol{T}} \frac{E^e A^e}{L^e} \begin{bmatrix} 1 & -1 \\ -1 & 1 \end{bmatrix} \begin{Bmatrix} u_1 \\ u_2 \end{Bmatrix}_b.$$

In order to convert that original bar relation to a truss member stiffness relation the node transformation above must be applied to both of the end nodes of the bar:

$$\begin{Bmatrix} u_1 \\ u_2 \end{Bmatrix}_b = \begin{bmatrix} \cos\theta_x & \cos\theta_y & 0 & 0 \\ 0 & 0 & \cos\theta_x & \cos\theta_y \end{bmatrix} \begin{Bmatrix} u_{x1} \\ u_{y1} \\ u_{x2} \\ u_{y2} \end{Bmatrix}, \tag{9.1-2}$$

$$\boldsymbol{u_L^e} = [\boldsymbol{T}(\theta)]\boldsymbol{u_G^e} = \begin{bmatrix} \boldsymbol{t}(\theta) & \boldsymbol{0} \\ \boldsymbol{0} & \boldsymbol{t}(\theta) \end{bmatrix} \boldsymbol{u_G^e}$$

$$2 \times 1 = (2 \times 4)\,(4 \times 1).$$

In other words, the four truss components of displacement are reduced to the two bar end displacements by multiplying by a rectangular geometry transformation matrix.

The scalar integral contribution to equilibrium must be the same in any coordinate system. So it is the same in the global system:

$$\begin{gathered} I_S = \boldsymbol{u_L^T S^e u_L} = \boldsymbol{u_G^T S_G^e u_G} \\ 1 \times 1 = (1 \times 2)\,(2 \times 2)\,(2 \times 1) = (1 \times 4)\,(4 \times 4)\,(4 \times 1)\,. \end{gathered} \tag{9.1-3}$$

Substituting the bar transformation:

$$I_S = \left([\boldsymbol{T}(\theta)]\,\boldsymbol{u_G^e}\right)^{\boldsymbol{T}} \boldsymbol{S}^e \left([\boldsymbol{T}(\theta)]\,\boldsymbol{u_G^e}\right) = \boldsymbol{u_G^T S_G^e u_G},$$

$$I_S = \boldsymbol{u_G^T}\left[[\boldsymbol{T}(\theta)]^{\boldsymbol{T}}\,\boldsymbol{S}^e\,[\boldsymbol{T}(\theta)]\right]\boldsymbol{u_G} = \boldsymbol{u_G^T}[\boldsymbol{S_G^e}]\boldsymbol{u_G},$$

gives the global truss stiffness as

$$\begin{gathered} \boldsymbol{S_G^e} = [\boldsymbol{T}(\theta)]^{\boldsymbol{T}}\ \ \boldsymbol{S}^e\ \ [\boldsymbol{T}(\theta)] \\ 4 \times 4 = (4 \times 2)\,(2 \times 2)\,(2 \times 4). \end{gathered} \tag{9.1-4}$$

It is probably easier to evaluate the matrix $\boldsymbol{S}^e$, since we already have it, and $\boldsymbol{T}(\theta)$, and have the computer do the multiplications, but the truss stiffness can be written in detail in terms of the length components as

$$\begin{aligned} \boldsymbol{S_G^e} &= \frac{EA}{L}\begin{bmatrix} C_xC_x & C_xC_y & -C_xC_x & -C_xC_y \\ C_xC_y & C_yC_y & -C_xC_y & -C_yC_y \\ -C_xC_x & -C_xC_y & C_xC_x & C_xC_y \\ -C_xC_y & -C_yC_y & C_xC_y & C_yC_y \end{bmatrix} \\ &= \frac{EA}{L^3}\begin{bmatrix} \Delta x\Delta x & \Delta x\Delta y & -\Delta x\Delta x & -\Delta x\Delta y \\ \Delta x\Delta y & \Delta y\Delta y & -\Delta x\Delta y & -\Delta y\Delta y \\ -\Delta x\Delta x & -\Delta x\Delta y & \Delta x\Delta x & \Delta x\Delta y \\ -\Delta x\Delta y & -\Delta y\Delta y & \Delta x\Delta y & \Delta y\Delta y \end{bmatrix}. \end{aligned} \tag{9.1-5}$$

As a spot check, degenerate the truss into a single horizontal bar. Then, $\Delta y = 0$ and $\Delta x = L$ and the truss stiffness becomes

$$\boldsymbol{S_G^e} = \frac{EA}{L^3}\begin{bmatrix} L^2 & 0 & -L^2 & 0 \\ 0 & 0 & 0 & 0 \\ -L^2 & 0 & L^2 & 0 \\ 0 & 0 & 0 & 0 \end{bmatrix} = \frac{EA}{L}\begin{bmatrix} 1 & 0 & -1 & 0 \\ 0 & 0 & 0 & 0 \\ -1 & 0 & 1 & 0 \\ 0 & 0 & 0 & 0 \end{bmatrix},$$

which shows that a horizontal bar member has no vertical stiffness. Enforcing the EBCs that the two vertical displacements are zero reduces the effective horizontal truss member stiffness back to that of the bar

$$\boldsymbol{S}^e = \frac{EA}{L}\begin{bmatrix} 1 & -1 \\ -1 & 1 \end{bmatrix}.$$

Bars and truss members can be subjected to thermal loads. For the bar, it was shown in Section 8.4 that the thermal load is

$$\boldsymbol{c}_{\boldsymbol{\alpha}}^{\boldsymbol{e}} = EA\alpha\Delta T \begin{Bmatrix} -1 \\ 1 \end{Bmatrix}. \tag{9.1-6}$$

This bar load is also transformed to a truss member load by using the scalar work term in the governing integral form: $I_c = \boldsymbol{u}_{\boldsymbol{L}}^{\boldsymbol{T}} \boldsymbol{c}^e = \boldsymbol{u}_{\boldsymbol{G}}^{\boldsymbol{T}} \boldsymbol{c}_{\boldsymbol{G}}^{\boldsymbol{e}}$. Substituting the rectangular member orientation transformation matrix gives:

$$\begin{aligned} \boldsymbol{c}_{\boldsymbol{G}}^{\boldsymbol{e}} &= [\boldsymbol{T}(\theta)]^{\boldsymbol{T}}\ \boldsymbol{c}^e \\ 4 \times 1 &= (4 \times 2)\,(2 \times 1), \end{aligned} \tag{9.1-7}$$

which converts any thermal load in a truss member to

$$\boldsymbol{c}_{\boldsymbol{\alpha}}^{\boldsymbol{e}} = EA\alpha\Delta T \begin{Bmatrix} -C_x \\ -C_y \\ C_x \\ C_y \end{Bmatrix} = \frac{EA\alpha\Delta T}{L} \begin{Bmatrix} -\Delta x \\ -\Delta y \\ \Delta x \\ \Delta y \end{Bmatrix}.$$

When a truss has all members receive the same temperature change and is free to expand, it just changes shape and no net member forces develop. However, if the truss is not free to expand, then a temperature change in even one member can produce additional axial forces in some or all of the other members.

To form a kinematically stable truss the truss elements and/or the support connections must form a structure made up of triangular regions. A region with only four truss elements combined into the shape of a quadrilateral will be kinematically unstable and would collapse under its own weight. Mentioning the weight, for trusses it is assumed that the weight of a truss element is split equally at its two ends as vertical forces:

$$c_{\gamma}^{G} = \frac{\gamma AL}{2}\begin{Bmatrix} 0 \\ -1 \\ 0 \\ -1 \end{Bmatrix} = \frac{wL}{2}\begin{Bmatrix} 0 \\ -1 \\ 0 \\ -1 \end{Bmatrix}, \tag{9.1-8}$$

where γ denote the specific weight of the material and $w = \gamma A$ is the weight per unit length.

Now that each node has two degrees of freedom, the packed integer code that flags the EBC at each node can have the following packed values: 00 a free joint, 10 only u is given, 01 only v is given, 11 both u and v are given (a pin joint), etc. Usually, the given values are zero, but any small deflection value can be imposed as required by the application. If any unit value in the flag is replaced with a 2, then that means that component is coupled to another degree of freedom with a type 2 multipoint constraints (MPC). These BC code flags are used in the application software for planar truss analysis, with limited graphical support, as supplied in the application library as *Planar_Truss.m*.

Example 9.1-1 Given: The two-bar steel truss in Fig. 9.1-2 supports a downward vertical load of $P = -20\,kN$ at their junction (node 3). The two member connections to the vertical wall are

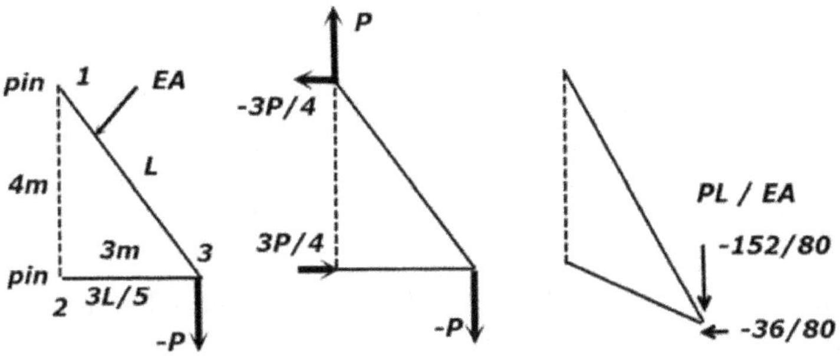

Fig. 9.1-2: Two bar planar truss with a point load.

pinned against displacement. Both elements have the same cross-sectional area, $A = 0.001\,\text{m}^2$. Find the deflection of the load and the system reactions. Check the reaction forces using statics. The truss data are as follows:

Node	1	2	3	Element	Connections	$\Delta x(m)$	$\Delta y(m)$	$L(m)$	C_x	C_y
x(m)	0	0	3	1	2, 3	3	0	3	1	0
y(m)	4	0	0	2	1, 3	3	-4	5	3/5	$-4/5$
DOF	1, 2	3, 4	5, 6							

Solution: First, note that the two wall connections form the third side of a stable triangle. Steel has an elastic modulus of $E = 200\text{e}9\ \text{N/m}^2$. The vertical sign load is at node 3 in the negative vertical direction. It corresponds to system DOF number of $2*(3-1)+2=6$. The null external horizontal point load there is at DOF number $2*(3-1)+1=5$. So the system external point load and reaction force vector is

$$\boldsymbol{c_P^T} = [R_{x_1}\ R_{y_1}\ R_{x_2}\ R_{y_2}\ 0\ -P].$$

Let the inclined member have a length L so that the length of the horizontal member is $3L/5$. Substitute the numerical direction cosine values and use the inclined bar as a reference length. The horizontal truss member stiffness and loads are

$$\boldsymbol{S^h} = \frac{EA}{(3L/5)}\begin{bmatrix} 1 & 0 & -1 & 0 \\ 0 & 0 & 0 & 0 \\ -1 & 0 & 1 & 0 \\ 0 & 0 & 0 & 0 \end{bmatrix} = \frac{125EA}{75L}\begin{bmatrix} 1 & 0 & -1 & 0 \\ 0 & 0 & 0 & 0 \\ -1 & 0 & 1 & 0 \\ 0 & 0 & 0 & 0 \end{bmatrix},$$

$$\boldsymbol{c_\gamma^h} = \frac{w(3L/5)}{2}\begin{Bmatrix} 0 \\ -1 \\ 0 \\ -1 \end{Bmatrix}, \quad \boldsymbol{c_\alpha^h} = EA\alpha\Delta T\begin{Bmatrix} -1 \\ 0 \\ 1 \\ 0 \end{Bmatrix}.$$

The pre- and post-multiplying of the bar stiffness by the rotation matrix of direction cosines gives the inclined stiffness matrix as

$$\boldsymbol{S}^i = \frac{EA}{25L}\begin{bmatrix} 9 & -12 & -9 & 12 \\ -12 & 16 & 12 & -16 \\ -9 & 12 & 9 & -12 \\ 12 & -16 & -12 & 16 \end{bmatrix}$$

$$= \frac{EA}{75L}\begin{bmatrix} 27 & -36 & -27 & 36 \\ -36 & 48 & 36 & -48 \\ -27 & 36 & 27 & -36 \\ 36 & -48 & -36 & 48 \end{bmatrix}.$$

Since the reactions are required, the full 6×6 equilibrium system will be assembled even though only the partition at node 3 is needed to find the displacements. Assembling the two truss members and their loads gives

$$\frac{EA}{75L}\begin{bmatrix} 27 & -36 & 0 & 0 & -27 & 36 \\ -36 & 48 & 0 & 0 & 36 & -48 \\ 0 & 0 & 125 & 0 & -125 & 0 \\ 0 & 0 & 0 & 0 & 0 & 0 \\ -27 & 36 & -125 & 0 & 152 & -36 \\ 36 & -48 & 0 & 0 & -36 & 48 \end{bmatrix}\begin{Bmatrix} u_{x1} \\ u_{y1} \\ u_{x2} \\ u_{y2} \\ u_{x3} \\ u_{y3} \end{Bmatrix}$$

$$= \begin{Bmatrix} R_{x_1} \\ R_{y_1} \\ R_{x_2} \\ R_{y_2} \\ 0 \\ -P \end{Bmatrix} + \frac{wL}{2}\begin{Bmatrix} 0 \\ -1 \\ 0 \\ -3/5 \\ 0 \\ -1-3/5 \end{Bmatrix} + EA\alpha\Delta T\begin{Bmatrix} -3/5 \\ 4/5 \\ -1 \\ 0 \\ 1+3/5 \\ -4/5 \end{Bmatrix}.$$

Note that the rows and columns associated with u_{y_2} are all zero. If no EBC is applied to that degree of freedom, the system stiffness will be singular. In that case, the system would be kinematically unstable since the horizontal bar could rotate about node 3. The pinned boundary condition prevents that rotation and renders the system non-singular. Consider the case where the weight per unit length is neglected ($w = \gamma A = \rho g A = 0$) and there is no temperature change ($\Delta T = 0$); then the independent equilibrium equations, in rows and columns 5 and 6, reduce to

$$\frac{EA}{75L}\begin{bmatrix} 152 & -36 \\ -36 & 48 \end{bmatrix}\begin{Bmatrix} u_{x3} \\ u_{y3} \end{Bmatrix} = \begin{Bmatrix} 0 \\ -P \end{Bmatrix}.$$

Multiplying by the inverse of the stiffness gives $\begin{Bmatrix} u_{x3} \\ u_{y3} \end{Bmatrix} = \frac{-PL}{80EA}\begin{Bmatrix} 36 \\ 152 \end{Bmatrix}$ so the third node deflects down and to the left. Multiplying all of the displacements times the fixed partition of the stiffness gives the reactions as

$$\begin{Bmatrix} R_{x_1} \\ R_{y_1} \\ R_{x_2} \\ R_{y_2} \end{Bmatrix} = \frac{P}{4}\begin{Bmatrix} -3 \\ 4 \\ 3 \\ 0 \end{Bmatrix}.$$

The reaction results are also sketched in Fig. 9.1-2. By inspection, the sum of the horizontal forces is zero, as is the sum of the vertical forces, and the sum of the moments about any of the three nodes.

Example 9.1-2 Given: For the truss, of Fig. 9.1-2, given in Example 9.1-1, subject to just a point load determine the local axial displacements of each truss member and the axial force in each bar.

Solution: Equation (9.1-2) gives the two axial displacements of a bar in terms of the four displacements of the ends of the truss member. For the inclined member (1), those axial displacements are

$$\begin{bmatrix} \cos\theta_x & \cos\theta_y & 0 & 0 \\ 0 & 0 & \cos\theta_x & \cos\theta_y \end{bmatrix}\begin{Bmatrix} u_{x1} \\ u_{y1} \\ u_{x2} \\ u_{y2} \end{Bmatrix},$$

$$\begin{Bmatrix} u_1 \\ u_2 \end{Bmatrix}_b = \frac{1}{5}\begin{bmatrix} 3 & -4 & 0 & 0 \\ 0 & 0 & 3 & -4 \end{bmatrix}\frac{PL}{80EA}\begin{Bmatrix} 0 \\ 0 \\ -36 \\ -152 \end{Bmatrix} = \frac{PL}{4EA}\begin{Bmatrix} 0 \\ 5 \end{Bmatrix}.$$

The mechanical axial strain in that element is

$$\varepsilon = \boldsymbol{B}^e \boldsymbol{u}^e = \frac{1}{L}[-1 \quad 1]\frac{PL}{4EA}\begin{Bmatrix} 0 \\ 5 \end{Bmatrix} = \frac{5}{4}\frac{P}{EA},$$

and the force in the element is $F = EA\varepsilon = 5P/4$ tension. Of course, since it is the only member at the upper pin support, that pin reaction must be providing the same force. From Example 9.1-1, the first two reaction components were

$$\begin{Bmatrix} R_{x_1} \\ R_{y_1} \end{Bmatrix} = \frac{P}{4}\begin{Bmatrix} -3 \\ 4 \end{Bmatrix},$$

so reaction magnitude at node 1 is $R_1 = \sqrt{R_x^2 + R_y^2} = \sqrt{(-3P/4)^2 + P^2} = 5P/4$, as expected. Likewise, for the horizontal member (element 2) the two axial displacements are

$$\begin{Bmatrix} u_1 \\ u_2 \end{Bmatrix}_2 = \begin{bmatrix} 1 & 0 & 0 & 0 \\ 0 & 0 & 1 & 0 \end{bmatrix}\frac{PL}{80EA}\begin{Bmatrix} 0 \\ 0 \\ -36 \\ -152 \end{Bmatrix} = \frac{PL}{80EA}\begin{Bmatrix} 0 \\ -36 \end{Bmatrix}.$$

Its strain is

$$\varepsilon = \frac{1}{(3L/5)}[-1 \ 1]\frac{PL}{80EA}\begin{Bmatrix} 0 \\ -36 \end{Bmatrix} = \frac{-3}{4}\frac{P}{EA'}$$

and the force is $F = EA\varepsilon = -3P/4$, compression. By inspection that agrees with the third and fourth reaction in Example 9.1-1. The reactions are also shown in Fig. 9.1-2.

Example 9.1-3 Given: The two-bar truss in Example 9.1-2 is subjected only to a temperature increase of ΔT. Find the displacement of the free node (3) and the reaction forces.

Solution: Starting with the system matrices only the thermal load vector has changed:

$$\boldsymbol{c}_{\boldsymbol{\alpha}}^{\boldsymbol{T}} = EA\alpha\Delta T[-3 \quad 4 \quad -5 \quad 0 \quad (3+5) \quad (-4+0)]/5.$$

Retaining the free partition, the new equilibrium equations are

$$\frac{EA}{75L}\begin{bmatrix} 152 & -36 \\ -36 & 48 \end{bmatrix}\begin{Bmatrix} u_{x3} \\ u_{y3} \end{Bmatrix} = \frac{EA\alpha\Delta T}{5}\begin{Bmatrix} 8 \\ -4 \end{Bmatrix}.$$

Thus, the free displacements are

$$\begin{Bmatrix} u_{x3} \\ u_{y3} \end{Bmatrix} = \frac{L\alpha\Delta T}{5}\begin{Bmatrix} 3 \\ -4 \end{Bmatrix}.$$

The support reaction portions of the system matrices are

$$\frac{EA}{75L}\begin{bmatrix} -27 & 36 \\ 36 & -48 \\ -125 & 0 \\ 0 & 0 \end{bmatrix}\frac{L\alpha\Delta T}{5}\begin{Bmatrix} 3 \\ -4 \end{Bmatrix} = \begin{Bmatrix} R_{x_1} \\ R_{y_1} \\ R_{x_2} \\ R_{y_2} \end{Bmatrix} + \frac{EA\alpha\Delta T}{5}\begin{Bmatrix} -3 \\ 4 \\ -5 \\ 0 \end{Bmatrix}.$$

Simplifying:

$$\frac{EA\alpha\Delta T}{5}\begin{Bmatrix} -3 \\ 4 \\ -5 \\ 0 \end{Bmatrix} = \begin{Bmatrix} R_{x_1} \\ R_{y_1} \\ R_{x_2} \\ R_{y_2} \end{Bmatrix} + \frac{EA\alpha\Delta T}{5}\begin{Bmatrix} -3 \\ 4 \\ -5 \\ 0 \end{Bmatrix} \rightarrow \begin{Bmatrix} R_{x_1} \\ R_{y_1} \\ R_{x_2} \\ R_{y_2} \end{Bmatrix} = \mathbf{0}.$$

Therefore, the external reactions are all identically zero. Also the forces in each truss member are zero because, for this connectivity set, each member is free to expand. Node 3 of the inclined member moves on an arc, centered at support node 1, of radius $(1 + \alpha\Delta T)\,L$, and node 3 of the horizontal member moves on an arc, centered at support node 2, of radius $(1 + \alpha\Delta T)\,3L/5$. Where those two arcs intersect is where node 3 displaces to, without causing any member forces.

The free expansion leading to no member forces found here would not occur if any other restrained members were present in the truss. For example, if a third bar was added to the truss between node 3 and a new node 4 at the mid-point between nodes 1 and 2, then an increase in temperature would cause non-zero reactions as well as non-zero member forces. Such thermal-induced reaction forces are shown in Fig. 9.1-3, and they clearly satisfy Newton's equations of equilibrium by inspection.

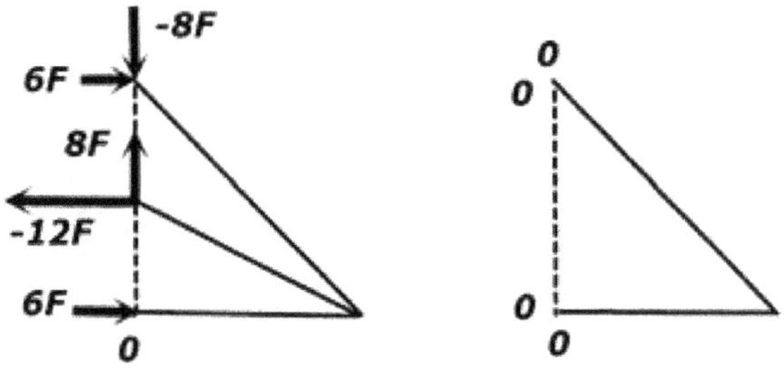

Fig. 9.1-3: Three- and two-bar (right) reactions for uniform temperature increase.

Example 9.1-4 Given: The three-member truss given in Fig. 9.1-4 has an inclined roller support that requires a multipoint constraints (MPC). Omitting the weight and the thermal loads, apply the single horizontal force at node 2 to numerically determine the displacements, the reactions, and the member axial loads by using the Matlab script. Check the reactions with Newton's Laws.

Solution: The property data were edited to set the specific weight and temperature change to zero. The roller constraint is

$$\vec{u} \cdot \vec{n} \equiv 0 = \left(u_{3x}\vec{i} + u_{3y}\vec{j}\right) \cdot \left(\frac{-4}{5}\vec{i} + \frac{3}{5}\vec{j}\right) = \frac{-4}{5}u_{3x} + \frac{3}{5}u_{3y} = 0$$

The MPC data input is planned such that the first unknown is multiplied by unity; thus, the two-point constraint equation is re-written as

$$u_{3x} - \frac{3}{4}u_{3y} = 0.$$

In the provided script this MPC is input as the two integer DOF numbers followed by the last two decimal coefficients in the constraint. In this case, that data stream is

$$3, 1 \quad 3, 2 \; -1.333333, \quad 0.0$$

The data sets were submitted to the planar truss script *Planar_Truss.m*, which is in the separate Application Library. The computed system displacements and reactions are:

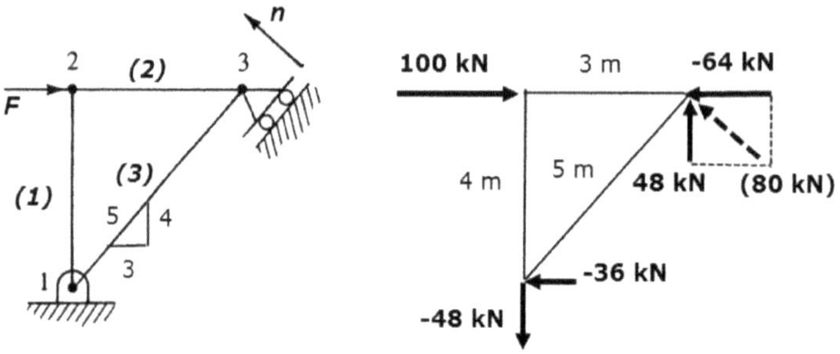

Fig. 9.1-4: Loads and reactions in a truss with an MPC.

Computed solution: (m)			System reactions (kN)			Axial force (kN)	
Node,	u_x	u_y	**Node,**	**DOF,**	**Reaction value**	**Elem,**	**Value**
1	0.0	0.0	1	1	−36,000	1	0.0
2	0.229713	0.0	1	2	−48,000	2	−1e5
3	0.0861728	0.114796	3	1	−64,000	3	6e4
			3	2	48,000		

Checking, the sum of the x-forces are $\sum F_x = 100{,}000 - 36{,}000 - 64{,}000 = 0$, as required. The sum of the y-forces are $\sum F_y = -48{,}000 + 48{,}000 = 0$, as required. Note that the reactions at node 3 from the MPC gives a vector resultant of 80,000 N perpendicular to the inclined support surface. Checking the moments about node 1 (with CCW positive) gives

$$\sum M_z = -100{,}000\,\text{N} \times 4\,\text{m} + 48{,}000\,\text{N} \times 3\,\text{m} + 64{,}000\,\text{N} \times 4\,\text{m} = 0.$$

The external load and reactions are shown in Fig. 9.1-4. Note that substituting displacement components at node 3 into the MPC gives

$$0.0861728 - \frac{3}{4}(0.114796) = 0.000076 \neq 0$$

which is not exactly satisfied but represents about a 0.01% error in the MPC equation. The accuracy of an MPC depends on how it is implemented and can be made to be exact. In the provided script the MPCs are implemented by the "penalty method" of Section 7.7 and can be made more accurate by changing one constant.

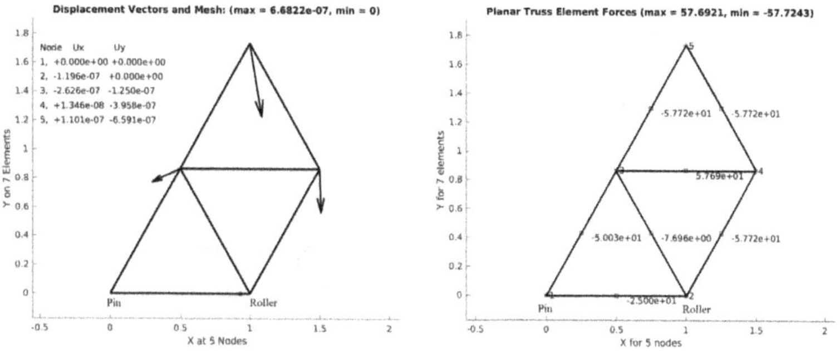

Fig. 9.1-5: Displacement vectors (left) and member axial forces in a planar truss.

```
File msh_remarks.txt
============ Begin Application Remarks ===============
 Seven bar steel planar truss of isosceles triangles
     weight loads and thermal loads not applied
         n_g = 2, n_e = 7, n_m = 5, n_d = 10
          Length in meters, Force in Newtons
============ End Application Remarks =================

File msh_bc_xyz.txt       File msh_typ_nodes.txt
 11  0.0     0.0           1  1, 2
 01  1.0     0.0           1  2, 3
 00  0.5     0.8667        1  1, 3
 00  1.5     0.8667        1  2, 4
 00  1.0     1.7334        1  3, 4
                           1  3, 5
                           1  5, 4

File msh_ebc.txt          File msh_load_pt.txt
 1    1  0.0               3  1  -50.
 1    2  0.0               5  2  -100.
 2    2  0.0

File msh_properties.txt (Area, E, Gamma, Alpha, del_T)
 2.0e-3 2.0e+11 0.0 1.000e-06 0.0
```

Fig. 9.1-6: Data files for the seven-bar planar truss model.

As another illustration of its application, it was applied to a seven-bar truss shown in Fig. 9.1-5. All of the members had the same properties. The steel truss was pinned at the lower left, supported by a horizontal roller at the lower right. The top point carried a vertical load, the middle left point, a horizontal load, and the weights were omitted. These data are superimposed on the node displacement plot on the left of that figure. The right portion of the figure shows the computed axial forces in each bar member, with negative being compression. To review the inputs to the general finite element library, the input files are summarized in Fig. 9.1-6.

9.2 Space Truss

Unlike beam and frame members, for any truss member only the value of its cross-sectional area matters. The orientation of the area about the local member axis does not matter. That means that the extension from planar truss analysis to space truss analysis is relatively simple. The z-coordinates of the nodes are required to define their locations, and their differences on a member define a third direction cosine required for an expanded transformation matrix to relate the local bar axial displacements to the six displacement components of the space truss member. Therefore, (9.1-2) expands to be

$$\begin{Bmatrix} u_1 \\ u_2 \end{Bmatrix}_b = \begin{bmatrix} \cos\theta_x & \cos\theta_y & \cos\theta_z & 0 & 0 & 0 \\ 0 & 0 & 0 & \cos\theta_x & \cos\theta_y & \cos\theta_z \end{bmatrix} \times \begin{Bmatrix} u_{x_1} \\ u_{y_1} \\ u_{z_1} \\ u_{x_2} \\ u_{y_2} \\ u_{z_2} \end{Bmatrix}. \tag{9.2-1}$$

The local bar stiffness matrix expands in the same way as (9.1-4) and (9.1-7):

$$\begin{array}{cc} \boldsymbol{S}^{\boldsymbol{e}}_{\boldsymbol{G}} = [\boldsymbol{T}(\theta)]^{\boldsymbol{T}}\, \boldsymbol{S}^e\, [\boldsymbol{T}(\theta)] \quad \text{and} & \boldsymbol{c}^{\boldsymbol{e}}_{\boldsymbol{G}} = [\boldsymbol{T}(\theta)]^{\boldsymbol{T}}\, \boldsymbol{c}^e \\ 6\times 6 = (6\times 2)\,(2\times 2)\,(2\times 6) & 6\times 1 = (6\times 2)\,(2\times 1)\,. \end{array}$$

Of course, point forces at any node can be applied in any or all of the three directions. Likewise, any or all of the three displacement components at a node can have prescribed values. That also means that the packed boundary condition flag assigned to each node now contains three digits: the left-most flags the x-displacement; the center one flags the y-displacement, etc. A packed flag value of 000 means that the joint is completely free, a value of 100 means only the

x-displacement is prescribed. A value of 111 means all displacements at the node are prescribed. Clearly, any mixture of prescribed displacements can be flagged by other combinations of the three digits. An application script *Space_Truss.m* was obtained from the planar truss script *Planar_Truss.m* by mainly changing the joint DOF transformation matrix (9.1-2) to

$$\begin{Bmatrix} u_1 \\ u_2 \end{Bmatrix}_b = \begin{bmatrix} \cos\theta_x & \cos\theta_y & \cos\theta_z & 0 & 0 & 0 \\ 0 & 0 & 0 & \cos\theta_x & \cos\theta_y & \cos\theta_z \end{bmatrix} \times \begin{Bmatrix} u_{x_1} \\ u_{y_1} \\ u_{z_1} \\ u_{x_2} \\ u_{y_2} \\ u_{z_2} \end{Bmatrix}, \qquad (9.2\text{-}2)$$

and to extend helpful plots from two-dimensional to three-dimensional. Increasing the number of displacement components from two to three simply required editing the beginning control section and setting $n_g = 3$.

Example 9.2-1: Figure 9.2-1 shows a space truss made of structural steel (E = 30e6 psi) with horizontal and vertical forces at the top. Prepare the required data files for this truss and obtain the displacements and member forces using a *Space_Truss.m* script.

Solution: While commercial codes often allow mixed units and convert those to a hidden SI system, for this software the user must provide the data in consistent units. Having accepted the above value and units for the modulus of elasticity that requires that coordinates be given in inches, areas in inches^2, forces in pounds. That also means that the results will appear with the displacements in inches, reaction forces in pounds, member lengths in inches, member axial forces in pounds, and member stresses in psi.

In addition, the member descriptions are all 24 WF 100. That is an American standard Wide Flange beam and a web search shows it

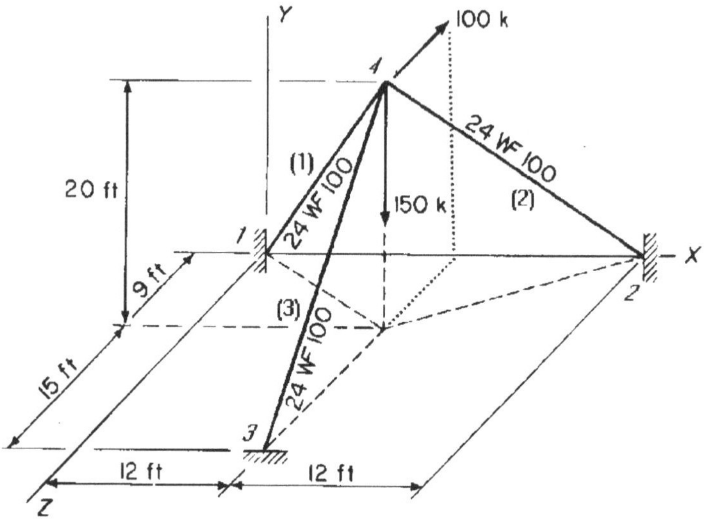

Fig. 9.2-1: Sample space truss.

has a nominal depth of 24 inches and weighs about 100 pounds per foot. Additional tabulated details include the cross-sectional area of 29.6 inches, and the area moments of inertias. The weight per unit length has been neglected, but could be input as the optional third property of 8.333 pounds per inch. The fourth and fifth omitted optional properties in the script are the coefficient of thermal expansion and the uniform change in temperature to allow the inclusion of thermal loads. The utilized data are echoed in Fig. 9.2-2, and the computed results are given in Fig. 9.2-3. This truss is statically determinate. Taking the moments about a line through two of the supports will give the reaction force, and member force, of the off-line member. However, the displacements can only easily be found using a finite element simulation.

```
Space_Truss
User control variables
n_g number of DOF per node          = 3
n_n number of nodes per element     = 2
n_s dimension of physical space     = 3

User logic flags: turn on(1)/off(0)
echo_p   listing of properties           = 1
el_react listing of element reactions    = 1
load_pt  point source (can be zero)      = 1
post     post-processing option          = 1

Begin Phase 2, read application data sets
Read 4 nodes:
node, bc_flags, 3 coordinates
1, 111 0   0   0
2, 111 288 0   0
3, 111 144 0   288
4, 000 144 240 108

Read 3 elements with type & 2 nodes each
Element number, type, connection list
1, 1 1 4
2, 1 2 4
3, 1 3 4

Read 1 materials with 2 properties
2.9600e+01   3.0000e+07
Above properties are: A, E

Read 2 point sources:
Node, DOF,  Source_value
4  2  -150000
4  3  -100000
Total x input forces   = 0
Total y input forces   = -150000
Total z input forces   = -100000

Read 9 EBC sets:
Node, DOF, Value.
1     1     0
1     2     0
1     3     0
2     1     0
2     2     0
2     3     0
3     1     0
3     2     0
3     3     0
```

Fig. 9.2-2: Space truss input data.

```
Begin Phase 3, assemble (scatter) elements
Begin Phase 4, modify matrices for EBC
Begin Phase 5, solve modified system
Computed Solution:
Node, 3 displacements per node
1,    0.000e+00  0.000e+00  0.000e+00
2,    0.000e+00  0.000e+00  0.000e+00
3,    0.000e+00  0.000e+00  0.000e+00
4,    0.000e+00 -2.385e-02 -5.086e-02

Reactions at essential BCs
Node, DOF, Reaction Value
1     1     5.3125e+04
1     2     8.8542e+04
1     3     3.9844e+04
2     1    -5.3125e+04
2     2     8.8542e+04
2     3     3.9844e+04
3     1     0.0000e+00
3     2    -2.7083e+04
3     3     2.0312e+04
Total reaction values = [0 1.5E+5  1.0E+5]

Begin Phase 6, use the answers
Member Force          Stress        Length
1,     -1.107e+05   -3.739e+03   3.000e+02
2,     -1.107e+05   -3.739e+03   3.000e+02
3,      3.385e+04    1.144e+03   3.000e+02
WARNING: Negative forces can cause buckling
```

Fig. 9.2-3: Space truss results.

9.3 Summary

$n\_b \longleftrightarrow n_b$ $\equiv$ Number of boundary segments
$n\_d \longleftrightarrow n_d$ $\equiv$ Number of system unknowns $= n\_g \times n\_m$
$n\_e \longleftrightarrow n_e$ $\equiv$ Number of elements
$n\_g \longleftrightarrow n_g$ $\equiv$ Number of generalized DOF per node
$n\_i \longleftrightarrow n_i$ $\equiv$ Number of unknowns per element $= n\_g \times n\_n$
$n\_m \longleftrightarrow n_m$ $\equiv$ Number of mesh nodes
$n\_n \longleftrightarrow n_n$ $\equiv$ Number of nodes per element
$n\_p \longleftrightarrow n_p$ $\equiv$ Dimension of parametric space
$n\_q \longleftrightarrow n_q$ $\equiv$ Number of total quadrature points
$n\_r \longleftrightarrow n_r$ $\equiv$ Number of rows in the $\boldsymbol{B}^e$ matrix (and material matrix)
$n\_s \longleftrightarrow n_s$ $\equiv$ Dimension of physical space

b = boundary segment number e = element number

$\subset$= subset $\cup$ = union of sets

Boundary, element, and system unknowns: $\boldsymbol{\delta}^b \subset_b \boldsymbol{\delta}^e \subset_e \boldsymbol{\delta}$

Boolean extraction arrays: $\boldsymbol{\delta}^b \equiv \boldsymbol{\beta}_b \boldsymbol{\delta}, \boldsymbol{\delta}^e \equiv \boldsymbol{\beta}_e \boldsymbol{\delta}$

Geometry: $\Gamma^b \subset \Omega^e \equiv$ Boundary segment $\Omega^e \equiv$ Element domain

$\Omega = \cup_e \Omega^e \equiv$ Solution domain $\Gamma = \cup_b \Gamma^b \equiv$ Domain boundary

Interpolation: $u(\boldsymbol{x}) = H(r)\,\boldsymbol{\delta}^e = u(\boldsymbol{x})^T = \boldsymbol{\delta}^{e^T} \boldsymbol{H}(r)^T$.

Local gradient: $\partial u(r)/\partial r = (\partial \boldsymbol{H}(r)/\partial r)\,\boldsymbol{\delta}^e$.

Physical gradient: $\partial u(x)/\partial x = (\partial u(r)/\partial r)\,(\partial r/\partial x) = (\partial u(r)/\partial r)\,(\partial x/\partial r)^{-1}$,

$\partial u(x)/\partial x = [(\partial \boldsymbol{G}(r)/\partial r)\boldsymbol{x}^e]^{-1} (\partial \boldsymbol{H}(r)/\partial r)\,\boldsymbol{\delta}^e \equiv B(r)\,\boldsymbol{\delta}^e$.

Local line element stiffness matrix:

$$\boldsymbol{S}_{\boldsymbol{k}}^{\boldsymbol{e}} = \int_{L^e} \frac{d\boldsymbol{H}(r)}{dx}^T E(x)\,A(x) \frac{d\boldsymbol{H}(r)}{dx} dx.$$

A symmetry plane has a zero normal displacement.
Thermal loads for linear quadratic bar:

$$\boldsymbol{c}_{\boldsymbol{\alpha}}^{\boldsymbol{e}} = E^e A^e \alpha^e \Delta T^e \begin{Bmatrix} -1 \\ 1 \end{Bmatrix}.$$

Equilibrium equations for a linear bar element:

$$\frac{E^e A^e}{L^e} \begin{bmatrix} 1 & -1 \\ -1 & 1 \end{bmatrix} \begin{Bmatrix} u_1 \\ u_2 \end{Bmatrix} = \begin{Bmatrix} P_1 \\ P_2 \end{Bmatrix} + \frac{1}{6L^e} \begin{bmatrix} 2 & 1 \\ 1 & 2 \end{bmatrix} \begin{Bmatrix} q_1 \\ q_2 \end{Bmatrix} + E^e A^e \alpha^e \Delta T^e \begin{Bmatrix} -1 \\ 1 \end{Bmatrix}.$$

Planar truss element: $n_g = 2$, $n_n = 2$, $n_i = 4$, stiffness, thermal and gravity loads

$$\cos\theta_x \equiv C_x = \Delta x/L, \quad \cos\theta_y \equiv C_y = \sin\theta_x = \Delta y/L,$$
$$\cos\theta_z \equiv C_z = \Delta z/L.$$

Transforming from the local bar to global truss matrices

$$\boldsymbol{S_G^e} = [\boldsymbol{T}(\theta)]^{\boldsymbol{T}}\, \boldsymbol{S}^e\, [\boldsymbol{T}(\theta)], \quad \boldsymbol{c_G^e} = [\boldsymbol{T}(\theta)]^{\boldsymbol{T}}\, \boldsymbol{c}^e,$$

$$[\boldsymbol{T}(\theta)] = \begin{bmatrix} \boldsymbol{t}(\theta) & \mathbf{0} \\ \mathbf{0} & \boldsymbol{t}(\theta) \end{bmatrix}.$$

Planar truss bar without previous axial load:

$$\boldsymbol{S}^e = \frac{E^e A^e}{L^e} \begin{bmatrix} 1 & -1 \\ -1 & 1 \end{bmatrix}, \quad \boldsymbol{c}^e = E^e A^e \alpha^e \Delta T^e \begin{Bmatrix} -1 \\ 1 \end{Bmatrix},$$

$$\boldsymbol{t}(\theta) = [\cos\theta_x \;\; (\cos\theta_y = -\sin\theta_x)]$$

$$\begin{Bmatrix} u_1 \\ u_2 \end{Bmatrix}_b = \begin{bmatrix} \cos\theta_x & \cos\theta_y & 0 & 0 \\ 0 & 0 & \cos\theta_x & \cos\theta_y \end{bmatrix} \begin{Bmatrix} u_{x1} \\ u_{y1} \\ u_{x2} \\ u_{y2} \end{Bmatrix}.$$

Global planar stiffness matrix, thermal and gravity load vectors:

$$\boldsymbol{S_G^e} = [\boldsymbol{T}(\theta)]^{\boldsymbol{T}} \frac{E^e A^e}{L^e} \begin{bmatrix} 1 & -1 \\ -1 & 1 \end{bmatrix} [\boldsymbol{T}(\theta)]$$

$$= \frac{E^e A^e}{L^e} \begin{bmatrix} C_x C_x & C_x C_y & -C_x C_x & -C_x C_y \\ C_x C_y & C_y C_y & -C_x C_y & -C_y C_y \\ -C_x C_x & -C_x C_y & C_x C_x & C_x C_y \\ -C_x C_y & -C_y C_y & C_x C_y & C_y C_y \end{bmatrix},$$

$$(4 \times 2)\,(2 \times 2)\,(2 \times 4) = (4 \times 4)$$

$$\boldsymbol{c_\alpha^e} = [\boldsymbol{T}(\theta)]^{\boldsymbol{T}}\, E^e A^e \alpha^e \Delta T^e \begin{Bmatrix} -1 \\ 1 \end{Bmatrix} = E^e A^e \alpha^e \Delta T^e \begin{Bmatrix} -C_x \\ -C_y \\ C_x \\ C_y \end{Bmatrix},$$

$$\boldsymbol{c_\gamma^e} = \frac{\gamma A L}{2} \begin{Bmatrix} 0 \\ -1 \\ 0 \\ -1 \end{Bmatrix}$$

$$(4 \times 1) = (4 \times 2)\,(2 \times 1).$$

Space truss bar without previous axial load:

$$\boldsymbol{S}^e = \frac{E^e A^e}{L^e}\begin{bmatrix} 1 & -1 \\ -1 & 1 \end{bmatrix}, \quad \boldsymbol{c}^e = E^e A^e \alpha^e \Delta T^e \begin{Bmatrix} -1 \\ 1 \end{Bmatrix},$$

$$\boldsymbol{t}(\theta) = [\cos\theta_x \ \cos\theta_y \ \cos\theta_z],$$

$$\begin{Bmatrix} u_1 \\ u_2 \end{Bmatrix}_b = \begin{bmatrix} \cos\theta_x & \cos\theta_y & \cos\theta_z & 0 & 0 & 0 \\ 0 & 0 & 0 & \cos\theta_x & \cos\theta_y & \cos\theta_z \end{bmatrix} \begin{Bmatrix} u_{x1} \\ u_{y1} \\ u_{z1} \\ u_{x2} \\ u_{y2} \\ u_{z2} \end{Bmatrix}.$$

Planar truss bar with previous tension load N; axial stiffness and initial (geometric) stiffness:

$$\boldsymbol{S}^e = \frac{E^e A^e}{L^e}\begin{bmatrix} 1 & 0 & -1 & 0 \\ 0 & 0 & 0 & 0 \\ -1 & 0 & 1 & 0 \\ 0 & 0 & 0 & 0 \end{bmatrix}, \quad \boldsymbol{S}_i^e = \frac{N^e}{L^e}\begin{bmatrix} 0 & 0 & 0 & 0 \\ 0 & 1 & 0 & -1 \\ 0 & 0 & 0 & 0 \\ 0 & -1 & 0 & 1 \end{bmatrix},$$

$$\boldsymbol{t}(\theta) = \begin{bmatrix} C_x & C_y & 0 & 0 \\ -C_y & C_x & 0 & 0 \end{bmatrix}$$

9.4 Review

1. Re-solve Example 9.1-1 where the two bar steel truss in Fig. 9.1-2 supports a downward vertical downward load of $P = -20\,\text{kN}$ at node 3, along with a horizontal force of $F = 20\,\text{kN}$. Begin with the previously assembled equilibrium equations:

$$\frac{EA}{75L}\begin{bmatrix} 27 & -36 & 0 & 0 & -27 & 36 \\ -36 & 48 & 0 & 0 & 36 & -48 \\ 0 & 0 & 125 & 0 & -125 & 0 \\ 0 & 0 & 0 & 0 & 0 & 0 \\ -27 & 36 & -125 & 0 & 152 & -36 \\ 36 & -48 & 0 & 0 & -36 & 48 \end{bmatrix} \begin{Bmatrix} u_{x1} \\ u_{y1} \\ u_{x2} \\ u_{y2} \\ u_{x3} \\ u_{y3} \end{Bmatrix} = \begin{Bmatrix} R_{x1} \\ R_{y1} \\ R_{x2} \\ R_{y2} \\ F \\ -P \end{Bmatrix}.$$

   Enforce the four Dirichlet boundary conditions, solve for the two displacements, and determine the four reaction forces.

Chapter 10

Applications of One-Dimensional Hermite Elements

10.1 Introduction

Most one-dimensional applications of Hermite polynomials involve ODEs of even degree four and higher because their equivalent integral forms require the inter-element continuity of at least the first derivative of the solution. A vast number of fourth-order ODEs for beam and frame (the bending extension of trusses) studies have been published. Since those structural elements are very common, many solutions of the fourth-order ODEs, with several different boundary conditions and/or various source (loading) terms, are available in engineering handbooks. To introduce the engineering terminology, a beam is a one-dimensional structure intended to support loads (forces and moments) perpendicular to its axis. In other works, axial effects are not considered in a beam. A beam-column is a beam that is also subjected to axial displacements and forces (like those in Chapter 8). A frame is a structural system formed by connecting beam-columns in a non-collinear manner.

Hermite interpolation can also be applied to lower-order ODEs if and only if the coefficients and sources (material properties and loads) are constant or smoothly varying over the entire domain. Those applications can improve the accuracy of the result when using a small number of degrees of freedom (DOF). Also, some non-essential boundary conditions (NBCs) can be exactly satisfied in the system matrices resulting from a Hermite interpolation model.

That contrasts with C^0 interpolations where the NBC are only satisfied in a weak sense.

All of the prior examples in Chapter 8 were based on the Galerkin method of weighted residuals. For completeness, the same ODE in Example 8.2-5 solved by the Galerkin method will be solved now by the Least Squares method of weighted residuals which is quite different. The least-squares approach always yields a symmetric set of matrix equations (which is desirable), but it also requires a higher level of interpolation continuity (which is difficult in higher dimensional physical spaces).

Example 10.1-1* Given: Using the classic least squares method of weighted residuals, formulate the approximation of the ODE:

$$d^2u^*/dx^2 + cx = 0, x =]0, L[.$$

Then set $c = L = 1$ and apply the boundary conditions that $u*(0) = 0$ and $du*(L)/dx = 0$ and compare the result to the cubic exact solution

$$u^*(x) = cL^2x/2 - cx^3/6.$$

Solution: To employ classic least squares, it is necessary to first define the residual error in terms of the unknown solution, $\boldsymbol{u^e}$. Approximate $u^*(x) \cong u(x) = \boldsymbol{H}(x)\boldsymbol{u^e}$ and assume a linear geometry mapping of $x(r) = x_1 + rL^e$ so the Jacobian is constant. Then the residual error is

$$R^e(x) = \frac{d^2\boldsymbol{H}(x)}{dx^2}\boldsymbol{u^e} + cx \neq 0.$$

The least-squares weighting is

$$w_k(x) = \frac{\partial R^e(x)}{\partial u_k^e} = \frac{d^2H_k(x)}{dx^2}, \quad \text{and} \quad \boldsymbol{w}(x)^T = \frac{d^2\boldsymbol{H^T}(x)}{dx^2}.$$

Then the weighted residual null vector is

$$\boldsymbol{I} = \int_0^L \boldsymbol{w}(x)^T R^e(x)\,dx = \boldsymbol{0}$$
$$= \int_0^L \frac{d^2\boldsymbol{H^T}(x)}{dx^2}\left(\frac{d^2\boldsymbol{H}(x)}{dx^2}\boldsymbol{u^e} + cx\right)dx.$$

The highest derivative in this integral is two. To eventually replace the integral as one of an assembly of elements, calculus requires that the solution across element interfaces must be continuous to one derivative less. In other words, the interpolations for this approach must have C^1 continuity between elements. That means the function and its slope must be continuous. Such interpolations are members of the Hermite polynomial family and have $u(x)$ and $du(x)/dx \equiv \theta(x)$ as the nodal DOF ($n_g = 2$). The element matrix system becomes

$$\left[\int_0^{L^e} \frac{d^2\boldsymbol{H}^{\boldsymbol{T}}(x)}{dx^2}\frac{d^2\boldsymbol{H}(x)}{dx^2} L^e dr\right] \boldsymbol{u}^{\boldsymbol{e}} + \left\{\int_0^{L^e} \frac{d^2\boldsymbol{H}^{\boldsymbol{T}}(x)}{dx^2} cxL^e dr\right\} = \{\boldsymbol{0}\}.$$

The simplest element in that family is the two-node Hermite line element with two DOFs per node. Thus, the element includes $n_n n_g = n_i = 2 \times 2 = 4$ independent DOFs. They define a cubic polynomial in one-dimensional space. The resulting interpolations, given previously in the summary of Chapter 2, are listed in the library function *Hermite_1D_C1_library.m* and are

$$u(x) = \left[\left(1 - 3r^2 + 2r^3\right) \ \left(r - 2r^2 + r^3\right) L^e \ \left(3r^2 - 2r^3\right) \right.$$
$$\left.\left(r^3 - r^2\right) L^e\right] \begin{Bmatrix} u_1 \\ \theta_1 \\ u_2 \\ \theta_2 \end{Bmatrix}^e .$$

The second x-derivative is

$$\frac{d^2u}{dx^2} = \frac{d^2u}{dr^2}\frac{dr^2}{dr^2} = \frac{d^2u}{dr^2}\frac{1}{(L^e)^2} = \frac{1}{(L^e)^2}\frac{d^2\boldsymbol{H}(r)}{dr^2},$$

$$\frac{d^2u}{dx^2} = \frac{1}{(L^e)^2}[(-6 + 12r) \ (-4 + 6r)L^e \ (6 - 12r) \ (6r - 2)L^e]$$
$$\times \begin{Bmatrix} u_1 \\ \theta_1 \\ u_2 \\ \theta_2 \end{Bmatrix}^e .$$

Substituting $d^2\boldsymbol{H}(x)/dx^2$ into the above two integrals yields the governing matrix system, before enforcing the essential conditions as

$$\frac{1}{L^{e^3}}\begin{bmatrix} 12 & 6L^e & -12 & 6L^e \\ 6L^e & 4L^{e2} & -6L^e & -12 \\ -12 & -6L^e & 12 & -6L^e \\ 6L^e & 2L^{e2} & -6L^e & 4L^{e2} \end{bmatrix}\begin{Bmatrix} u_1 \\ \theta_1 \\ u_2 \\ \theta_2 \end{Bmatrix} = \begin{Bmatrix} -1 \\ x_1 \\ 1 \\ -L^e(L^e x_1 + 1) \end{Bmatrix}.$$

Note here that the quantities ($du(0)/dx \equiv \theta_1$ and $du(L)/dx \equiv \theta_2$) that are usually defined as the NBCs appear as nodal DOFs in the Hermite form and can be specifically enforced. That is because Hermite interpolation requires that the source (here cx) not be discontinuous, yet the Galerkin assumption does not have that restriction. Here the essential boundary condition (EBC) $u_1 = 0 = u(0)$ and the NBC of $du(L)/dx \equiv \theta_2 = 0$ can also be specified. Multiply columns 1 and 4 by their known values (an EBC and a NBC) and carry those known values to the right-hand side. Then, only two independent equations remain in the second and third rows (the left slope and right solution value):

$$\frac{1}{L^{e^3}}\begin{bmatrix} 4L^{e2} & -6L^e \\ -6L^e & 4L^{e2} \end{bmatrix}\begin{Bmatrix} \theta_1 \\ u_2 \end{Bmatrix} = \begin{Bmatrix} x_1 \\ 1 \end{Bmatrix} - \frac{u_1}{L^{e^3}}\begin{Bmatrix} 6L^e \\ -12 \end{Bmatrix}$$

$$- \frac{\theta_2}{L^{e^3}}\begin{Bmatrix} -12 \\ -6L^e \end{Bmatrix} = \begin{Bmatrix} x_1 \\ 1 \end{Bmatrix}.$$

Inverting gives the following solution:

$$\begin{Bmatrix} \theta_1 \\ u_2 \end{Bmatrix} = \frac{L^e}{6}\begin{Bmatrix} 3(L^e + 2x_1) \\ L^e(2L^e + 3x_1) \end{Bmatrix}.$$

The solution is exact because the exact solution is included in the cubic interpolation.

10.2 General Case Fourth-Order Beam Equation

Figure 10.2-1 shows the transverse displacement, $v(x)$, of a beam on an elastic foundation. The beam is connected to a continuous series of foundation springs, of stiffness k per unit length. The other end of the foundation spring has a known displacement, v_f, which is almost always zero. The differential equation of transverse equilibrium of a beam, of flexural stiffness *EI*, resting on a foundation, with a transverse load per unit length of $w(x)$, subjected to a tensile axial load N is

$$\frac{d^2}{dx^2}\left[EI(x)\frac{d^2v}{dx^2}\right] - \frac{d}{dx}\left[N(x)\frac{dv}{dx}\right] + k(x)[v - v_\infty] - w(x) = 0$$

or

$$\frac{d^2}{dx^2}\left[EI(x)\frac{d^2v}{dx^2}\right] - N(x)\frac{d^2v}{dx^2} - \frac{dN(x)}{dx}\frac{dv}{dx} + k(x)[v - v_\infty] - w(x) = 0, \qquad (10.2\text{-}1)$$

where $v(x)$ is the transverse displacement of the beam. When the foundation effect is present, the structure is usually called a beam on an elastic foundation, which is abbreviated as BOEF. The beam equation is a fourth-order ordinary differential equation. Therefore, it will generally need four boundary conditions.

Each beam has a cross-section with two principle axes associated with the second-moments of inertia, I_{zz}, I_{yy} and I_{zy}. For the coordinate system shown above, the principle inertia is the former: $I \equiv I_{zz} = \int_A y^2 dA$. Its defining axis is the z-axis coming out of the

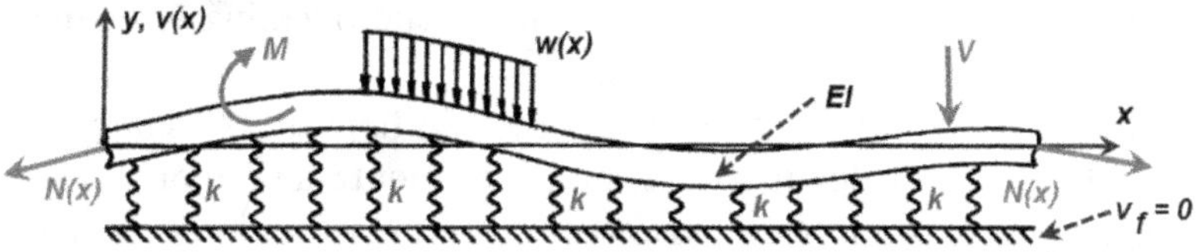

Fig. 10.2-1: A beam-column on an elastic foundation.

paper and lies in the horizontal plane. Conversely, the minor inertia y-axis lies in the vertical plane of the paper. Any changes in the two inertia axis directions becomes important if the beam is part of a space frame member located in general three-dimensional space, as discussed later.

The distributed load per unit length can include point transverse shear loads, V, by using the Dirac Delta distribution. Likewise, employing a doublet distribution in defining $f(x)$ allows for the inclusion of point couples, or moments, M. Related physical quantities are the slope (angle of rotation $\ll 1$), $\theta(x) = v'(x)$, the bending moment, $M(x) = EIv''(x)$, and the transverse shear force, $V(x) = EIv'''(x)$. Engineers designing beams are usually interested in the last two quantities since they define the stress levels and the material failure criteria. That means that a model used in designing a beam should have accurate third derivatives, or a fine mesh. The sign conventions are that the position, x, is positive to the right, the deflection, v, point forces, P, and the line load, w, are positive in the y-direction (upward), and the slopes and moments are positive in the counter-clockwise direction.

The axial force, $N(x)$, is positive when it is in tension, which stabilizes the system, and negative when in compression, which de-stabilizes the system. Those two cases are typically called a "tensioned-beam" and a "beam-column", respectively. When the axial force is in tension, the solution to the homogeneous equation tends to smoothly decay away from the supports. Conversely, when the axial force is in compression, the solution to the homogeneous solution oscillates and decays very slowly. Frequently, the axial force of interest is an unknown global constant to be computed. Then the ODE becomes an eigenproblem to determine the axial force that causes buckling. Eigenproblems, including the buckling of beams are covered later in Chapter 12.

The rate of change in the axial force, $dN(x)/dx$, is usually small, especially over the length of a single element. Therefore, it could be neglected in some cases. However, if the axial force is a given function of x, then the gradient of $N(x)$ needs to be retained in the approximate solution. As seen in what follows, the retention of the $dN(x)/dx$ contribution leads to a non-symmetric set of system matrix equations.

Since the foundation springs are restrained by the displacement v_∞ at their end not connected to the beam, there can be no rigid body motion of the beam. In other words, the assembled equations should never be singular and it is acceptable to just have NBCs applied to the beam. A simple Winkler foundation model like this one can push or pull on the beam as needed and no gaps can occur. If a foundation is not present, then enough EBCs must be supplied to prevent rotation about the z-axis and to prevent translation in the y-direction.

The exact solution of the homogeneous ($f = 0$) general form of (10.2-1) is given in terms of hyperbolic sines and cosines. Based on Tong's Theorem, exact solutions at the nodes are obtained if such functions are used in a finite element model. Advanced elements of that type have been applied with excellent results. Only when there is no foundation support ($k = 0$) and no axial force ($N = 0$) will the simplified homogeneous solution of

$$\frac{d^2}{dx^2}\left[EI\frac{d^2v}{dx^2}\right] - f(x) = 0 \tag{10.2-2}$$

be a cubic polynomial. All of the Hermite polynomials include at least the cubic. Therefore, a finite element model of (10.2-3) using a Hermite interpolation will *always* give exact values of $v(x)$ at the nodes in the mesh, even if it is only approximate at other points in the element.

When the model ODE represents a beam, then the following quantities are considered in engineering studies:

$EIv''''(x) = f(x)$	load per unit length,	Differential equation
$EIv'''(x) = V(x)$	transverse shear force,	Non-essential boundary condition
$EIv''(x) = M(x)$	bending moment,	Non-essential boundary condition
$v'(x) = \theta(x)$	slope,	Essential boundary condition
$v(x) =$	deflection,	Essential boundary condition.

There are six exact solution cases for the homogeneous portion of (10.2-1) that depend on the relative magnitudes of the coefficients EI, N, and k. Those solutions depend on the eigenvalue solution of the homogeneous equation and will not be considered in general in this section (eigenproblems are covered in Chapter 12). Of course, a numerical solution of that equation is also dependent on the relative values of those coefficients but automatically finds the best approximate solution.

10.3 Integral Form

To apply the Galerkin weak form, the governing ODE is multiplied by $v(x)$ and the integral over the length of the beam is set to zero. The highest (fourth) derivative term is always present, and needs to be integrated twice by parts to reduce the inter-element continuity requirement. That integral becomes

$$I_E = \int_0^L v \frac{d^2}{dx^2}\left(E(x)I(x)\frac{d^2v}{dx^2}\right)dx, \tag{10.3-1}$$

$$I_E = \left[v\frac{d}{dx}\left(E(x)I(x)\frac{d^2v}{dx^2}\right)\right]_0^L - \int_0^L \frac{dv}{dx}\frac{d}{dx}\left(E(x)I(x)\frac{d^2v}{dx^2}\right)dx,$$

$$I_E = \left[v\frac{d}{dx}\left(E(x)I(x)\frac{d^2v}{dx^2}\right)\right]_0^L - \left[\frac{dv}{dx}\left(E(x)I(x)\frac{d^2v}{dx^2}\right)\right]_0^L + \int_0^L \frac{d^2v}{dx^2}\left(E(x)I(x)\frac{d^2v}{dx^2}\right)dx. \tag{10.3-2}$$

The integration by parts brings the two possible NBCs, or reactions, into the integral form. Those terms are the transverse shear force, $d\left(EId^2v/dx^2\right)/dx$, and the moment, EId^2v/dx^2. The first NBC term is the product of the displacement and the transverse shear force at the endpoints, while the second term is the product of the slope (angle) and the point moment at the endpoints. Both of those products are definitions of mechanical work. Thus, the contributions from the fourth derivative term in the ODEs of (10.2-1) or (10.2-2), for $N = 0$, are

$$I_E = [vV(x)]_0^L - \left[\frac{dv}{dx}M(x)\right]_0^L + \int_0^L \frac{d^2v}{dx^2}\left(E(x)I(x)\frac{d^2v}{dx^2}\right)dx.$$

The second integral term originally is non-symmetric because it also has unbalanced derivative orders. Creating a symmetric form requires integration by parts:

$$I_N = \int_0^L v\left(-N(x)\frac{d^2v}{dx^2}\right)dx = \left[v\left(-N(x)\frac{dv}{dx}\right)\right]_0^L + \int_0^L \frac{dv}{dx}N\frac{dv}{dx}dx. \tag{10.3-3}$$

For small deflections, the slope is approximately equal to its tangent. Thus, the boundary term $N dv/dx \approx N_y$ is the transverse (y-) component of the axial force in the deformed beam. The final integral form contains second derivatives (d^2v/dx^2) as its highest derivative term. The presence of second derivatives in the integral form means that calculus requires the elements to have inter-element continuity of the deflection and the slope, $v(x)$ and $\theta(x) = v'(x)$. Such elements are said to have an inter-element continuity of C^1. Therefore, each shared beam node must have two DOFs, at least. The Galerkin models for the other terms in (10.2-1) were covered in Chapter 8 and are now appended to give the complete governing Galerkin integral form of the beam-column equilibrium equation:

$$\begin{aligned} I = &\left[v\left\{\frac{d}{dx}\left(E(x)I(x)\frac{d^2v}{dx^2}\right) - N(x)\frac{dv}{dx}\right\}\right]_0^L \\ &- \left[\frac{dv}{dx}\left(E(x)I(x)\frac{d^2v}{dx^2}\right)\right]_0^L \\ &+ \int_0^L \frac{d^2v}{dx^2}\left(E(x)I(x)\frac{d^2v}{dx^2}\right)dx \\ &+ \int_0^L \frac{dv}{dx}N\frac{dv}{dx}\,dx + \int_0^L \frac{dN}{dx}\frac{dv}{dx}dx \\ &+ \int_0^L vkv\,dx - \int_0^L vv_\infty dx - \int_0^L vf\,dx = 0. \end{aligned} \tag{10.3-4}$$

The first NBC states that when $N \neq 0$, the consistent definition of the transverse shear force is

$$V(x) = \left\{d\left(EI(x)\, d^2v/dx^2\right)/dx - N(x)dv/dx\right\} \equiv V_E - V_N. \tag{10.3-5}$$

Equation (10.3-4) must be satisfied along with any EBCs.

The finite element model now has at least two DOFs per node ($n_g = 2$). At node number k (local or system) they will be denoted as v_k and θ_k. Likewise, the element DOFs are locally numbered sequentially over the n_n number of nodes per element to create a total of $n_i = n_g \times n_n$ independent DOFs per element:

$$\boldsymbol{\delta}^{e^T} = [v_1\ \theta_1\ v_2\ \theta_2\ \cdots\ \theta_{n_n}]. \tag{10.3-6}$$

Likewise, the point sources at any node are a transverse shear force, V_k, and/or a point moment (couple), M_k. The possible point load vector for an element is

$$\boldsymbol{c}_{\boldsymbol{P}}^{\boldsymbol{e}^T} = [V_1\ M_1\ V_2\ M_2\ \cdots\ M_{n_n}]. \tag{10.3-7}$$

It would typically be a mixture of reaction terms from the EBC and externally applied point sources (most of which are identically zero. The element generalized displacements are a subset of the n_m system unknowns, $\boldsymbol{\delta}^e \subset_e \boldsymbol{\delta}$:

$$\boldsymbol{\delta}^T = [v_1\ \theta_1\ v_2\ \theta_2\ v_3\ \theta_3\ \cdots\ \theta_{n_m}],$$

which correspond to a total of $n_d = n_g \times n_m$ independent equations in the system (before EBC).

10.4 Element Arrays

As before, substituting the Hermite interpolation function for the beam's transverse deflection and slope:

$$v(x) = \boldsymbol{H}^e(x)\boldsymbol{\delta}^e \text{ and } v'(x) = dv/dx = \theta(x) = d\boldsymbol{H}^e/dx\boldsymbol{\delta}^e,$$

leads to the definitions of the element matrices. Expressed in matrix notation the equilibrium equation in (10.3-3) becomes

$$I = \boldsymbol{\delta}^T \boldsymbol{c}_{\mathbf{NBC}} + \boldsymbol{\delta}^T \boldsymbol{S}_{\boldsymbol{E}}\boldsymbol{\delta} + \boldsymbol{\delta}^T \boldsymbol{S}_{\boldsymbol{N}}\boldsymbol{\delta} + \boldsymbol{\delta}^T \boldsymbol{S}_{\boldsymbol{k}}\boldsymbol{\delta}$$
$$- \boldsymbol{\delta}^T \boldsymbol{S}_{\boldsymbol{w}}\boldsymbol{\delta} - \boldsymbol{\delta}^T \boldsymbol{c}_{\infty} - \boldsymbol{\delta}^T \boldsymbol{c}_{\boldsymbol{f}} = 0.$$

This leads to the matrix system

$$[\boldsymbol{S_E} + \boldsymbol{S_N} + \boldsymbol{S_w} + \boldsymbol{S_k}]\boldsymbol{\delta} = \boldsymbol{c}_{\mathbf{NBC}} + \boldsymbol{c_P} + \boldsymbol{c}_\infty + \boldsymbol{c_f}, \tag{10.4-1}$$

which is assembled from the corresponding element matrices of

$$\boldsymbol{S}^e_{\boldsymbol{E}} = \int_{L^e} \frac{d^2\boldsymbol{H}(x)}{dx^2}^T E^e I^e \frac{d^2\boldsymbol{H}(x)}{dx^2} dx,$$

$$\boldsymbol{S}^e_{\boldsymbol{E}} \equiv \int_{L^e} \boldsymbol{B}^e(x)^T EI^e \boldsymbol{B}^e(x) dx,$$

$$\boldsymbol{B}^e(x) \equiv \frac{d^2\boldsymbol{H}(x)}{dx^2}, \quad \boldsymbol{S}^e_{\boldsymbol{N}} = \int_{L^e} \frac{d\boldsymbol{H}(x)}{dx}^T N^e \frac{d\boldsymbol{H}(x)}{dx} dx,$$

$$\boldsymbol{S}^e_{\boldsymbol{w}} = -\int_{L^e} \boldsymbol{H}(x)^T \frac{dN}{dx}\frac{d\boldsymbol{H}(x)}{dx} dx, \quad \boldsymbol{S}^e_{\boldsymbol{k}} = \int_{L^e} \boldsymbol{H}(x)^T k^e \boldsymbol{H}(x) dx,$$

$$\boldsymbol{c}^e_{\boldsymbol{f}} = \int_{L^e} \boldsymbol{H}(x)^T f^e(x) dx, \quad \boldsymbol{c}^e_\infty = \int_{L^e} \boldsymbol{H}(x)^T v^e_\infty dx. \tag{10.4-2}$$

In the vast majority of cases (excluding long drill stings), the axial force within an element, N^e, can be taken as a constant, so $dN/dx = 0$, and the non-symmetric contribution, $\boldsymbol{S}^e_{\boldsymbol{w}}$, does not appear.

The new matrix, $\boldsymbol{S}^e_{\boldsymbol{N}}$, which is dependent on the axial force stress, and thus the axial stress, is usually called a "geometric stiffness matrix" in the finite element literature. The bending stiffness matrix is $\boldsymbol{S}^e_{\boldsymbol{E}}$, the foundation stiffness matrix is $\boldsymbol{S}^e_{\boldsymbol{k}}$, while the axial force gradient matrix has no common name.

Referring to (10.3-5), the first row of the reaction/natural boundary condition vector, $\boldsymbol{c}_{\mathbf{NBC}}$, contains the transverse shear $\{V_E(0) - V_N(0)\}$, the second row contains the point bending moment $\{-M(0)\}$, the next-to-last row contains the transverse shear force $\{-V_E(L) + V_N(L)\}$, and the last row contains the endpoint bending moment $\{M(L)\}$.

Any distributed transverse load per unit length is usually defined by the value of that load input at the element nodes and approximated with a Lagrangian interpolation function. Assume that $f^e(x) = \boldsymbol{h}^w(x)\boldsymbol{f}^e$. Then the resultant element load vector changes into an alternate rectangular integral:

$$\boldsymbol{c}_{\boldsymbol{f}}^{e} = \int_{L^e} \boldsymbol{H}(x)^T \boldsymbol{h}^w(x) \boldsymbol{f}^e dx = \left[\int_{L^e} \boldsymbol{H}(x)^T \boldsymbol{h}^w(x) dx\right] \boldsymbol{f}^e \equiv \boldsymbol{R}^e \boldsymbol{f}^e,$$

$$\boldsymbol{R}^e \equiv \int_{L^e} \boldsymbol{H}(x)^T \boldsymbol{h}^w(x) dx, \tag{10.4-3}$$

$$n_i \times n_n = (n_i \times 1)(1 \times n_n).$$

Temperature changes along the length of the beam do not affect the transverse deflections or generalized forces. However, a temperature change, ΔT, through the thickness, t^e, from top to bottom does affect them. It is possible to include those thermal effects in a beam model. Thermal bending is not common, but the result of including it gives another load vector acting on the element:

$$\begin{aligned}\boldsymbol{c}_{\boldsymbol{\alpha}}^{\boldsymbol{e}} &= \int_{L^e} \boldsymbol{B}^{\boldsymbol{e}^{\boldsymbol{T}}} EI^e(x) \frac{\alpha^e \Delta T(x)^e}{t(x)} dx \\ &= \frac{\alpha^e \Delta T^e EI^e}{t^e} \int_{L^e} \boldsymbol{B}^{\boldsymbol{e}^{\boldsymbol{T}}}(x) dx,\end{aligned} \tag{10.4-4}$$

where α^e is the coefficient of thermal expansion of the material.

The foundation stiffness matrix, $\boldsymbol{S}_{\boldsymbol{k}}^{e}$, has the form previously called a generalized mass matrix. If this model is later extended to be time dependent, then the literal mass matrix will be required. In this case, it is

$$\boldsymbol{m}^e = \int_{L^e} \boldsymbol{H}(x)^T \rho^e A^e \boldsymbol{H}(x) dx, \tag{10.4-5}$$

where ρ^e is the mass density of the material, and A^e is the cross-sectional area of the beam. Of course, the volume of the beam is $A^e L^e$ and its total scalar mass is $m^e = \rho^e A^e L^e$.

10.5 C¹ Element Models

The summary of Chapter 2 gives the cubic (two-noded) and quintic (three-noded) Hermite C^1 line interpolations. The C^2 quintic (two-noded) interpolations are also given there. The cubic beam model is by far the most widely used beam element. However, being a cubic polynomial, its third derivative (shear force) is constant along the length of the element. That requires a large number of elements to generate a reasonable estimate of the transverse shear force which is a key parameter in actual beam design. Therefore, it is recommended that a quintic (fifth degree) polynomial model be used since its quadratic third derivative will give the exact shear force in the vast majority of applications of beams. The element matrices for both of those C^1 Hermite interpolations are summarized here.

If a single two-noded cubic C^1 beam element is in equilibrium, then its matrix system is

$$\frac{EI^e}{L^3}\begin{bmatrix} 12 & 6L & -12 & 6L \\ 6L & 4L^2 & -6L & 2L^2 \\ -12 & -6L & 12 & -6L \\ 6L & 2L^2 & -6L & 4L^2 \end{bmatrix}\begin{Bmatrix} v_1 \\ \theta_1 \\ v_2 \\ \theta_2 \end{Bmatrix}$$

$$+\frac{N^e}{30L}\begin{bmatrix} 36 & 3L & -36 & 3L \\ 3L & 4L^2 & -3L & -L^2 \\ -36 & -3L & 36 & -3L \\ 3L & -L^2 & -3L & 4L^2 \end{bmatrix}\begin{Bmatrix} v_1 \\ \theta_1 \\ v_2 \\ \theta_2 \end{Bmatrix}\cdots$$

$$-\frac{dN}{dx}\frac{1}{60}\begin{bmatrix} -30 & 6L & 30 & -6L \\ -6L & 0 & 6L & -L^2 \\ -30 & -6L & 30 & 6L \\ 6L & -L^2 & -6L & 0 \end{bmatrix}\begin{Bmatrix} v_1 \\ \theta_1 \\ v_2 \\ \theta_2 \end{Bmatrix}$$

$$+\frac{k^e L}{420}\begin{bmatrix} 156 & 22L & 54 & -13L \\ 22L & 4L^2 & 13L & -3L^2 \\ 54 & 13L & 156 & -22L \\ -13L & -3L^2 & -22L & 4L^2 \end{bmatrix}\begin{Bmatrix} v_1 \\ \theta_1 \\ v_2 \\ \theta_2 \end{Bmatrix}\cdots$$

$$=\begin{Bmatrix} V_1 \\ M_1 \\ V_2 \\ M_2 \end{Bmatrix}+\frac{L}{60}\begin{bmatrix} 21 & 9 \\ 3L & 2L \\ 9 & 21 \\ -2L & -3L \end{bmatrix}\begin{Bmatrix} f_1 \\ f_2 \end{Bmatrix}$$

$$+\frac{v_\infty^e L}{12}\begin{Bmatrix} 6 \\ L \\ 6 \\ -L \end{Bmatrix}+\frac{\alpha^e \Delta T^e EI^e}{t^e}\begin{Bmatrix} 0 \\ 1 \\ 0 \\ -1 \end{Bmatrix}. \qquad (10.5\text{-}1)$$

The rectangular load transfer matrix in the above equation is (10.4-2) with a scalar interpolation for a linear variation of the load per unit length between the two nodes. The four square matrices would be combined into a single square symmetric stiffness matrix. Note that an axial compression force ($N^e < 0$) reduces the stiffness, and the extra support from a foundation increases the overall stiffness. Also, note that a temperature change through the thickness of the beam only causes bending effects, not the transverse shear.

If the recommended three-noded quintic C^1 beam element is in equilibrium, then its matrix system is

$$\frac{EI}{35L^3}\begin{bmatrix} 5{,}092 & 1{,}138L & -3{,}584 & 1{,}920L & -1{,}508 & 242L \\ 1{,}138L & 332L^2 & -896L & 320L^2 & -242L & 38L^2 \\ -3{,}584 & -896L & 7{,}168 & 0 & -3{,}584 & 896L \\ 1{,}920L & 320L^2 & 0 & 1{,}280L^2 & -1{,}920L & 320L^2 \\ -1{,}508 & -242L & -3{,}584 & -1{,}920L & 5{,}092 & -1{,}138L \\ 242L & 38L^2 & 896L & 320L^2 & -1{,}138L & 332L^2 \end{bmatrix}$$

$$\times \begin{Bmatrix} v_1 \\ \theta_1 \\ v_2 \\ \theta_2 \\ v_3 \\ \theta_3 \end{Bmatrix} \cdots$$

$$+\frac{N}{630L}\begin{bmatrix} 1{,}668 & 39L & -1{,}536 & 240L & -132 & -9L \\ 39L & 28L^2 & -48L & -8L^2 & 9L & -5L^2 \\ -1{,}536 & -48L & 3{,}072 & 0 & -1{,}536 & 48L \\ 240L & -8L^2 & 0 & 256L^2 & -240L & -8L^2 \\ -132 & 9L & -1{,}536 & -240L & 1{,}668 & -39L \\ -9L & -5L^2 & 48L & -8L^2 & -39L & 28L^2 \end{bmatrix}$$

$$\times \begin{Bmatrix} v_1 \\ \theta_1 \\ v_2 \\ \theta_2 \\ v_3 \\ \theta_3 \end{Bmatrix} \cdots$$

$$
-\frac{dN}{dx}\frac{1}{1,260}\begin{bmatrix} -630 & 46L & 480 & -128L & 150 & -14L \\ -46L & 0 & 32L & -8L^2 & 14L & -L^2 \\ -480 & -32L & 0 & 256L & 480 & -32L \\ 128L & 8L^2 & -256L & 0 & 128L & -8L^2 \\ -150 & -14L & -480 & -128L & 630 & 46L \\ 14L & L^2 & 32L & 8L^2 & -46L & 0 \end{bmatrix}
$$

$$
\times \begin{Bmatrix} v_1 \\ \theta_1 \\ v_2 \\ \theta_2 \\ v_3 \\ \theta_3 \end{Bmatrix} \cdots
$$

$$
+\frac{kL}{13,860}\begin{bmatrix} 2{,}092 & 114L & 880 & -160L & 262 & -29L \\ 114L & 8L^2 & 88L & -12L^2 & 29L & -3L^2 \\ 880 & 88L & 5{,}632 & 0 & 880 & -88L \\ -160L & -12L^2 & 0 & 128L^2 & 160L & -12L^2 \\ 262 & 29L & 880 & 160L & 2{,}092 & -114L \\ -29L & -3L^2 & -88L & -12L^2 & -114L & 8L^2 \end{bmatrix}
$$

$$
\times \begin{Bmatrix} v_1 \\ \theta_1 \\ v_2 \\ \theta_2 \\ v_3 \\ \theta_3 \end{Bmatrix} \cdots
$$

$$
= \begin{Bmatrix} V_1 \\ M_1 \\ V_2 \\ M_2 \\ V_3 \\ M_3 \end{Bmatrix} + \frac{L}{420}\begin{bmatrix} 57 & 44 & -3 \\ 3L & 4L & 0 \\ 16 & 192 & 16 \\ -8L & 0 & 8L \\ -3 & 44 & 57 \\ 0 & -4L & -3L \end{bmatrix} \begin{Bmatrix} f_1 \\ f_2 \\ f_3 \end{Bmatrix}
$$

$$
+\frac{v_{\infty}^{e}L}{420}\begin{Bmatrix}98\\7L\\224\\0\\98\\-7L\end{Bmatrix}+\frac{\alpha^{e}\Delta T^{e}EI^{e}}{t^{e}}\begin{Bmatrix}0\\1\\0\\0\\0\\-1\end{Bmatrix}. \tag{10.5-2}
$$

The rectangular load transfer matrix in (10.4-2) is for a quadratic variation of the load per unit length between the three nodes. The Matlab symbolic integration of (10.4-3) to construct that rectangular matrix is given in Fig. 10.5-1. A constant transverse load per unit length (f) reduces the resultant load and moment vector to

$$
c_f^T = fL[98\ 7L\ 224\ 0\ 98\ \ -7L]/420,
$$

while a triangular load ($f_1 = 0$, $f_2 = f/2$,$f_3 = f$) reduces to

$$
c_f^T = fL[19\ 2L\ 112\ 8L\ 79\ \ -5L]/420.
$$

These line load conversions are symbolically calculated in Figs. 10.5-2 and 10.5-3, respectively.

The associated mass matrix for both beam elements is like their elastic foundation matrix, except for the leading constant, kL, which is replaced with the total mass of the beam element, $m = \rho^e A^e L^e$.

```
%  Line load conversion rectangle matrix for quintic beam element
syms r L real                                   % mathematical limits
r2 = r^2 ; r3 = r^3 ; r4 = r^4 ; r5 = r^5 ;            % shorthand
%                fifth degree three-node beam interpolation, L3_C1
H(r)=[(1-23*r2+66*r3-68*r4+24*r5) (r-6*r2+13*r3-12*r4+4*r5)*L ...
      (16*r2-32*r3+16*r4 )        (-8*r2+32*r3-40*r4+16*r5)*L ...
      (7*r2-34*r3+52*r4-24*r5)    (-r2+5*r3-8*r4+4*r5 )*L] ;
% second degree three-node line interpolation
h(r)=[(1 - 3*r + 2*r^2), (4*r - 4*r^2), (2*r^2 - r)] ;     % L3_C0
%                               Integrate over length, Jacobian = L
R_e = int (H' * h, r, 0, 1) * L    % rectangular conversion matrix
%                                                  %  Running gives
% R_e = [  (19*L)/140, (11*L)/105,       -L/140]
%       [     L^2/140,    L^2/105,            0]
%       [   (4*L)/105,  (16*L)/35,    (4*L)/105]
%       [-(2*L^2)/105,          0, (2*L^2)/105]
%       [      -L/140, (11*L)/105,   (19*L)/140]
%       [           0,   -L^2/105,     -L^2/140]
```

Fig. 10.5-1: Symbolic integration to form the rectangular line-load conversion matrix.

```
%  Quadratic load to quintic beam transfer rectangle
syms L w real                           % mathematical limits
R_e = L * [57    44    -3   ;           % 6 by 3 rectangle
           3*L   4*L   0    ;
           16    192   16   ;
          -8*L   0     8*L  ;
          -3     44    57   ;
           0    -4*L  -3*L ] / 420 ;
Load = [0  w/2  w]'                     % triangle w(x) =w*x/L
c_w = R_e * Load                       % triangular load result
c_w=c_w*420 %B
Load = [0   w   0]' % approximate w(x) = w sin(pi*x/L)
c_w = R_e * Load                  % approx. sine load result
c_w=c_w*420 %B
Load = [w  3*w/4  0]'               % w(x)  = w *(1-x^2/L^2)
c_w = R_e * Load                  % approx. sine load result
c_w=c_w*420 %B
%                                                running gives
% c_w = [19   2*L   112    8*L   79   -5*L]*w*L / 420
% c_w = [44   4*L   192    0     44   -4*L]*w*L / 420
% c_w = [90   6*L   160   -8*L   30   -3*L]*w*L / 420
```

Fig. 10.5-2: Symbolically computing the resultant source vector from line-loads.

```
% Single 5-th degree element symbolic solution of fix-fix beam
syms EI L L_e k w real                               % mathematical limits
L_e = L ; L_2 = L_e^2                                       ; % shorthand
K   = EI / (35 * L_e^3)                     ; % quintic beam stiffness
%                                                 Beam stiffness matrix
S_e=[5092       1138*L_e  -3584     1920*L_e  -1508       242*L_e    ;
     1138*L_e   332*L_2   -896*L_e  320*L_2   -242*L_e    38*L_2     ;
    -3584      -896*L_e   7168      0         -3584       896*L_e    ;
     1920*L_e   320*L_2   0         1280*L_2  -1920*L_e   320*L_2    ;
    -1508      -242*L_e   -3584    -1920*L_e   5092      -1138*L_e   ;
     242*L_e    38*L_2    896*L_e   320*L_2   -1138*L_e   332*L_2]*K;

% Resultant source, triangular load from nodes 1 to 3, f(x) upward
c_f = f * L_e *[665 70* L_e 3920 280 *L_e 2765 -175*L_e]' /14700 ;
%                                                     Define zero EBCs
Fixed_L = [1, 2]; Free  = [3, 4]; Fixed_R = [5, 6];% Eq partitions
%                                              Effective system A * x = b
A = S_e (Free, Free)            % free partition of total stiffness
b = c_f (Free)                     % free partition of total loads
x = A \ b                                    % Solve free equations
React_L = S_e (Fixed_L, Free) * x - c_f (Fixed_L) % Left reactions
React_R = S_e (Fixed_R, Free) * x - c_f (Fixed_R)   % Rt reactions
%                                                        Check answers
Down = 0.5 * L_e * f ; Moment = Down * 2 * L_e / 3 ;        % Statics
Up = React_L(1) + React_R(1) ;                              % Statics
Oppose = React_L(2) + React_R(2) + L * React_R(1) ;         % Statics
Sum_F = Down + Up                                      % Newton's Law
Sum_M = Moment + Oppose                                % Newton's Law
%                                                        Running gives
% x' = [(L^4*f)/(768*EI)  (L^3*f)/(1920*EI)]                   Result
% React_L' = [-(3*L*f)/20 -(L^2*f)/30]                         Result
% React_R' = [-(7*L*f)/20 (L^2*f)/20]                          Result
% Sum_F = 0 ; Sum_M = 0 ;                                      Checks
```

Fig. 10.5-3: Symbolic solution of a quintic fixed–fixed beam with a triangular line load.

The associated mass matrix for the cubic element is

$$\boldsymbol{m}^e = \frac{\rho^e A^e L^e}{420}\begin{bmatrix} 156 & 22L^e & 54 & -13L^e \\ 22L^e & 4L^{e^2} & 13L^e & -3L^{e^2} \\ 54 & 13L^e & 156 & -22L^e \\ -13L^e & -3L^{e^2} & -22L^e & 4L^{e^2} \end{bmatrix}. \tag{10.5-3}$$

The first three stiffness matrix calculations can be executed in scripts *matrix_S_E_L3_C1.m, matrix_S_N_L3_C1.m,* and *matrix_S_K_L3_C1.m.* The rectangular transform matrix is included in *matrix_c_f_L3_C1.m* to accept three line-load values and build their resultant vector. The basic bending stiffness matrix is always required in any structure; the distributed line-load resultant is commonly needed. The elastic foundation stiffness is sometimes needed; as is the thermal bending matrix. The axial load "geometric stiffness" matrix is rarely needed, except for pipelines and buckling studies. The node point load vector is frequently needed for optional reaction recovery. Point sources are usually directly scattered to the system vector, but can be input at an element level.

10.6 Classic Beams

The analysis and design of beams have been important for at least 200 years. In a current textbook on the Mechanics of Materials, 97 of its 750 pages (13%) were devoted to the deflections and shear and moments in a beam. The above matrix system in (10.5-3) alone, or in combination with the derivatives of the C^1 interpolation functions, will give the same exact solutions for point forces, point couples, and line-loads that are constant, linear, or quadratic along the element. Such textbooks generally do not cover the influence of elastic foundations. If an elastic foundation is present, the results of (10.4-3) are only approximate (because the analytic solution includes hyperbolic and trigonometric functions). Then, a finer mesh of three-noded elements is required. If that mesh is not fine enough, then the shear force graph will show small jumps in the shear force at element interfaces within a single span. Now that each node has two DOFs, the packed integer code that flags the boundary condition at each node can have the following packed values: 00 free joint, 10 v is given (a roller joint),

01 the slope is given, or 11, both v and the slope are given (a fixed joint).

It is misleading to just observe from Tong's Theorem that for common line load distributions two cubic elements and a single quintic element can both give the exact deflections at the nodes and the exact reactions when using the same number of unknowns. The important items in designing beams are the moment distribution and the transverse shear force distribution along the beam. The moment and shear estimates from the classic cubic beam are linear and constant, respectively; while for the quintic element they are cubic and quadratic quantities. The shear force in a beam is very rarely constant, but it frequently varies quadratically along the beam. To obtain reliable shear design data with the cubic beam requires a very large number of elements along the beam. Better shear estimates can be obtained with a few quintic elements. In both cases, there still must be an element interface where any discontinuity in the data occurs. Figure 10.6-1 shows a fixed–fixed beam span with a triangular line load and Fig. 10.6-2 graphs element moment and shear force estimates. The classic cubic beam results are the dashed lines. The solid lines are the quintic (and exact) values of the moment and shear distributions.

Equations 10.6-1 show that the partitioning of the system matrices through the use of vector subscripts is quite useful in symbolic solutions. It is less useful in large numerical solutions because the vector subscripts create temporary hidden arrays (if memory permits) which are automatically deleted after their use. Figure 10.6-3 shows detailed manipulations when all of the EBCs are zero. However, it is common for some of the EBC values to be given to be zero while others have non-zero values specified. For example, Fig. 10.6-3 shows a fixed-end beam where a support movement has raised the right end

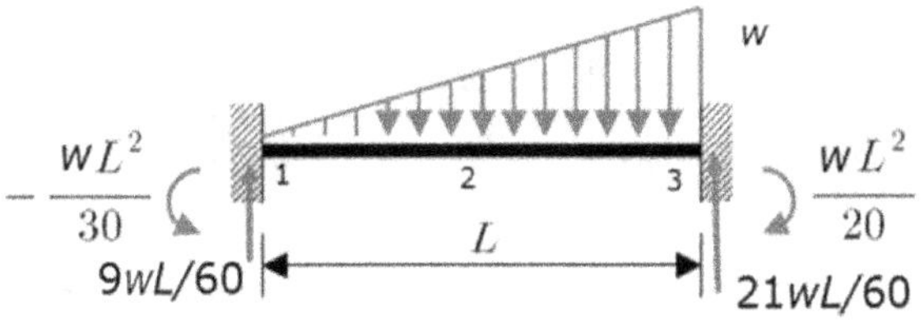

Fig. 10.6-1: Fixed–Fixed beam with a triangular line load.

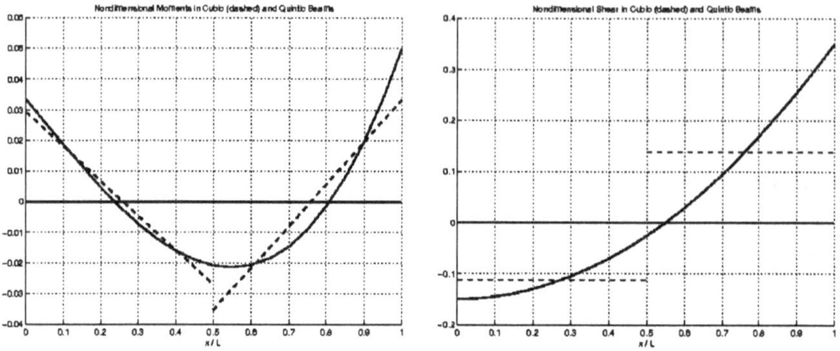

Fig. 10.6-2: Moment (left) and shear for L2 (dashed) and L3 beams.

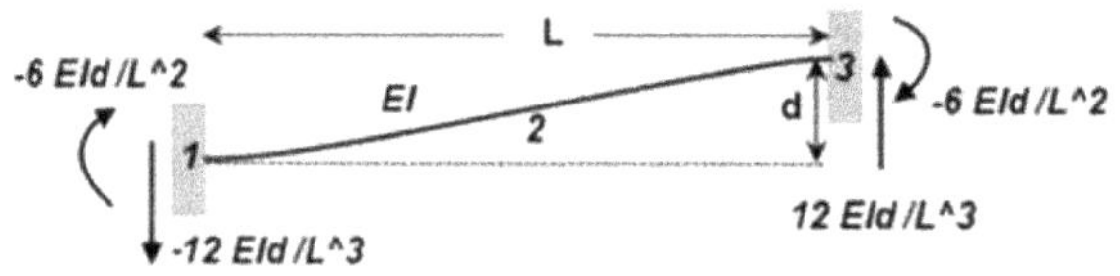

Fig. 10.6-3: Fixed-end beam with support motion.

of the beam (or a settlement lowers the left end). The end displacement is an EBC.

Whether other loadings are present or not, the known displacement of a support introduces other loads on the structure. To calculate what the reactions are due to a settlement (a non-zero EBC), the system matrices can be partitioned (via three vector subscripts) into regions of zero displacements, non-zero displacements, and unknown displacements, where $\{\boldsymbol{r}\}$ denotes the reactions at EBCs:

$$\begin{bmatrix} \boldsymbol{S}_{ff} & \vdots & \boldsymbol{S}_{fn} & \vdots & \boldsymbol{S}_{fz} \\ \cdots & & \cdots & & \cdots \\ \boldsymbol{S}_{nf} & \vdots & \boldsymbol{S}_{nn} & \vdots & \boldsymbol{S}_{nz} \\ \cdots & & \cdots & & \cdots \\ \boldsymbol{S}_{zf} & \vdots & \boldsymbol{S}_{zn} & \vdots & \boldsymbol{S}_{zz} \end{bmatrix} \begin{Bmatrix} u_{\text{free}} \\ u_{\text{not}} \\ u_{\text{zero}} \end{Bmatrix} = \begin{Bmatrix} c_{\text{free}} \\ c_{\text{not}} \\ c_{\text{zero}} \end{Bmatrix} + \begin{Bmatrix} 0 \\ r_{\text{not}} \\ r_{\text{zero}} \end{Bmatrix}. \tag{10.6-1}$$

The top partition gives the free displacements

$$\boldsymbol{u}_{\mathbf{free}} = \boldsymbol{S}_{ff}^{-1}\left\{\boldsymbol{c}_{\mathbf{free}} + \mathbf{0} - \boldsymbol{S}_{fn}\boldsymbol{u}_{\mathbf{not}} - \boldsymbol{S}_{fz} \times \mathbf{0}\right\},$$

the reactions at the non-zero EBCs are

$$\boldsymbol{r}_{\mathbf{not}} = \boldsymbol{S}_{nf}\boldsymbol{u}_{\mathbf{free}} + \boldsymbol{S}_{nn}\boldsymbol{u}_{\mathbf{not}} + \boldsymbol{S}_{nz} \times \mathbf{0} - \boldsymbol{c}_{\mathbf{not}},$$

and the bottom partition yields the reactions at the zero EBCs:

$$\boldsymbol{r}_{\mathbf{zero}} = \boldsymbol{S}_{zf}\boldsymbol{u}_{\mathbf{free}} + \boldsymbol{S}_{zn}\boldsymbol{u}_{\mathbf{not}} + \boldsymbol{S}_{\mathbf{zz}} \times \mathbf{0} - \boldsymbol{c}_{\mathbf{zero}}.$$

In general, the non-zero EBC values in the partitioned arrays of (10.6-1) can be assigned to multiple DOFs so the **Not_0** vector subscript will also have several DOF numbers, instead of one as shown in Fig. 10.6-3. For example, in that figure if the right support had also rotated counter-clockwise by an angle of θ, then the vector subscripts become **Is_0**= [1, 2]; **Not_0** = [5, 6]; and **Free** = [3, 4].

Now, a new vector is required to specify the non-zero boundary condition value for each DOF in the subscript array **Not_0**, say **Not** = [d θ]. Figure 10.6-4 shows the full Matlab details for symbolically partitioning a matrix system into three groups of DOF. Here, the total number of DOFs is only six, but for numerical calculations there is no theoretical limit on the size of the three vector subscript arrays that govern the solution of the system and the reaction recovery.

Example 10.6-1 Given: For the beam in Fig. 10.6-3, modify the Matlab script in Fig. 10.6-4 to symbolically compute the mid-span deflection and slope, the induced reactions and check the reaction values with statics.

Solution: To easily find the mid-span deflection use a three-noded quintic beam element (or two two-noded beam elements, since both methods give exact results). The system DOFs are 1, 2; 3, 4; and 5, 6. Clearly, the center displacements (3, 4) are free, while the right vertical displacement (5) has a non-zero value. The other support DOFs (1, 2, and 6) are zero. Those distinctions can be defined by vector subscripts, say Is_0 = [1, 2, 6]; Not_0 = [5]; and Free = [3, 4]

```
% Single 5-th degree element symbolic solution of fix-fix beam
%     with a vertical settlement of right support of +D3y
%          and a counter-clockwise rotation of +Ang
syms EI L L_e k D3y Ang real                      % mathematical limits
L_e = L ; L_2 = L_e^2                                    ; % shorthand
K   = EI / (35 * L_e^3)                   ; % quintic beam stiffness
%                                             Beam stiffness matrix
S_e=[5092       1138*L_e  -3584     1920*L_e  -1508     242*L_e   ;
     1138*L_e  332*L_2   -896*L_e  320*L_2   -242*L_e  38*L_2    ;
    -3584      -896*L_e  7168      0         -3584     896*L_e   ;
     1920*L_e  320*L_2   0         1280*L_2  -1920*L_e 320*L_2   ;
    -1508      -242*L_e  -3584    -1920*L_e  5092     -1138*L_e ;
     242*L_e   38*L_2    896*L_e   320*L_2   -1138*L_e 332*L_2]*K;

%                                    Define zero End non-zero BCs
Is_0 = [1, 2]; Not_0 = [5, 6] ; Free  = [3, 4];  % 3 Eq partitions
Not = [D3y  Ang]'                                ; % support movements

%                                     Effective system A * u = b
A =  S_e (Free, Free)         ; % free partition of total stiffness
b = -S_e (Free, Not_0) * Not      ; % non-0 support movement loads
u = A \ b                                      % solve free equations

%                                               Reactions at EBCs
React_0 = S_e (Is_0,  Free)*u + S_e (Is_0,  Not_0)*Not ;  % at 0's
React_0 = simplify (React_0)
React_N = S_e (Not_0, Free)*u + S_e (Not_0, Not_0)*Not ;  % at not
React_N = simplify (React_N)
Reacts (Is_0) = React_0 ; Reacts (Not_0) = React_N ;  % gather all
%                                                  Check answers
Up     = Reacts(1) + Reacts(5)                         ; % Statics
Up     = simplify (Up)                                   % pretty
Mom_1 = Reacts(2) + Reacts(6) + L * Reacts(5)          ; % Statics
Mom_1 = simplify (Mom_1)                                 % pretty
%                                                   Running gives
% u = [(D3y/2 - (Ang*L)/8) (6*D3y - Ang*L)/(4*L)]'
% React_0 = [-(6*EI*(2*D3y-Ang*L))/L^3 - |(2*EI*(3*D3y-Ang*L))/L^2]
% React_N = [(6*EI*(2*D3y-Ang*L))/L^3 -(2*EI*(3*D3y-2*Ang*L))/L^2]
% Up = 0 ; Mom_1 = 0                                     % All exact
```

Fig. 10.6-4: Partitioning the displacements into three sets.

which partition the matrix equations:

$$\begin{bmatrix} \boldsymbol{S}_{3:4,3:4} & \vdots & \boldsymbol{S}_{3:4,5} & \vdots & \boldsymbol{S}_{3:4,(1,2,6)} \\ \cdots & & \cdots & & \cdots \\ \boldsymbol{S}_{5,3:4} & \vdots & \boldsymbol{S}_{5,5} & \vdots & \boldsymbol{S}_{5(1,2,6)}, \\ \cdots & & \cdots & & \cdots \\ \boldsymbol{S}_{(1,2,6),3:4,} & \vdots & \boldsymbol{S}_{(1,2,6),5} & \vdots & \boldsymbol{S}_{(1,2,6),(1,2,6)} \end{bmatrix} \begin{Bmatrix} \boldsymbol{u}_{3:4} \\ \boldsymbol{u}_5 \\ \boldsymbol{u}_{(1,2,6)} \end{Bmatrix}$$

$$= \begin{Bmatrix} \boldsymbol{c}_{3:4} \\ \boldsymbol{c}_5 \\ \boldsymbol{c}_{(1,2,6)} \end{Bmatrix} + \begin{Bmatrix} \boldsymbol{0} \\ \boldsymbol{r}_5 \\ \boldsymbol{r}_{(1,2,6)} \end{Bmatrix}.$$

Solving for the mid-span displacements $\boldsymbol{u}_{3:4} = \boldsymbol{S}^{-1}_{3:4,3:4}$ $\{\boldsymbol{c}_{3:4} + \boldsymbol{0} - \boldsymbol{S}_{3:4,5}\boldsymbol{u}_5 + \boldsymbol{0}\}$:

$$\frac{EI}{35L^3}\begin{bmatrix} 7{,}168 & 0 \\ 0 & 1{,}280L^2 \end{bmatrix}\begin{Bmatrix} v_2 \\ \theta_2 \end{Bmatrix} = \left\{\frac{(f=0)L}{14{,}700}\begin{Bmatrix} 3{,}920 \\ 280L \end{Bmatrix}\right.$$

$$\left. + \begin{Bmatrix} 0 \\ 0 \end{Bmatrix} - \frac{EI}{35L^3}\begin{Bmatrix} -3{,}584 \\ -1{,}920L \end{Bmatrix}\{d\} + \begin{Bmatrix} 0 \\ 0 \end{Bmatrix}\right\}$$

$$= -\frac{EId}{35L^3}\begin{Bmatrix} -3{,}584 \\ -1{,}920L \end{Bmatrix},$$

$$\begin{Bmatrix} v_2 \\ \theta_2 \end{Bmatrix} = \frac{d}{7,168\,(1{,}280L^2)}\begin{bmatrix} 1{,}280L^2 & 0 \\ 0 & 7{,}168 \end{bmatrix}$$

$$\times \begin{Bmatrix} -3{,}584 \\ -1{,}920L \end{Bmatrix} = \begin{Bmatrix} d/2 \\ 3d/2L \end{Bmatrix}.$$

As outlined above, the reaction load at the non-zero EBC is found to be $\{\boldsymbol{r}_5\} = \{12EId/L^3\}$, which agrees with the upward right reaction force of Fig. 10.6-3. Likewise, the bottom partition gives the other exact reactions in that figure.

Example 10.6-2 Given: A fixed–fixed three-noded beam with a triangular line-load, as shown in Fig. 10.6-1. The EBCs are $v_1 = 0$, $\theta_1 = 0$, $v_3 = 0$, and $\theta_3 = 0$. The external point force and moment at center node 2 are zero ($V_2 = 0, M_2 = 0$). Here, there is no axial force, $N = 0$, and no elastic foundation, $k = 0$ and $v_\infty = 0$, and no thermal load, $\alpha = 0$. Determine the deflections and reactions using a single three-noded (fifth degree) beam element.

Solution: For a single element the equilibrium equations are given in (10.5-2). The middle two rows define the remaining unknown center point generalized displacements: After enforcing the EBCs:

$$\frac{EI}{35L^3}\begin{bmatrix} 7{,}168 & 0 \\ 0 & 1{,}280L^2 \end{bmatrix}\begin{Bmatrix} v_2 \\ \theta_2 \end{Bmatrix} = \begin{Bmatrix} 0 \\ 0 \end{Bmatrix} + \frac{fL}{14{,}700}\begin{Bmatrix} 3{,}920 \\ 280L \end{Bmatrix} + \begin{Bmatrix} 0 \\ 0 \end{Bmatrix}.$$

Multiplying by the inverse of the square matrix gives the middle node solutions:

$$\begin{Bmatrix} v_2 \\ \theta_2 \end{Bmatrix} = \frac{35L^3}{EI}\begin{bmatrix} 1/7{,}168 & 0 \\ 0 & 1/1{,}280L^2 \end{bmatrix}\frac{fL}{14{,}700}\begin{Bmatrix} 3{,}920 \\ 280L \end{Bmatrix}$$
$$= \frac{fL^3}{3{,}840EI}\begin{Bmatrix} 5L \\ 2 \end{Bmatrix},$$

which are the exact mid-span deflection and slope. Here, the reactions on the left are found from the first two rows of the equilibrium equations (since all the displacements are now known):

$$\frac{EI}{35L^3}\begin{bmatrix} -3{,}584 & 1{,}920L \\ -896L & 320L^2 \end{bmatrix}\frac{fL^3}{3{,}840EI}\begin{Bmatrix} 5L \\ 2 \end{Bmatrix}$$
$$= \begin{Bmatrix} V_1 \\ M_1 \end{Bmatrix} + \frac{fL}{14{,}700}\begin{Bmatrix} 665 \\ 70L \end{Bmatrix}, \text{ giving } \begin{Bmatrix} V_1 \\ M_1 \end{Bmatrix} = \frac{-fL}{60}\begin{Bmatrix} 9 \\ 2L \end{Bmatrix}.$$

Likewise, at the right end, utilizing the last two rows of the equilibrium equations gives the reactions at node 3:

$$\begin{Bmatrix} V_3 \\ M_3 \end{Bmatrix} = \frac{-fL}{20}\begin{Bmatrix} 7 \\ -L \end{Bmatrix}.$$

Both of the reactions are exact. Note that the net resultant force is $-fL/2$, which is equal and opposite to the applied triangular-shaped transverse load. The net external moment is zero. Static equilibrium is usually taught in undergraduate classes with Newton's Laws. You can use them to verify that the computed reactions do indeed satisfy that the sum of the forces is zero, and that the sum of the moments, taken at any reference point, is zero. The interpolated deflection of a quintic beam with these EBCs is

$$v(x) = v_2\left(16r^2 - 32r^3 + 16r^4\right) + \theta_2\left(-8r^2 + 32r^3 - 40r^4 + 16r^5\right)L.$$

Substituting the above values for the mid-point deflection and slope, the deflection estimate reduces to a fifth-order polynomial

$$v(x) = fL^4r^2(r-1)^2(r+2)/120EI = fL^4[r^5 - 3r^3 + 2r^2]/120EI,$$

where $r = x/L$. Handbook solutions show that the exact displacement is the above fifth-degree polynomial and therefore this single element model gives the exact deflection, slope, moment, and transverse shear force everywhere along the length of the beam. The finite element solution does not utilize Newton's Laws, but they can be used to validate the results. This solution is executed symbolically, and the results are checked, in Fig. 10.6-4.

Example 10.6-3 Given: Repeat Example 10.6-2 using two two-noded cubic beam elements.

Solution: The element lengths are both $L^e = L/2$ and the line load values at the left and right elements are [0 f/2] and $[f/2\ f]$, respectively. From (10.6-1), the left element nodal resultant values are

$$c_f^T = fL[9 \quad 2L/2 \quad 21 \quad -3L/2]/240,$$

and the right ones are

$$c_f^T = fL[39 \quad 7L/2 \quad 51 \quad -8L/2]/240,$$

respectively. Adding the force rows (1 and 3) gives $fL(9+21+39+51)/240 = fL/2$, which, as expected, is the total load caused by the variable line load. The two elements share DOFs three and four so the assembled system is

$$\frac{EI}{\left(\frac{L}{2}\right)^3}\begin{bmatrix} 12 & 6L/2 & -12 & 6L/2 & 0 & 0 \\ 6L/2 & 4L^2/4 & -6L/2 & 2L^2/4 & 0 & 0 \\ -12 & -6L/2 & (12+12) & (-6L/2+6L/2) & -12 & 6L/2 \\ 6L/2 & 2L^2/4 & (-6L/2+6L/2) & (4L^2/4+4L^2/4) & -6L/2 & 2L^2/4 \\ 0 & 0 & -12 & -6L/2 & 12 & -6L/2 \\ [3pt]0 & 0 & 6L/2 & 2L^2/4 & -6L/2 & 4L^2/4 \end{bmatrix}$$

$$\times\begin{Bmatrix} v_1 \\ \theta_1 \\ v_2 \\ \theta_2 \\ v_3 \\ \theta_3 \end{Bmatrix} = \begin{Bmatrix} V_1 \\ M_1 \\ V_2 \\ M_2 \\ V_3 \\ M_3 \end{Bmatrix} + \frac{fL}{240}\begin{Bmatrix} 9 \\ 2L/2 \\ 21+39 \\ -3L/2+7L/2 \\ 51 \\ -8L/2 \end{Bmatrix} + \mathbf{0}.$$

Since the two ends are fixed (have zero deflections and slopes), the middle two rows define the remaining unknown center point displacements:

$$\frac{8EI}{L^3}\begin{bmatrix} 24 & 0 \\ 0 & 2L^2 \end{bmatrix}\begin{Bmatrix} v_2 \\ \theta_2 \end{Bmatrix} = \begin{Bmatrix} 0 \\ 0 \end{Bmatrix} + \frac{fL}{240}\begin{Bmatrix} 60 \\ 2L \end{Bmatrix} + \begin{Bmatrix} 0 \\ 0 \end{Bmatrix}$$

$$\begin{Bmatrix} v_2 \\ \theta_2 \end{Bmatrix} = \frac{L^3}{8EI}\begin{bmatrix} 1/24 & 0 \\ 0 & 1/2L^2 \end{bmatrix}\frac{fL}{240}\begin{Bmatrix} 60 \\ 2L \end{Bmatrix} = \frac{fL^3}{3{,}840EI}\begin{Bmatrix} 5L \\ 2 \end{Bmatrix},$$

which again is exact, as expected. However, the solution is only exact at the nodes and is inexact along the length of each of the two elements. The four end reactions are exact.

Example 10.6-4 Given: A two-span indeterminate beam structure is shown in Fig. 10.6-5, along with its exact bending moments and transverse shear forces. The bending stiffness, *EI*, is constant along the full length. Calculate the analytic solution the slope at the interior roller support. Also, verify the analytic values of the reactions at all supports.

Solution: Rather than solve the governing differential equation, recall that for a constant or linear line-load the cubic beam element

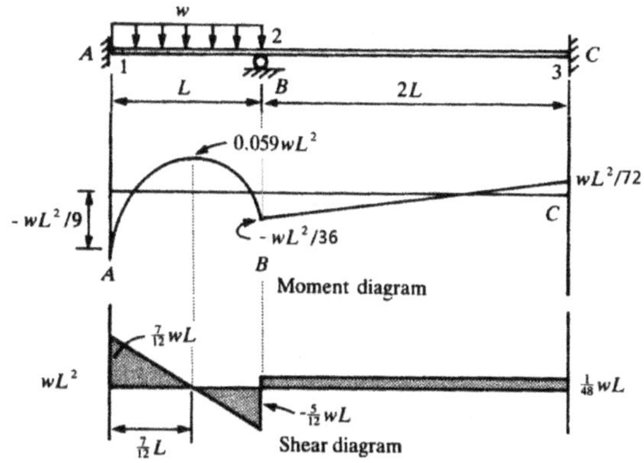

Fig. 10.6-5: Two-span continuous beam with a partial line-load.

yields the exact deflections and slopes at its nodes as well as exact reactions (but non-exact moments and shears along the member). Thus, use two cubic beam elements to solve this structure. The two ends fix both the deflection and slope, and the roller prevents the transverse deflection; so the requested slope at B is the only unknown of the DOF. For the left span, the stiffness matrix and line-load contributions are given in (10.5-1). That expression will occupy the top four rows of the system equilibrium equations. The right span has a similar stiffness matrix, but with the symbol L replaced with the value $2L$. That element will occupy the bottom four rows of the system equations and overlap at the two rows for node 2. Assembling the two elements gives the six equilibrium equations before the five EBCs are enforced, as follows:

$$\frac{EI}{L^3}\begin{bmatrix} 12 & 6L & -12 & 6L & 0 & 0 \\ 6L & 4L^2 & -6L & 2L^2 & 0 & 0 \\ -12 & -6L & (12+12/8) & (-6L+12L/8) & -12/8 & 12L/8 \\ 6L & 2L^2 & (-6L+12L/8) & (4L^2+16L^2/8) & -12L/8 & 8L^2/8 \\ 0 & 0 & -12/8 & -12L/8 & 12 & -12L/8 \\ 0 & 0 & 12L/8 & 8L^2/8 & -12L/8 & 16L^2/8 \end{bmatrix}$$

$$\times \begin{Bmatrix} v_1 \\ \theta_1 \\ v_2 \\ \theta_2 \\ v_3 \\ \theta_3 \end{Bmatrix} = \begin{Bmatrix} V_1 \\ M_1 \\ V_2 \\ 0 \\ V_3 \\ M_3 \end{Bmatrix} + \frac{wL}{12} \begin{Bmatrix} -6 \\ -L \\ -6+0 \\ L+0 \\ 0 \\ 0 \end{Bmatrix}.$$

The system boundary conditions make all node displacements except θ_2 zero. The only remaining independent displacement equation is row four:

$$\frac{EI}{L^3}\left[4L^2+2L^2\right]\theta_2=\{0\}+\left\{\frac{wL^2}{12}\right\}+\{0\},\quad \text{or}\quad \theta_2=\frac{wL^3}{72EI}.$$

Now that all node displacements are known, they can be substituted into the remaining five equations for the system reactions:

$$\frac{EI}{L^3}\begin{bmatrix} 12 & 6L & -12 & 6L & 0 & 0 \\ 6L & 4L^2 & -6L & 2L^2 & 0 & 0 \\ -12 & -6L & \frac{108}{8} & 60L/8 & -12/8 & 12L/8 \\ 6L & 2L^2 & 60L/8 & 6L^2 & -12L/8 & 8L^2/8 \\ 0 & 0 & -12/8 & -12L/8 & 12 & -12L/8 \\ 0 & 0 & 12L/8 & 8L^2/8 & -12L/8 & \frac{16L^2}{8} \end{bmatrix}\begin{Bmatrix} 0 \\ 0 \\ 0 \\ \theta_2 \\ 0 \\ 0 \end{Bmatrix}$$

$$=\begin{Bmatrix} V_1 \\ M_1 \\ V_2 \\ 0 \\ V_3 \\ M_3 \end{Bmatrix}+\frac{wL}{12}\begin{Bmatrix} -6 \\ -L \\ -6 \\ L \\ 0 \\ 0 \end{Bmatrix}\rightarrow\begin{Bmatrix} V_1 \\ M_1 \\ V_2 \\ 0 \\ V_3 \\ M_3 \end{Bmatrix}=wL\begin{Bmatrix} 28/48 \\ 8L/72 \\ 21/48 \\ 0 \\ -1/48 \\ L/72 \end{Bmatrix}.$$

Checking with Newton's Laws of equilibrium, the sum of the vertical forces is zero by inspection. Taking the moment sums about the left support:

$$M_1-(wL)(L/2)+V_2L+M_3+V_3(3L)=0,$$

$$8wL^2/72-(wL)(L/2)+(21wL/48)L+wL^2/72$$
$$+-wL/48(3L)=0,$$

which becomes $wL^2[32-144+126+4-18]/288=0$, as expected.

10.7 Structural Symmetry

Often a problem has a symmetry or anti-symmetry condition that allows half of the one-dimensional domain to be modeled. When an analyst uses that condition, the edge of the omitted domain must be replaced by a new boundary condition. Figure 8.1-1 showed the concepts of one-dimensional symmetry and anti-symmetry for a scalar unknown. A symmetry (mirror) plane is one where the domain and its material (coefficients in the ODE) are mirror images, as are the EBCs. For the symmetry condition, half of the line is meshed and at the point falling on the plane of symmetry the boundary conditions are enforced. When displacement vectors and (infinitesimal) rotation vectors are present, the distinctions between symmetric and anti-symmetric problems are as sketched in Fig. 10.7-1.

For an anti-symmetry plane, the domain and its material are mirror images, but the EBCs have equal and opposite changes in value, relative to the value at the point in the plane. The line is cut in half, and the removed material is replaced with an EBC at the point in the plane where the displacement components in the plane are zero, and the rotational component normal to the plane is zero. Thus, an anti-symmetry solution over half of the line gives the change in the solution value $\Delta v(x)$, with respect to the plane value, v_p, so the actual solution is $v(x) = v_p + \Delta v(x)$. On the other (omitted) half of the line, the change is the solution has its sign reversed and the actual solution is $v(x) = v_p - \Delta v(x)$. (As the figure indicates, v_p is usually zero for vector DOF.)

When the computer memory is insufficient to solve a problem with symmetric geometry and a general load state, it is possible to solve two half-size models by decomposing the general load into

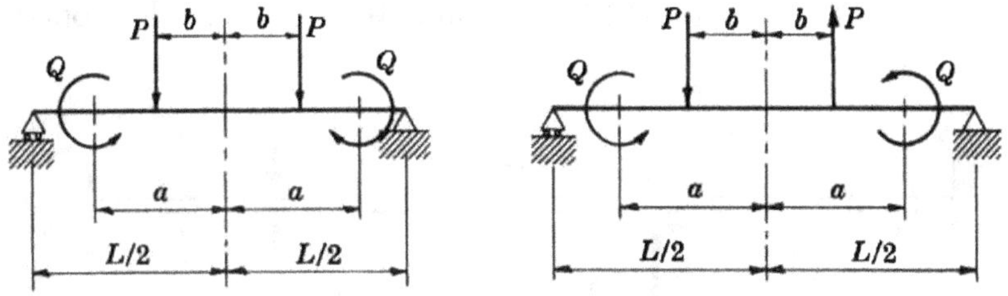

Fig. 10.7-1: Symmetric (left) and anti-symmetric Hermite models.

symmetric loads and anti-symmetric loads. Some commercial finite element systems have the ability to automatically carry out the post-processing and to display the results as if the complete structure had been analyzed.

10.8 Multiple Span Beams*

Many beams have more than a single span. Figure 10.8-1 shows a typical two-span beam. The first span has a constant uniform line-load, while the second span has point load at the two-thirds point. It is classified as a "statically indeterminate" beam since there are six unknown reactions at the supports. Points A and B rest on rollers that prevent any vertical displacement and fixed-end C prevents any vertical displacement or rotation. The EBCs at those three points introduce discontinuities in the shear forces and the end moment. Therefore, element interfaces must occur there. The point load also causes a shear discontinuity so it too must be at an element interface. To get exact shear and moments under the uniform line load requires the three-noded quintic beam. Using that same beam element on both sides of the point load leads to a mesh with seven nodes and three elements.

Note that the beam has a constant *EI* product value. Here *E* is the material modulus of elasticity of the material and *I* is the geometric moment of inertia of the cross-section of the beam. Often, the inertia is not known to begin with since it must be selected based on the values of the extreme moment and/or shear values in the system. It is a common practice to set the *EI* product to unity (with the proper units) and solve the problem with that value since the results are directly proportional to that product.

To begin illustrating how to automate a multi-span beam analysis the Matlab script in Figs. 10.8-2(a) and 10.8-2(b) was developed to

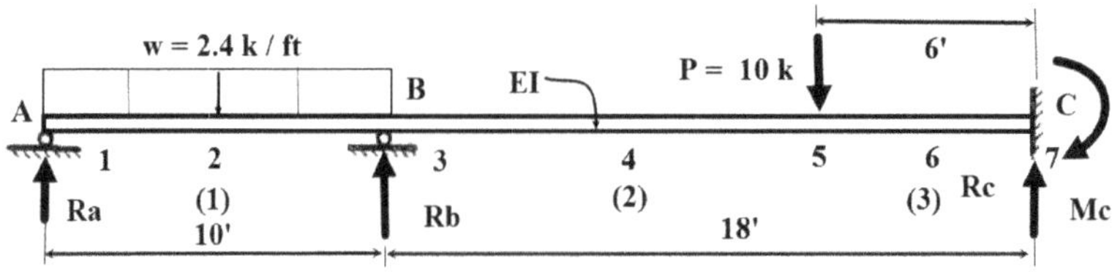

Fig. 10.8-1: Two-span, constant *EI* beam.

determine the deflections and rotations for the indeterminate system in Fig. 10.8-1. It does not have the usual for loop over all elements, but addresses each element sequentially (which is a much less efficient process.) The stiffness matrices and line-load resultant arrays are in (10.3-1). However, each of the beams has a different length and a different connectivity list. The vertical point load will be inserted directly into the system load vector, **c**, in the row corresponding to the vertical displacement at that node.

The system equation number for DOF j at node number N is $row\,(j) = n_g\,(N-1) + j, 1 \le j \le n_g$. For this beam $n_g = 2$ with $j = 1$ corresponding to a vertical displacement and $j = 2$ being the small rotation angle (in radians) at the node. For the point load the equation number is $2*(5-1)+1 = 9$. The required script is too long to fit a single page so its major stages are presented in Figs. 10.8-2(a)

```
function Two_span_three_L3_C1_beam
%      f=2,400 lb/ft                           P=10,000 lb
%            (1)              (2)              |   (3)
%      ffffffffffff                            V
%    1 *-----*-----*--------*---------*---*---*
% roller     2      3,roller 4          5    6    7,fixed
%     x=0    5     10        16        22   25   28 ft.
% DOF 1,2  3,4   5,6       7,8      9,10 11,12 13,14
% EI == 1 lb ft^2.  Reaction results are:
% R1 = 9,957 R3 = 17,226 R7 = -6,816 lb. M7 = -23,121 ft lb
%                        problem controls
n_g = 2 ;                                  % number of DOF per node
n_e = 3 ;                                      % number of elements
n_m = 7 ;                             % number of nodes in the mesh
n_n = 3 ;                             % number of nodes per element
n_d = n_g * n_m ;                      % number of system equations
n_i = n_g * n_n ;                           % nmber of element DOF

%                        allocate input arrays
x = zeros (n_m, 1) ; Connect = zeros (n_e, n_n) ;       % inputs
Connect = [1  2  3 ;                       % element 1 connections
           3  4  5 ;                       % element 2 connections
           5  6  7 ] ;                     % element 3 connections
x = [0 5 10 16 22 25 28]'              ;    % system x-coordinates

%                        allocate required arrays
S   = zeros (n_d, n_d) ; c   = zeros (n_d, 1) ;  % system arrays
S_e = zeros (n_i, n_i) ; c_f = zeros (n_i, 1) ;    % elem arrays
index = zeros (n_i, 1) ;                 % element scatter numbers
u     = zeros (n_d, 1) ;        % system deflections and slopes
React = zeros (n_d, 1) ;                       % system reactions
```

Fig. 10.8-2(a): Beam sketch, controls, basic data, and memory allocation.

```
%           zero EBC and free DOF vector subscripts
Fixed = [1 5 13 14] ; Free = [2 3 4 6 7 8 9 10 11 12];
%                       insert point load scatter
P_n = 5 ;  P_v = -1e4  ; % node & value of vertical point load
P_eq = n_g*(P_n - 1) + 1 ; % equation of vertical displacement
c(P_eq) = P_v       ; % insert (scatter) point load into system

e = 1 ;                                  % assemble 1 of 3 elements
e_nodes = Connect (e, 1:3)                ;  % nodes on the element
L = abs ( x(e_nodes(3)) - x(e_nodes(1)) )    ; % compute length
E = 1 ; I = 1 ;                              % constant properties
Line_Load = -2.4e3 * [1  1  1]' ;            % constant line load
[index] = get_element_index (n_g, n_n, e_nodes); % sys numbers
[S_e] = matrix_S_E_L3_C1 (E, I, L)          ; % bending stiffness
[c_f] = matrix_c_f_L3_C1 (L, Line_Load)       ; % load resultant
S (index, index) = S (index, index) + S_e   ; % e = 1 assembled
c (index)        = c (index)        + c_f   ; % e = 1 assembled

e = 2 ;                                  % assemble 2 of 3 elements
E = 1 ; I = 1 ;                       % constant properties, length
e_nodes = Connect (e, 1:3)                 ; % nodes on the element
L = abs ( x(e_nodes(3)) - x(e_nodes(1)) )    ; % compute length
[index] = get_element_index (n_g, n_n, e_nodes); % sys numbers
[S_e] = matrix_S_E_L3_C1 (E, I, L)          ; % bending stiffness
S (index, index) = S (index, index) + S_e   ; % e = 2 assembled

e = 3 ;                                  % assemble 3 of 3 elements
E = 1 ; I = 1 ;                       % constant properties, length
e_nodes = Connect (e, 1:3)                 ; % nodes on the element
L = abs ( x(e_nodes(3)) - x(e_nodes(1)) )    ; % compute length
[index] = get_element_index (n_g, n_n, e_nodes); % sys numbers
[S_e] = matrix_S_E_L3_C1 (E, I, L)          ; % bending stiffness
S (index, index) = S (index, index) + S_e; % assembly complete

% independent equations A * p = b.          Partition and solve
A = S (Free, Free) ; b = c (Free) ;                 % known arrays
p = A \ b                             ; % non-zero displacements
u (Free) = p                      ; % gather back into full list
fprintf('\n u*EI= ') ; disp(u')                   ; % pretty print

React(Fixed) = S(Fixed, Free)*p - c(Fixed); % system reactions
fprintf('\n React*EI= ') ; disp(React')          ; % pretty print
graph_L3_C1_result (u, x, Connect)          ; % plot the solution
graph_L3_C1_moment (u, x, Connect)            ; % plot the moment
graph_L3_C1_shear  (u, x, Connect)             ; % plot the shear
```

Fig. 10.8-2(b): Assemble beam matrices, solve for displacements, and recover reactions.

and 10.8-2(b). Figure 10.8-2(a) has comments to summarize the problem, manually sets several of the controlling integers, and manually sets the spatial coordinates and the mesh connectivity list. The last portion allocates the memory required for the major arrays to ensure an efficient execution. Beginning with defining the vector subscripts for the unknown DOF, and the zero ones, Fig. 10.8-2(b) assembles the point load, and manually "loops" over each element, creates their arrays, and scatters them.

For each element in Fig. 10.8-2(b), the connecting nodes are gathered and used to get the nodal x-coordinates in order to compute the element length. The connections are used again with the control integers to generate the system DOF numbers for the element. That is done with the *get_element_index.m* script given in Fig. 7.2-1. That script is always used for each element being assembled. All three elements use the script *matrix_S_E_L3_C1.m* to form their bending stiffness. Only the first element uses the script *matrix_c_f_L3_C1.m* to form its resultant due to the constant line-load. Each element array is scattered into the system matrices using its vector subscript, ***index***. When the assembly process is complete, the partitioned system matrices are solved for the unknown displacements. Then all of the displacements are used to calculate the reactions at the EBCs. Finally, selected results are graphed.

The short script in Fig. 10.8-2 showed that there are several actions that must be completed to fully automate a FEA. Almost all studies require the input of the location and value of all EBCs. The library of scripts includes *get_point_sources.m* for that purpose. It reads the text file *msh_load_pt.txt* which has three columns: the node number where the EBC occurs ($\leq n_m$), the DOF direction ($\leq n_g$), and the value assigned to that generalized force. The user must always specify the coordinates of all of the nodes. Those node location inputs are read by script *get_mesh_nodes.m* which reads those data from the sequential text file *msh_bc_xyz.txt*. The number of lines in that file defines the total number of nodes in the mesh, n_m.

Every application must also specify the node connection lists of all of the element types (volumes, areas, lines, and/or points). They are read by script *get_mesh_elements.m* from the user supplied sequential text file *msh_typ_nodes.txt*. The number of lines in that file defines the total number of elements in the mesh, n_e, and the number of different types of elements, n_t. The provided general finite element software system allows a mixture of compatible element types to be input. For example, it may contain a mixture of element types; say quadrilaterals and triangles and/or line elements. For a mixed mesh, the connection list must be padded with zeros to assure that the input text file has a constant number of columns (in Matlab, but not in Fortran).

Most problems also have specified properties, or coefficients in the ODE, which are application dependent. Their order of input depends on the person that writes the application script. The script *get_mesh_properties.m* reads the element or type properties from the text file *msh_properties.txt* and counts the number of properties *n_vals* (columns of data) and it counts the number of rows of data, *n_mats*. The number of rows of properties must equal either the number of elements or the number of different types of elements. A mixed mesh can also have different properties for each element type. When needed, the properties list for an element type must be padded with zeros to assure that the input text file has a constant number of columns.

Figure 10.8-3 shows numerical data required had the two-span beam in Fig. 10.8-1 been solved numerically using the supplied general finite element library. The computed results are graphed in Fig. 10.8-4.

```
%msh_remarks.txt: remarks about the application
Two-span indeterminate beam with three L3_C1 elements
EI constant (1), one point load, one line load
n_g=2, n_e=3, n_m=7, n_n=3, Reaction M7 = -23,121 ft-lb
% msh_bc_xyz.txt:  n_g digit BC flag, x-coord, y-, z-coord
01  0.0
00  5.0
01  10.0
00  16.0
00  22.0
00  25.0
11  28.0
% msh_typ_nodes.txt: element-type, connection list
1    1, 2, 3
1    3, 4, 5
1    5, 6, 7
% msh_ebc.txt:  node-number, dof-number, assigned value
1   2   0.0
3   2   0.0
7   1   0.0
7   2   0.0
% msh_properties.txt: one line per element OR element type
% for BOEF:  E, I, k, f
1.0   1.0  0.0  -2400.0
1.0   1.0  0.0  0.0
1.0   1.0  0.0  0.0
% msh_load_pt.txt: node-number, dof-number, assigned value
5  2  -10000.0
```

Fig. 10.8-3: Numerical data equivalent to the beam in Fig. 10.8-1 for FEA library.

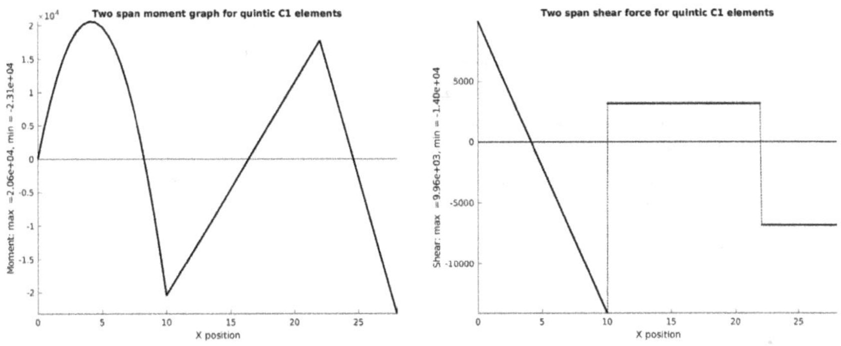

Fig. 10.8-4: Moment and shear diagrams for Fig. 10.8-1.

10.9 Beam on Elastic Foundation*

The presence of an elastic foundation is not uncommon and significantly changes the analysis by requiring the foundation stiffness term, $k(x)$, in (10.2-1). That means that the mathematical nature of the solution to the homogeneous (i.e., unloaded) differential equation changes from polynomials to hyperbolic cosines and its coupled beam structural response. That makes it more difficult to get an accurate solution using polynomials, as has been done so far. The mesh must be much finer, or the polynomial degree must be increased, or both.

In theory, the foundation everywhere pushes back against the beam. It is not unusual for the beam to have a segment of its length that does reverse direction. Then part of the foundation is theoretically pulling on the beam, instead of pushing against it. If the foundation is soil, then a gap would often develop there instead of having the soil pull on the beam. That means the model would have to be changed by putting an element interface at the liftoff point, and the prior foundation stiffness removed for the new element. An accurate location of a "lift-off-point" is a trial and error process.

Figure 10.9-1 shows a more practical BOEF where the exact analytic solution has been given. Since there are discontinuous loadings, any finite element model must split this beam into at least four spans. The first runs from the left end to the point load. The second covers the gap from the point load to the beginning of the line load. The third spans the length of the line load, and the last one covers from the end of the line load to the right end of the beam. The pressure

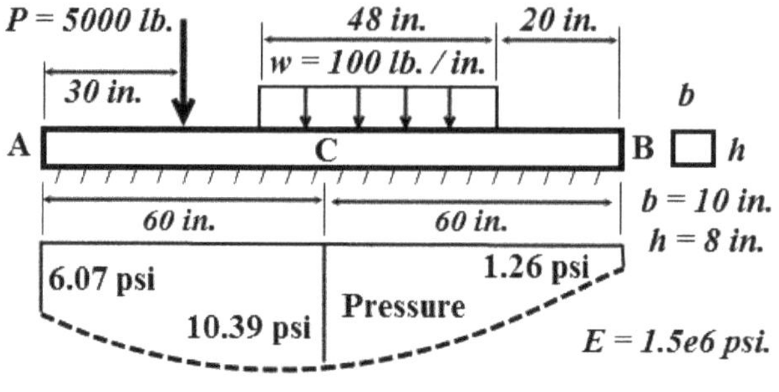

Fig. 10.9-1: BOEF with changing loadings.

distribution shown in that figure is actually computed from the final beam deflection as $p = -kv$ in a post-solution calculation and is proportional to the deformed shape of the beam.

Also, note that there is no change in sign of the pressure or the corresponding deflections so no lift-off corrections need to be considered. The elastic modulus of this wooden BOEF is $E = 1.5\,\text{e6}\,\text{psi}$, the moment of inertia is $I = 426.7\,\text{in.}^4$, and the foundation modulus is $k = bk_0 = 10\,\text{in.} \times 200\,\text{lb./in.}^3 = 2\text{e3 lb./in.}^2$.

This beam was run with both the cubic and quintic beam elements using the same number of nodes in the mesh. Each span had a mid-point node added. Thus, there are two cubic elements per span compared to one quintic element per span. Both models yield essentially the same displacements of the beam. The differences in the solutions again become clear in the moment and shear force evaluations. The moment and shear graphs for a nine-noded mesh are shown in Figs. 10.9-2 and 10.9-3, respectively. The cubic element mesh underestimated the maximum shear force by about 42%. Doubling the number of quintic elements only changed the shear results in the fourth significant figure (too small to see). Thus, that quintic element mesh is probably sufficient. Doubling the number of cubic elements in a 17 node mesh gives the moment and shear results in Fig. 10.9-4. It is still possible to spot jumps (see oval) in the moment graph. The cubic beam element is by far the most widely used beam element and is included in most commercial finite element software. These examples remind the users that if that element is utilized, then the mesh must be very fine and at least two meshes should be investigated.

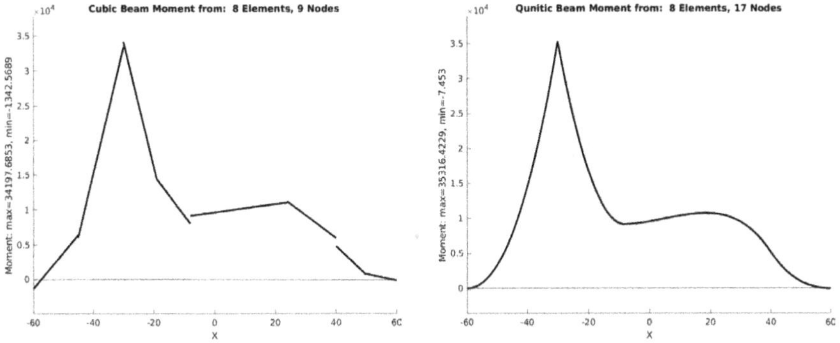

Fig. 10.9-2: Moments from cubic (left) and quintic BOEF elements (nine nodes).

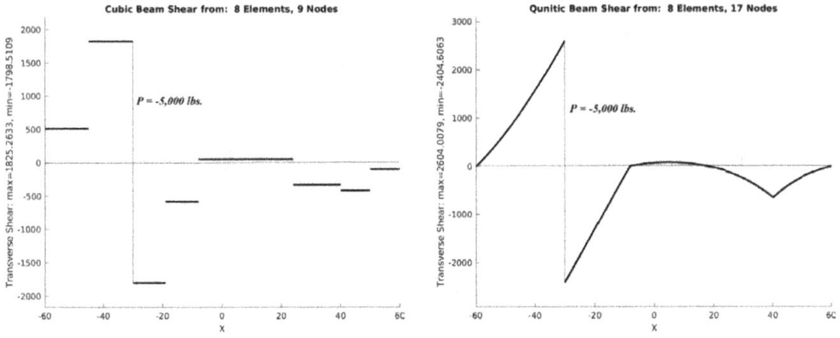

Fig. 10.9-3: Shear force from cubic (left) and quintic BOEF elements (nine nodes).

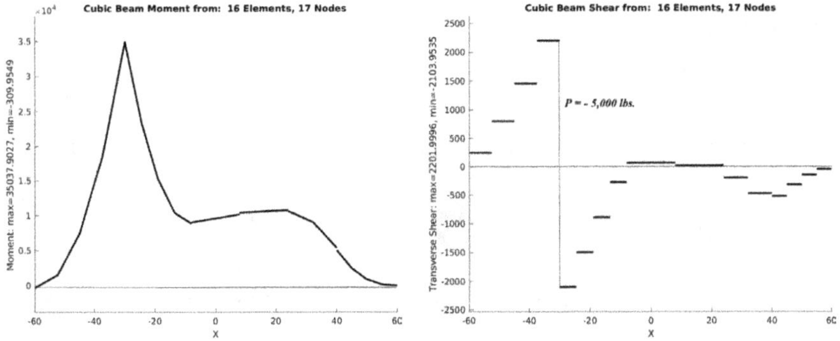

Fig. 10.9-4: Moment and shear from cubic BOEF with a 17-noded mesh.

10.10 Summary

$n\_d \longleftrightarrow n_d$ $\equiv$ Number of system unknowns $= n\_g \times n\_m$
$n\_e \longleftrightarrow n_e$ $\equiv$ Number of elements
$n\_g \longleftrightarrow n_g$ $\equiv$ Number of generalized DOFs per node
$n\_i \longleftrightarrow n_i$ $\equiv$ Number of unknowns per element $= n\_g \times n\_n$
$n\_m \longleftrightarrow n_m$ $\equiv$ Number of mesh nodes
$n\_n \longleftrightarrow n_n$ $\equiv$ Number of nodes per element
$n\_p \longleftrightarrow n_p$ $\equiv$ Dimension of parametric space
$n\_q \longleftrightarrow n_q$ $\equiv$ Number of total quadrature points
$n\_r \longleftrightarrow n_r$ $\equiv$ Number of rows in the $\boldsymbol{B^e}$ matrix (and material matrix)
$n\_s \longleftrightarrow n_s$ $\equiv$ Dimension of physical space

Classic beam ($n_g = 2$, $n_p = 1$, $n_r = 1$, $n_s = 1$) quantities:

$EI\, v''''(x)$	$= f(x)$ load per unit length,	Differential equation
$EI\, v'''(x)$	$= V(x)$ transverse shear force,	Natural boundary condition
$EI\, v''(x)$	$= M(x)$ bending moment,	Natural boundary condition
$v'(x)$	$= \theta(x)$ slope,	Essential boundary condition
$v(x)$	$=$ deflection,	Essential boundary condition

Element degrees of freedom

$$\boldsymbol{\delta}^{\mathbf{e}^T} = [v_1\ \theta_1\ v_2\ \theta_2\ \cdots\ \theta_{n_n}].$$

Beam with a transverse force per unit length, $f(x)$:

$$\frac{d^2}{dx^2}\left[EI(x)\frac{d^2 v}{dx^2}\right] - f(x) = 0.$$

Beam on an elastic foundation (BOEF) with a stiffness of $k(x)$:

$$\frac{d^2}{dx^2}\left[EI(x)\frac{d^2 v}{dx^2}\right] + k(x)[v - v_\infty] - f(x) = 0.$$

Beam with a constant axial load, N:

$$\frac{d^2}{dx^2}\left[EI(x)\frac{d^2v}{dx^2}\right] - N\frac{d^2v}{dx^2} - f(x) = 0.$$

Beam with a variable axial force, $N(x)$:

$$\frac{d^2}{dx^2}\left[EI(x)\frac{d^2v}{dx^2}\right] - \frac{d}{dx}\left[N(x)\frac{dv}{dx}\right] - f(x) = 0.$$

Beam with an axial force and an elastic foundation:

$$\frac{d^2}{dx^2}\left[EI(x)\frac{d^2v}{dx^2}\right] - \frac{d}{dx}\left[N(x)\frac{dv}{dx}\right] + k(x)[v - v_\infty] - f(x) = 0.$$

Bending stiffness:

$$\boldsymbol{S}_{\boldsymbol{E}^e} = \int_{L^e} \frac{d^2\boldsymbol{H}(x)}{dx^2}^T EI^e \frac{d^2\boldsymbol{H}(x)}{dx^2}\, dx \equiv \int_{L^e} \boldsymbol{B}^e(x)^T EI^e \boldsymbol{B}^e(x)\, dx.$$

Foundation stiffness and load:

$$\boldsymbol{S}_{\boldsymbol{k}}^e = \int_{L^e} \boldsymbol{H}(x)^T k^e \boldsymbol{H}(x)\, dx, \quad \boldsymbol{c}_{\infty}^e = \int_{L^e} \boldsymbol{H}(x)^T v_\infty^e\, dx.$$

Axial load stiffness(es):

$$\boldsymbol{S}_{\boldsymbol{N}}^e = \int_{L^e} \frac{d\boldsymbol{H}(x)}{dx}^T N^e \frac{d\boldsymbol{H}(x)}{dx}\, dx,\ \boldsymbol{S}_{\boldsymbol{w}}^e = -\int_{L^e} \boldsymbol{H}(x)^T \frac{dN}{dx}\frac{d\boldsymbol{H}(x)}{dx}\, dx.$$

Line load resultant:

$$\boldsymbol{c}_{\boldsymbol{f}}^e = \int_{L^e} \boldsymbol{H}(x)^T f^e(x)\, dx = \int_{L^e} \boldsymbol{H}(x)^T \boldsymbol{h}(x)\boldsymbol{f}^e\, dx \equiv \boldsymbol{R}^e \boldsymbol{f}^e.$$

Beam transverse thermal moment:

$$\boldsymbol{c}_{\boldsymbol{\alpha}}^{\boldsymbol{e}} = \int_{L^e} \boldsymbol{B}^{\boldsymbol{e}^T} EI^e(x) \frac{\alpha^e \Delta T(x)^e}{t(x)}\, dx = \frac{\alpha^e \Delta T^e EI^e}{t^e} \int_{L^e} \boldsymbol{B}^{\boldsymbol{e}^T}\, dx.$$

Beam element mass matrix:

$$\boldsymbol{m}^e = \int_{L^e} \boldsymbol{H}(x)^T \rho^e A^e \boldsymbol{H}(x)\, dx.$$

Beam force and moment point sources:

$$\boldsymbol{c}_{\boldsymbol{P}}^{\boldsymbol{e}T} = [V_1\ M_1\ V_2\ M_2\ \cdots\ M_{n_n}].$$

Cubic beam stiffness matrix:

$$\boldsymbol{K}^{\boldsymbol{e}} = \frac{EI^e}{L^3}\begin{bmatrix} 12 & 6L & -12 & 6L \\ 6L & 4L^2 & -6L & 2L^2 \\ -12 & -6L & 12 & -6L \\ 6L & 2L^2 & -6L & 4L^2 \end{bmatrix}.$$

Quintic beam stiffness matrix:

$$\boldsymbol{K}^{\boldsymbol{e}} = \frac{EI}{35L^3}\begin{bmatrix} 5{,}092 & 1{,}138L & -3{,}584 & 1{,}920L & -1{,}508 & 242L \\ 1{,}138L & 332L^2 & -896L & 320L^2 & -242L & 38L^2 \\ -3{,}584 & -896L & 7{,}168 & 0 & -3{,}584 & 896L \\ 1{,}920L & 320L^2 & 0 & 1{,}280L^2 & -1{,}920L & 320L^2 \\ -1{,}508 & -242L & -3{,}584 & -1{,}920L & 5{,}092 & -1{,}138L \\ 242L & 38L^2 & 896L & 320L^2 & -1{,}138L & 332L^2 \end{bmatrix}.$$

Cubic beam line load resultant:

$$\boldsymbol{c}_{\boldsymbol{f}}^{\boldsymbol{e}} = \frac{L}{60}\begin{bmatrix} 21 & 9 \\ 3L & 2L \\ 9 & 21 \\ -2L & -3L \end{bmatrix}\begin{Bmatrix} f_1 \\ f_2 \end{Bmatrix}.$$

Quintic beam quadratic line load resultant:

$$\boldsymbol{c}_{\boldsymbol{f}}^{\boldsymbol{e}} = \frac{L}{420}\begin{bmatrix} 57 & 44 & -3 \\ 3L & 4L & 0 \\ 16 & 192 & 16 \\ -8L & 0 & 8L \\ -3 & 44 & 57 \\ 0 & -4L & -3L \end{bmatrix}\begin{Bmatrix} f_1 \\ f_2 \\ f_3 \end{Bmatrix}.$$

Cubic beam thermal moment (ΔT^e through depth t^e):

$$\boldsymbol{c}_{\boldsymbol{\alpha}}^{\boldsymbol{e}} = \frac{\alpha^e \Delta T^e EI^e}{t^e}[0\ 1\ 0\ -1]^T.$$

Quintic beam thermal moment (ΔT^e through depth t^e):

$$\boldsymbol{c}^e_\alpha = \frac{\alpha^e \Delta T^e E I^e}{t^e}[0 \quad 1 \quad 0 \quad 0 \quad 0 \quad -1]^T.$$

Cubic beam consistent mass matrix:

$$\boldsymbol{m}^e = \frac{\rho^e A^e L}{420}\begin{bmatrix} 156 & 22L & 54 & -13L \\ 22L & 4L^2 & 13L & -3L^2 \\ 54 & 13L & 156 & -22L \\ -13L & -3L^2 & -22L & 4L^2 \end{bmatrix}.$$

Quintic beam consistent mass matrix:

$$\boldsymbol{m}^e = \frac{\rho^e A^e L}{13860}\begin{bmatrix} 2{,}092 & 114L & 880 & -160L & 262 & -29L \\ 114L & 8L^2 & 88L & -12L^2 & 29L & -3L^2 \\ 880 & 88L & 5,632 & 0 & 880 & -88L \\ -160L & -12L^2 & 0 & 128L^2 & 160L & -12L^2 \\ 262 & 29L & 880 & 160L & 2{,}092 & -114L \\ -29L & -3L^2 & -88L & -12L^2 & -114L & 8L^2 \end{bmatrix}.$$

Cubic beam averaged mass matrix:

$$\boldsymbol{m}^e = \frac{\rho^e A^e L}{70560}\begin{bmatrix} 30744 & 1848L & 4536 & -1092L \\ 1848L & 420L^2 & 1092L & -252L^2 \\ 4536 & 1092L & 30744 & -1848L \\ -1092L & -252L^2 & -1848L & 420L^2 \end{bmatrix}.$$

Quintic beam averaged mass matrix:

$$\boldsymbol{m}^e = \frac{\rho^e A^e L}{11337480}\begin{bmatrix} 2063758 & 46626L & 359920 & -65440L & 107158 & -11861L \\ 46626L & 5317L^2 & 35992L & -4908L^2 & 11861L & -1227L^2 \\ 359920 & 35992L & 5555968 & 0 & 359920 & -35992L \\ -65440L & -4908L^2 & 0 & 85072L^2 & 65440L & -4908L^2 \\ 107158 & 11861L & 359920 & 65440L & 2063758 & -46626L \\ -11861L & -1227L^2 & -35992L & -4908L^2 & -46626L & 5317L^2 \end{bmatrix}.$$

Cubic beam diagonalized mass matrix:

$$\boldsymbol{m}^e = \frac{\rho^e A^e L}{420}\begin{bmatrix} 210 & 0 & 0 & 0 \\ 0 & L^2 & 0 & 0 \\ 0 & 0 & 210 & 0 \\ 0 & 0 & 0 & L^2 \end{bmatrix}.$$

Quintic beam diagonalized mass matrix:

$$\boldsymbol{m}^e = \frac{\rho^e A^e L}{1133748}\begin{bmatrix} 241626 & 0 & 0 & 0 & 0 & 0 \\ 0 & 409L^2 & 0 & 0 & 0 & 0 \\ 0 & 0 & 650496 & 0 & 0 & 0 \\ 0 & 0 & 0 & 6544L^2 & 0 & 0 \\ 0 & 0 & 0 & 0 & 241626 & 0 \\ 0 & 0 & 0 & 0 & 0 & 409L^2 \end{bmatrix}.$$

Cubic beam geometric stiffness matrix:

$$\boldsymbol{K}_G^e = \frac{N}{30L}\begin{bmatrix} 36 & 3L & -36 & 3L \\ 3L & 4L^2 & -3L & -L^2 \\ -36 & -3L & 36 & -3L \\ 3L & -L^2 & -3L & 4L^2 \end{bmatrix}.$$

Quintic beam geometric stiffness matrix:

$$\boldsymbol{K}_G^e = \frac{N}{630L}\begin{bmatrix} 1{,}668 & 39L & -1{,}536 & 240L & -132 & -9L \\ 39L & 28L^2 & -48L & -8L^2 & 9L & -5L^2 \\ -1{,}536 & -48L & 3{,}072 & 0 & -1{,}536 & 48L \\ 240L & -8L^2 & 0 & 256L^2 & -240L & -8L^2 \\ -132 & 9L & -1{,}536 & -240L & 1{,}668 & -39L \\ -9L & -5L^2 & 48L & -8L^2 & -39L & 28L^2 \end{bmatrix}.$$

10.11 Review

1. A symmetry plane divides mirror images of the _____.

   (a) Geometric shape
   (b) Distribution of material properties
   (c) Dirichlet boundary conditions
   (d) External loadings
   (e) All of the above
   (f) None of the above

2. At a point on a plane of structural symmetry, which items are zero? _____

   (a) Tangential displacements
   (b) Normal displacement
   (c) Tangential flux
   (d) Temperature
   (e) Normal rotations
   (f) Tangential rotations
   (g) Both (a) and (f)
   (h) All of the above

Chapter 11

Frame Analysis

11.1 Planar Frames

If the bar member, which carries only loads along its axis, and a beam, which carries only loads transverse to its axis, are combined, the new element is the so-called beam-column or frame member which is illustrated in Fig. 11.1-1. The one-dimensional version of that element has three generalized nodal degrees of freedom ($n_g = 3$): an axial displacement vector, a transverse displacement vector, and a rotation vector (perpendicular to the other two), in that order. Analogous to a planar truss, which is the extension of a simple two force axial member to a planar assembly that resists loads by axial loads only, a frame is an assembly of beam-column members that adds the ability to also transmit moments (couples) through its joints. In other words, a planar frame is a combination of individual beam-column elements that resist loadings by a combination of bending, axial member forces, and transverse (shear) forces. Therefore, a planar frame is a more efficient load transferring structure than a planar truss structure. A plane frame also has all of its joints and forces in the same plane, with any couples applied about an axis normal to that plane.

Each beam component of the member has a cross-section with two principle axes associated with the second moments of inertia, I_{zz} and I_{yy}. For the coordinate system shown above, the principle inertia is the former: $I \equiv I_{zz} = \int_A y^2 dA$. Its defining axis is the z-axis coming out of the paper and lies in the horizontal plane.

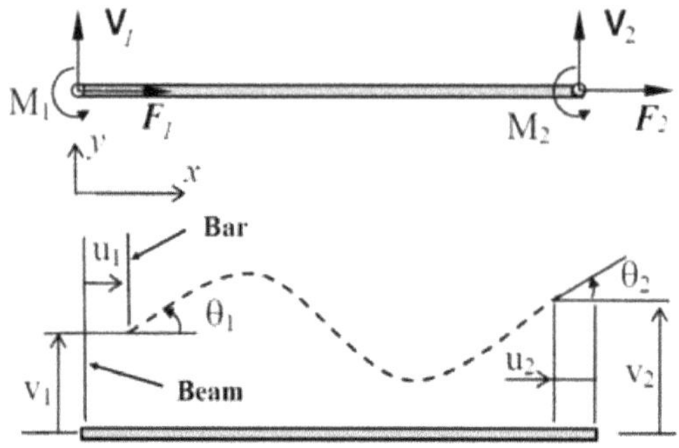

Fig. 11.1-1: A plane frame member with axial (1) and transverse (2) displacements, and an in-plane rotation (3) at each node, $n_g = 3$.

Conversely, the minor inertia y-axis lies in the vertical plane of the paper. Any changes in the two inertia axis directions becomes important if the beam is part of a space frame member located in general three-dimensional space, and they are discussed later.

Recall that the stiffness of the linear axial two-node bar element depends on the "axial stiffness", EA/L, of the member and it has the equilibrium equation of

$$\begin{aligned}
&\frac{EA}{L}\begin{bmatrix} 1 & -1 \\ -1 & 1 \end{bmatrix}\begin{Bmatrix} u_1 \\ u_2 \end{Bmatrix} \\
&= \begin{Bmatrix} F_1 \\ F_2 \end{Bmatrix} + \frac{L}{6}\begin{bmatrix} 2 & 1 \\ 1 & 2 \end{bmatrix}\begin{Bmatrix} w_{x1} \\ w_{x2} \end{Bmatrix} + EA\alpha\Delta T_x \begin{Bmatrix} -1 \\ 1 \end{Bmatrix}, [\boldsymbol{S^a}]\{\boldsymbol{\delta^a}\} \\
&= \{\boldsymbol{F^a}\} + \{\boldsymbol{F^a_w}\} + \{\boldsymbol{F^a_T}\} \qquad (11.1\text{-}1)
\end{aligned}$$

where E is the modulus of elasticity, A is the cross-sectional area, L is the length, F_x denotes the axial force at node k, w_{xk} is the axial load per unit length at node k, α is the coefficient of thermal expansion, and ΔT_x is the constant increase in temperature along the axis of the bar. These axial effects are associated with the first and third degrees of freedom of a frame element thus a vector subscript, Bar $= [1\,4]$, to insert its terms into the combined matrices. The two-node beam equilibrium equation depends on the "bending stiffness", EI/L^3, and has the form

$$\frac{EI}{L^3}\begin{bmatrix} 12 & 6L & -12 & 6L \\ 6L & 4L^2 & -6L & 2L^2 \\ -12 & -6L & 12 & -6L \\ 6L & 2L^2 & -6L & 4L^2 \end{bmatrix}\begin{Bmatrix} v_1 \\ \theta_1 \\ v_2 \\ \theta_2 \end{Bmatrix}$$

$$+\frac{N}{30\,L}\begin{bmatrix} 36 & 3L & -36 & 3L \\ 3L & 4L^2 & -3L & -L^2 \\ -36 & -3L & 36 & -3L \\ 3L & -L^2 & -3L & 4L^2 \end{bmatrix}\begin{Bmatrix} v_1 \\ \theta_1 \\ v_2 \\ \theta_2 \end{Bmatrix}$$

$$=\begin{Bmatrix} V_1 \\ M_1 \\ V_2 \\ M_2 \end{Bmatrix}+\frac{L}{60}\begin{bmatrix} 21 & 9 \\ 3L & 2L \\ 9 & 21 \\ -2L & -3L \end{bmatrix}\begin{Bmatrix} w_{y1} \\ w_{y2} \end{Bmatrix}+\frac{EI\alpha\Delta T_y}{t}\begin{Bmatrix} 0 \\ 1 \\ 0 \\ -1 \end{Bmatrix},$$

$$\left[\boldsymbol{S^b}\right]\left\{\boldsymbol{\delta^b}\right\}=\left\{\boldsymbol{F^b}\right\}+\left\{\boldsymbol{F^b_w}\right\}+\left\{\boldsymbol{F^b_T}\right\}, \tag{11.1-2}$$

but with the axial force, N, identically zero unless a prior iteration has provided the axial force in the bar element. The other items are I the moment inertia of the area evaluated at its centroid, V_k is the external transverse shear force applied at node k, M_k is the external couple (moment) applied at node k, w_{yk} is the transverse line load at node k, t is the depth of the beam, and ΔT_y is the increase in temperature from the top of the beam through its depth. For now, the axial force N is taken as zero, until it becomes necessary to study buckling (instability) of frames. The degrees of freedom of the bar are identified by the vector subscript Bend = [2 3 5 6]. In other words, the combined element degrees of freedom are

$$\boldsymbol{\delta^e}\left(\boldsymbol{Bar}\right)=\boldsymbol{\delta^e}\begin{pmatrix} 1 \\ 4 \end{pmatrix}=\begin{Bmatrix} u_1 \\ u_2 \end{Bmatrix}, \quad \boldsymbol{\delta^e}\left(\boldsymbol{Bend}\right)=\boldsymbol{\delta^e}\begin{pmatrix} 2 \\ 3 \\ 5 \\ 6 \end{pmatrix}=\begin{Bmatrix} v_1 \\ \theta_1 \\ v_2 \\ \theta_2 \end{Bmatrix}$$

$$\boldsymbol{\delta^{e^T}}=[u_1 \quad v_1 \quad \theta_1 \quad u_2 \quad v_2 \quad \theta_2]. \tag{11.1-3}$$

Let $\boldsymbol{K}$ be the combined frame 6×6 stiffness matrix, it is made up of, and programmed as, the scattering of the 2×2 axial stiffness matrix, $\boldsymbol{K}(\boldsymbol{Bar}, \boldsymbol{Bar})=\boldsymbol{S^a}(:, :)$, and the scattering of the 4×4 axial stiffness matrix, $\boldsymbol{K}\left(\boldsymbol{Bend}, \boldsymbol{Bend}\right)=\boldsymbol{S^b}(:, :)$. In the provided application script *Plane_frame_MPC.m*, the axial and bending stiffnesses are written in the above forms and then combined using vector subscripts. That makes it easier to understand where the entries in matrix $\boldsymbol{K}$ came from. The completed stiffness in the local coordinate axes (with element length L) is

$$\boldsymbol{K_L^e} = \frac{E}{L}\begin{bmatrix} A & 0 & 0 & -A & 0 & 0 \\ 0 & 12\beta/L & 6\beta & 0 & -12\beta/L & 6\beta \\ 0 & 6\beta & 4I & 0 & -6\beta & 2I \\ -A & 0 & 0 & A & 0 & 0 \\ 0 & -12\beta/L & -6\beta & 0 & 12\beta/L & -6\beta \\ 0 & 6\beta & 2I & 0 & -6\beta & 4I \end{bmatrix}, \quad \beta \equiv \frac{I}{L}. \tag{11.1-4}$$

The combined external point loads are scattered the same way:

$$\boldsymbol{F^T} = \begin{bmatrix} F_1 & V_1 & M_1 & F_2 & V_2 & M_2 \end{bmatrix}$$

as are the initial thermal loads

$$\boldsymbol{F_T} = E\alpha\begin{bmatrix} -A\Delta T_x & 0 & I\Delta T_y/t & A\Delta T_x & 0 & -I\Delta T_y/t \end{bmatrix}.$$

The resultant of the element forces, and moments, are written as a rectangular matrix times the input nodal line loads as $\{\boldsymbol{F_w^b}\} \equiv [\boldsymbol{R^b}]\{\boldsymbol{w^b}\}$ and it probably makes sense to calculate the resultant axial and bending (generalized) forces and scatter them. But, since the line load components will come in as a vector in the property data, the element rectangular matrix could also be assembled and simply post-multiplied by that load vector. The assembled 6×4 rectangular load transfer matrix and the line load inputs for the frame element are

$$\{\boldsymbol{F_w^e}\} \equiv [\boldsymbol{R^e}]\{\boldsymbol{w^e}\}, \quad \boldsymbol{R^e} = \frac{L}{60}\begin{bmatrix} 20 & 0 & 10 & 0 \\ 0 & 21 & 0 & 0 \\ 0 & 3L & 0 & 2L \\ 10 & 0 & 20 & 0 \\ 0 & 9 & 0 & 21 \\ 0 & -2L & 0 & -3L \end{bmatrix},$$

$$\boldsymbol{w^e} = \begin{Bmatrix} w_{x1} \\ w_{y1} \\ w_{x2} \\ w_{y2} \end{Bmatrix}. \tag{11.1-5}$$

Usually, several of the frame members in a structure do not lie parallel to the global axis. For any inclined frame member, the relationship between the above local coordinate equations and their form for assembly into the system matrix equations of equilibrium depends on its orientation in the plane, as sketched in Fig. 11.1-2. As with a truss element, one must consider how the nodal degrees of freedom transform from the element axes to the global axes.

The rotation of the frame member at node k, θ_k, is unchanged by rotation of the coordinate system about a parallel axis, so a unity term is added to the truss transformation rule. The frame transformation matrices for the generalized displacements at a node (similar to 9.1-2) are

$$\{\delta\}_L = \begin{Bmatrix} u \\ v \\ \theta \end{Bmatrix}_L = \begin{bmatrix} \cos(\theta_x) & \cos(\theta_y) & 0 \\ -\cos(\theta_y) & \cos(\theta_x) & 0 \\ 0 & 0 & 1 \end{bmatrix} \begin{Bmatrix} u \\ v \\ \theta \end{Bmatrix}_G \quad \text{or} \quad \boldsymbol{\delta}_{\boldsymbol{L}} = \boldsymbol{t}(\theta)\boldsymbol{\delta}_{\boldsymbol{G}}.$$

Applying the same transformation to both ends gives the element transformation law

$$\boldsymbol{\delta}^e_{\boldsymbol{L}} = [\boldsymbol{T}(\theta)]\,\boldsymbol{\delta}^e_{\boldsymbol{G}} = \begin{bmatrix} \boldsymbol{t}(\theta) & \boldsymbol{0} \\ \boldsymbol{0} & \boldsymbol{t}(\theta) \end{bmatrix} \boldsymbol{\delta}^e_{\boldsymbol{G}}, \tag{11.1-6}$$

$$6 \times 1 = (6 \times 6)(6 \times 1)$$

In its detail form this block diagonal transformation matrix is

$$[\boldsymbol{T}(\theta)] = \begin{bmatrix} \cos(\theta_x) & \cos(\theta_y) & 0 & & & \\ -\cos(\theta_y) & \cos(\theta_x) & 0 & & \boldsymbol{0} & \\ 0 & 0 & 1 & & & \\ & & & \cos(\theta_x) & \cos(\theta_y) & 0 \\ & \boldsymbol{0} & & -\cos(\theta_y) & \cos(\theta_x) & 0 \\ & & & 0 & 0 & 1 \end{bmatrix}.$$

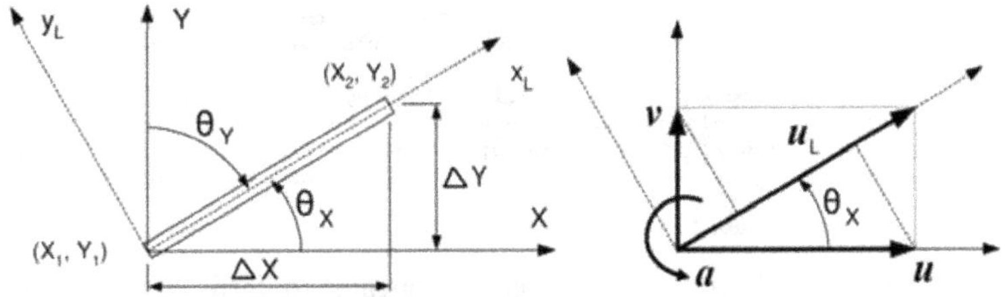

Fig. 11.1-2: An inclined frame member.

Finally, the transformed global coordinate form of the combined frame member stiffness matrix and force vectors is

$$\boldsymbol{K}_{\boldsymbol{G}}^{\boldsymbol{e}} = [\boldsymbol{T}(\theta)]^{\boldsymbol{T}} \boldsymbol{K}_{\boldsymbol{L}}^{\boldsymbol{e}} [\boldsymbol{T}(\theta)], \quad \boldsymbol{F}_{\boldsymbol{G}}^{\boldsymbol{e}} = [\boldsymbol{T}(\theta)]^{\boldsymbol{T}} \boldsymbol{F}_{\boldsymbol{L}}^{\boldsymbol{e}}. \tag{11.1-7}$$

The above element generation, combination, and assembly are illustrated in the script segment in Fig. 11.1-3, which is taken from the application script *Planar_Frame.m*.

```
%     Define vector subscripts for combined element DOF
axial = [1, 4] ;  bend   = [2, 3, 5, 6] ; % DOF maps

for k = 1:n_e; % loop over elements ===>> ====>> ====>> ====>>
  e_nodes = nodes (k, 1:n_n)            ; % garther connectivity
  type    = el_type (k)          ; % current element type number
  xy_e (1:n_n, 1) = x(e_nodes)            ; % x coord at el nodes
  xy_e (1:n_n, 2) = y(e_nodes)            ; % y coord at el nodes

%   Set constant element properties& Allocate element arrays
  . . .
%          Find member length and direction cosines
  dx  = x(e_nodes(n_n)) - x(e_nodes(1))             ; % x length
  dy  = y(e_nodes(n_n)) - y(e_nodes(1))             ; % y length
  L_e = sqrt (dx * dx + dy * dy)                ; % total length
  cx  = dx / L_e ; cy   = dy / L_e        ; % direction cosines
  IbL = I / L_e   ; IbL2 = I / L_e^2       ; % bending constants

% Local coordinate stiffness (axial dof 1&4 bending 2,3 & 5,6)
  bar = A * E * [1,  -1 ; -1,    1] / L_e      ; % bar stiffness
  beam = [12*IbL2,  6*IbL,  -12*IbL2,  6*IbL ;% beam stiffness
          6*IbL,     4*I,    -6*IbL,    2*I   ;
         -12*IbL2, -6*IbL,   12*IbL2, -6*IbL ;
          6*IbL,     2*I,    -6*IbL,    4*I   ] * E / L_e ;
%     Transform line load to member end forces and moments
  R_b = [21, 9; 3*L_e, 2*L_e; 9, 21; -2*L_e -3*L_e ]*L_e / 60;
  w_L = R_b * w_e            ; % transverse line load resultants

%               Combine local axial and bending
  s_L (axial, axial) = bar             ; % insert bar stiffness
  s_L (bend,  bend ) = beam           ; % insert beam stiffness
  c_L (bend)            = w_L ; % transverse line load resultants

%     Define local to system DOF transformation matrix
  t_L = [ cx    cy    0    0    0    0 ;                % joint 1
         -cy    cx    0    0    0    0 ;
          0     0     1    0    0    0 ;
          0     0     0    cx   cy   0 ;                % joint 2
          0     0     0   -cy   cx   0 ;
          0     0     0    0    0    1 ] ;

% Transform from local coordinates to system coordinates
  S_e = t_L' * s_L * t_L                           ; % stiffness
  C_e = t_L' * c_L             ; % resultant forces and moments
%  Save element arrays needed for post-processing stresses
  . . .
% Insert completed element matrices into system matrices
  [rows] = get_element_index (n_g, n_n, e_nodes); % eq numbers
  S (rows, rows) = S (rows, rows) + S_e    ; % add to system sq
  C (rows) = C (rows) + C_e               ; % add to sys column

end ; % for each k element in mesh <<==== <<==== <<==== <<====
```

Fig. 11.1-3: Combining axial and bending arrays to form a frame member stiffness.

Now that each node has three degrees of freedom, the packed integer code that flags the essential boundary conditions (EBCs) at each node can have the following packed values: 000, which is a free joint, 100, where only u is given, 010, where only v is given, 001, only the slope is given, 110, where both u and v are given (a pinned joint), 111, where all are given (usually a fixed joint), etc.

Usually, the given boundary condition flag values are zero, but any small deflection value can be imposed as required by the application. If any unit value in the flag is replaced with a 2, then that means that component is coupled to another degree of freedom with a type-2 multipoint constraints (MPC). For example, some frames contain hinges that release the moment there. Hinges are modeled by two nodes having the same coordinates and having the vertical displacements constrained to be equal and also having the horizontal displacements constrained to be equal. The rotations at the two nodes become independent (they no longer transmit a moment). Then there are two type-2 MPCs at those nodes.

11.2 Frame Member Reactions

To design buildings utilizing frame members, it is important to be able to determine the element reactions (member end forces and moments) and or to graph its moment and shear diagrams. Once the entire structure has been solved to give all of the nodal displacements, each element is post-processed and its subset of displacements is gathered back to the element. Assuming that the element is in equilibrium with those displacements, then (11.11-1) and/or (11.11-2) are re-arranged to solve for the generalized forces at its endpoints. In other words, the saved element stiffness matrix, in global coordinates, is multiplied by the element displacements to give a vector of generalized forces, say $\{\boldsymbol{F}^e_\delta\} \equiv [\boldsymbol{S}^e]\,\{\boldsymbol{\delta}^e\}$, so that the equilibrium of the generalized element forces becomes $\{\boldsymbol{F}^e_\delta\} = \{\boldsymbol{F}^e\} + \{\boldsymbol{F}^e_w\} + \{\boldsymbol{F}^e_T\}$, which is simply rearranged to find the member end reactions as

$$\{\boldsymbol{F}^e\} = \{\boldsymbol{F}^e_\delta\} - \{\boldsymbol{F}^e_w\} - \{\boldsymbol{F}^e_T\}. \tag{11.2-1}$$

To find the member axial force and the two endpoint transverse shear forces, it is necessary to transform the global element reactions back to the local member coordinates. The transformation matrices have the property of being "orthogonal matrices" which means that their inverse is simply their transpose: $[\boldsymbol{T}(\theta)]^{-1} = \boldsymbol{T}(\theta)^T$, so the array used to rotate from an inclined member axis to the global member axis gets re-used. The above element reactions recovery in first the global system and then in the member local coordinate system are illustrated in the script segment in Fig. 11.2-1, which is taken from the application script *Planar_Frame.m*.

```
for k = 1:n_e; % loop over elements ====>> ====>> ====>> ====>> ====>>

  type    = el_type (k)                  ; % current element type number
  e_nodes = nodes (k, 1:n_n)                          ; % connectivity
  [rows]  = get_element_index (n_g, n_n, e_nodes)       ; % eq numbers
  Ans_e (1:n_i, 1) = Ans(rows)        ;  % gather element displacements

%  Recover previously calculated element arrays
  [t_L] = fread (el_unit, [n_i, n_i], 'double')     ; % rotation matrix
  . . .
  if ( el_react )                   ; % list member end forces and moments
%   Assign any point source n C_pt to the first element with that node
    if ( load_pt )                ; % then point sources to assign (once)
      for eq = 1:n_i                          ; % loop over element nodes
        n = rows (eq)                          ; % find system DOF number
        if ( C_pt (n) ~= 0 )               ; % found an input point value
          C_e (eq) = C_e (eq) + C_pt (n)          ; % copy to this node
          C_pt (n) = 0                          ; % prevent a second use
        end                  ; % if first appearance of this point source
      end                         ; % for eq node of the current element
    end                   ; % if load_pt has been assigned to this element

%   Get the element reactions and list them in global coordinates
%         S_e * Ans_e = C_e + F_e, F_e = global reactions
    C_m = S_e * Ans_e     ; % global member forces due to displacements
    F_e = C_m - C_e      ; % less external loads for reaction on member

%   Transform back to element local coordinates and list
    fprintf('\n'); fprintf('Element number %i, length %g \n', k, L_e);

    fprintf('Global Element Reactions: \n');
    fprintf('Fx_1G    Fy_1G    Mz_1G    Fx_2G    Fy_2G    Mz_2G \n');
    fprintf('%11.4e  %11.4e  %11.4e  %11.4e  %11.4e  %11.4e \n', ...
             F_e(1), F_e(2), F_e(3), F_e(4), F_e(5), F_e(6) );

    c_L = t_L * F_e         ; % overwrite c_L storage w local reactions
    fprintf ('Local Element Reactions  \n');
    fprintf('x-Axial & y-Transverse Forces & Moment: \n');
    fprintf('Fx_1L     Fy_1L    Mz_1L    Fx_2L    Fy_2L    Mz_2L \n');
    fprintf ('%11.4e  %11.4e  %11.4e  %11.4e  %11.4e  %11.4e \n', ...
             c_L(1), c_L(2), c_L(3), c_L(4), c_L(5), c_L(6) );
  end                                               ; % if el_react list

end ; % for each k element in mesh  <<==== <<==== <<==== <<==== <<====
```

Fig. 11.2-1: Recovering the frame member global and local reactions.

Example 11.2-1 Given: The plane frame in Fig. 11.2-2 is a statically determinate plane frame with the shown point loads and line loads. Joints occur anywhere there is a discontinuity in the loading or the member properties. It was analyzed numerically using frame elements consisting of two-node cubic bending elements combined with two-node linear axial elements. The analysis used values of $EI = 1{,}000$ and $A = 1$. Compute the displacements of the frame using Matlab script *Planar_Frame.m.*

Solution: The application data in Fig. 11.2-3 are similar to most applications and the major change is the application properties. For a plane frame, those data are the cross-sectional area, the section moment of inertia about an axis normal to the plane, the material elastic modulus, material weight per unit area, coefficient of thermal expansion, axial temperature increase, line load value at the first end joint, and the line load value at the other end joint. Any line load acting to the left from the first end to the second is considered as positive (applies a CCW moment). The Matlab script utilized the data in Fig. 11.2-3 and numerically gives the system displacements as

Node, 3 displacements per node (u_x, u_y, θ radians))			
1,	0.0000e + 00	0.0000e + 00	3.7190e − 01
2,	−1.3674e + 00	−2.1500e − 01	1.1903e − 02
3,	−1.5274e + 00	−1.7667e − 01	3.8569e − 02
4,	−1.5036e + 00	−8.8333e − 02	−1.4306e − 03
5,	−1.5065e + 00	0.0000e + 00	−1.4306e − 03,

which match the analytically exact values. That script recovers the system reaction forces as

Recovered Reactions at Displacement BCs

Node,	DOF	(1 = Fx, 2 = Fy), Value [which are exact]
1,	1,	30.0000
1,	2,	35.8333
5,	2,	44.1667

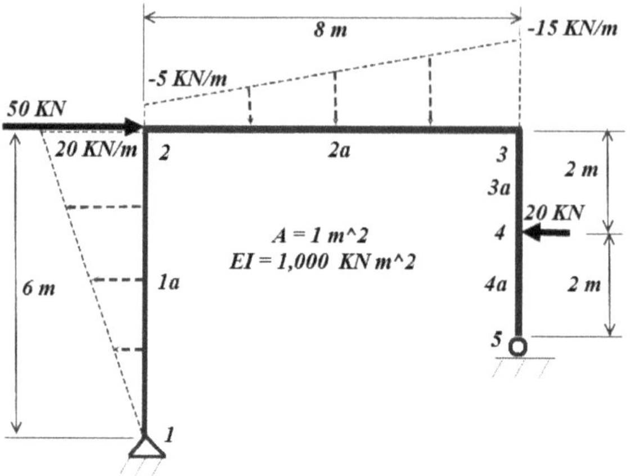

Fig. 11.2-2: Plane frame structure.

```
msh_remarks.txt
Determinate frame using L2_C1 elements

msh_bc_xyz.txt            msh_typ_nodes.txt
110  0.   0.                1       1     2
000  0.   6.                1       2     3
000  8.   6.                1       3     4
000  8.   4.                1       4     5
000  8.   2.

msh_properties
1  1.   1000.  0.   0.   0.   0.   20.
1  1.   1000.  0.   0.   0.  -5.  -15.
1  1.   1000.  0.   0.   0.   0.   0.
1  1.   1000.  0.   0.   0.   0.   0.

msh_load_pt.txt            msh_ebc.txt
2  1   50.                  1   1   0.
4  1  -20.                  1   2   0.
                            5   2   0.
```

Fig. 11.2-3: Data for Fig. 11.2-2.

Example 11.2-2 Given: Since cubic beams give poor moment and shear values (see Fig. 10.9-3), unless there are many of them, repeat the frame study in Example 11.2-1 using the three-noded quintic beam element combined with the three-noded quadratic bar element, and graph the deflection, slope, moment, and shear along the member lengths.

Solution: For point loads, constant line loads, and linear line loads, this element gives the analytic exact results along each member

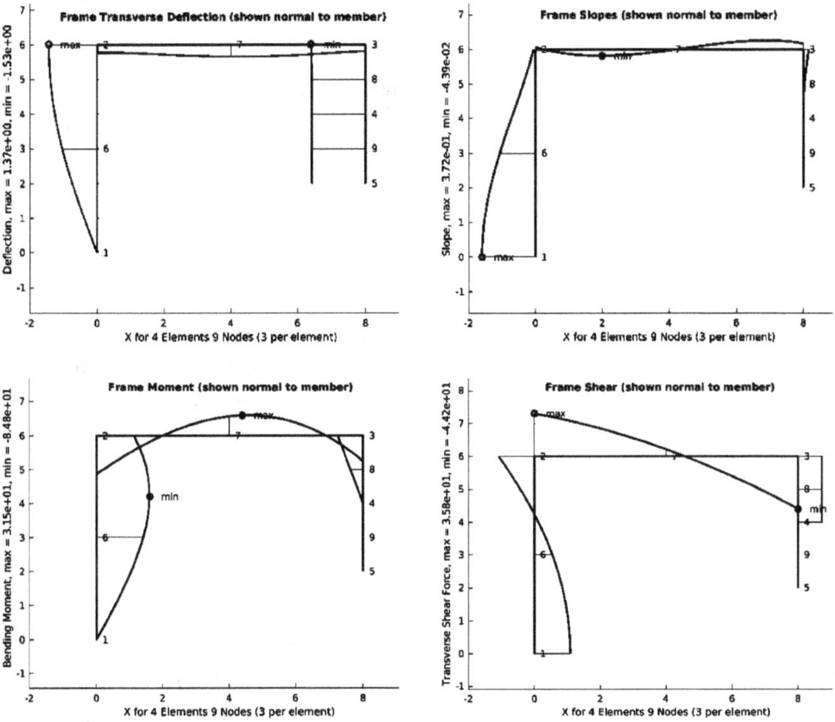

Fig. 11.2-4: Deflection, slope, moments, and shears from quintic frame members.

length. Thus, still, only four elements are required but each must have a mid-length node added to each span and each element connection list. In other words, the reference locations 1a through 4a in Fig. 11.2-2 are made new node locations 6 through 9 (see Fig. 11.2-4). The interpolated magnitudes of the deflections, slopes, moments, and transverse shear forces are plotted perpendicular to the member axes in Fig. 11.2-2. In that figure, the top left plot of the displacements shows that the right vertical member, with the bottom roller, mainly just translates to the left and causes the pinned left vertical member to bend. Actually, there is a small change in the slope of the right member, but it is too small to see on the plot. That is confirmed by comparing the above u_x values in Example 11.2-1 at nodes 3, 4, and 5 (since cubic beam only yield exact displacements at the nodes).

Example 11.2-3 Given: The plane frame structure in Fig. 11.2-5 has one horizontal member and one inclined member with the same bending stiffness, EI, and the same length, L. The horizontal span is loaded with a constant line-load per unit length of w. Both members have the same local stiffness matrices in (11.1-4), and the horizontal member's local stiffness matrix is the same as its value in system coordinates. Determine the system stiffness matrix of the inclined member.

Solution: The inclined stiffness must be rotated using the rotation matrix in (11.1-7) as $\boldsymbol{K}_G^e = [\boldsymbol{T}(\theta)]^T \boldsymbol{K}_L^e [\boldsymbol{T}(\theta)]$ with $[\boldsymbol{T}(300°)]$. Evaluating the direction cosines and pre- and post-multiplying gives

$$\boldsymbol{K}_G^{(2)} = 250{,}000$$

$$\times \begin{bmatrix} 2.563 & -4.294 & 4.330 & -2.563 & -4.294 & -4.330 \\ & 7.521 & 2.5 & 4.294 & -7.521 & 2.5 \\ & & 400. & -4.330 & -2.5 & 200. \\ & & & -2.563 & -4.294 & -4.330 \\ & & & & 7.521 & -2.5 \\ & \text{Symmetric} & & & & 400. \end{bmatrix}$$

$\times$ lb/in.

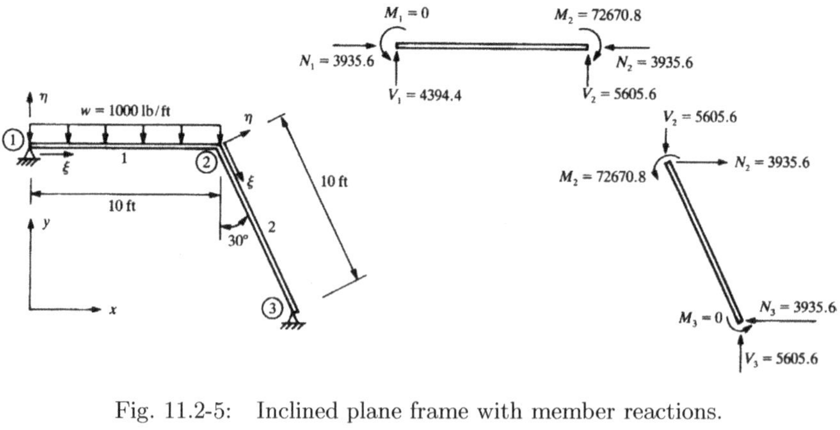

Fig. 11.2-5: Inclined plane frame with member reactions.

Example 11.2-4 Given: After assembly of the stiffnesses and loads in Fig. 11.2-4 and enforcing the four Dirichlet BC, the remaining five non-zero generalized displacements (in inches and radians) are computed to be

$$\begin{aligned}\boldsymbol{\delta} &= [\theta_1 \quad u_2 \quad v_2 \quad \theta_2 \quad \theta_3]^T \\ &= e^{-3}\,[-1.5495 \quad -1.5746 \quad -4.0601 \quad 0.9972 \quad -.4562].\end{aligned}$$

Use the now known six displacements on member 2 and its system stiffness matrix in Example 11.2-3 to find its system reactions shown in Fig. 11.2-5.

Solution: The subset of the element displacements for member 2 are

$$\boldsymbol{\delta}^e = [u_2 \quad v_2 \quad \theta_2 \quad 0 \quad 0 \quad \theta_3]^T.$$

Assuming each element is in equilibrium, the element reactions are

$$[\boldsymbol{S}^e]\,\{\boldsymbol{\delta}^e\} = \{\boldsymbol{F}^e\} + \{\boldsymbol{F}^e_{\boldsymbol{w}}\} + \{\boldsymbol{F}^e_{\boldsymbol{T}}\}.$$

Element 2 has no line load or temperature change so $\{\boldsymbol{F}^e_{\boldsymbol{w}}\} = \{\boldsymbol{F}^e_{\boldsymbol{T}}\} = \mathbf{0}$ and the only unknown at the element are the node point reactions $\boldsymbol{F}^e = [N_2 \quad V_2 \quad M_2 \quad N_3 \quad V_3 \quad M_3]^{\boldsymbol{T}}$ in Fig. 11.2-5 (in lb. and in-lb.). Multiplying the element stiffness in Example 11.2-3 by the current displacement vector gives the element point reactions as

$$\boldsymbol{F}^e = [3{,}935.6 \quad -5{,}605.6 \quad 72{,}670.0 \quad -3{,}935.6 \quad 5{,}605.6 \quad 0.0]^{\boldsymbol{T}}.$$

Example 11.2-5 Given: Now that the system reaction at node 3, in Fig. 11.2-5, are known from Example 11.2-4, use basic statics to check the system reactions at node 1.

Solution: Sum the system external horizontal forces:

$$\sum f_x = 0 = N_1 + N_3 = N_1 - 3{,}935.6 \rightarrow N_1 = 3{,}935.6\,\text{lb}.$$

Sum the vertical forces:

$$\sum f_y = 0 = V_1 - w\,L + V_3 = V_1 - (1{,}000)(10) + 5{,}605.6$$

$$\rightarrow V_1 = 4{,}394.4\,\text{lb}.$$

(Check the results by taking moments about node 3 or about node 2.)

11.3 Space Frames*

A space frame is made up of frame members that are connected together in three-dimensional space. That means that each node now has three displacement components and three rotational components. A space frame member is required to resist three force components and three-moment components at each node, see Fig. 11.3-1. The bar element carries the axial force, say F_x, a torsional shaft element carries the moment about the axis, say M_x, the previous beam element, with inertia I_{yy}, carries the first transverse force, say F_y, and the moment, say M_z, is perpendicular to F_x and F_y, and a second beam element, with the same axis, is set in the plane perpendicular to the first beam and it transmits the transverse force, say F_z, and the moment, say M_y, perpendicular to the axis and M_z. The second beam has a different moment of inertia (I_{zz}) since it also lies at the centroid of the cross-sectional area, but is in a plane perpendicular to that of the first beam section.

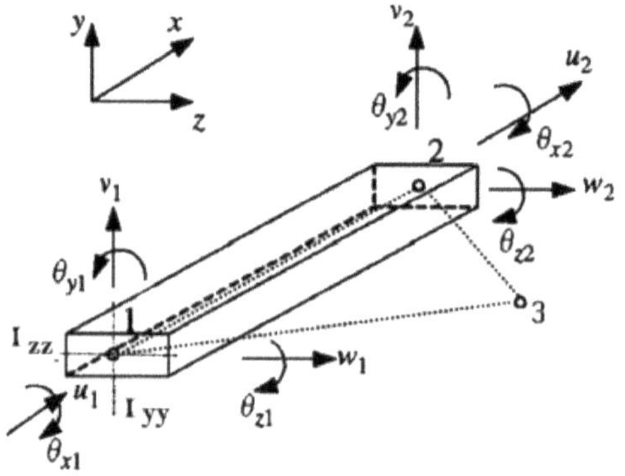

Fig. 11.3-1: Space frame degrees of freedom and reference node.

The direction cosine rotation matrix, in (11.1-6), of a space frame is often very similar to that of the planar frame. If the axes of the two principle inertia axis continue to lie in the horizontal plane and vertical plane, as they did for planar frames, then the nodal displacements and rotations transform into three-dimensional space just like the space truss displacements. However, for the more powerful case where a space frame member is rotated about its axis causing the principle inertia axes to no longer be in the horizontal and vertical planes, then more detailed user data are required in order to correctly orientate the axis and inertia planes of the frame member in three-dimensional space. In general, the additional orientation data needed to locate the local I_{yy} bending inertia axis, in Fig. 11.3-1, is set by including a third node in the element connection list. Those three points define the plane in which the bending about the major inertia axis occurs. Usually, that node can be found at another joint. Otherwise, the reference point is input like a node, but is fully restrained so that the system stiffness matrix does not become singular.

11.4 Numerically Integrated Frame Members*

The results of important studies should be validated by some other technique like analytical solutions, experiments, or a different type of FEA. There are long irregularly shaped solids carrying bending loads that can be modeled as space frame members where the area, moment of inertia tensor, and/or modulus of elasticity vary along the length of the frame members. They can be reasonably approximated as numerically integrated space frame elements.

One such structure is a human long bone. The data for long bones are extracted from computer tomography (CT) images taken at multiple scan planes. The extracted data give the inner and outer perimeters of the cortical bone and thereby give the centroid, cross-sectional area, and the moment of inertias about orthogonal axes in each plane slice. Every pixel in the CT slice gives the density of the bone at that point. There is an equation that converts bone density to bone modulus of elasticity. The elastic modulus value, E, at every point in the slice is used to obtain the average modulus. A space frame element can be established between the centroids of two adjacent slices. Then the slice area, inertias, and average modulus at the two (or three) member nodes are interpolated to define the variations along the length of the member.

Such space frame models are more efficient than using solid models and can give similar accuracy. The element stiffness must be evaluated by numerical integration. Then the standard constant property bending stiffness matrix generalizes from (10.4-2) to

$$\boldsymbol{S}_b^e = \int_{L^e} \boldsymbol{B}_b^e(x)^T E(x) I(x) \boldsymbol{B}_b^e(x) dx,$$

with $E(x) = \boldsymbol{H}(r)\boldsymbol{E}^e$, $I(x) = \boldsymbol{H}(r)\boldsymbol{I}^e$. The axial stiffness matrix generalizes to

$$\boldsymbol{S}_a^e = \int_{L^e} \boldsymbol{B}_a^e(x)^T E(x) A(x) \boldsymbol{B}_a^e(x) dx,$$

with $A(x) = \boldsymbol{H}(r)\boldsymbol{A}^e$. Those terms are integrated numerically, using the larger number of quadrature points required by the bending contribution:

$$\boldsymbol{S}_b^e = \sum_{q=1}^{n_q} \boldsymbol{B}_b^e(r_q)^T \{\boldsymbol{H}(r_q)\boldsymbol{E}^e\}\{\boldsymbol{H}(r_q)\boldsymbol{I}^e\}\boldsymbol{B}_b^e(r_q)|J|w_q,$$

$$\boldsymbol{S}_a^e = \sum_{q=1}^{n_q} \boldsymbol{B}_a^e(r_q)^T \{\boldsymbol{H}(r_q)\boldsymbol{E}^e\}\{\boldsymbol{H}(r_q)\boldsymbol{A}^e\}\boldsymbol{B}_a^e(r_q)|J|w_q. \quad (11.4\text{-}1)$$

For the cubic beam the $\boldsymbol{B}_b^e$ is degree 1, the elastic and geometry interpolations $\boldsymbol{H}$ are each degree 2, and the Jacobian, $|J|$, is probably not constant and should be taken as degree 1. Thus, the total degree of the integrand is $D = 1+2+2+1+1 = 7$ and the minimum integer number of quadrature points is $n_q \geq (D+1)/2 = 4$.

A numerically integrated space frame model was used as a validation check for a three-dimensional solid element study of an artificial hip replacement for the femur bone in Fig. 11.4-1. The space frame model ran 2,000 times faster than the custom solid model mainly because the modulus of elasticity was different at every point and required a higher than normal number of integration points in each solid element. Of course, after the displacements were obtained a more complicated post-processing was required to estimate the equivalent solid stresses. The outer perimeter of each of the bone slices was divided into several stress recovery points. At each such point around the perimeter the axial stress, torsional shear stress, coupled bending stress, and bending shear stresses were combined to

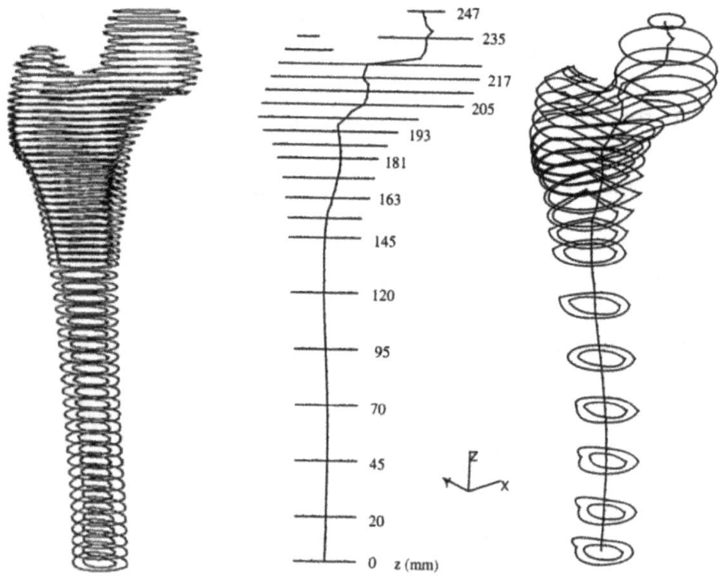

Fig. 11.4-1: Femur slices and frame with variable areas and moment of inertias.

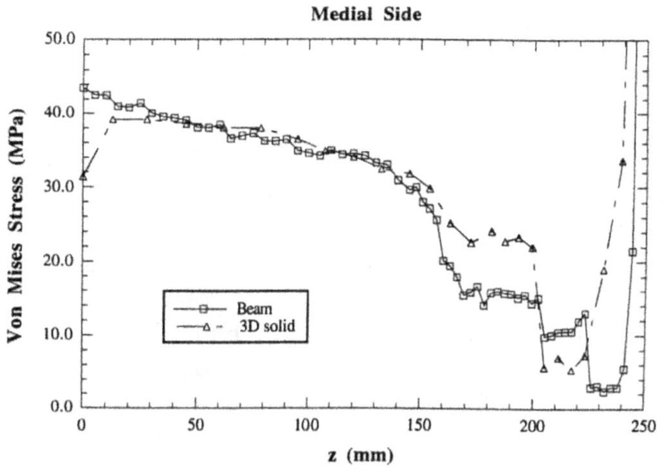

Fig. 11.4-2: Von Mises failure criteria from a bone space frame and a solid model.

define the three-dimensional stresses at the point. The general three-dimensional stresses yielded the principal stresses, which in turn were combined to evaluate a few likely yield criteria, including the von Mises equivalent stress. Figure 11.4-2, shows one such comparison where the base was fixed and the femur was loaded with the "one-leg-stance" case. The two graphs show the maximum von Mises effective stress in each slice from the numerically integrated space frame and the eight-noded solid brick simulation. This illustrates that one-dimensional models can sometimes provide useful validation checks of some classes of relatively long three-dimensional solid objects.

11.5 Summary

$n\_d \longleftrightarrow n_d$ ≡ Number of system unknowns $= n\_g \times n\_m$
$n\_e \longleftrightarrow n_e$ ≡ Number of elements
$n\_g \longleftrightarrow n_g$ ≡ Number of generalized DOF per node
$n\_i \longleftrightarrow n_i$ ≡ Number of unknowns per element $= n\_g \times n\_n$
$n\_m \longleftrightarrow n_m$ ≡ Number of mesh nodes
$n\_n \longleftrightarrow n_n$ ≡ Number of nodes per element
$n\_p \longleftrightarrow n_p$ ≡ Dimension of parametric space
$n\_q \longleftrightarrow n_q$ ≡ Number of total quadrature points
$n\_r \longleftrightarrow n_r$ ≡ Number of rows in the $\boldsymbol{B^e}$ matrix (and material matrix)
$n\_s \longleftrightarrow n_s$ ≡ Dimension of physical space

Classic beam ($n_g = 2$, $n_n = 2$ or 3, $n_p = 1$, $n_r = 1$, $n_s = 1$) quantities:

$EI\,v''''(x)$	$= f(x)$ load per unit length,	Differential equation
$EI\,v'''(x)$	$= V(x)$ transverse shear force,	Natural boundary condition
$EIv''(x)$	$= M(x)$ bending moment,	Natural boundary condition
$v'(x)$	$= \theta(x)$ slope,	Essential boundary condition
$v(x)$	= Deflection,	Essential boundary condition

Beam element degrees of freedom:

$$\boldsymbol{\delta^{eT}} = [v_1 \quad \theta_1 \quad v_2 \quad \theta_2 \quad \cdots \quad \theta_{n_n}].$$

Beam with a transverse force per unit length, $f(x)$:

$$\frac{d^2}{dx^2}\left[EI(x)\frac{d^2 v}{dx^2}\right] - f(x) = 0.$$

Beam on an elastic foundation (BOEF) with a stiffness of $k(x)$.

$$\frac{d^2}{dx^2}\left[EI(x)\frac{d^2 v}{dx^2}\right] + k(x)[v - v_\infty] - f(x) = 0.$$

Beam with a constant axial load, N:

$$\frac{d^2}{dx^2}\left[EI(x)\frac{d^2 v}{dx^2}\right] - N\frac{d^2 v}{dx^2} - f(x) = 0.$$

Beam with a variable axial force, $N(x)$:

$$\frac{d^2}{dx^2}\left[EI(x)\frac{d^2 v}{dx^2}\right] - \frac{d}{dx}\left[N(x)\frac{dv}{dx}\right] - f(x) = 0.$$

Beam with an axial force and an elastic foundation:

$$\frac{d^2}{dx^2}\left[EI(x)\frac{d^2 v}{dx^2}\right] - \frac{d}{dx}\left[N(x)\frac{dv}{dx}\right] + k(x)[v - v_\infty] - f(x) = 0.$$

Bending stiffness:

$$\boldsymbol{S}^e_{\boldsymbol{E}} = \int_{L^e} \frac{d^2\boldsymbol{H}(x)}{dx^2}^T EI^e \frac{d^2\boldsymbol{H}(x)}{dx^2}\, dx \equiv \int_{L^e} \boldsymbol{B}^e(x)^T EI^e \boldsymbol{B}^e(x) dx.$$

Foundation stiffness (and load):

$$\boldsymbol{S}^e_{\boldsymbol{k}} = \int_{L^e} \boldsymbol{H}(x)^T k^e \boldsymbol{H}(x)\, dx, \quad \left(\boldsymbol{c}^e_\infty = \int_{L^e} \boldsymbol{H}(x)^T v^e_\infty\, dx\right).$$

Foundation axial load stiffness:

$$\boldsymbol{S}^e_{\boldsymbol{N}} = \int_{L^e} \frac{d\boldsymbol{H}(x)}{dx}^T N^e \frac{d\boldsymbol{H}(x)}{dx}\, dx$$

Line load resultant:

$$\boldsymbol{c}_{\boldsymbol{f}}^{e} = \int_{L^e} \boldsymbol{H}(x)^T f^e(x)dx = \int_{L^e} \boldsymbol{H}(x)^T \boldsymbol{h}(x)\boldsymbol{f}^{\boldsymbol{e}}dx \equiv \boldsymbol{R}^{\boldsymbol{e}}\boldsymbol{f}^{\boldsymbol{e}}.$$

Transverse thermal moment:

$$\boldsymbol{c}_{\boldsymbol{\alpha}}^{\boldsymbol{e}} = \int_{L^e} \boldsymbol{B}^{\boldsymbol{e}^T} EI^e(x)\frac{\alpha^e \Delta T(x)^e}{t(x)}dx = \frac{\alpha^e \Delta T^e EI^e}{t^e}\int_{L^e} \boldsymbol{B}^{\boldsymbol{e}^T} dx.$$

Element mass matrix:

$$\boldsymbol{m}^e = \int_{L^e} \boldsymbol{H}(x)^T \rho^e A^e \boldsymbol{H}(x)\, dx.$$

Force and moment point sources:

$$\boldsymbol{c}_{\boldsymbol{P}}^{\boldsymbol{e}^{\boldsymbol{T}}} = [V_1 \quad M_1 \quad V_2 \quad M_2 \quad \cdots \quad M_{n_n}].$$

Two-noded beam stiffness:

$$\boldsymbol{S}_{\boldsymbol{E}}^{e} = \frac{EI}{L^3}\begin{bmatrix} 12 & 6L & -12 & 6L \\ 6L & 4L^2 & -6L & 2L^2 \\ -12 & -6L & 12 & -6L \\ 6L & 2L^2 & -6L & 4L^2 \end{bmatrix}\begin{Bmatrix} v_1 \\ \theta_1 \\ v_2 \\ \theta_2 \end{Bmatrix}.$$

Two-noded beam line load and thermal bending loads are

$$\boldsymbol{c}_{\boldsymbol{f}}^{e} = \frac{L}{60}\begin{bmatrix} 21 & 9 \\ 3L & 2L \\ 9 & 21 \\ -2L & -3L \end{bmatrix}\begin{Bmatrix} w_{y1} \\ w_{y2} \end{Bmatrix} \quad \text{and} \quad \boldsymbol{c}_{\boldsymbol{\alpha}}^{\boldsymbol{e}} = \frac{EI\alpha\Delta T_y}{t}\begin{Bmatrix} 0 \\ 1 \\ 0 \\ -1 \end{Bmatrix}.$$

Two-noded planar frame local stiffness:

$$\boldsymbol{K}_{\boldsymbol{L}}^{\boldsymbol{e}} = \frac{E}{L}\begin{bmatrix} A & 0 & 0 & -A & 0 & 0 \\ 0 & 12\beta/L & 6\beta & 0 & -12\beta/L & 6\beta \\ 0 & 6\beta & 4I & 0 & -6\beta & 2I \\ -A & 0 & 0 & A & 0 & 0 \\ 0 & -12\beta/L & -6\beta & 0 & 12\beta/L & -6\beta \\ 0 & 6\beta & 2I & 0 & -6\beta & 4I \end{bmatrix}, \quad \beta \equiv \frac{I}{L}.$$

Two-noded planar frame local line load and thermal load resultants:

$$c_f^e = \frac{L}{60}\begin{bmatrix} 20 & 0 & 10 & 0 \\ 0 & 21 & 0 & 9 \\ 0 & 3L & 0 & 2L \\ 10 & 0 & 20 & 0 \\ 0 & 9 & 0 & 21 \\ 0 & -2L & 0 & -3L \end{bmatrix} \begin{Bmatrix} w_{x1} \\ w_{y1} \\ w_{x2} \\ w_{y2} \end{Bmatrix}$$

$$\boldsymbol{F_T^T} = E\alpha\begin{bmatrix} -A\Delta T_x & 0 & I\Delta T_y/t & A\Delta T_x & 0 & -I\Delta T_y/t \end{bmatrix}.$$

Planar frame transformation from local (L) to global (G) coordinates:

$$\boldsymbol{K_G^e} = [\boldsymbol{T}(\theta)]^{\boldsymbol{T}}\ \boldsymbol{K_L^e}[\boldsymbol{T}(\theta)], \quad \boldsymbol{F_G^e} = [\boldsymbol{T}(\theta)]^{\boldsymbol{T}}\boldsymbol{F_L^e}.$$

Two-noded planar frame transformation matrix:

$$[\boldsymbol{T}(\theta)] = \begin{bmatrix} \cos(\theta_x) & \cos(\theta_y) & 0 & & & \\ -\cos(\theta_y) & \cos(\theta_x) & 0 & & \mathbf{0} & \\ 0 & 0 & 1 & & & \\ & & & \cos(\theta_x) & \cos(\theta_y) & 0 \\ & \mathbf{0} & & -\cos(\theta_y) & \cos(\theta_x) & 0 \\ & & & 0 & 0 & 1 \end{bmatrix}.$$

Chapter 12

Scalar Fields and Thermal Analysis

12.1 Introduction

Field analysis covers many areas of physics and engineering governed by the partial differential equations known as the Helmholtz Equation, the Poisson Equation, and the Laplace Equation. These equations define several physical problems with scalar unknowns. They describe heat transfer by conduction, convection, and radiation; the torsion of non-circular shafts, ideal fluid motion by a velocity potent or by a stream function; seepage of a viscous fluid through a porous media; electrostatics; magnetostatics; and others. As their names imply, these equations have been in use for more than two-hundred years and a huge number of solutions have been published using analytical and numerical approaches. The application of these problems requires the satisfaction of the essential boundary conditions (EBCs) and/or non-essential boundary conditions (NBCs) described earlier. After introducing the mathematical foundations, field studies will be undertaken on the torsional analysis of bars, and then on the more common study of heat transfer analysis.

Many of the early analytic models dealt with domains that were assumed to contain a single, constant, isotropic material property, say κ, that defined a scalar unknown, say u, driven by a source term, say Q, and satisfying the two-dimensional homogeneous Poisson equation as follows:

$$\frac{\partial^2 u}{\partial x^2} + \frac{\partial^2 u}{\partial y^2} = \frac{Q(x, y)}{\kappa}.$$

In applications where the material property was non-homogeneous or varied with position, the governing equation changed to a more difficult form:

$$\kappa_x(x, y)\frac{\partial^2 u}{\partial x^2} + \kappa_y(x, y)\frac{\partial^2 u}{\partial y^2} = Q(x, y)$$

where the application involved materials with two-directional properties, like a layered soil or wood.

The most general form of the scalar field equations involve fully directionally dependent (anisotropic) and position-dependent (non-homogeneous) material properties associated with the highest derivatives in the governing differential equation. Relatively few materials are isotropic and homogeneous. Modern materials science creates new advanced materials and almost all of those materials are anisotropic. Any anisotropic material has an orthogonal set of principal directions. The material properties are experimentally measured with respect to those axes. Next, the fully anisotropic material formulation of the scalar field problem is presented and converted to an equivalent finite element formulation.

The boundary conditions for second-order field problems are the same as discussed for the one-dimensional equations, except that some involve the derivative of the solution in the direction normal to the boundary where they are applied. They are sketched in Fig. 12.1-1. The default boundary condition on any surface is that the normal gradient of the solution (and the normal flux) are zero. This is called the natural boundary condition (NatBC), and it does

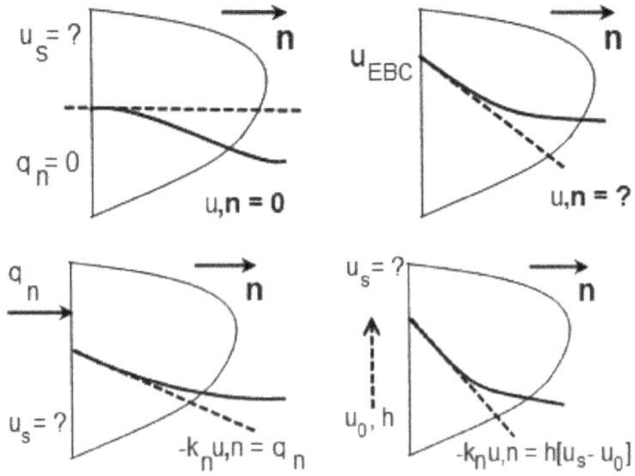

Fig. 12.1-1: Natural, essential, known flux, and convection boundary conditions.

not require any input data. It is usually necessary to have EBCs that specify the value of the solution at one or more points. Often the normal flux entering the body is known and is specified as one of the NBCs. It indirectly specifies the normal gradient of the solution at a point. The more complicated non-essential condition is the mixed condition that couples the normal gradient of the solution to the unknown value of the solution. That mixed boundary condition (MBC) usually occurs as a convection boundary condition (CBC) or as a radiation boundary condition (RBC) in nonlinear applications. Only a radiation condition requires the use of the Kelvin temperature scale.

12.2 General Field Problem

The anisotropic (directionally dependent) Helmholtz equation is a good example of one of the most common problems in engineering and physics that solves for scalar unknowns. The one-dimensional form was covered earlier. In three dimensions, the transient model equation is

$$\begin{aligned}\boldsymbol{\nabla}\left([\boldsymbol{\kappa}]\,\nabla^{\boldsymbol{T}} u\,(x, y, z,\, \tau)\right) + m\,\boldsymbol{v}\,\boldsymbol{\nabla}^{\boldsymbol{T}} u\,(x, y, z,\, \tau) - a\,u\,(x, y, z, \tau)\\ - Q\,(x, y, z, \tau) = \rho \partial u / \partial \tau \qquad (12.2\text{-}1)\end{aligned}$$

where "a" is a convection like term, "Q" is a source rate per unit volume, "ρ" is a mass density term, and "τ" denotes time. Often there is a known velocity vector, $\boldsymbol{v}$, with an associated transport property, "m". If they are not zero, then this is known as an advection-diffusion equation; otherwise, it is just called the diffusion equation.

If the coefficients $m = 0, a = 0$, and, $\rho = 0$ that form (12.2-1) is called the Poisson equation. If the source term, Q, is also zero, then it is called the Laplace equation. If just $m = 0$, (12.2-1) is known as the Helmholtz Equation. If the Helmholtz Equation also contains the term "a" as an unknown system constant (eigenvalue) to be determined, then it requires an eigenproblem analysis which utilizes the same finite element matrices covered here. The solution of eigenproblems, using the same matrices, is addressed in Chapter 14.

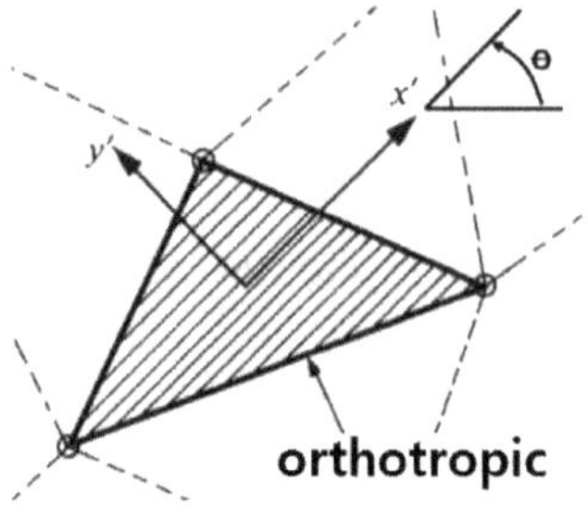

Fig. 12.2-1: Element principle material directions.

The gradient operator in (12.2-1) is

$$\boldsymbol{\nabla}^{T} = \begin{Bmatrix} \partial/\partial x \\ \partial/\partial y \\ \partial/\partial z \end{Bmatrix} = \vec{\boldsymbol{\nabla}}. \tag{12.2-2}$$

The material square matrix $[\boldsymbol{\kappa}]$ contains the symmetric, directionally dependent material properties, like shown in Fig. 12.2-1, evaluated in the system coordinate directions:

$$[\boldsymbol{\kappa}] = \begin{bmatrix} k_{xx} & k_{xy} & k_{xz} \\ k_{xy} & k_{yy} & k_{yz} \\ k_{xz} & k_{yz} & k_{zz} \end{bmatrix} = [\boldsymbol{\kappa}]^{T}, \quad |\boldsymbol{\kappa}| > 0. \tag{12.2-3}$$

For orthotropic materials, $[\boldsymbol{\kappa}]$ is a diagonal array. In two dimensions, the second-order diffusion operator becomes

$$\boldsymbol{\nabla}\,[\boldsymbol{\kappa}]\,\boldsymbol{\nabla}^{T}u = \frac{\partial}{\partial x}\left(k_{xx}\frac{\partial u}{\partial x}\right) + \frac{\partial}{\partial x}\left(k_{xy}\frac{\partial u}{\partial y}\right) + \frac{\partial}{\partial y}\left(k_{yx}\frac{\partial u}{\partial x}\right) + \frac{\partial}{\partial y}\left(k_{yy}\frac{\partial u}{\partial y}\right) \tag{12.2-4}$$

For isotropic materials, the material matrix (constitutive matrix) becomes a single property value times an identity matrix, $[\boldsymbol{\kappa}] = k\,[\boldsymbol{I}]$. The non-symmetric element matrix for the second term in the advection operator

$$m\,\boldsymbol{v}\,\boldsymbol{\nabla}^{T}u\,(x, y, z,\, \tau) = m\left(v_x\frac{\partial u}{\partial x} + v_y\frac{\partial u}{\partial y}\right) \tag{12.2-5}$$

is included here just for completeness because unless the leading coefficient, m, is relatively small, then the presented approach gives widely oscillating solutions and a more advanced approach known as the Petrov–Galerkin approach must be used to bias the solution in the "upwind" direction, $-\boldsymbol{v}$. In the prior one-dimensional formulations, only the first and fourth terms in (12.2-1) were considered.

12.3 Common Flux Components

In this chapter, the unknown, $u(x, y, z)$, is a scalar which may or may not have physical meaning. The components of the solution gradient, combined with any physical properties, usually do have physical meaning as components of a vector or tensor quantity, as sketched in Fig. 12.3-1. Here some of the more common two-dimensional relations are summarized.

In heat transfer, Fourier's Law defines a heat flux vector per unit area, $\boldsymbol{q}$, in terms of the gradient as

$$\vec{q} = \begin{Bmatrix} q_x \\ q_y \end{Bmatrix} = \boldsymbol{q} = -\,[\boldsymbol{\kappa}]\,\boldsymbol{\nabla}^{\boldsymbol{T}} u = -\begin{bmatrix} k_{xx} & k_{xy} \\ k_{xy} & k_{yy} \end{bmatrix} \begin{Bmatrix} \partial u/\partial x \\ \partial u/\partial y \end{Bmatrix} \qquad (12.3\text{-}1)$$

where $[\boldsymbol{\kappa}]$ contains the anisotropic thermal conductivity coefficients, u represents the temperature, and where the area is normal to the gradient vector. Often, the heat flow crossing a surface has importance. The heat flow crossing a surface is the integral, over the surface, of the normal component of the heat flux vector:

$$f = \int_S \boldsymbol{q} \cdot \boldsymbol{n}\, dS = \int_S q_n\, dS. \qquad (12.3\text{-}2)$$

For fluid flow through a porous media, Darcy's Law has the same form as (12.3-1), but with $\vec{q}$ being the fluid velocity vector at the

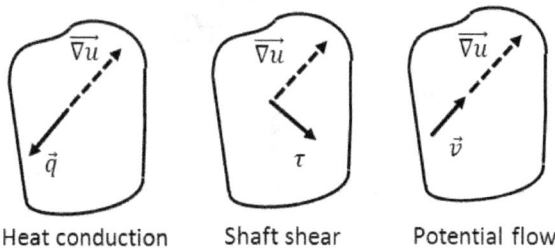

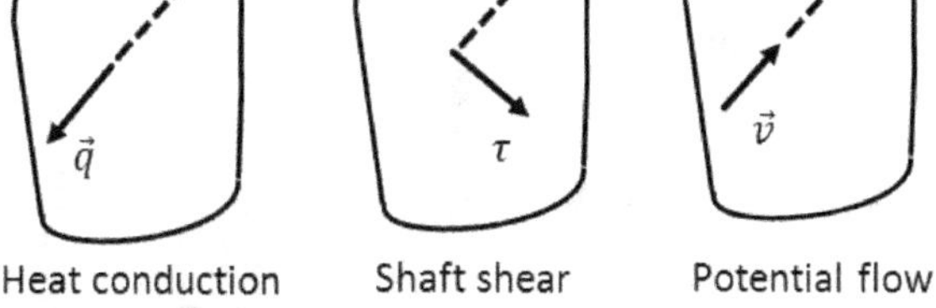

Fig. 12.3-1: The field's solution gradient defines physical "flux" components.

point where the gradient is computed. The material media properties in $[\boldsymbol{\kappa}]$ are the anisotropic permeability coefficients, and u represents the pressure at the point. The flow, f, is the volume of fluid that crosses the surface.

For the analysis of the concentration of substances, Fick's First Law has the same form as (12.3-1), with $\boldsymbol{q}$ being the diffusion flux vector which measures the amount of a substance, per unit area, that will flow through during a unit time interval. The solution, u, is the concentration (the amount of the substance per unit volume). The $[\boldsymbol{\kappa}]$ array contains the diffusivity (diffusion coefficients) at the point.

For electrostatics, u corresponds to the voltage, $[\boldsymbol{\kappa}]$ contains the anisotropic electric conductivities, and $\boldsymbol{q}$ gives the electric charge flux vector. In some applications, u represents a non-physical mathematical potential and $[\boldsymbol{\kappa}]$ contains zeros and ones that convert the gradient of the potential into physical components. In the study of the torsion of a straight non-circular shaft (along the z-axis), u represents a stress function which is zero on the outer boundary of the cross-section and its gradient components are re-arranged by $[\boldsymbol{\kappa}]$ to define the shear stress components in the plane of the cross-section:

$$\boldsymbol{\tau} = \begin{Bmatrix} \tau_{zx} \\ \tau_{zy} \end{Bmatrix} = \begin{Bmatrix} +\partial u/\partial y \\ -\partial u/\partial x \end{Bmatrix} = \begin{bmatrix} 0 & 1 \\ -1 & 0 \end{bmatrix} \begin{Bmatrix} \partial u/\partial x \\ \partial u/\partial y \end{Bmatrix}. \tag{12.3-3}$$

In some applications, the integral of the solution has a physical significance. For example, the applied torque, in a torsional analysis, acting along the shaft is twice the integral of the stress function

$$T = 2 \int_A u(x, y) dA. \tag{12.3-4}$$

Similarly, in potential (inviscid fluid) flow u corresponds to a non-physical velocity potential whose gradient components are the components of the velocity vector ($[\boldsymbol{\kappa}] = [\boldsymbol{I}]$). Then q_n is the velocity component normal to a surface and corresponds to the volume of flow entering the domain.

12.4 Galerkin Integral Form

Applying the Galerkin method of weighted residuals, only the first term needs to be integrated by parts, and that will define additional terms in the element matrices. That integral term is

$$I_k \equiv \int_{\Omega} u(x,y)[\boldsymbol{\nabla}\,[\boldsymbol{\kappa}]\,\boldsymbol{\nabla}^{\boldsymbol{T}} u(x,y)]d\Omega. \tag{12.4-1}$$

Recalling Green's theorem for variables $A(x,\, y,\, z)$ and $B(x,\, y,\, z)$:

$$\begin{aligned}\iiint_V A\,\nabla^2 B\, dV &= \iint_S A\vec{\nabla}B\cdot\vec{n}dS - \iiint_V \vec{\nabla}A\cdot\vec{\nabla}B\,dV\\ &= \iint_S A\frac{\partial B}{\partial n}dS - \iiint_V \vec{\nabla}A\cdot\vec{\nabla}B\,dV,\end{aligned}$$

the Galerkin integral becomes

$$I_k = \int_{\Gamma} u\,\left[[\boldsymbol{\kappa}]\,\boldsymbol{\nabla}^{\boldsymbol{T}} u\right]\cdot\boldsymbol{n}\,d\Gamma - \int_{\Omega} \boldsymbol{\nabla} u\,\left[[\boldsymbol{\kappa}]\,\boldsymbol{\nabla}^{\boldsymbol{T}} u\right]d\Omega \tag{12.4-2}$$

where Γ is the boundary of the domain Ω, and the unit normal vector on the boundary is $\boldsymbol{n}$. The boundary term introduces the derivatives normal to the boundary and the material property at the surface in the direction of its normal vector:

$$[\boldsymbol{\kappa}]\;\boldsymbol{\nabla}^{\boldsymbol{T}} u\cdot\boldsymbol{n} = (k_{xx}+k_{yx})\frac{\partial u}{\partial x}n_x + (k_{yy}+k_{xy})\frac{\partial u}{\partial y}n_y \equiv k_n\frac{\partial u}{\partial n}. \tag{12.4-3}$$

That product appears in the Neumann or NBCs (including any MBCs). Once again, when an EBC (on u on Γ_u) is specified and the normal flux ($k_n\partial u/\partial n$ on Γ_{NBC}) will be recovered as a reaction:

$$\int_{\Gamma} u\,(\,[\boldsymbol{\kappa}]\,\boldsymbol{\nabla}^{\boldsymbol{T}} u)\cdot\boldsymbol{n}\,d\Gamma = \int_{\Gamma} u\left(k_n\frac{\partial u}{\partial n}\right)d\Gamma. \tag{12.4-4}$$

The most common NBC is that of heat convection on the surface of a heat conducting solid. Then the mixed secondary boundary condition is of the form

$$-k_n\frac{\partial u}{\partial n} = h^b\left(u - u_{\infty}^b\right) \tag{12.4-5}$$

and requires boundary segment matrices that integrate the data, h^b and/or u_{∞}^b, over the boundary segment.

For a three-dimensional analysis, the boundary segment is most likely the face of some element. In a two-dimensional analysis, the boundary segment is most likely one or more of the edges of the element. But if the two-dimensional element were part of a cooling fin, the boundary segment could include the front and or back surface of the element. These are mainly modeling details, but the programmer must allow for any valid description of a "boundary segment".

When the finite element method is applied (see what follows) to this three-dimensional equation, the same element matrices occur as with the one-dimensional models. In one dimension, the secondary boundary conditions occurred at a point (actually the integral over an area at the point), but in higher-dimensional applications they enter as integrals over curves or surfaces. Conceptually, the second derivative term in the original equation leads to the same symbolic element square matrix as in the one-dimensional case. The differences are that the arrays are larger in size and the integration takes place over an area or volume:

$$\int_{\Omega} \boldsymbol{\nabla} u([\boldsymbol{\kappa}] \boldsymbol{\nabla}^{\boldsymbol{T}} u)\, d\Omega \Longrightarrow \boldsymbol{S}^{\boldsymbol{e}} = \int_{\Omega^e} \boldsymbol{B}^{\boldsymbol{e}^T} \boldsymbol{\kappa}^e \boldsymbol{B}^{\boldsymbol{e}}\, d\Omega. \tag{12.4-6}$$

Here, the symbol $\boldsymbol{B}^{\boldsymbol{e}}$ arises from a differential operator, in this application it is the gradient, acting on the interpolated solution. In the finite element literature, the symbol $\boldsymbol{B}^{\boldsymbol{e}}$ is used to represent some differential operator acting on the element interpolation functions. Inside each element

$$\boldsymbol{\nabla}^{\boldsymbol{T}} u = \boldsymbol{\nabla}^{\boldsymbol{T}} \boldsymbol{H}^e(x,\, y,\, z)\ \boldsymbol{u}^e \equiv \boldsymbol{B}^e(x,\, y,\, z)\ \boldsymbol{u}^e,$$

$$\boldsymbol{B}^e \equiv \begin{bmatrix} \partial \boldsymbol{H}^e(x,\, y,\, z)/\partial x \\ \partial \boldsymbol{H}^e(x,\, y,\, z)/\partial y \\ \partial \boldsymbol{H}^e(x,\, y,\, z)/\partial z \end{bmatrix}. \tag{12.4-7}$$

Before, the material data involved a scalar, but now they have become a square symmetric matrix, $\boldsymbol{\kappa}^{\boldsymbol{e}}$. To be a valid matrix product in (12.4-6), the number of rows in the operator matrix, $\boldsymbol{B}^{\boldsymbol{e}}$, must be the same as those in $\boldsymbol{\kappa}^{\boldsymbol{e}}$. Here, it will be shown in what follows that number is the same as the physical space dimension, $\boldsymbol{n_s}$. However, in later applications the number of rows in $\boldsymbol{B}^{\boldsymbol{e}}$ is larger, say $\boldsymbol{n_r} \geq \boldsymbol{n_s}$. The enlarged size of the arrays combined with any curved element geometry means that the above element integral is almost always evaluated numerically in practice. The exceptions are the three-noded triangle, the four-noded rectangle parallel to the global axes, and the four-noded tetrahedron that have constant Jacobians. Those three elements were used in the first published solutions of two- and three-dimensional finite element solutions of field problems and eigenproblems.

12.5 Corresponding Element and Boundary Matrices

Following the prior process where volume integrals are replaced by the sum of the element volume integrals, the boundary integrals are replaced by the sum of the boundary segment integrals, $u(x, y)$ is replaced by its interpolated value, and the governing integral is converted to the assembly (scatter) of individual element and boundary segment integrals to define their respective local matrices. The symmetric diffusion matrix is always present:

$$\int_{\Omega} \nabla \mathrm{u} \left([\boldsymbol{\kappa}] \, \nabla^T u \right) d\Omega \Rightarrow \sum_{e=1}^{n_e} \boldsymbol{u}^{e^T} \left[\int_{\Omega^e} \boldsymbol{B}^{e^T} \boldsymbol{\kappa}^e \boldsymbol{B}^e \, d\Omega \right]$$

$$\boldsymbol{u}^e = \sum_{e=1}^{n_e} \boldsymbol{u}^{e^T} \left[\boldsymbol{S}_{\kappa}^e \right] \boldsymbol{u}^e$$

The non-symmetric advection square matrix may be present:

$$\int_{\Omega} u m \boldsymbol{v} \, \nabla^T u \, d\Omega \Rightarrow \sum_{e=1}^{n_e} \boldsymbol{u}^{e^T} \left[\int_{\Omega^e} \boldsymbol{H}^{e^T} m^e v^e \boldsymbol{B}^e \, d\Omega \right] \boldsymbol{u}^e$$

$$= \sum_{e=1}^{n_e} \boldsymbol{u}^{e^T} \left[\boldsymbol{A}_v^e \right] \boldsymbol{u}^e$$

The convection-like square and column matrices may be present:

$$\int_{\Omega} u a u \, d\Omega \Rightarrow \sum_{e=1}^{n_e} \boldsymbol{u}^{e^T} \left[\int_{\Omega^e} \boldsymbol{H}^{e^T} a^e \boldsymbol{H}^e \, d\Omega \right] \boldsymbol{u}^e$$

$$= \sum_{e=1}^{n_e} \boldsymbol{u}^{e^T} \left[\boldsymbol{M}_a^e \right] \boldsymbol{u}^e$$

$$-\int_{\Omega} u a u_{\infty} \, d\Omega \Rightarrow \sum_{e=1}^{n_e} \boldsymbol{u}^{e^T} \left[\int_{\Omega^e} \boldsymbol{H}^{e^T} a^e u_{\infty} \, d\Omega \right] \boldsymbol{u}^e$$

$$= \sum_{e=1}^{n_e} \boldsymbol{u}^{e^T} \left\{ \boldsymbol{c}_{\infty}^e \right\}$$

The resultant source column matrix may be present:

$$\int_{\Omega} uQ\, d\Omega \Rightarrow \sum_{e=1}^{n_e} \boldsymbol{u}^{\boldsymbol{e}^T} \left[\int_{\Omega^e} \boldsymbol{H}^{\boldsymbol{e}^T} Q^e\, d\Omega \right] = \sum_{e=1}^{n_e} \boldsymbol{u}^{\boldsymbol{e}^T} \{\boldsymbol{c}_Q^e\}$$

The square symmetric capacitance matrix may be present. If so, a separation of variables is assumed here (unlike space–time finite elements):

$$u\,(x,\, y,\, z,\, \tau) \equiv \boldsymbol{H}\,(x,\, y,\, z)\boldsymbol{u}^e(\tau)$$

$$\partial u/\partial\tau = \ \boldsymbol{H}\,(x,\, y,\, z)\ \partial \boldsymbol{u}^e(\tau)/\partial\tau \equiv \boldsymbol{H}\,(x,\, y,\, z)\dot{u}^e$$

$$\int_{\Omega} u\, \rho\partial u/\partial\tau d\Omega \Rightarrow \sum_{e=1}^{n_e} \boldsymbol{u}^{\boldsymbol{e}^T} \left[\int_{\Omega^e} \boldsymbol{H}^{\boldsymbol{e}^T} \rho^e \boldsymbol{H}^{\boldsymbol{e}}\, d\Omega \right] \dot{u}^e$$

$$= \sum_{e=1}^{n_e} \boldsymbol{u}^{\boldsymbol{e}^T} [\boldsymbol{M}_\rho^e] \dot{u}^e.$$

The mixed or NBC may be non-zero on some boundary segments:

$$-k_{nn}\frac{\partial u}{\partial n} = g\, u + h \ \text{ or } \ - k_{nn}\frac{\partial u}{\partial n} = q_n \text{ on } \Gamma^b$$

$$\int_{\Gamma} u\, k_{nn}\frac{\partial u}{\partial n} d\Gamma \Rightarrow \sum_{b=1}^{n_b} \boldsymbol{u}^{\boldsymbol{b}^T} \left[\int_{\Gamma^b} \boldsymbol{H}^{\boldsymbol{b}^T} \left(k_{nn}\frac{\partial u}{\partial n} \right)^b d\Gamma \right]$$

$$\Rightarrow \sum_{b=1}^{n_b} \boldsymbol{u}^{\boldsymbol{b}^T} \left\{ \boldsymbol{c}_{NBC}^b \right\}.$$

The zero normal flux condition, $k_{nn}\partial u/\partial n = 0$, on a boundary segment is called the natural boundary condition (NatBC). In finite elements it requires no action whatsoever, because there is no need to add (scatter) zeros to the system arrays. The natural condition is the default on all surfaces until replaced with an EBC or a non-zero NBC.

12.6 Governing Matrix Form

The assembled system matrix form, before the enforcement of the application's EBCs, is

$$I = \sum_{b=1}^{n_b} \boldsymbol{u}^{\boldsymbol{b}^T} \left\{ \boldsymbol{c}_{\text{NBC}}^b \right\} - \sum_{e=1}^{n_e} \boldsymbol{u}^{\boldsymbol{e}^T} [\boldsymbol{S}_\kappa^e]\, \boldsymbol{u}^{\boldsymbol{e}} - \sum_{e=1}^{n_e} \boldsymbol{u}^{\boldsymbol{e}^T} [\boldsymbol{A}_v^e]\, \boldsymbol{u}^{\boldsymbol{e}}$$

$$-\sum_{e=1}^{n_e} \boldsymbol{u}^{\boldsymbol{e}^T} [\boldsymbol{M}_a^e]\, \boldsymbol{u}^{\boldsymbol{e}} \cdots$$

$$\sum_{e=1}^{n_e} \boldsymbol{u}^{\boldsymbol{e}^T} [\boldsymbol{M}_\rho^e]\, \dot{\boldsymbol{u}}^e - \sum_{e=1}^{n_e} \boldsymbol{u}^{\boldsymbol{e}^T} \{\boldsymbol{c}_Q^e\} = 0.$$

Using the element and boundary segment connectivity lists as before gives the full system array:

$$I = \boldsymbol{u}^T \left[\boldsymbol{S_k} + \boldsymbol{A_v} + \boldsymbol{M_a}\right] \boldsymbol{u} + \boldsymbol{u}^T \left[\boldsymbol{M_\rho}\right] \dot{\boldsymbol{u}} - \boldsymbol{u}^T \left(\boldsymbol{c}_Q - \boldsymbol{c}_{\text{NBC}}\right) = 0$$

which defines the general time-dependent (transient) field matrix system:

$$\left[\boldsymbol{S_k} + \boldsymbol{A_v} + \boldsymbol{M_a}\right] \boldsymbol{u}\left(\tau\right) + \left[\boldsymbol{M_\rho}\right] \dot{\boldsymbol{u}}\left(\tau\right) = \boldsymbol{c}\left(\tau\right). \tag{12.6-1}$$

The steady-state matrix system ($\dot{\boldsymbol{u}}\left(\tau\right) = \mathbf{0}$, and before EBCs) is

$$\left[\boldsymbol{S_k} + \boldsymbol{A_v} + \boldsymbol{M_a}\right] \boldsymbol{u} = \boldsymbol{c}. \tag{12.6-2}$$

Remember that the advection matrix, $\boldsymbol{A_v}$, is non-symmetric and introduces non-physical oscillations in the solution unless the given velocity is small (has a small dimensionless Peclet number). Removal of any advection oscillations requires using the Petrov–Galerkin method, which is not covered in this introductory text. In many problems, $\boldsymbol{S_k}$ is a heat conduction matrix and $\boldsymbol{M_a}$ is from heat convection contributions.

12.7 The Classic Linear Triangle Field Element

Historically, one of the first uses of a finite element for heat transfer analysis was developed by structural engineers who were conducting the stress analysis of the cross-section of a concrete dam. The stress model could include the initial strains due to the non-uniform temperature in the cross-section of the dam. They knew that the curing concrete chemical reaction caused a known heat generation per unit volume, $Q(x, y)$. There were cooling pipes through the cross-section that removed part of that generated heat. The engineers needed to calculate the non-uniform temperature at every node in the mesh of triangular structural elements having three nodes. Thus, using physical energy balances, instead of a differential equation, they developed and applied the three-noded triangular heat transfer element and used the output of the thermal study as the thermal load input of the stress simulation. The governing differential equation, and its corresponding integral form used here, yields exactly the same element matrices.

The linear element appeared in much of the early literature with the interpolation functions given in terms of the physical coordinates.

That approach involves nine geometric constants to define the interpolation:

$$u(x, y) = \boldsymbol{H}(x, y)\, \boldsymbol{u}^{\boldsymbol{e}} = \sum_{k=1}^{3} H_k(x, y) u_k^e,$$

$$H_k(x, y) = (a_k^e + b_k^e x + c_k^e y)/2A^e,$$

$$a_1^e = x_2^e y_3^e - x_3^e y_2^e,\ b_1^e = y_2^e - y_3^e,\ c_1^e = x_3^e - x_2^e, \qquad (12.7\text{-}1)$$

$$a_2^e = x_3^e y_1^e - x_1^e y_3^e,\ b_2^e = y_3^e - y_1^e,\ c_2^e = x_1^e - x_3^e,$$

$$a_3^e = x_1^e y_2^e - x_2^e y_1^e,\ b_3^e = y_1^e - y_2^e,\ c_3^e = x_2^e - x_1^e,$$

$$2A^e = a_1^e + a_2^e + a_3^e = b_2^e c_3^e - b_3^e c_2^e,$$

where A^e is the physical area of the triangle, and where the vertices are numbered in a counter-clockwise order. In this form, the gradient components of the interpolations can be written by inspection:

$$\frac{\partial u}{\partial \boldsymbol{\Omega}} = \begin{Bmatrix} \frac{\partial u}{\partial x} \\ \frac{\partial u}{\partial y} \end{Bmatrix} = \begin{bmatrix} \frac{\partial \boldsymbol{H}(x,y)}{\partial x} \\ \frac{\partial \boldsymbol{H}(x,y)}{\partial y} \end{bmatrix} \boldsymbol{u}^{\boldsymbol{e}} = \frac{1}{2A^e} \begin{bmatrix} b_1^e & b_2^e & b_3^e \\ c_1^e & c_2^e & c_3^e \end{bmatrix} \begin{Bmatrix} u_1 \\ u_2 \\ u_3 \end{Bmatrix}^{\boldsymbol{e}} \equiv \boldsymbol{B}^{\boldsymbol{e}} \boldsymbol{u}^{\boldsymbol{e}} \qquad (12.7\text{-}2)$$

$$2 \times 1 = (2 \times 3)(3 \times 1).$$

These derivatives are constant, as expected for a linear interpolation.

As the applications of finite elements expanded to parts with curved boundaries, it was learned that the interpolations had to be formulated in parametric coordinate systems. Here, this element will be re-formulated in parametric unit coordinates to illustrate how numerically integrated curved triangles (of higher degree) are implemented. At (4.6-1), it was proved that the parametric interpolation functions for $u(r, s) = \boldsymbol{H}(r, s)\, \boldsymbol{u}^{\boldsymbol{e}}$ are

$$\boldsymbol{H}(r, s) = \big[(1 - r - s) \quad r \quad s\big] = \big[H_1(r, s) \quad H_2(r, s) \quad H_3(r, s)\big]. \qquad (12.7\text{-}3)$$

As for elements with curved boundaries, the x- and y-coordinates are interpolated in the same way:

$$x(r, s) = \boldsymbol{H}(r, s)\, \boldsymbol{x}^{\boldsymbol{e}} = \big[(1 - r - s) \quad r \quad s\big] \begin{Bmatrix} x_1 \\ x_2 \\ x_3 \end{Bmatrix}^{\boldsymbol{e}}$$

and

$$y(r,s) = \boldsymbol{H}(r,s)\,\boldsymbol{y}^{\boldsymbol{e}} = \begin{bmatrix}(1-r-s) & r & s\end{bmatrix}\begin{Bmatrix} y_1 \\ y_2 \\ y_3 \end{Bmatrix}^{\boldsymbol{e}}.$$

This form allows the parametric partial derivatives of the physical coordinates:

$$\frac{\partial x}{\partial r} = \begin{bmatrix}-1 & 1 & 0\end{bmatrix}\begin{Bmatrix} x_1 \\ x_2 \\ x_3 \end{Bmatrix}^{\boldsymbol{e}} = (x_2^e - x_1^e),\ \text{and}\ \frac{\partial y}{\partial s} = \begin{bmatrix}-1 & 0 & 1\end{bmatrix}\begin{Bmatrix} y_1 \\ y_2 \\ y_3 \end{Bmatrix}^{\boldsymbol{e}}$$
$$= (y_3^e - y_1^e),\ \text{etc.}$$

That in turn defines the Jacobian matrix of the geometric map from the parametric space to the physical space

$$\boldsymbol{J}^{\boldsymbol{e}} = \begin{bmatrix}\partial x/\partial r & \partial y/\partial r \\ \partial x/\partial s & \partial y/\partial s\end{bmatrix}^e = \begin{bmatrix}\partial \boldsymbol{H}(r,s)/\partial r \\ \partial \boldsymbol{H}(r,s)/\partial s\end{bmatrix}\begin{bmatrix} x_1 & y_1 \\ x_2 & y_2 \\ x_3 & y_3\end{bmatrix}^e,$$

$$\boldsymbol{J}^{\boldsymbol{e}} = \begin{bmatrix}-1 & 1 & 0 \\ -1 & 0 & 1\end{bmatrix}\begin{bmatrix} x_1 & y_1 \\ x_2 & y_2 \\ x_3 & y_3\end{bmatrix}^e = \begin{bmatrix}(x_2-x_1) & (y_2-y_1) \\ (x_3-x_1) & (y_3-y_1)\end{bmatrix}^e. \quad (12.7\text{-}4)$$

The determinant of the Jacobian matrix is also constant with a value of twice the physical area of the triangle:

$$|\boldsymbol{J}^{\boldsymbol{e}}| = (x_2-x_1)^e(y_3-y_1)^e - (x_3-x_1)^e(y_2-y_1)^e = 2A^e. \quad (12.7\text{-}5)$$

This term is always used in the formulation of the element integrals to represent the differential area, $\mathrm{dA} = |\boldsymbol{J}^{\boldsymbol{e}}|\,dr\,ds$. Since the straight-sided triangle has a constant 2×2 Jacobian matrix, its inverse Jacobian matrix can be written in closed form as follows:

$$\boldsymbol{J}^{\boldsymbol{e}^{-1}} = \frac{1}{2A^e}\begin{bmatrix}(y_3-y_1) & (y_1-y_2) \\ (x_1-x_3) & (x_2-x_1)\end{bmatrix}^e = \frac{1}{2A^e}\begin{bmatrix} b_2^e & b_3^e \\ c_2^e & c_3^e\end{bmatrix}. \quad (12.7\text{-}6)$$

This inverse is used to compute the physical gradient components of the interpolation functions as the simple numerical product of two matrices:

$$\frac{\partial \boldsymbol{H}}{\partial \boldsymbol{\Omega}} = \begin{bmatrix} \partial \boldsymbol{H}(r,s)/\partial x \\ \partial \boldsymbol{H}(r,s)/\partial y \end{bmatrix} = \boldsymbol{J}^{e^{-1}} \begin{bmatrix} \partial \boldsymbol{H}(r,s)/\partial r \\ \partial \boldsymbol{H}(r,s)/\partial s \end{bmatrix},$$

$$\begin{bmatrix} \partial \boldsymbol{H}(r,s)/\partial x \\ \partial \boldsymbol{H}(r,s)/\partial y \end{bmatrix} = \frac{1}{2A^e} \begin{bmatrix} b_2^e & b_3^e \\ c_2^e & c_3^e \end{bmatrix} \begin{bmatrix} -1 & 1 & 0 \\ -1 & 0 & 1 \end{bmatrix} = \frac{1}{2A^e} \begin{bmatrix} b_1^e & b_2^e & b_3^e \\ c_1^e & c_2^e & c_3^e \end{bmatrix}, \tag{12.7-7}$$

which exactly agrees with (12.7-2), which was originally based on physical interpolation space. The square conduction matrix of (12.4-6), in the usual finite element notation, is

$$\boldsymbol{S}_\kappa^e = \int_{\Omega^e} \boldsymbol{B}^{e^T} \boldsymbol{\kappa}^e \boldsymbol{B}^e \, d\Omega,$$

where for heat conduction (and scalar fields) the differential operator matrix is simply defined by the gradient components

$$\boldsymbol{B}^e \equiv \begin{bmatrix} \partial \boldsymbol{H}(r,s)/\partial x \\ \partial \boldsymbol{H}(r,s)/\partial y \end{bmatrix},$$

and for an anisotropic (directionally dependent) material the constitutive properties are

$$\boldsymbol{\kappa}^e = \begin{bmatrix} k_{xx}^e & k_{xy}^e \\ k_{xy}^e & k_{yy}^e \end{bmatrix} = \boldsymbol{\kappa}^{e^T}.$$

For an orthotropic material ($k_{xy}^e = 0$) of constant thickness, t^e, this matrix becomes

$$\boldsymbol{S}_\kappa^e = \int_A^e \begin{bmatrix} \partial \boldsymbol{H}(r,s)/\partial x \\ \partial \boldsymbol{H}(r,s)/\partial y \end{bmatrix}^T \begin{bmatrix} k_x^e & 0 \\ 0 & k_y^e \end{bmatrix} \begin{bmatrix} \partial \boldsymbol{H}(r,s)/\partial x \\ \partial \boldsymbol{H}(r,s)/\partial y \end{bmatrix} (t^e \, dA),$$

$$\boldsymbol{S}_\kappa^e = \frac{t^e}{2A^e} \begin{bmatrix} b_1^e & b_2^e & b_3^e \\ c_1^e & c_2^e & c_3^e \end{bmatrix}^T \begin{bmatrix} k_x^e & 0 \\ 0 & k_y^e \end{bmatrix} \frac{1}{2A^e} \begin{bmatrix} b_1^e & b_2^e & b_3^e \\ c_1^e & c_2^e & c_3^e \end{bmatrix} \int_A^e dA,$$

$$\boldsymbol{S}_\kappa^e = \frac{t^e}{4\,A^e} \left[k_x^e \begin{bmatrix} b_1 b_1 & b_1 b_2 & b_1 b_3 \\ b_2 b_1 & b_2 b_2 & b_3 b_3 \\ b_3 b_1 & b_3 b_2 & b_3 b_3 \end{bmatrix} + k_y^e \begin{bmatrix} c_1 c_1 & c_1 c_2 & c_1 c_3 \\ c_2 c_1 & c_2 c_2 & c_2 c_3 \\ c_3 c_1 & c_3 c_2 & c_3 c_3 \end{bmatrix} \right]. \tag{12.7-8}$$

This is known as the element conduction matrix, or the thermal stiffness matrix, and it allows for orthotropic thermal conductivities in the x- and y-directions. Note that the heat conduction in the x-direction depends on the size of the element in the y-direction (b_k), and vice versa. When a heat generation per unit volume is present in the element, the general resultant source vector is

$$\boldsymbol{c}_{\boldsymbol{Q}}^{\boldsymbol{e}} = \int_{\Omega^e} \boldsymbol{H}^{\boldsymbol{e}^T} \mathrm{Q}^{\mathrm{e}}\, \mathrm{d}\Omega = \int_{\square} \boldsymbol{H}^{\boldsymbol{e}^T} Q^e \, (t^e \, |\boldsymbol{J}^{\boldsymbol{e}}| \, d\square). \qquad (12.7\text{-}9)$$

Assume that source and thickness are constant across the element and evaluate the integral numerically:

$$\boldsymbol{c}_{\boldsymbol{Q}}^{\boldsymbol{e}} = t^e Q^e \int_0^1 \int_0^{1-r} \begin{Bmatrix} (1-r-s) \\ r \\ s \end{Bmatrix} (2A^e ds\, dr)$$

$$= 2A^e t^e Q^e \sum_{k=1}^{n_q} \begin{Bmatrix} 1 - r_q - r_q \\ r_q \\ s_q \end{Bmatrix} w_q.$$

Since this is a linear polynomial, the tabulated quadrature data show that only one point is needed to evaluate this integral (and the above constant $\boldsymbol{S}_{\kappa}^{e}$ integral). The tabulated data give a quadrature weight of $w_1 = 1/2$, and locate the point at the centroid of the unit triangle having the coordinates of $r_1 = 1/3 = s_1$. Substituting those data gives

$$\boldsymbol{c}_{\boldsymbol{Q}}^{\boldsymbol{e}} = 2A^e t^e Q^e \begin{Bmatrix} 1 - 1/3 - 1/3 \\ 1/3 \\ 1/3 \end{Bmatrix} \frac{1}{2} = \frac{A^e t^e Q^e}{3} \begin{Bmatrix} 1 \\ 1 \\ 1 \end{Bmatrix}. \qquad (12.7\text{-}10)$$

This means that the total heat generated in the element, $A^e t^e Q^e$, has been divided equally into thirds and placed as point sources at each of the three nodes of the element.

Convection can occur on the front and/or back of the triangular element and/or along any of its three edges. Their contribution to the element square matrix is

$$\boldsymbol{M}_h^e = \int_{\Omega^e} \boldsymbol{H}^{e^T} h^e \boldsymbol{H}^e \, d\Omega = \frac{h^e A^e}{12} \begin{bmatrix} 2 & 1 & 1 \\ 1 & 2 & 1 \\ 1 & 1 & 2 \end{bmatrix}, \quad \boldsymbol{M}_h^b = \frac{h^b t^b L^b}{6} \begin{bmatrix} 2 & 1 \\ 1 & 2 \end{bmatrix} \tag{12.7-11}$$

and their face contribution to the source vector is

$$\boldsymbol{c}_h^b = \frac{h^b u_\infty^b A^b}{3} \begin{Bmatrix} 1 \\ 1 \\ 1 \end{Bmatrix},$$

and an edge contribution

$$\boldsymbol{c}_h^b = \int_\Gamma^b \boldsymbol{H}^{b^T} h^b u_\infty^b d\Gamma = \frac{h^b u_\infty^b t^b L^b}{2} \begin{Bmatrix} 1 \\ 1 \end{Bmatrix}. \tag{12.7-12}$$

Likewise, a specified normal heat flux, per unit area, into the edge of the element contributes to the source vector as

$$\boldsymbol{c}_q^b = \int_\Gamma^b \boldsymbol{H}^{b^T} q_n d\Gamma = \frac{q_n^b t^b L^b}{2} \begin{Bmatrix} 1 \\ 1 \end{Bmatrix}. \tag{12.7-13}$$

The use of a one-point numerical integration rule to form both the $\boldsymbol{S}_\kappa^e$ and the $\boldsymbol{c}_{\boldsymbol{Q}}^e$ matrices would be used in an application using this element. Those calculations would occur within a loop over every element in the mesh. Once the element matrices are calculated, they are scattered into the system matrices. Upon completing that loop the EBCs would be enforced, the unknowns would be calculated and saved, and optionally the reaction at each EBC would be calculated.

The primary unknowns are scalar quantities. Thus, there is almost always a need to have another loop over the elements to recover the solution gradient vector at selected locations within the element. Often, the gradient vector components are used to calculate other vector or tensor components of importance.

Of course, any implementation requires other auxiliary functions that are needed for things like reading the input data, gathering the integration data, enforcing the EBCs, saving the solution, extracting the reactions, and saving the gradient calculations. Those scripts do not change from one application to another.

12.8 Jacobian Matrix for Equal Space Dimensions

Having picked a type of the parametric element (the parametric shape, its number of nodes, and the number of degrees of freedom per node), the geometry interpolation functions can be looked up in a library of parametric functions. Since all the common parametric interpolation functions are known in terms of the parametric coordinates (r, s, t) that also means that all of the parametric local derivatives are known and can be stored in the same library of functions. Those parametric derivatives of the solution are denoted here as the vector (column vector) with as many rows as the dimension of the parametric space, n_p. For a line or curve, $n_p = 1$, for an area or curved surface, $n_p = 2$, while for a solid, $n_p = 3$. In the last case, there are three parametric derivatives, defined as

$$\boldsymbol{\partial}_{\square}(\ ) = \begin{Bmatrix} \partial(\ )/\partial r \\ \partial(\ )/\partial s \\ \partial(\ )/\partial t \end{Bmatrix}. \tag{12.8-1}$$

Therefore, the parametric local derivatives of any interpolated item, say $u(r, s, t)$, is

$$\boldsymbol{\partial}_{\square}\boldsymbol{u}^e = \begin{Bmatrix} \partial u/\partial r \\ \partial u/\partial s \\ \partial u/\partial t \end{Bmatrix} = \begin{bmatrix} \partial \boldsymbol{H}(r,s,t)/\partial r \\ \partial \boldsymbol{H}(r,s,t)/\partial s \\ \partial \boldsymbol{H}(r,s,t)/\partial t \end{bmatrix} \{\boldsymbol{u}^e\}. \tag{12.8-2}$$

If u is replaced with the physical spatial coordinate x, then the interpolations $\boldsymbol{H}(r, s, t)$ could be replaced with a different geometry interpolation $\boldsymbol{G}(r, s, t)$. Then the local derivative of physical position x becomes the first column of the geometric Jacobian matrix:

$$\begin{Bmatrix} \partial x/\partial r \\ \partial x/\partial s \\ \partial x/\partial t \end{Bmatrix} = \begin{bmatrix} \partial \boldsymbol{G}(r,s,t)/\partial r \\ \partial \boldsymbol{G}(r,s,t)/\partial s \\ \partial \boldsymbol{G}(r,s,t)/\partial t \end{bmatrix} \{\boldsymbol{x}^e\}. \tag{12.8-3}$$

Usually, the solution and geometric interpolations are the same, $\boldsymbol{G}(r, s, t) \equiv \boldsymbol{H}(r, s, t)$, and that case is referred to as an isoparametric analysis. Replacing the right column data with a rectangular array constructed by adding a column of the n_n coordinates $\boldsymbol{y}^e$ and a column for the $\boldsymbol{z}^e$ coordinates, the full geometric Jacobian matrix, for that specific element, is obtained as follows:

$$\boldsymbol{J}^e = \begin{bmatrix} \partial x/\partial r & \partial y/\partial r & \partial z/\partial r \\ \partial x/\partial s & \partial y/\partial s & \partial z/\partial s \\ \partial x/\partial t & \partial y/\partial t & \partial z/\partial t \end{bmatrix}^e = \begin{bmatrix} \partial \boldsymbol{G}(r,s,t)/\partial r \\ \partial \boldsymbol{G}(r,s,t)/\partial s \\ \partial \boldsymbol{G}(r,s,t)/\partial t \end{bmatrix} \begin{bmatrix} \boldsymbol{x}^e & \boldsymbol{y}^e & \boldsymbol{z}^e \end{bmatrix}$$
$$n_p \times n_s = (n_p \times n_n)(n_n \times n_s). \tag{12.8-4}$$

Note that the element Jacobian matrix, $\boldsymbol{J}^e$, is generally a rectangular matrix and is only a square (and invertible) matrix when the dimension of the parametric space, n_p, equals the dimension of the physical space, n_s. In other words, the element Jacobian matrix is square except when the element is a line element on a two- or three-dimensional curve, or if it is an area element on a three-dimensional surface. The vast majority of practical finite element calculations utilize a square Jacobian matrix, but there are times (like convection on a non-flat surface) when the rectangular format must be employed.

In the above equation, (r, s, t) represents any local point in the element where it is desired to evaluate the Jacobian matrix. Usually, the point is a tabulated quadrature point. To numerically evaluate the $\boldsymbol{\partial}_{\square}\boldsymbol{G}$ matrix, at a specific point, the local coordinates are provided as arguments to the function that contains the parametric interpolation equations, and the equations for their parametric derivatives. Those data, along with the parametric element type, defining its spatial dimension, n_p, and the number of nodes, n_n, provide for its automatic evaluation. The rectangular array of element nodal coordinates is *gathered* as a set of input numbers. Then, the simple numerical matrix multiplication of (12.4-4) provides all the numerical entries of the element Jacobian matrix, $\boldsymbol{J}^e$. Having a current numerical value for a square element Jacobian matrix, $\boldsymbol{J}^e$, it is straightforward to numerically evaluate its determinant, J^e, and its inverse matrix, ${\boldsymbol{J}^e}^{-1}$.

Recall that the determinant of the geometric Jacobian relates a physical differential volume to the corresponding parametric differential volume, at the point where it was computed. In simplex elements, (straight lines, straight-edged triangles and tetrahedrons in physical space) the determinant of the element Jacobian is constant everywhere in the element. Constant determinants can occur in other special cases, like straight-edged rectangles and bricks with their edges parallel to the physical axes. Of course, a constant determinant implies that the Jacobian matrix, like its inverse, is also constant in such special element geometries in physical space.

Consider the programming aspects of the above numerical matrix evaluation. To obtain the necessary geometric data there must be a function that reads and stores all the physical coordinates of all the nodes in the mesh. The list of coordinates defines the number of physical spatial dimensions, n_s. There must also be another function that reads and stores the node connection list for each and every element in the mesh. That list of connections defines the number of nodes on each element, n_n. For the element of interest, there must be another function that will gather the list of nodes on that particular element. That list (a vector) is then used to extract the subset of coordinates on that particular element: $\boldsymbol{x}^e \subset_e \boldsymbol{x}$, $\boldsymbol{y}^e \subset_e \boldsymbol{y}$, $\boldsymbol{z}^e \subset_e \boldsymbol{z}$. Those three vectors are substituted into the three columns of the rightmost matrix in the Jacobian matrix product. The numerical values of the left matrix are inserted by another function that evaluates the $\boldsymbol{\partial}_{\boxdot}\boldsymbol{G}$ matrix at the specified local parametric point, (r, s, t). Finally, the numerical matrix multiplication is executed to create the numerical values in the element Jacobian matrix. Having a square element Jacobian matrix allows the physical gradient of any quantity to be numerically evaluated, at the specified parametric point, by inverting the Jacobian matrix and multiplying it times the parametric gradient of the quantity:

$$\vec{\boldsymbol{\nabla}}^e u = \boldsymbol{\partial}_{\Omega}^e u = \boldsymbol{J}^{e^{-1}} \boldsymbol{\partial}_{\boxdot} u = \begin{Bmatrix} \partial u/\partial x \\ \partial u/\partial y \\ \partial u/\partial z \end{Bmatrix}^e = \boldsymbol{J}^{e^{-1}} \begin{Bmatrix} \partial u/\partial r \\ \partial u/\partial s \\ \partial u/\partial t \end{Bmatrix}. \tag{12.8-5}$$

Here, the number of components in the gradient vector (and the size of the square matrix to invert) will be the same as the dimension of the physical space, $n_s = n_p$.

The concept of using the element connection lists to gather those local coordinate data is illustrated in Fig. 7.2-2, for a one-dimensional mesh. Most of the examples herein will illustrate one item per node occurring in a gather-scatter process. However, practical applications deal with an arbitrary number of generalized unknowns per node, denoted as n_g. The next section gives the simple equations for identifying the associated element and system equation numbers

Example 12.8-1 Given: A two-dimensional four-noded ($n_n = 4$) bi-linear Lagrangian quadrilateral ($n_p = 2$) element has nodal coordinates of $\boldsymbol{x}^{e^T} = \begin{bmatrix} 1 & 3 & 3 & 1 \end{bmatrix}$ cm and $\boldsymbol{y}^{e^T} = \begin{bmatrix} 1 & 1 & 3 & 2 \end{bmatrix}$ cm. Evaluate the Jacobian and determine if it is variable or constant. Determine the physical derivatives of the interpolation functions.

Solution: In unit coordinates, the parametric interpolation functions (also called shape functions) are an incomplete quadratic polynomial in the two-dimensional parametric space (they are missing the r^2 and s^2 terms):

$$\boldsymbol{H}(r, s) = \begin{bmatrix} H_1(r, s) & H_2(r, s) & H_3(r, s) & H_4(r, s) \end{bmatrix}$$

$$H_1(r, s) = 1 - r - s + rs, \quad H_2(r, s) = r - rs, \quad H_3(r, s) = rs,$$

$$H_4(r, s) = s - rs,$$

and their $n_p \times n_n$ parametric derivatives are

$$\partial_{\square}\boldsymbol{H}(r, s) = \begin{bmatrix} \partial\boldsymbol{H}/\partial r \\ \partial\boldsymbol{H}/\partial s \end{bmatrix} = \begin{bmatrix} (-1+s) & (1-s) & s & -s \\ (-1+r) & -r & r & (1-r) \end{bmatrix}.$$

The Jacobian is the product of the parametric derivatives and the nodal coordinates:

$$\boldsymbol{J}^e(r, s) = \begin{bmatrix} (-1+s) & (1-s) & s & -s \\ (-1+r) & -r & r & (1-r) \end{bmatrix} \begin{bmatrix} x_1 & y_1 \\ x_2 & y_2 \\ x_3 & y_3 \\ x_4 & y_4 \end{bmatrix}^e$$

$$\boldsymbol{J}^e(r, s) = \begin{bmatrix} (-1+s) & (1-s) & s & -s \\ (-1+r) & -r & r & (1-r) \end{bmatrix} \begin{bmatrix} 1 & 1 \\ 3 & 1 \\ 3 & 3 \\ 1 & 2 \end{bmatrix}^e$$

$$\text{cm} = \begin{bmatrix} 2 & s \\ 0 & (r+1) \end{bmatrix} \text{cm}.$$

For the current element node coordinates, this Jacobin is not constant but is linear in the local coordinates. Thus, the element Jacobian matrix, for this element type, will not be constant, unless its sides happen to be input parallel to the physical axes. The determinant is $|\boldsymbol{J}^e(r,\, s)| = (2 + 2r)\ \mathrm{cm}^2$ and the inverse matrix is

$$\boldsymbol{J}^e(r,\, s)^{-1} = \begin{bmatrix} \frac{1}{2} & \frac{-s}{2(r+1)} \\ 0 & \frac{1}{(r+1)} \end{bmatrix} \frac{1}{\mathrm{cm}},$$

and that gives the physical derivatives of $\boldsymbol{H}$ as

$$\boldsymbol{\partial}_\Omega \boldsymbol{H}(r,\, s) = \begin{bmatrix} \partial \boldsymbol{H}/\partial x \\ \partial \boldsymbol{H}/\partial y \end{bmatrix} = \boldsymbol{J}^e(r,\, s)^{-1}\, \boldsymbol{\partial}_\square \boldsymbol{H}(r,\, s)$$

$$\begin{bmatrix} \partial \boldsymbol{H}/\partial x \\ \partial \boldsymbol{H}/\partial y \end{bmatrix} = \begin{bmatrix} \frac{1}{2} & \frac{-s}{2(r+1)} \\ 0 & \frac{1}{(r+1)} \end{bmatrix} \frac{1}{\mathrm{cm}} \begin{bmatrix} (-1+s) & (1-s) & s & -s \\ (-1+r) & -r & r & (1-r) \end{bmatrix}$$

$$\begin{bmatrix} \partial \boldsymbol{H}/\partial x \\ \partial \boldsymbol{H}/\partial y \end{bmatrix} = \begin{bmatrix} \frac{2s-r-1}{2r+2} & \frac{r-s+1}{2r+2} & \frac{s}{2r+2} & \frac{-s}{r+1} \\ \frac{r-1}{r+1} & \frac{-r}{r+1} & \frac{r}{r+1} & \frac{1-r}{r+1} \end{bmatrix} \frac{1}{\mathrm{cm}}.$$

Note that the determinant and the physical derivatives, for this geometry, are no longer polynomials but ratios of polynomials (rational functions). Therefore, when using numerical integration the minimum number of points should be raised by at least one in both directions.

Example 12.8-2 Given: A four-noded quadrilateral element has the nodal spatial coordinates of $\boldsymbol{x}^{e^T} = \begin{bmatrix} 4 & 7 & 8 & 3 \end{bmatrix}$, and $\boldsymbol{y}^{e^T} = \begin{bmatrix} 4 & 5 & 12 & 8 \end{bmatrix}$ m, and pressure values of $\boldsymbol{p}^{e^T} = \begin{bmatrix} 22 & 24 & 30 & 28 \end{bmatrix}\ N/\mathrm{m}^2$. What is the physical pressure gradient at the centroid of that element, $(r = 1/2,\ s = 1/2)$?

Solution: To answer that question it is first necessary to numerically evaluate the Jacobian matrix for that isoparametric element at the specific point of interest (usually a quadrature point):

$$\boldsymbol{J}^e(r,\, s) = \boldsymbol{\partial}_\square \boldsymbol{G}(r,\, s) \begin{bmatrix} \boldsymbol{x}^e & \boldsymbol{y}^e \end{bmatrix}.$$

From Example, 12.10-1 $\boldsymbol{J}^e(r,\, s)$ is

$$\boldsymbol{J}^e(r,\, s) = \begin{bmatrix} (-1+s) & (1-s) & s & -s \\ (-1+r) & -r & r & (1-r) \end{bmatrix} \begin{bmatrix} x_1 & y_1 \\ x_2 & y_2 \\ x_3 & y_3 \\ x_4 & y_4 \end{bmatrix}^e$$

$$\boldsymbol{J}^e\,(0.5,\, 0.5) = \begin{bmatrix} -0.5 & 0.5 & 0.5 & -0.5 \\ -0.5 & -0.5 & 0.5 & 0.5 \end{bmatrix} \begin{bmatrix} 4 & 4 \\ 7 & 5 \\ 8 & 12 \\ 3 & 8 \end{bmatrix} \mathrm{m} = \begin{bmatrix} 4 & 3/2 \\ 0 & 9/2 \end{bmatrix} \mathrm{m}.$$

So the determinant at that point is $J^e = 4\,(9/2\,) - 0 = 18\,\mathrm{m}^2$ and the inverse Jacobian matrix is

$$\boldsymbol{J}^{e^{-1}} = \frac{1}{18} \begin{bmatrix} 9/2 & -3/2 \\ 0 & 4 \end{bmatrix} 1/\mathrm{m}.$$

The parametric pressure gradient component here is $\boldsymbol{\partial}^e_{\boxdot} p\,(r,\, s) = \boldsymbol{\partial}_{\boxdot} \boldsymbol{H}\,(r,\, s)\; \boldsymbol{p}^e$, or

$$\begin{Bmatrix} \frac{\partial p}{\partial r} \\ \frac{\partial p}{\partial s} \end{Bmatrix}^e = \begin{bmatrix} (-1+s) & (1-s) & s & -s \\ (-1+r) & -r & r & (1-r) \end{bmatrix} \begin{Bmatrix} p_1 \\ p_2 \\ p_3 \\ p_4 \end{Bmatrix}^e.$$

Substituting the centroidal coordinates, (0.5, 0.5), gives the numerical values

$$\begin{Bmatrix} \frac{\partial p(0.5, 0.5)}{\partial r} \\ \frac{\partial p(0.5, 0.5)}{\partial s} \end{Bmatrix}^e = \begin{bmatrix} -0.5 & 0.5 & 0.5 & -0.5 \\ -0.5 & -0.5 & 0.5 & 0.5 \end{bmatrix} \begin{Bmatrix} 22 \\ 24 \\ 30 \\ 28 \end{Bmatrix}^e \mathrm{N/m^2}$$

$$\boldsymbol{\partial}^e_{\square} p\,(0.5,\,0.5) = \begin{Bmatrix} 2 \\ 6 \end{Bmatrix} \mathrm{N/m^2/1},$$

and the physical pressure gradient components, at the point, are $\vec{\boldsymbol{\nabla}}^e p = \boldsymbol{\partial}^e_{\Omega} p = \boldsymbol{J}^{e^{-1}}\ \boldsymbol{\partial}^e_{\square} p$, or

$$\begin{Bmatrix} \frac{\partial p}{\partial x} \\ \frac{\partial p}{\partial y} \end{Bmatrix}^e = \frac{1}{18} \begin{bmatrix} 9/2 & -3/2 \\ 0 & 4 \end{bmatrix} \begin{Bmatrix} 2 \\ 6 \end{Bmatrix} = \frac{1}{3} \begin{Bmatrix} 0 \\ 4 \end{Bmatrix} (\mathrm{N/m^2})/\mathrm{m}.$$

Here, the pressure gradient is different at every point in the element.

Example 12.8-3 Given: Let the quadrilateral in Example 12.8-2 be degenerated to a rectangle, parallel to the x-y axes, with the same nodal pressures. Let $x_2 = (x_1 + \Delta x) = x_3$, $x_4 = x_1$ and $y_2 = y_1$, $y_3 = y_4 = (y_1 + \nabla y)$. Determine the value of the Jacobian and the center pressure gradient for that element physical shape.

Solution: The Jacobian matrix becomes

$$\boldsymbol{J}^e(r,\,s) = \begin{bmatrix} (-1+s)\,(1-s) & s & -s \\ (-1+r) & -r & r & (1-r) \end{bmatrix} \begin{bmatrix} x_1 & y_1 \\ x_2 & y_2 \\ x_3 & y_3 \\ x_4 & y_4 \end{bmatrix}^e$$

$$\boldsymbol{J}^e\,(r,\,s) = \begin{bmatrix} (-1+s) & (1-s) & s & -s \\ (-1+r) & -r & r & (1-r) \end{bmatrix}$$

$$\begin{bmatrix} x_1 & y_1 \\ x_1 + \Delta x & y_1 \\ x_1 + \Delta x & y_1 + \Delta y \\ x_1 & y_1 + \Delta y \end{bmatrix} = \begin{bmatrix} \Delta x & 0 \\ 0 & \Delta y \end{bmatrix} \mathrm{m}$$

which is a constant diagonal Jacobian. Its determinant is $J^e = \Delta x\, \Delta y\, \mathrm{m}^2 = A^e = A^e/1$, which is the physical area of the element divided by the measure of the unit parametric square space.

Example 12.8-4 Given: Consider the second boundary edge of the quadrilateral in Example 12.8-2, between points 2 and 3 (where $r = 1$). Determine the length of that line and the pressure gradient (directional derivative) along that edge.

Solution: Since that edge has only two nodes, the quadrilateral interpolation functions degenerate to a parametric linear function:

$$\boldsymbol{G}(r,\ s) = \begin{bmatrix} G_1(r,\ s) & G_2(r,\ s) & G_3(r,\ s) & G_4(r,\ s) \end{bmatrix}$$

$$G_1(r,s) = 1 - r - s + rs, \quad G_2(r,s) = r - rs, \quad G_3(r,s) = rs,$$

$$G_4\,(r,s) = s - rs$$

and for $r = 1$ the interpolation functions not on that edge vanish, and the ones on that edge simplify: $G_1(1,s) = 0,\ G_2(1,s) = 1 - s$, $G_3(1,s) = s$, $G_4\,(1,s) = 0$. That is, the four interpolations in the two-dimensional parametric space reduce to two non-zero functions in one-parametric space. The reduced forms are called the boundary interpolations, $\boldsymbol{G^b}\,(s)$.

$$\boldsymbol{G^e}\,(r = 1,\ s) \Longrightarrow \boldsymbol{G^b}\,(s) = [G_1\ \ G_2] = [\,(1 - s)\ \ s]$$

Then the physical coordinates on the edge become linear, and the interpolation subset on the boundary, $\boldsymbol{G^b} \subset \boldsymbol{G^e}$, is

$$x\,(s) = \boldsymbol{G^b}\,(s)\ \boldsymbol{x^b} = \boldsymbol{G^b}\,(s) \begin{Bmatrix} x_1 \\ x_2 \end{Bmatrix}^b = [(1 - s)\ \ s] \begin{Bmatrix} x_3 \\ x_4 \end{Bmatrix},$$

and likewise for the y-coordinates. This means that the edge is a straight line in physical space. The general length relations are

$$L^b = \int_{L^b} dL = \int_{\boxdot} \frac{dL}{ds} ds,$$

with

$$\left(\frac{dL}{ds}\right)^2 = \left(\frac{dx}{ds}\right)^2 + \left(\frac{dy}{ds}\right)^2,$$

where

$$\frac{dx}{ds} = \frac{d\boldsymbol{G}^{\boldsymbol{b}}}{ds}(s)\,\boldsymbol{x}^{\boldsymbol{b}} = \begin{bmatrix}-1 & 1\end{bmatrix}\begin{Bmatrix}x_3\\x_4\end{Bmatrix} = (x_4 - x_3) \equiv \Delta x = 1\,\text{m},$$

and similarly for the y-coordinates it gives a constant $\Delta\text{y} = 5$ meters and $dL/ds = \sqrt{\Delta x^2 + \Delta y^2}$, so $dL/ds = 5.12\,\text{m}$. Since that row of the Jacobian was constant, in this example, it comes out of the integral and the length of the edge is

$$L^b = \frac{dL}{ds}\int_0^1 ds = 5.12\,\text{m}.$$

The pressure gradient along that line is $\partial p/\partial L = \partial p/\partial s\;(\partial s/\partial L)$ where the parametric pressure gradient is

$$\frac{\partial p}{\partial s} = \frac{d\boldsymbol{H}^{\boldsymbol{b}}}{ds}(s)\,\boldsymbol{p}^{\boldsymbol{b}} = \begin{bmatrix}-1 & 1\end{bmatrix}\begin{Bmatrix}p_3\\p_4\end{Bmatrix} = (p_4 - p_3) \equiv \Delta p = 6\,\text{N}/\text{m}^2,$$

and finally, the physical pressure gradient is

$$\partial p/\partial L = 6\,\text{N}/\text{m}^2\,(1/5.12\,\text{m}) = 1.18\,\text{N}/\text{m}^2/\text{m}.$$

Example 12.8-5 Given: For the above pressure element find the pressure gradient at the local center in the direction parallel to physical edge 1-2.

Solution: This is the directional derivative of the pressure obtained from the pressure gradient previously calculated at the center of the quadrilateral. The directional derivative is the dot product of the gradient vector and a unit vector in the direction of interest. That requires the unit tangent vector for the edge of interest:

$$\vec{T}^b(s) = \frac{\partial x}{\partial s}\vec{i} + \frac{\partial y}{\partial s}\vec{j} = \left(1\vec{i} + 5\vec{j}\right)m,$$

which has a unit tangent vector of $\vec{t}^b(s) = (0.196\,\vec{i} + 0.980\,\vec{j})$ and the directional derivative at the center of the quadrilateral and parallel to edge 1-2 is

$$\vec{\nabla} p \cdot \vec{t}^b = \left(0\,\vec{i} + 4/3\vec{j}\right) \frac{\mathrm{N/m^2}}{\mathrm{m}} \cdot \left(0.196\,\vec{i} + 0.980\,\vec{j}\right) = 1.31\mathrm{N/m^2/m},$$

which is similar to the edge gradient.

12.9 Field Flux Vector at a Point

When the material properties are not an identity matrix, the solution has an associated "flux vector" that usually has an important physical meaning, even if the scalar unknown does not. For example, for the torsion of non-circular bars the primary unknown is the stress-function, which has no physical importance, and its gradient is not physically important. However, the material matrix times the gradient of the solution defines components of the shear stress in the material.

Probably the most widely used and important flux vector is the heat flux vector at a point defined from Fourier's Law

$$\vec{q}\,(x,\,y,z) = \boldsymbol{q} = \begin{Bmatrix} q_x \\ q_x \\ q_x \end{Bmatrix} = -[\boldsymbol{\kappa}]\ \boldsymbol{\nabla}^{\boldsymbol{T}} u\,(x,\,y,z), \qquad (12.9\text{-}1)$$

where u represents the temperature, $\boldsymbol{\kappa}$ contains the anisotropic thermal conductivities, and $\vec{q}$ is the heat flux per unit area in the direction of the gradient vector. The x-component in the general case expands to

$$q_x = -\left(k_{xx}\frac{\partial u}{\partial x} + k_{xy}\frac{\partial u}{\partial y} + k_{xz}\frac{\partial u}{\partial z}\right).$$

There are some applications where the flux vector is defined with a positive sign.

The heat flux vector is calculated at numerous points in each element in the post-processing phase of a finite element study. Often those vectors (or their averaged nodal values) are then plotted. The magnitude of the flux, $|\vec{q}\,|$, is also computed for contouring. That element post-processing is usually evaluated at the numerical integration points by utilizing the operator matrix:

$$\begin{aligned} \boldsymbol{q}^e &= -\boldsymbol{\kappa}^e \boldsymbol{\nabla}^{e^T} u\,(x, y, z) = -\boldsymbol{\kappa}^e \boldsymbol{\nabla}^{e^T} \boldsymbol{H}^e\,(x,\, y,\, z)\boldsymbol{u}^e \\ &\equiv -\boldsymbol{\kappa}^e \boldsymbol{B}^e\,(x,\, y,\, z)\boldsymbol{u}^e. \end{aligned} \tag{12.9-2}$$

The normal component on a boundary surface is important because it is related to secondary boundary conditions, and its integral over a boundary surface gives the heat flow into or out of the body. The flux component in any direction is found by taking the scalar product of the heat flux vector with a unit vector in the direction of interest. On a boundary surface the unit outward normal is used to define the normal heat flux per unit area leaving or entering the body: $q_n = \vec{q}\cdot\vec{n} = \boldsymbol{q}^T\boldsymbol{n} = \boldsymbol{n}^T\ \boldsymbol{q} = q_x n_x + q_y n_y + q_z n_z$. For the general anisotropic material, the scalar normal flux becomes $q_n = -\boldsymbol{n}^T \boldsymbol{\kappa}^e \boldsymbol{\nabla}^{e^T} u$, or

$$\begin{aligned} q_n = &-\left(k_{xx}\frac{\partial u}{\partial x} + k_{xy}\frac{\partial u}{\partial y} + k_{xz}\frac{\partial u}{\partial z}\right) n_x \\ &-\left(k_{yx}\frac{\partial u}{\partial x} + k_{yy}\frac{\partial u}{\partial y} + k_{yz}\frac{\partial u}{\partial z}\right) n_y \cdots \\ &-\left(k_{zx}\frac{\partial u}{\partial x} + k_{zy}\frac{\partial u}{\partial y} + k_{zz}\frac{\partial u}{\partial z}\right) n_z \equiv -k_{nn}\frac{\partial u}{\partial n}, \end{aligned} \tag{12.9-3}$$

where the unit normal vector components are $\boldsymbol{n}^T = \begin{bmatrix} n_x & n_y & n_z \end{bmatrix}$, and where k_{nn} is defined as the (transformed) material property in the direction normal to the surface.

This sheds light on the signs encountered in the one-dimensional secondary boundary conditions. There $n_y = n_z = 0 = \partial/\partial y = \partial/\partial z$ and the normal flux per unit area at a boundary surface reduces to $q_n = -k_{nn}\partial u/\partial n = -k_{xx}\partial u/\partial x n_x$. Evaluating the heat flow at the ends, $x = 0$ and $x = L$, as the product of the end areas and the flux gives

$$\begin{aligned} f\,(0) = -A\,(0)\,k_{xx}\frac{\partial u}{\partial x}n_x = -A\,(0)\,k_{xx}\frac{\partial u}{\partial x}\,(-1) = +A\,(0)\,k_{xx}\frac{\partial u}{\partial x} \\ f\,(L) = -A\,(L)\,k_{xx}\frac{\partial u}{\partial x}, \end{aligned} \tag{12.9-4}$$

where a positive sign is heat flow entering the one-dimensional body.

12.10 Evaluation of Integrals with Constant Jacobian

When the Jacobian of a geometric transformation is constant, it is possible to develop the closed-form exact integrals of parametric polynomials. Tables 12.10-1–12.10-4 give a few element matrices for straight-sided triangles obtained in closed form by using constant and/or diagonal Jacobians. Some of the integrals for the other special case of rectangular elements are given in Tables 12.10-5 and 12.10-6. In practice, most element arrays in two and three dimensions (and space–time) are obtained by numerical integration.

12.11 Symmetry and Anti-Symmetry

The concepts of symmetry and anti-symmetry for thermal and other scalar field problems were introduced in Fig. 8.1-1. Now, that figure can be considered as depicting descriptions along any line that is perpendicular to the plane of symmetry or anti-symmetry. Thermal studies often have multiple planes of symmetry. Horizontal and vertical ones are usually spotted, but diagonal ones are often missed. The top of Fig. 12.11-1, shows a simple example where a region is subjected to known constant temperatures (EBCs) on its inner and outer

Table 12.10-1: Interpolation integrals for straight-edged triangles.

Type	$\int_\Omega \boldsymbol{H}^T d\Omega$	$\int_\Omega \boldsymbol{H}^T \boldsymbol{H} d\Omega$
$2A^e = (x_2 - x_1)(y_3 - y_1) - (x_3 - x_1)(y_2 - y_1) = b_2c_3 - b_3c_2 = a_i + a_j + a_k$ $a_i = x_j y_k - x_k y_j,\ b_i = y_j - y_k,\ c_i = x_k - x_j:\ ijk \to 123 \to 231 \to 312$		
T3	$\frac{A^e}{3}\begin{Bmatrix} 1 \\ 1 \\ 1 \end{Bmatrix}$	$\frac{A^e}{12}\begin{bmatrix} 2 & 1 & 1 \\ 1 & 2 & 1 \\ 1 & 1 & 2 \end{bmatrix}$
T6	$\frac{A^e}{3}\begin{Bmatrix} 0 \\ 0 \\ 0 \\ 1 \\ 1 \\ 1 \end{Bmatrix}$	$\frac{A^e}{180}\begin{bmatrix} 6 & -1 & -1 & 0 & -4 & 0 \\ -1 & 6 & -1 & 0 & 0 & -4 \\ -1 & -1 & 6 & -4 & 0 & 0 \\ 0 & 0 & -4 & 32 & 16 & 16 \\ -4 & 0 & 0 & 16 & 32 & 16 \\ 0 & -4 & 0 & 16 & 16 & 32 \end{bmatrix}.$

Table 12.10-2: Diffusion integrals for isotropic straight-edged triangles.

Type	$\int_\Omega \vec{\nabla} \boldsymbol{H}^T \boldsymbol{\kappa} \vec{\nabla} \boldsymbol{H} d\Omega$	$\boldsymbol{\kappa} = \begin{bmatrix} k^e & 0 \\ 0 & k^e \end{bmatrix}$
T3	$\frac{k^e}{4A^e}\begin{bmatrix} (b_1b_1+c_1c_1) & (b_1b_2+c_1c_2) & (b_1b_3+c_1c_3) \\ (b_2b_1+c_2c_1) & (b_2b_2+c_2c_2) & (b_2b_3+c_2c_3) \\ (b_3b_1+c_3c_1) & (b_3b_2+c_3c_2) & (b_3b_3+c_3c_3) \end{bmatrix}$	

Special cases:

90° triangle, corner at node 1: $A^e = L_x^e\, L_y^e/2$

T3_90 (90° at node 1)

$$\frac{k^e}{4\,A^e}\begin{bmatrix} \left(L_x^{e^2} + L_y^{e^2}\right) & -L_y^{e^2} & -L_x^{e^2} \\ -L_y^{e^2} & L_y^{e^2} & 0 \\ -L_x^{e^2} & 0 & L_x^{e^2} \end{bmatrix} \quad \underset{L_x^e = L_y^e}{\to\to} \quad \frac{k^e}{2}\begin{bmatrix} 2 & -1 & -1 \\ -1 & 1 & 0 \\ -1 & 0 & 1 \end{bmatrix}$$

T3_90 (90° at node 2)

$$\frac{k^e}{4\,A^e}\begin{bmatrix} L_x^{e^2} & -L_x^{e^2} & 0 \\ -L_x^{e^2} & \left(L_x^{e^2} + L_y^{e^2}\right) & -L_y^{e^2} \\ 0 & -L_y^{e^2} & L_y^{e^2} \end{bmatrix} \quad \underset{L_x^e = L_y^e}{\to\to} \quad \frac{k^e}{2}\begin{bmatrix} 1 & -1 & 0 \\ -1 & 2 & -1 \\ 0 & -1 & 1 \end{bmatrix}$$

T6_90_45 (90° at node 1)

$$\frac{k^e}{6}\begin{bmatrix} 6 & 1 & 1 & -4 & 0 & -4 \\ 1 & 3 & 0 & -4 & 0 & 0 \\ 1 & 0 & 3 & 0 & 0 & -4 \\ -4 & -4 & 0 & 16 & -8 & 0 \\ 0 & 0 & 0 & -8 & 16 & -8 \\ -4 & 0 & -4 & 0 & -8 & 16 \end{bmatrix}.$$

Note: The sum of all the terms in brackets is zero.

surfaces, and an insulated top surface. It has a vertical plane of symmetry that is easy to spot. For the lengths given, each symmetric half also has another plane of symmetry through the lower corner at 45°. Thus, symmetry is applied twice resulting in a "quarter-symmetry" model. It will require only one-fourth as many elements as the full model and will execute about 64 times faster.

Assume that the part in Fig. 12.11-1 is a very thick solid part, perpendicular to the paper, then the middle plane would be another plane of symmetry (with zero normal flux). That would allow a "one-eighth symmetry" analysis of the solid part and would result in a huge reduction in execution time compared to that required for a full middle.

Table 12.10-3: Diffusion integrals for orthotropic straight-edged triangles.

Type	$\int_\Omega \vec{\nabla} \boldsymbol{H}^T \boldsymbol{\kappa} \vec{\nabla} \boldsymbol{H} d\Omega, \quad \boldsymbol{\kappa} = \begin{bmatrix} k_x & 0 \\ 0 & k_y \end{bmatrix}$
T3	$\frac{1}{4\,A^e} \left[k_x^e \begin{bmatrix} b_1b_1 & b_1b_2 & b_1b_3 \\ b_2b_1 & b_2b_2 & b_2b_3 \\ b_3b_1 & b_3b_2 & b_3b_3 \end{bmatrix} + k_y^e \begin{bmatrix} c_1c_1 & c_1c_2 & c_1c_3 \\ c_2c_1 & c_2c_2 & c_2c_3 \\ c_3c_1 & c_3c_2 & c_3c_3 \end{bmatrix} \right]$
Special case: 90° corner at node 1:	
T3_90	$\frac{k_x^e\, L_y^e}{2\,L_x^e} \begin{bmatrix} 1 & -1 & 0 \\ -1 & 1 & 0 \\ 0 & 0 & 0 \end{bmatrix} + \frac{k_y^e\, L_x^e}{2\,L_y^e} \begin{bmatrix} 1 & 0 & -1 \\ 0 & 0 & 0 \\ -1 & 0 & 1 \end{bmatrix}$
T6_90	$\frac{k_x^e\, L_y^e}{6\,L_x^e} \begin{bmatrix} 3 & 1 & 0 & -4 & 0 & 0 \\ 1 & 3 & 0 & -4 & 0 & 0 \\ 0 & 0 & 0 & 0 & 0 & 0 \\ -4 & -4 & 0 & 8 & 0 & 0 \\ 0 & 0 & 0 & 0 & 8 & -8 \\ 0 & 0 & 0 & 0 & -8 & 8 \end{bmatrix} + \frac{k_y^e L_x^e}{6L_y^e} \begin{bmatrix} 3 & 0 & 1 & 0 & 0 & -4 \\ 0 & 0 & 0 & 0 & 0 & 0 \\ 1 & 0 & 3 & 0 & 0 & -4 \\ 0 & 0 & 0 & 8 & -8 & 0 \\ 0 & 0 & 0 & -8 & 8 & 0 \\ -4 & 0 & -4 & 0 & 0 & 8 \end{bmatrix}.$

Note: The sum of all the terms in brackets is zero.

Table 12.10-4: Interpolation integrals for rectangular elements.

Type	$\int_\Omega \boldsymbol{H}^T d\Omega$	$\int_\Omega \boldsymbol{H}^T \boldsymbol{H} d\Omega$ Rectangle: $A^e = L_x^e\, L_y^e$
R4	$\frac{A^e}{4} \begin{Bmatrix} 1 \\ 1 \\ 1 \\ 1 \end{Bmatrix}$	$\frac{L_x^e\, L_y^e}{36} \begin{bmatrix} 4 & 2 & 1 & 2 \\ 2 & 4 & 2 & 1 \\ 1 & 2 & 4 & 2 \\ 2 & 1 & 2 & 4 \end{bmatrix}$
R8	$\frac{A^e}{12} \begin{Bmatrix} -1 \\ -1 \\ -1 \\ -1 \\ 4 \\ 4 \\ 4 \\ 4 \end{Bmatrix}$	$\frac{L_x^e\, L_y^e}{360} \begin{bmatrix} 12 & 4 & 6 & 4 & -12 & -16 & -16 & -12 \\ 4 & 12 & 4 & 6 & -12 & -12 & -16 & -16 \\ 6 & 4 & 12 & 4 & -16 & -12 & -12 & -16 \\ 4 & 6 & 4 & 12 & -16 & -16 & -12 & -12 \\ -12 & -12 & -16 & -16 & 64 & 40 & 32 & 40 \\ -16 & -12 & -12 & -16 & 40 & 64 & 40 & 32 \\ -16 & -16 & -12 & -12 & 32 & 40 & 64 & 40 \\ -12 & -16 & -16 & -12 & 40 & 32 & 40 & 64 \end{bmatrix}$
R9	$\frac{A^e}{36} \begin{Bmatrix} 1 \\ 1 \\ 1 \\ 1 \\ 4 \\ 4 \\ 4 \\ 4 \\ 16 \end{Bmatrix}$	$\frac{A^e}{900} \begin{bmatrix} 16 & -4 & 1 & -4 & 8 & -2 & -2 & 8 & 4 \\ -4 & 16 & -4 & 1 & 8 & 8 & -2 & -2 & 4 \\ 1 & -4 & 16 & -4 & -2 & 8 & 8 & -2 & 4 \\ -4 & 1 & -4 & 16 & -2 & -2 & 8 & 8 & 4 \\ 8 & 8 & -2 & -2 & 64 & 4 & -16 & 4 & 32 \\ -2 & 8 & 8 & -2 & 4 & 64 & 4 & -16 & 32 \\ -2 & -2 & 8 & 8 & -16 & 4 & 64 & 4 & 32 \\ 8 & -2 & -2 & 8 & 4 & -16 & 4 & 64 & 32 \\ 4 & 4 & 4 & 4 & 32 & 32 & 32 & 32 & 256 \end{bmatrix}.$

Note: For these two integrals, the sum of all the terms in the brackets is one.

Table 12.10-5: Diffusion integrals for orthotropic rectangles.

Type $\int_\Omega \vec{\nabla} \boldsymbol{H}^T \boldsymbol{\kappa} \vec{\nabla} \boldsymbol{H} d\Omega, \qquad \boldsymbol{\kappa} = \begin{bmatrix} k_x & 0 \\ 0 & k_y \end{bmatrix}$

R4

$$\frac{k_x^e L_y^e}{6 L_x^e} \begin{bmatrix} 2 & -2 & -1 & 1 \\ -2 & 2 & 1 & -1 \\ -1 & 1 & 2 & -2 \\ 1 & -1 & -2 & 2 \end{bmatrix} + \frac{k_y^e L_x^e}{6 L_y^e} \begin{bmatrix} 2 & 1 & -1 & -2 \\ 1 & 2 & -2 & -1 \\ -1 & -2 & 2 & 1 \\ -2 & -1 & 1 & 2 \end{bmatrix}.$$

R8

$$\frac{k_x^e L_y^e}{360 L_x^e} \begin{bmatrix} 52 & 28 & 23 & 17 & -80 & -6 & -40 & 6 \\ 28 & 52 & 28 & 23 & -80 & 6 & -40 & -6 \\ 23 & 28 & 52 & 28 & -40 & 6 & -80 & -6 \\ 17 & 23 & 28 & 52 & -40 & 0 & -80 & 6 \\ -80 & -80 & -40 & -40 & 160 & 0 & 80 & 0 \\ -6 & 6 & 6 & 0 & 0 & 48 & 0 & -48 \\ -40 & -40 & -80 & -80 & 80 & 0 & 160 & 0 \\ 6 & -6 & -6 & 6 & 0 & -48 & 0 & 48 \end{bmatrix} \cdots$$

$$+\frac{k_y^e L_x^e}{360 L_y^e} \begin{bmatrix} 52 & 17 & 23 & 28 & 6 & -40 & -6 & -80 \\ 17 & 52 & 28 & 23 & 6 & -80 & -6 & -40 \\ 23 & 28 & 52 & 17 & -6 & -80 & 6 & -40 \\ 28 & 23 & 17 & 52 & -6 & -40 & 6 & -80 \\ 6 & 6 & -6 & -6 & 48 & 0 & -48 & 0 \\ -40 & -80 & -80 & -40 & 0 & 160 & 0 & 80 \\ -6 & -6 & 6 & 6 & -48 & 0 & 48 & 0 \\ -80 & -40 & -40 & -80 & 0 & 80 & 0 & 160 \end{bmatrix}.$$

R9

$$\frac{k_x^e L_y^e}{360 L_x^e} \begin{bmatrix} 28 & 4 & -1 & -7 & -32 & 2 & 8 & 14 & -16 \\ 4 & 28 & -7 & -1 & -32 & 14 & 8 & 2 & -16 \\ -1 & -7 & 28 & 4 & 8 & 14 & -32 & 2 & -16 \\ -7 & -1 & 4 & 28 & 8 & 2 & -32 & 14 & -16 \\ -32 & -32 & 8 & 8 & 64 & -16 & -16 & -16 & 32 \\ 2 & 14 & 14 & 2 & -16 & 112 & -16 & 16 & -128 \\ 8 & -32 & -32 & -32 & -16 & -16 & 64 & -16 & 32 \\ 14 & 2 & 2 & 14 & -16 & 16 & -16 & 112 & -128 \\ -16 & -16 & -16 & -16 & 32 & -128 & 32 & -128 & 256 \end{bmatrix}$$

$$+\frac{k_y^e L_x^e}{360 L_y^e} \begin{bmatrix} 28 & -7 & -1 & 4 & 14 & 8 & 2 & -32 & -16 \\ -7 & 28 & 4 & -1 & 14 & -32 & 2 & 8 & -16 \\ -1 & 4 & 28 & -7 & 2 & -32 & 14 & 8 & -16 \\ 4 & -1 & -7 & 28 & 2 & 8 & 14 & -32 & -16 \\ 14 & 14 & 2 & 2 & 112 & -16 & 16 & -16 & -128 \\ 8 & -32 & -32 & 8 & -16 & 64 & -16 & -16 & 32 \\ 2 & 2 & 14 & 14 & 16 & -16 & 112 & -16 & -128 \\ -32 & 8 & 8 & -32 & -16 & -16 & -16 & 64 & 32 \\ -16 & -16 & -16 & -16 & -128 & 32 & -128 & 32 & 256 \end{bmatrix}$$

Notes: The sum of all the terms in brackets is zero. Curved elements do not have a constant Jacobian and require numerical integration. Quadrilateral elements do not generally have a constant Jacobian, but they do if the sides are parallel.

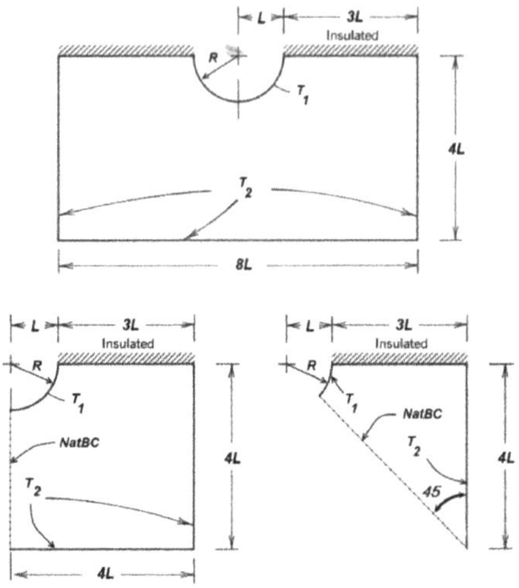

Fig. 12.11-1: A region and its half- and quarter-symmetry versions.

Many industrial parts have another type of symmetry where a "pie slice" of the part occurs an integer number of times as it is rotated about a part axis. That type of symmetry is called cyclic symmetry. The most common example is the turbine blades in a jet engine. Figure 12.11-2 shows a thermal example where the shaded area is either a different material or a different thickness to be modeled in a two and half-dimensional or three-dimensional study. Either way, any 90° slice of the part, relative to its center, is all that has to be analyzed (if the software has the necessary features). That figure shows two of an infinite number of cyclic symmetry regions. Any 90° slice of that part can be used, but some are more logical or easy to mesh than others. The top choice is the best of the two shown. Most commercial software allows the use of cyclic symmetry.

Note that Fig. 12.11-2 shows three pairs of points on each side of the slice, *a*-*b*-*c* and *A*-*B*-*C*. They represent any pair of nodes on the mesh. Each pair, say *a*-*A*, is the same radial distance from the center of the cyclic symmetry. For any field analysis each pair, *a*-*A*, *b*-*B*, *c*-*C*, has the same *unknown* solution value. In other words, all nodes in the plane *a*-*b*-*c* have the same unknown solution as any node in plane *A*-*B*-*C* if the nodes have the same radial distance from the center. The mesh generator (or human) must assure that on those two planes all of the nodes in the model occur in pairs having the same

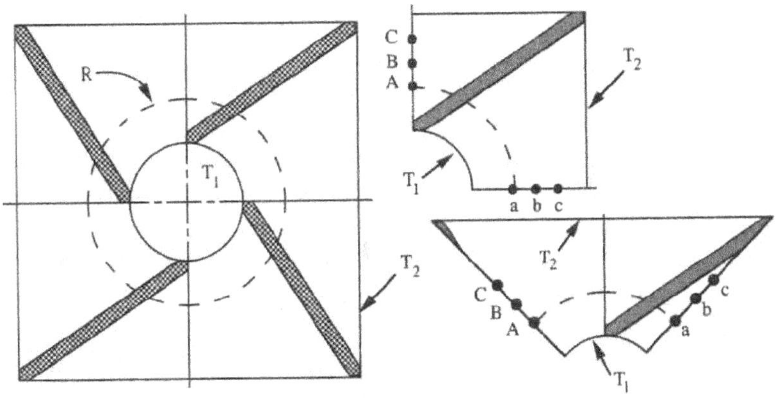

Fig. 12.11-2: A part with a 90° cyclic symmetry.

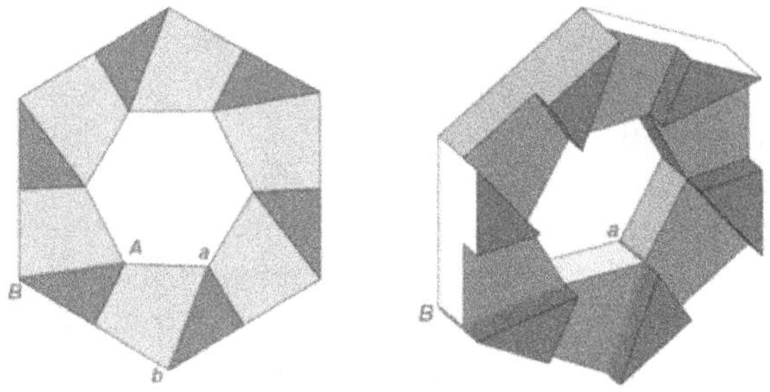

Fig. 12.11-3: A solid with 60° cyclic symmetry.

radial distance. In addition, the solver has to generate a multipoint constraints for each pair requiring that there solution values are the same.

An alternative to using MPCs to enforce cyclic symmetry is to have the solver recognize "repeated freedoms", shown in Fig. 12.11-3. That is, while node-a and node-A have different coordinates to allow the mesh to be plotted, the solver knows (through an input file) that node-A is a "repeat" of node-a and all of the element matrix terms to be assembled at node-A actually are scattered to node-a. Then the system is solved and the output solution at node-a is simply repeated at node-A for plotting the solution within the pie slice and for post-processing the elements.

12.12 Torsion of Non-Circular Shafts

Today it is common to encounter non-circular shafts, like thin-walled extruded members, and large torsional members. The behavior of any torsional member is directly related to a geometric parameter, J, called the "torsional constant" which is proportional to the polar moment of inertia of its cross-section, and its material shear modulus, G. The product of the two, GJ is called the "torsional stiffness" of the shaft.

The simple expressions for the shear stresses and deflections in circular were derived about 1,800. But the failures of shafts with non-circular cross-sections continued to be a common problem for another half a century. Then Saint-Venant, circa 1855, introduced a "warp function" that reduced the problem to solving a second-order partial differential equation over the cross-sectional area. In 1903, Ludwig Prandtl published a simpler solution by introducing the concept of a "stress function" that reduced the problem to solving a simpler second-order partial differential equation. That PDE is the same as the one that determines the shape of soap film surfaces. For many decades, before digital computers, the stresses in non-circular shafts were determined by very careful experimental measurements of the deflections and slopes of inflated membranes. Prandtl's equation is a form of Poisson's equation and is easily solved for any shape by FEA. Prandtl's equation for the stress function, $\varphi(x, y)$, of an isotropic elastic shaft is

$$\frac{\partial}{\partial x}\left(\frac{1}{G_x}\frac{\partial \varphi}{\partial x}\right) + \frac{\partial}{\partial y}\left(\frac{1}{G_y}\frac{\partial \varphi}{\partial y}\right) + 2\theta = 0, \tag{12.12-1}$$

where G_x and G_y are the orthotropic shear moduli of the material and θ is the angle of twist per unit length about an axis parallel to the shaft. The most common case is where the shaft is an isotropic material where $G_x = G_y = G$. The EBC is that the stress function is a constant on each peripheral boundary curve. When there is only one exterior boundary curve, the stress function is set to zero. When the shaft has interior boundaries around a hole or a different material (a different G), its constant value is not known and must be obtained by placing a constraint on the solution that computes the required additional constant(s) as part of the solution. In an FEA study that is accomplished by the use of a different material filling

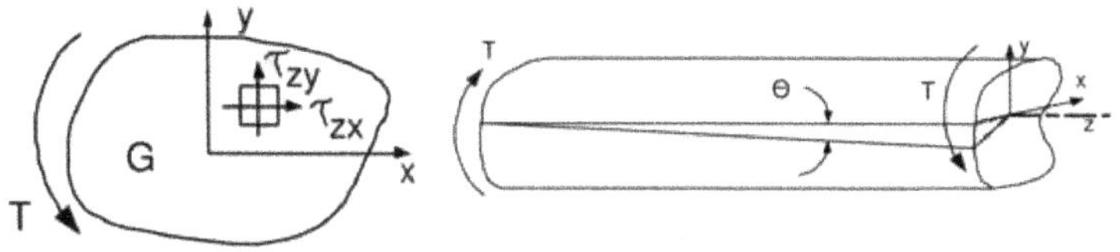

Fig. 12.12-1: Shaft shear stress components due to torsion.

the closed interior curve, or by a sophisticated algebraic constraint (usually known as repeated freedoms, which is not covered herein) applied to all nodes on that interior curve.

From the finite element point of view, the stress function is different because it does not have a physical meaning, but its integral does, and its gradient components do have physical importance. Let the cross-sectional area lie in xy plane. Then the angle of twist per unit length, θ, is about the z-axis as is the torque (couple) reaction, T, required to maintain that angular displacement. At all points in the boundary there are only two non-zero components of the stress tensor; namely the shear stress components, τ_{zx} and τ_{zy}, acting parallel to the x- and y-axes, respectively (see Fig. 12.12-1). The shear stress components are orthogonal to the gradient of the stress function:

$$\tau_{zx} = \frac{\partial \varphi}{\partial y} \text{ and } \tau_{zy} = -\frac{\partial \varphi}{\partial x}, \ \tau_{\max} = \sqrt{\tau_{zx}^2 + \tau_{zy}^2}. \tag{12.12-2}$$

The maximum shear stress at the point can be plotted as the "surface stress vector" ($\sigma_i = \sum_{j=1}^{3} \sigma_{ji} n_j$), which in this special case lies in the flat plane of the cross-section. From the membrane analogy, the slope of the bubble is maximum at, and perpendicular to, the boundary curve. That means that the maximum shear stress will occur at a point on the boundary. At an exterior corner the shear stress goes to zero. But, any sharp re-entrant corner is a singular point where the shear stress, in theory, goes to infinity. Therefore, any re-entrant corner should have a curved fillet that lowers the shear stress to an allowable material limit. For an area enclosed by a single boundary, the points of maximum shear stress are at locations on the boundary which touch the largest inscribed circle; such as the shapes in Fig. 12.12-2.

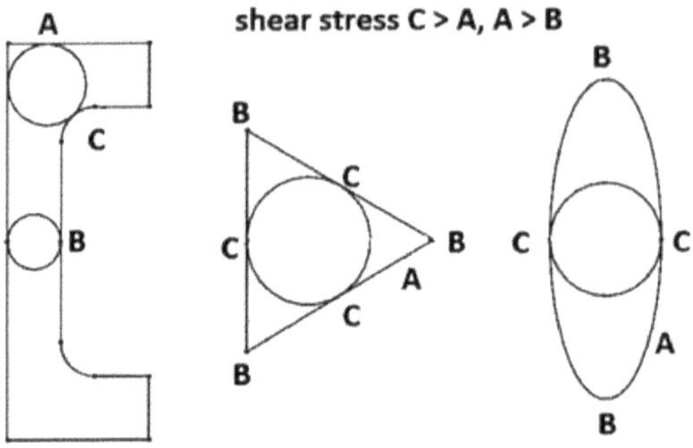

Fig. 12.12-2: Points of maximum (C) and minimum (B) torsional shear stress.

The externally applied torque, T, is defined by twice the integral, over the cross-section, of the stress function:

$$T = 2\int_{\Omega} \varphi(x,\, y)d\Omega \equiv (GJ)\,\theta. \tag{12.12-3}$$

In practice, however, we generally know the applied torque, T, and not the twist angle that appears in the differential equation. Thus, a unit twist angle ($\theta = 1$) is assumed and the finite element model is solved for the stress function. Then the integral of the stress function is computed to give the corresponding torque, say T_{fea}. Then, all of the stresses and the angle of twist are scaled by the ratio $T_{\text{actual}}/T_{\text{fea}}$ to obtain the results that correspond to the actual applied torque.

Two important analogies are useful in the calculation of torsional shear stresses because they share the same differential equation. They are the soap film "membrane analogy" and the "thermal analogy" (considered above). Their differential equations are as follows:

$$\text{soap film membrane: } \frac{\partial}{\partial x}\left(N_x\frac{\partial w}{\partial x}\right) + \frac{\partial}{\partial y}\left(N_y\frac{\partial w}{\partial y}\right) + P = 0,$$

$$\text{heat conduction: } \frac{\partial}{\partial x}\left(k_x\frac{\partial u}{\partial x}\right) + \frac{\partial}{\partial y}\left(k_x\frac{\partial u}{\partial y}\right) + Q = 0.$$

The thermal conduction analogy is important because it is available in most commercial FEA programs, while torsional analysis of a non-circular section is not specifically identified as an analysis option. To use heat conduction for torsion analysis, just change the meaning of its data (and edit the headings of its plotted results). The temperature, u, becomes the stress-function, φ. The input rate of heat generation becomes twice the rate of twist, $Q = 2\theta$, and the thermal conductivity is input as the reciprocal of the shear modulus, $k_x = 1/G_x$. Then the temperature gradient vector, ∇u, has the magnitude of the shear stress, but its direction is off by 90°.

The soap film membrane analogy is important because it lets an engineer visualize the shear stress distribution over the cross-section of the shaft. In a soap film membrane inflated over a boundary with the same shape as the torsional bar, the membrane deflection corresponds to the value of the stress function, $w = \varphi$, and its inflation pressure is proportional to the angle of twist, $P = 2\theta$, The membrane force per unit length is the reciprocal of the shear modulus, $N_x = 1/G_x$. The slope of the soap film is proportional to the shear stress at the same point, but the resultant shear stress acts in a direction perpendicular to that slope. On the bounding perimeter, the slope of the membrane is perpendicular to that curve; thus, the shaft shear stress is tangent to any closed bounding perimeter curve.

The membrane analogy makes it possible to visualize the expected torsional results for the two most common shapes of a circular and a rectangular cross-section. For a circular bar, the shear stress is zero at the center, increases radially, and is maximum and constant along its circular boundary. Therefore, the circular shaft has contours of shear stress that are concentric circles. The distribution of shear stress is more complicated for a rectangular cross-section. It is also zero at the center point, but the maximum shear stress occurs on the outer boundary at the two midpoints of the longest sides of the rectangle; while zero shear stress occurs at the corners of the rectangle (why?).

Two typical classes of the torsion of non-circular shafts will be illustrated. First, consider a symmetric aluminum circular shaft ($G = 3.92\text{e}6$ psi) with an eccentric circular hole. Had the hole been at the center, the problem would be the classic one-dimensional solution where the shear stress is directly proportional to the radius. The presence of the hole means that the condition of an unknown constant stress function value along the interior boundary curve must be enforced, or tricked into being satisfied. One trick is to fill the empty space with something like air which has a shear modulus of approximately zero compared to aluminum. That is, insert elements into the hole space and make the fake material modulus 10^4 or 10^5 times smaller than that of the surrounding material. The shape is shown on the left of Fig. 12.12-3, with $R = 4\,\text{in.}$, $d = 1\,\text{in.}$, $r = 1\,\text{in.}$ along with the half-symmetry upper half of the domain that was meshed with an unstructured group of six-noded curved triangular elements (T6). The center hole region was filled with four fake material (type 2) elements (63–66). The fake type 2 elements are shown in an exploded view in Fig. 12.12-4, and the EBC values applied to the outer boundary are shown in Fig. 12.12-5.

There is a matrix algebra way to enforce the requirement that all of the nodes on the boundary of the interior hole must have the same (unknown) constant value. That type of constraint is common in electrical engineering but rare in mechanical engineering, thus it is not included here. Instead, the trick of inserting a fake material having a shear modulus that is 10,000 times smaller was used. A unit angle of twist was input along with the true and fake shear moduli. The application script *field_2d_types.m* which is intended for planar scalar field solutions, was utilized to calculate the stress function and the shear stress components. The stress function value is shown with colored values and as approximate contours in Fig. 12.12-6. Figure 12.12-7 shows carpet plots over the

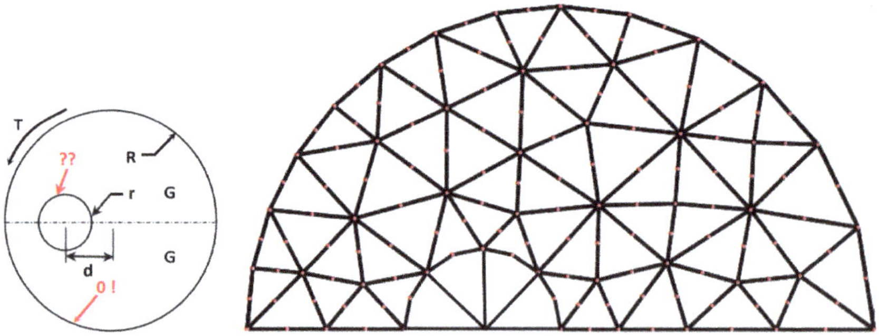

Fig. 12.12-3: Eccentric shaft and half-symmetry mesh with two-element types.

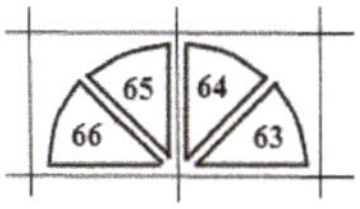

Fig. 12.12-4: The type-2 elements.

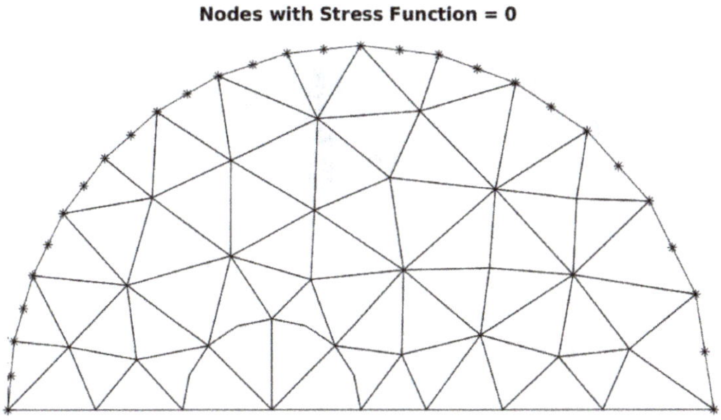

Fig. 12.12-5: Stars mark nodes with zero stress function.

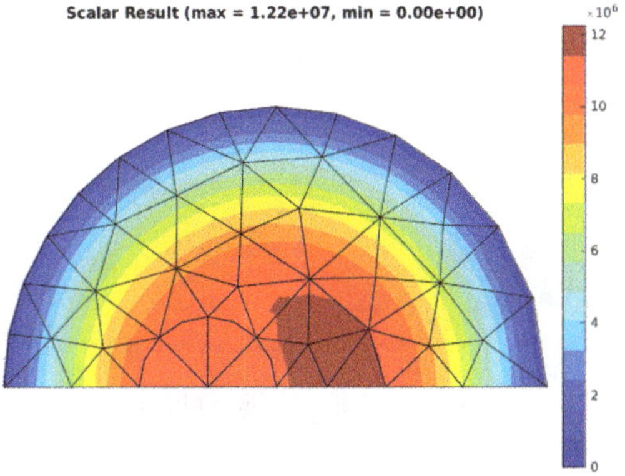

Fig. 12.12-6: Stress function.

cross-section where the vertical coordinate is the stress function value. Occasionally a graph of the results along a selected line is useful, and the stress function is plotted along the symmetry line in Fig. 12.12-8.

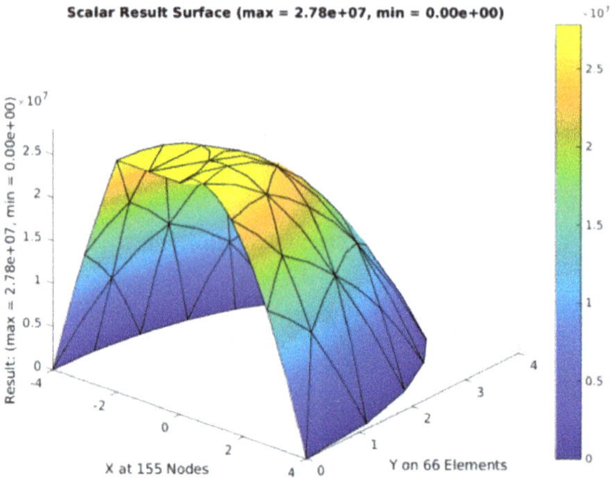

Fig. 12.12-7: Stress function carpet.

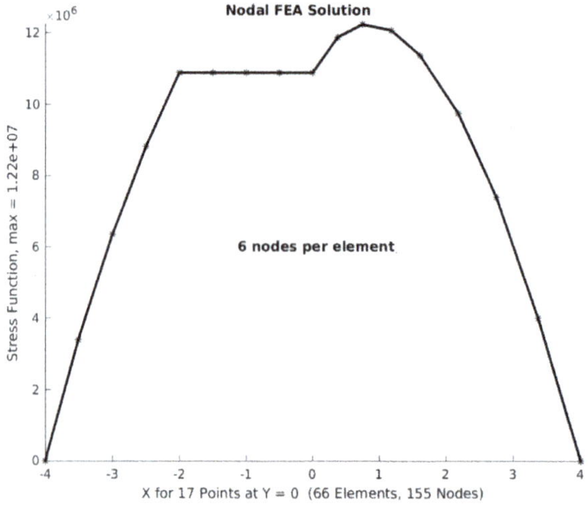

Fig. 12.12-8: Edge values.

The main quantities of interest are the magnitudes and directions of the resultant shear stress "vector" at points on the surface. The theory shows that the maximum values occur at points on the boundary. The FEA stress vector plots are most accurate at the Gauss points which usually do not fall on the boundary. However, as the number of quadrature points is increased, some of those points always get closer to the boundary. Therefore, torsion is an application

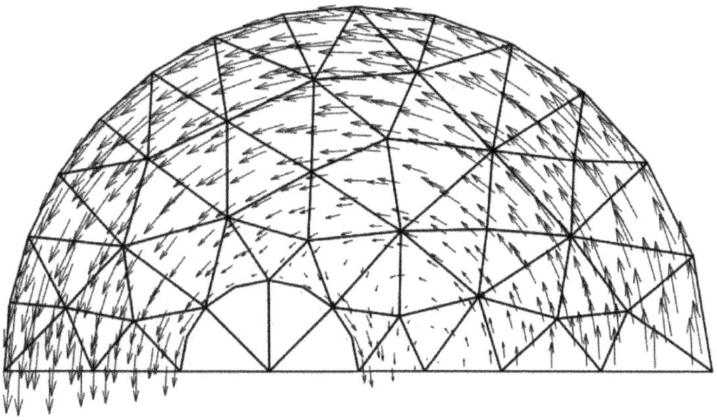

Fig. 12.12-9: Maximum shear stress distributions.

where it can be useful to increase the number of integration points beyond the number needed to integrate the element matrices, at least in a few selected elements. Here, seven quadrature points were used to enhance the stress "vector" plot even though only four points were needed to integrate the element matrices. The shear stress "vectors" for this domain are shown in Fig. 12.12-9 In this case, the topmost element in the left corner contains the maximum shear stress.

To obtain the above results and figures, the control integer *torsion* was manually set to true to activate the few alterations required for this class of solution. They include reading G_x and G_y as properties, but converting them to $k_x = 1/G_x$ and $k_y = 1/G_y$ for calculating the equivalent conduction matrix. The control integer *color* was manually set to true to produce color area and carpet plots of the stress function with *color_scalar_result.m* and *scalar_result_surface.m* which are on the left of Figs. 12.12-6 and 12.12-7. The stress function colored and contoured values show that the hole acted like an enlarged center hole. As such a hole approaches the outer radius, its effect on the shaft becomes more pronounced (as standard stress concentration tables suggest).

The standard output text files, *node_results.txt* file *node_reaction.txt*, and file *el_qp_xyz_fluxes.txt* are always saved upon completion of the analysis. The other graphs, contours, carpet plots, and resultant

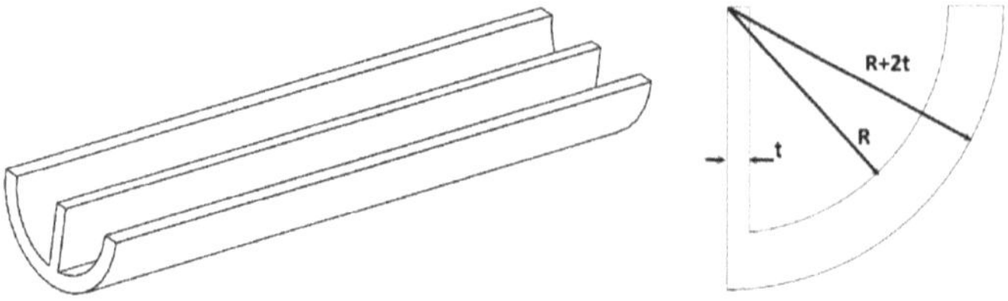

Fig. 12.12-10: A symmetric open thin-walled extrusion subject to torsion.

shear stress vectors were created after the execution was completed by selecting scripts from the supplied *Matlab_Plots* directory which only uses the data in the standard input and output files. Those scripts were the graph from the script *result_on_const_y.m*, the script (color) *contour_result_on_mesh.m*, the script *contour_qp_flux_on_mesh.m*, the script (color) *result_surface_plot.m*, and the script *hidden_result_surface.m*.

The next class of torsional analysis is that of open thin-walled members which are typical of extrusions in metal and plastic. They are called open if the section never closes back on itself, otherwise, they are called thin-walled tubes. The two types of thin-walled members have very different shear stress distributions. The current open extrusions have zero shear stress generally along the center of the thickness and maximum shear stress at the outer thicknesses, but running in opposite directions. In other words, along a line perpendicular to the thickness the shear stresses are equal but opposite relative to the line mid-point and thus form a small torque, but no net force. At free ends of a leg of the extrusion, the shear stress is tangent to the end. Figure 12.12-10 shows a typical extrusion with half-symmetry. The symmetric section was meshed with curved nine-noded quadratic Lagrange quadrilaterals with EBC values of zero on the perimeter excluding the lie of symmetry (see Fig. 12.12-11).

The *torsion* option in the application *field_2d_types.m* was utilized again to obtain the solution. It gave the stress function distribution in Fig. 12.12-12. The steep gradient at the re-entrant corner is hard to see there, but becomes apparent when graphed along the line of symmetry, and along the middle of the circular arc as shown in Fig. 12.12-13. Figure 12.12-14 shows that the maximum stress function, and thus the minimum shear stress, occurs on the symmetry line near where the centerlines of the two legs intersect. The resultant shear stress "vectors" were evaluated at each of the nine

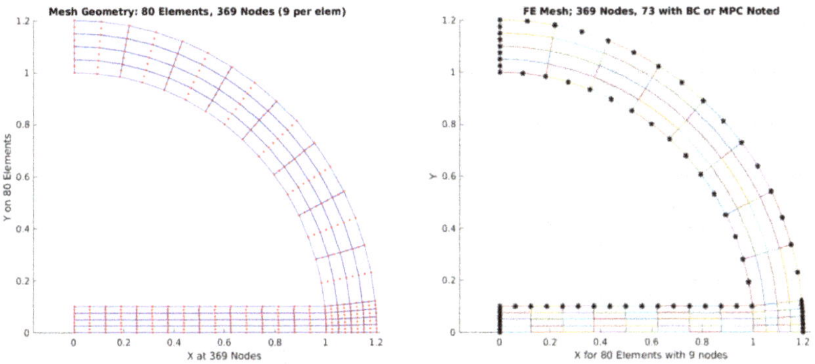

Fig. 12.12-11: Half-symmetry quadratic quadrilaterals mesh and EBC points.

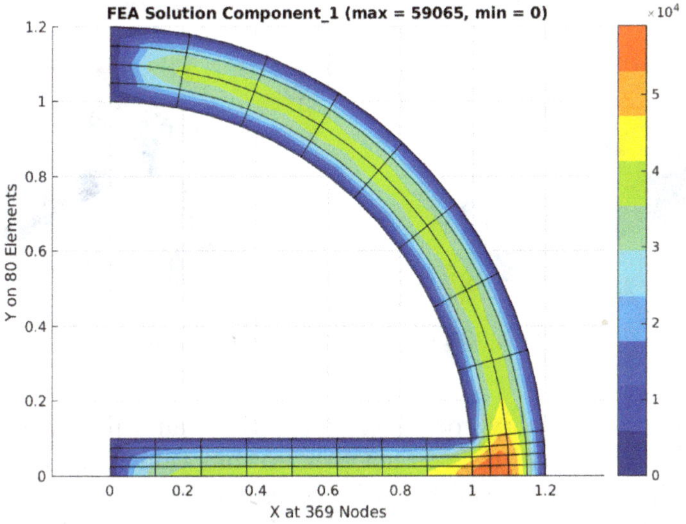

Fig. 12.12-12: Stress function colored values.

numerical integration points in each quadrilateral and are shown in Fig. 12.12-15. Along the thin arc it is easy to see that the shear stress is maximum along the perimeters but act in opposite direction on the other side perimeter.

The top right of that figure shows the shear stress approaching zero at the exterior corners, flowing parallel to the free end, and reversing direction to flow along the inner perimeter. The dashed arrow indicates the singular point at the re-entrant corner where the

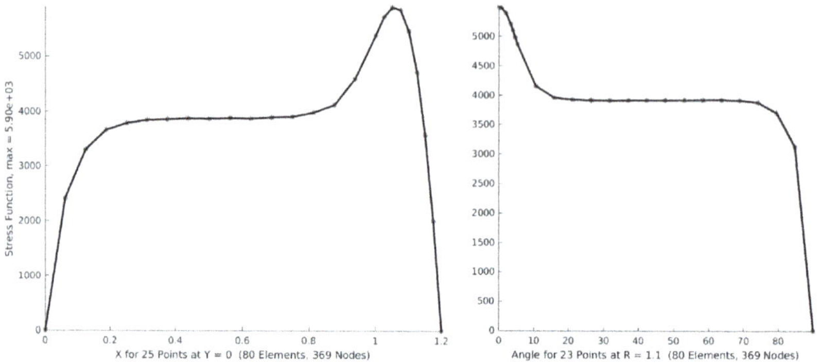

Fig. 12.12-13: Stress function values on symmetry line and arc center.

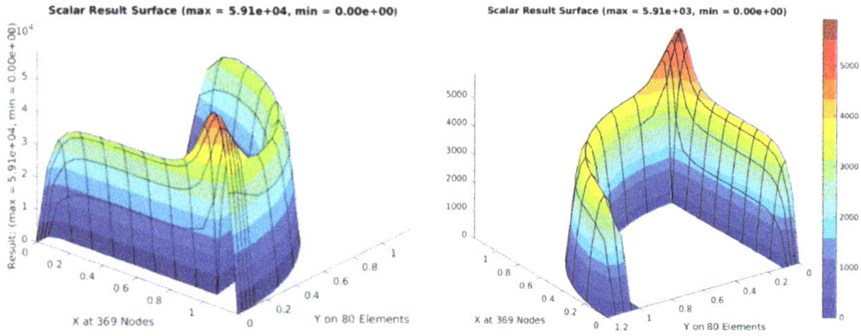

Fig. 12.12-14: Stress function carpet plot.

shear stress in theory goes to infinity. The Gauss points are offset from the corner and thus do not pick up that value. Any small fillet there will remove the mathematical singularity.

The third class of torsion analysis is where the shaft is a thin-walled closed tube. There, the shear stress "flows" around the perimeter with a constant value that is independent of the material modulus. For a tube with a constant thickness, the mechanics of materials theory gives the constant shear stress as $\tau = T/2At$ where t is the tube thickness and A is the area enclosed by the median line of the thickness of the tube. For multiple wall thicknesses, this becomes a slightly more complicated theory. For a closed tube with multiple closed cells, another mechanics theory is available to predict the shear stress flow distribution. The assumption of constant shear stress through the wall thickness is reasonable but not exact.

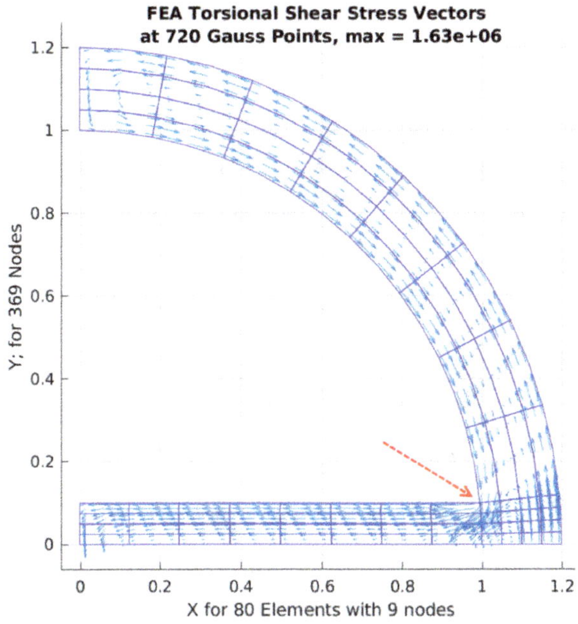

Fig. 12.12-15: Maximum shear stress directions with a singular point.

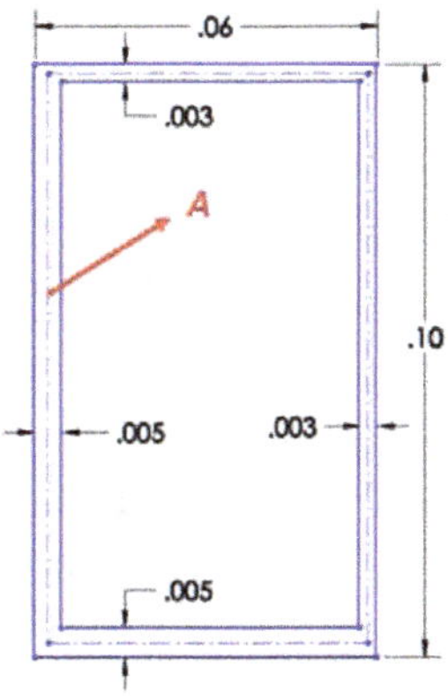

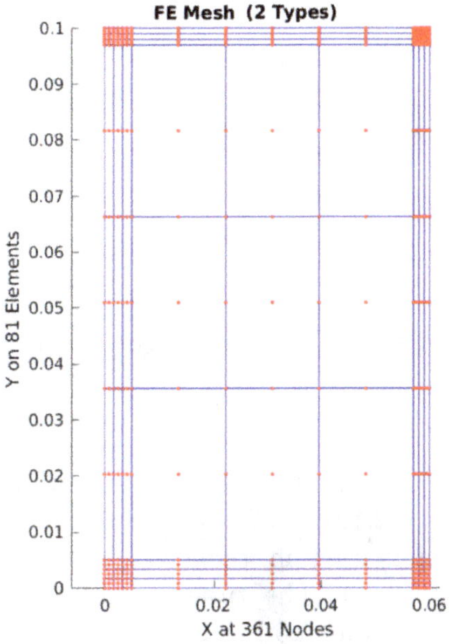

Fig. 12.12-16: A closed thin wall tube with piecewise constant thicknesses.

```
1ST NODE,   OTHER LAST DIGITS        ROW   ASSIGNED EBC FLAGS
  343       3456789012345678901       19   *******************
  324       4567890123456789012       18   *                 *
  305       5678901234567890123       17   *                 *
  286       6789012345678901234       16   *                 *
  267       7890123456789012345       15   *                 *
  248       8901234567890123456       14   *                 *
  229       9012345678901234567       13   *                 *
  210       0123456789012345678       12   *                 *
  191       1234567890123456789       11   *                 *
  172       2345678901234567890       10   *                 *
  153       3456789012345678901        9   *                 *
  134       4567890123456789012        8   *                 *
  115       5678901234567890123        7   *                 *
   96       6789012345678901234        6   *                 *
   77       7890123456789012345        5   *                 *
   58       8901234567890123456        4   *                 *
   39       9012345678901234567        3   *                 *
   20       0123456789012345678        2   *                 *
    1       1234567890123456789        1   *******************
```

Fig. 12.12-17: Compressed data for the structured tube mesh.

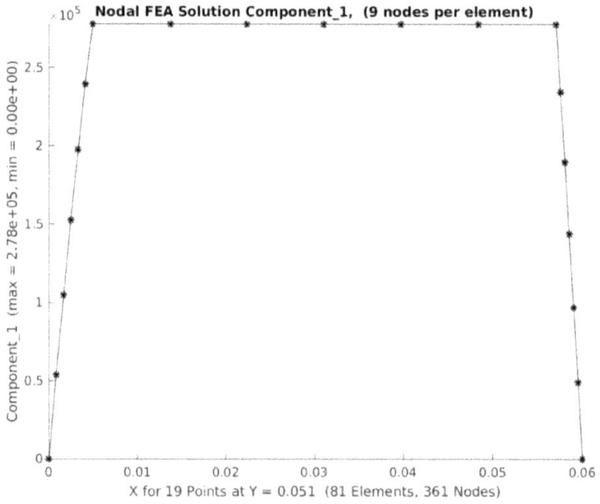

Fig. 12.12-18: The stress function values midlevel across the tube opening.

To illustrate that, consider the thin closed aluminum tube shown in Fig. 12.12-16. There the dashed centerline curve denotes the perimeter used in the elementary theory to calculate the reference area, A. The tube was modeled with a structured mesh of quadratic nine-noded quadrilateral elements, including nine fake interior elements to account for the unknown EBC value around

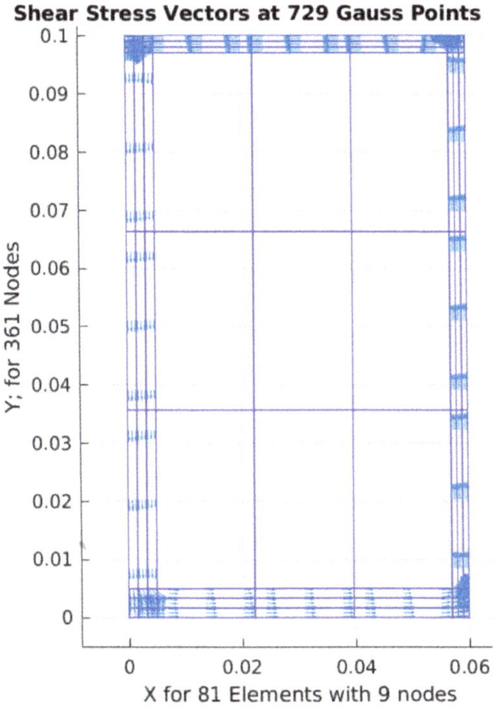

Fig. 12.12-19: Shear stress directions for the thin-walled closed tube.

the tube interior perimeter. The mesh was created with a structured mesh generator that created the condensed data summaries in Fig. 12.12-17. Again all of the nodes on the outer perimeter were assigned the EBC value of zero.

For a torque of 3,000 kPa-m, the mechanics of materials theory for this geometry predicts a constant shear stress in the 3 mm thick leg of 93.0 MPa and a value of 55.8 MPa in the walls with a thickness of 5 mm. The torsion differential equation was solved for this tube section. The graph of the stress function horizontally across the tube at the middle of the open segment is shown in Fig. 12.16-18. It shows that the value across the right wall has a nearly constant slope (shear stress value) while the section through the thicker left was a slightly changing slope. The distribution of the shear stress vectors for the full domain is in Fig. 12.12-19 and supports the reasonable assumption of approximate constant "shear flow" in each constant thickness section.

To compare to the elementary theory, the average shear stress was calculated in the elements in the middle of the vertical legs. From the lists in Fig. 12.12-18, they are elements 37, 38, and 39 in the 5 mm wall and 43, 44, and 45 in the 3 mm wall. The averages of the quadrature point values in those elements were 55.7 MPa and 99.6 MPa. Comparing to the mechanics of materials solutions of 55.8 MPa and 93.0 MPa, the simplified solution is only off by 7%.

12.13 Planar Heat Transfer

Heat transfer brings in the possibility that two or more element types can be active in a single solution. For example, a problem can have edge, area, or solid conducting elements, along with edge or face convecting elements. Likewise, source contributions can be applied at points, edges, faces, or volumes. To illustrate two such interactions, consider a simplified trapezoidal fin. It has in-plane conduction and face convection on its front and back faces (but not along the edges). The Dirichlet boundary conditions are a linear variation of a known temperature along its baseline. An approximate solution for the temperatures and convection losses is desired. Try two linear triangles or one quadrilateral element to approximate the temperatures and heat flows in the fin. The geometry and properties are shown in Fig. 12.13-1.

Choose two triangles with a conducting area and convecting face(s) and neglect the edges. Triangular elements were first published in FEA literature. The conduction matrices were given before

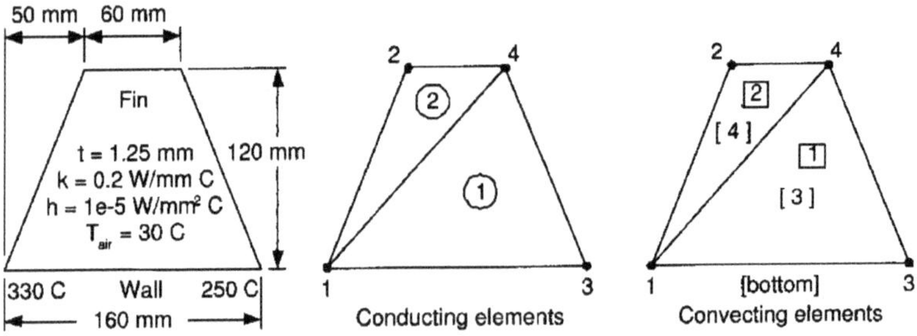

Fig. 12.13-1: A conducting and convecting fin.

as (Table 12.9).

$$\boldsymbol{S_k} = \int_\Omega \vec{\nabla}\boldsymbol{H}^{\boldsymbol{T}} \boldsymbol{\kappa}\, \vec{\nabla}\boldsymbol{H} d\Omega = \frac{t^e}{4\,A^e}\left[k_x^e \begin{bmatrix} b_1b_1 & b_1b_2 & b_1b_3 \\ b_2b_1 & b_2b_2 & b_2b_3 \\ b_3b_1 & b_3b_2 & b_3b_3 \end{bmatrix} + k_y^e \begin{bmatrix} c_1c_1 & c_1c_2 & c_1c_3 \\ c_2c_1 & c_2c_2 & c_2c_3 \\ c_3c_1 & c_3c_2 & c_3c_3 \end{bmatrix}\right],$$

$$\boldsymbol{c_q} = \frac{q^e t^e A^e}{3}\begin{Bmatrix} 1 \\ 1 \\ 1 \end{Bmatrix},$$

where the geometric constants are $a_i = x_j y_k - x_k y_j$, $b_i = y_j - y_k$, $c_i = x_k - x_j$, $ijk \to 123 \to 231 \to 312$ and where the face convection matrices are

$$\boldsymbol{S_h} = \int_\Omega \boldsymbol{H^T} h^e \boldsymbol{H}\, d\Omega = \frac{h^e\,A^e}{12}\begin{bmatrix} 2 & 1 & 1 \\ 1 & 2 & 1 \\ 1 & 1 & 2 \end{bmatrix},$$

$$\boldsymbol{c_h} = \int_\Omega \boldsymbol{H^T} h^e u_0\, d\Omega = \frac{h^e u_0 A^e}{3}\begin{Bmatrix} 1 \\ 1 \\ 1 \end{Bmatrix}.$$

Had convection along any of the edges also been active, then two smaller matrices for each such edge would also have to be assembled as

$$\boldsymbol{S_h} = \int_\Omega \boldsymbol{H^T} h^e \boldsymbol{H}\, d\Omega = \frac{h^e\, t^e L^e}{6}\begin{bmatrix} 2 & 1 \\ 1 & 2 \end{bmatrix},$$

$$\boldsymbol{c_h} = \int_\Omega \boldsymbol{H^T} h^e u_0\, d\Omega = \frac{h^e u_0 t^e L^e}{2}\begin{Bmatrix} 1 \\ 1 \end{Bmatrix}.$$

Note that since the linear triangle has a linear (two-noded) interpolation between edge end nodes, the linear Dirichlet BC on edge 1-3 of conducting element 1 and convection elements 1 and 3 is exactly satisfied once those conditions are imposed at nodes 1 and 3. These relations can be put into a single function to provide their numerical values, as in Fig. 12.13-2(a), and another script to recover convection loss across a face once all of the temperatures

```
function [S_k, S_h, c_q, c_h] = t3_conduct_convect (x, y, kx, ...
                                                    ky, h, q, u0)
% thermal conduction and convection square matrices; S_k, S_h
% thermal conduction and convection column matrices; c_h, c_q
% for orthotropic poisson equation in two dimensions with
% linear triangle, k_xx u,xx + k_yy u,yy + q = 0, conduction
% and face convection q_h = h(u - u0) (for one face)
% for a unit thickness
% x_i, x_j, x_k, y_i, y_j, y_k      % global coordinates
% a_i, a_j, a_k, b_i, b_j, b_k      % standard geometry
% c_i, c_j, c_k, two_a              % standard geometry

%   define nodal coordinates, ccw: i, j, k
x_i = x(1) ; x_j = x(2) ; x_k = x(3) ; % change notation
y_i = y(1) ; y_j = y(2) ; y_k = y(3) ; % change notation

%   geometric parameters: H_i (x,y) = (a_i + b_i*x + c_i*y)/two_a
a_i = x_j * y_k - x_k * y_j ; b_i = y_j - y_k ; c_i = x_k - x_j ;
a_j = x_k * y_i - x_i * y_k ; b_j = y_k - y_i ; c_j = x_i - x_k ;
a_k = x_i * y_j - x_j * y_i ; b_k = y_i - y_j ; c_k = x_j - x_i ;

%   calculate twice element area
two_a = a_i + a_j + a_k               ; % = b_j*c_k - b_k*c_j also

% form conduction and (one) face convection square matrices
b = [b_i, b_j, b_k] ; c = [c_i, c_j, c_k]       ; % for conduction
S_k = (kx*b'*b + ky*c'*c)/two_a/2                ; % conduction
S_h = h*two_a*[2  1  1; 1  2  1; 1  1  2]/ 24    ; % convection
c_q = q*two_a*[1; 1; 1]/6                       ; % heat generation
c_h = h*u0*two_a*[1; 1; 1]/6                   ; % convection source
% end t3_conduct_convect ==========================================
```

Fig. 12.13-2(a): Conduction and convection for a linear triangle.

```
function [q_loss] = t3_convection_loss (x, y, h, u_diff)
% convection heat loss from a convecting face is the area
% integral of the interpolated temperature difference,
% u_diff, times the convection coefficient. That is:
%          area_int [H(x,y)]'*[u_diff]* h dA
% face convection at a point q_h = h(u - u0) (for one face)

%   define nodal coordinates, ccw: i, j, k
x_i = x(1) ; x_j = x(2) ; x_k = x(3) ; % change notation
y_i = y(1) ; y_j = y(2) ; y_k = y(3) ; % change notation

%   interpolation: H_i (x,y) = (a_i + b_i*x + c_i*y)/two_a
a_i=x_j*y_k-x_k*y_j;b_i=y_j-y_k;c_i=x_k-x_j;
a_j=x_k*y_i-x_i*y_k;b_j=y_k-y_i;c_j=x_i-x_k;
a_k=x_i*y_j-x_j*y_i;b_k=y_i-y_j;c_k=x_j-x_i;

%   calculate twice element area
two_a = a_i + a_j + a_k        ; % = b_j*c_k - b_k*c_j also
H_integral = [1; 1; 1]*two_a/6      ; % integral of H(x,y)
q_loss = h*H_integral'*u_diff        ; % face heat exchange
% end t3_convection_loss ==================================
```

Fig. 12.13-2(b): Determining the convection transfer on a single convecting face.

and temperature differences are known at the nodes of the face (Fig. 12.13-2(b)). That loss, or gain, is just the post-processing of the normal heat flux, per unit area, at a point, $q_n(x,y) = h^b\left(u^b(x,y) - u_0\right)$ where the temperature, or the temperature difference, is interpolated

```
% Trapazoid fin with two convecting faces (not edges)
x = [0, 50, 160, 110]   ; % mm node coordinates
y = [0, 120, 0, 120]    ; % mm node coordinates
kx = 0.2 ; ky = 0.2     ; % W/mm C thermal conductivity
h = 1e-5                ; % W/mm^2 C convection coefficient
u0= 30                  ; % C fluid temperature
t = 1.25                ; % mm part thickness
q = 0                   ; % W/mm^3 heat generation per vol
faces = 2               ; % 0, 1, or 2 convecting faces
connect = [1  3  4; ...
           2  1  4]     ; % element connectivity
EBC_nodes = [1, 3]      ; % Dirichlet BC node locations
EBC_values = [330, 250]; % C Dirichlet values
Free = [2 4]            ; % temperatures to find

S = zeros(4, 4); c = zeros(4, 1); u = zeros(4, 1)      ; % allocate
r = zeros(4, 1)                                        ; % reactions
u(EBC_nodes) = EBC_values(:)                           ; % insert EBC

% first element
nodes = connect(1, :)                         ; % first connectivity
% unit thickness conduction, single face
[S_k, S_h, c_q, c_h] = t3_conduct_convect (x(nodes), y(nodes), ...
                                            kx, ky, h, q, u0) ;
% scale thickness, double faces
S(nodes, nodes) = t*S_k(:, :)                 ; % scale up conduction
c(nodes)        = t*c_q(:)                    ; % scale up generation
S(nodes, nodes) = S(nodes, nodes) + faces*S_h(:,:)  ; % convection
c(nodes)        = c(nodes)        + faces*c_h(:)    ; % convection

% second element
nodes = connect(2, :)                         ; % second connectivity
% unit thickness conduction, single face
[S_k, S_h, c_q, c_h] = t3_conduct_convect (x(nodes), y(nodes), ...
                                            kx, ky, h, q, u0) ;
% scale thickness, double faces
S(nodes, nodes) = S(nodes, nodes) + t*S_k(:, :);% scale conduction
c(nodes)        = c(nodes)        + t*c_q(:)   ; % scale conduction
S(nodes, nodes) = S(nodes, nodes) + faces*S_h(:,:)  ; % convection
c(nodes)        = c(nodes)        + faces*c_h(:)    ; % convection
```

Fig. 12.13-3(a): Manual assembly of the fin conduction and convection matrices.

as $u^b(r,s) = \boldsymbol{H^b}(r,s)^T \boldsymbol{u^b} - u_0 = \boldsymbol{H^b}(r,s)^T \left\{\boldsymbol{u^b} - \boldsymbol{u_0}\right\}$ so the total convection transfer at a face is

$$\text{lost} = \int_A^b q_n(x,y)\,dA = \int_A^b h^b \boldsymbol{H}^{\boldsymbol{b}}(r,s)^T dA \left\{\boldsymbol{u^b} - \boldsymbol{u_0}\right\}$$

$$= \frac{h^b A^b}{3} \begin{Bmatrix} 1 \\ 1 \\ 1 \end{Bmatrix}^T \left\{\boldsymbol{u^b} - \boldsymbol{u_0}\right\}.$$

Thus, this fin can be modeled with a main script to assemble (scatter) the two combined conduction and convection effects. The sample data and assembly phase of such a script is in Fig. 12.13-3(a); applying the Dirichlet BC, solving for the unknown

```
% Bring given Dirichlet BC to right hand side
c (Free) = c (Free) - S (Free, EBC_nodes) * u (EBC_nodes);% modify

% Now, the Free rows and columns are unique
u(Free) = S(Free, Free) \ c(Free)   ; % solve for free temperatures
fprintf ('Temperatures \n'); disp(u)

% get heat flow reactions
r(EBC_nodes) = S(EBC_nodes, :)*u(:)-c(EBC_nodes);% reaction values
fprintf ('Heat flows   \n'); disp(r)                % running gives

% recover any heat flow through face convection
if ( faces == 0 ) ; return; end                        ; % if no faces
u_diff = u(:) - u0               ; % temperature differences at faces
q_loss = 0                                          ; % initialize sum
for e = 1:2                      ; % loop over elements ===> ===> ===>
  nodes = connect (e, :)         ; % nodes on the face(s)
  [loss] = t3_convection_loss (x(nodes),y(nodes),h,u_diff(nodes));
  loss = loss * faces                           ; % loss at all faces
  fprintf ('Element %i convection loss = %g \n', e, loss); % print
  q_loss = q_loss + loss                   ; % increment total losses
end                                ; % for element e <=== <=== <===
fprintf ('Total convection loss is %g ', q_loss) ; % Running gives
% Temperatures    Heat flows  Convection losses
%    330.0000        39.9271  Element 1 convection loss = 42.763
%    205.5621              0  Element 2 convection loss = 14.9696
%    250.0000        17.8056  Total convection loss is 57.7327
%    178.1725              0
% end ; % of test_trapizoidal_fin
```

Fig. 12.13-3(b): Solving for the fin temperatures and the convection heat transfer.

temperatures, obtaining the heat flow reactions from the hot wall, and determining how the heat entering the part is convected away to the cooler air is shown in Fig. 12.13-3(b).

The solution temperatures, gradient vector components, and heat flows are summarized in Fig. 12.13-3(c). About 58 W enter the fin from the hot wall and are convected away by the cooler air over the four face elements. The constant temperature gradient components in that figure are at the centroid of each element for possible later use in a thermal stress model.

To illustrate more general field equations applied to heat transfer problems, the Matlab application *isopar_2d_fields.m* was developed to solve scalar field problems using curved numerically integrated elements. Since heat transfer problems often involve both conduction and convection, that tool allows for more than one element type in the mesh. For example, a curved conducting area element often joins with a curved line element where convection is being imposed. In that tool, a conducting triangle is the type $= 1$ element, a conducting

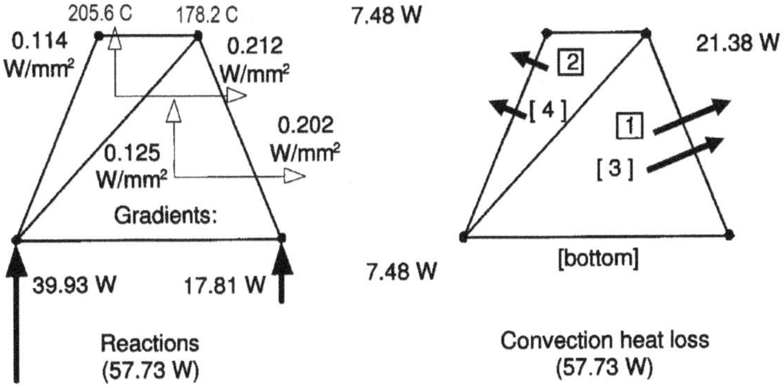

Fig. 12.13-3(c): Summary of the fin heat transfer results.

quadrilateral is the type = 2, an edge element with a entering normal flux is type = 3, and an edge element with a convection (Robin) condition is the type = 4. Most previous applications included a single type of element and the leading integer (type number) before the element connections list in the sequential file *msh_typ_nodes.txt* was always zero. Now that integer flag can be 1, 2, 3, or 4. Clearly, edge elements are connected to fewer nodes than an area element. Since Matlab requires input files to have a constant number of columns, the edge element node connections are padded with zeros until their line is the same length as that for the highest degree area element. The tool accepts any compatible set (same number of edge nodes) of area elements and line elements. There is a default set of control integers for planar studies that use numerically integrated quadratic triangles (T6). Otherwise, the user has to respond to interactive questions to set the necessary control integers for each application.

Consider the heat transfer in a circular area with a symmetric eccentric hole. The wall of the center hole is held at a high constant temperature while the outer wall convects heat to a cooler fluid. The conduction elements are curved T6 triangles which connect on the outer edge to curved L3 convection line elements. The problem domain and its half symmetry mesh are shown in Figs. 12.13-4 and 12.13-5. The mesh plots were produced by the Matlab library scripts *plot_input_2d_mesh.m* and *shrink_2d_mesh.m*. The area and line elements were created with an automatic mesh generator that populated

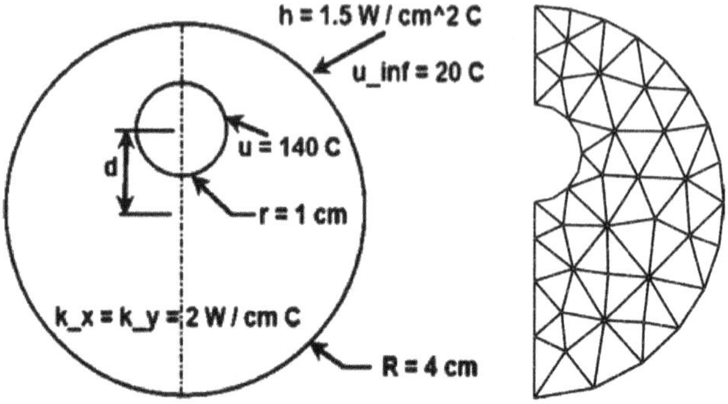

Fig. 12.13-4: Symmetric eccentric cylinder with T6 face elements and L3 line elements.

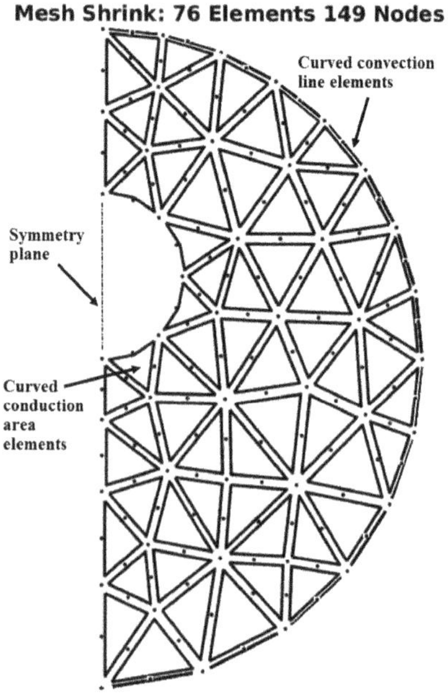

Fig. 12.13-5: A mesh of curved T6 area elements and curved L3 edge elements.

most of the standard input files with their required data. To illustrate some new flexibility, a partial listing of those files is shown in Fig. 12.13-6.

Since this application mixes different element types with different functions, some additional data are required to properly interface

```
msh_remarks.txt
"Offset cylinder test of convection", Segerlind "Applied FEA"
p. 405 cyl of r = 4 cm with hole of r= 1 cm at offset of 1 cm
k = 2 W/cm C, hole T= 140 C, convection h = 1.5 W/cm^2 C,
T_ref = 20 C. Edge value T_min = 36.1 C Heat inflow = 448.0 W
```

```
msh_bc_xyz.txt
0    0.0       -4
0    0.0       -3.37395
. . .
0    1.11941 -0.0999958
1    0.702124 0.287945
0    1.06709 0.423626
1    0.9238 0.6171
. . .
0    0.375506 3.96443
```

```
msh_typ_nodes.txt
1, 20 10 17 12 11 18
1, 13 24 33 15 23 14
. . .
1, 135 141 144 137 142 136
4, 88 69 67 0 0 0
4, 67 58 56 0 0 0
. . .
4, 110 98 96 0 0 0
4, 96 90 88 0 0 0
```

```
msh_properties.txt
2.0+00   2.0+00  0.  0.
0.       0.      0.  0.
0.       0.      0.  0.
3.0+01   1.5+00  0.  0.
```

```
msh_ebc.txt
85    1   140.
87    1   140.
. . .
66    1   140.
```

```
msh_ctrl_types.txt
6    2    4    6
8    2    4    8
3    1    3    3
3    1    3    3
```

Fig. 12.13-6: Partial input files with new element type control data.

with the supplied Matlab scripts. For every element type, the driver script needs to know the following: (1) How many nodes does it have? (Here 6 for conducting quadratic triangles, 8 for quadratic quadrilaterals, 3 for normal heat flux line elements, and 3 for heat convection line elements.) (2) In what dimension parametric space is it defined? (Here 2 for an area element and 1 for a line element.) (3) How many numerical integration points are needed to properly evaluate the matrices for that element type? (Here 4, 4, 3, 3.) (4). How many of its (solution) nodes define its geometrical shape? (Here all.) These data are stored in standard input file *msh_ctrl_types.txt.*

As mentioned before, properties data in file *msh_properties.txt* must be supplied for either every type of element (when there are fewer types than actual elements) or for every individual element. This heat transfer (scalar field analysis) tool is set up to allow four different types of elements in the same mesh. In the current application, only triangular conducting elements (type 1) and edge convection elements (type 4) are present. Thus, dummy zero values were assigned to the properties of element types 2 and 3. Since Matlab requires the same number of columns in a data file, the entries are

```
Computed Solution:
Node, 1 results per node
1     35.7995
2     43.994
. . .
149   55.5597
Max value is 140     at node 49
Min value is 35.7995 at node 1

Reactions at essential BCs
Node, DOF, Reaction Value
49 1 17.5776
. . .
118 1 20.1748
Totals = 448.0925

Element Post-processing:
El, Q_Pt, Coordinates       1, 1,  0.193605 -2.20448
El, Q_Pt, Gradient Vector   1, 1, -1.28685   19.8748
El, Q_Pt, Flux Vector       1, 1,  2.5737   -39.7496
. . .
El, Q_Pt, Coordinates      62, 4,  1.29848   3.41856
El, Q_Pt, Gradient Vector  62, 4, -12.6859  -25.7779
El, Q_Pt, Flux Vector      62, 4,  25.3718   51.5557

NOTE: skipped type 4 element number 63
. . .
NOTE: skipped type 4 element number 76

Total solution integral = 1644.86
Total domain volume     = 23.3318
```

Fig. 12.13-7: Selected output from the thermal study.

padded with zeros to match whichever element type has the most properties.

A selected portion of the optional printed output is shown in Fig. 12.13-7. After the computed temperatures are listed, the application lists the maximum and minimum temperatures and the loads at which they occur. The listed reactions are the total heat flow into (positive) the domain necessary to keep the node at its specified temperature. The total heat flow on the inner arc is about 448 W, or about 142.6 W/cm around the center hole. That heat flow is ejected through convection on the outer radius (and could be verified by post-processing the edge elements.

The partial output listing optionally includes the gradient vector and the heat flux vector, from Fourier's law, at each numerical integration point (since control integer *show_qp* was set to true). The domain volume (for a unit thickness) is also printed as a useful check.

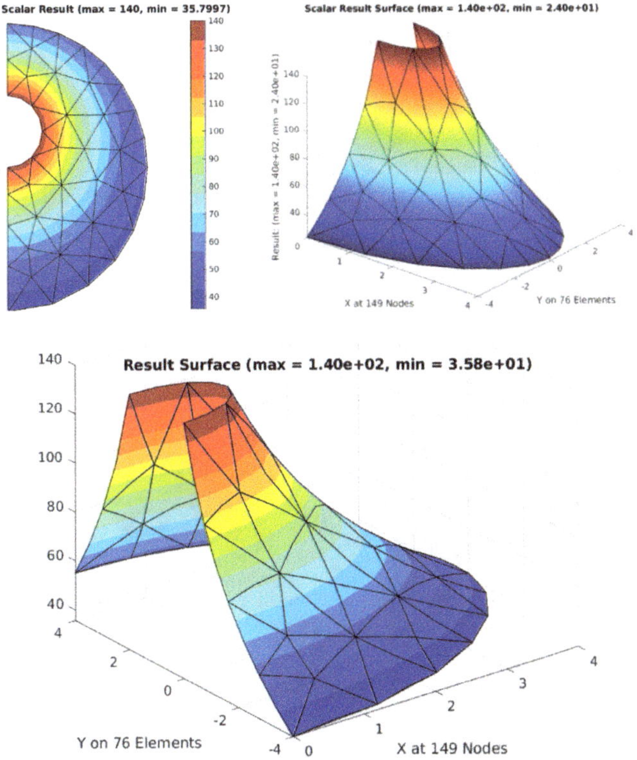

Fig. 12.13-8: Temperature values in a symmetric cylinder.

Note that the integral of the solution over the area was also given (since *integral* was true) even though it does not have physical importance in heat transfer, as it is important in other field problems. The amount of printed output can become huge and is usually suppressed by the user by setting various control integers in the driver script to false (such as *debug, echo_p, el_react, integral, show_bc, show_e, show_ebc, show_s*).

Generally, graphical presentation of the results is preferred. Two default plots are the filled colored distribution of the planar temperature (see Fig. 12.13-8) and the temperature represented vertically in a filled color surface plot. The temperature result value plots were produced by scripts *color_scalar_result.m* and *scalar_result_surface.m*, which are all called from the *field_2d_types.m* application software. When running Matlab interactively, that type of surface plot can be

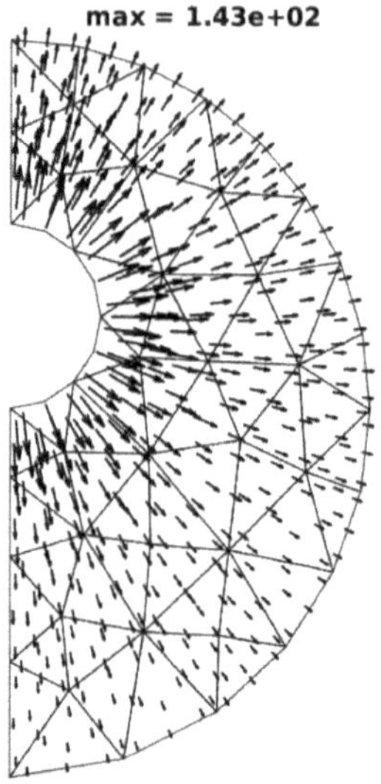

Fig. 12.13-9: Heat flux vectors in a symmetric cylinder.

rotated by changing the eye viewpoint (or manually with the Matlab *view* command).

While temperature is a scalar, the important heat flux is a vector quantity and both its vector display and its contoured magnitude should be displayed. The heat flux data are not available until all of the quadrature point results have been computed and the application closed. Those data are saved to the standard output file *el_qp_xyz_fluxes.txt*. After termination of the application the script *quiver_qp_flux_mesh.m* is run to plot the vectors using the Matlab function *quiver*, and the results are shown in Fig. 12.13-9.

Matlab provides the *contour* function. However, it expects to operate on a rectangular grid of values. When given values at unstructured node point or quadrature point locations, Matlab fits a rectangular grid over the shape and least square fits contours on that regular grid. For a finite element irregular mesh, that means that often the contours extend to regions outside the mesh boundary. Also, the least square fit values are often less accurate near rapidly changing FEA values. But its use is simpler than writing a contour script for all element types provided herein. To support many different applications of the FEA library, the author developed a directory (MatlabPlots) with hundreds of specialized plotting

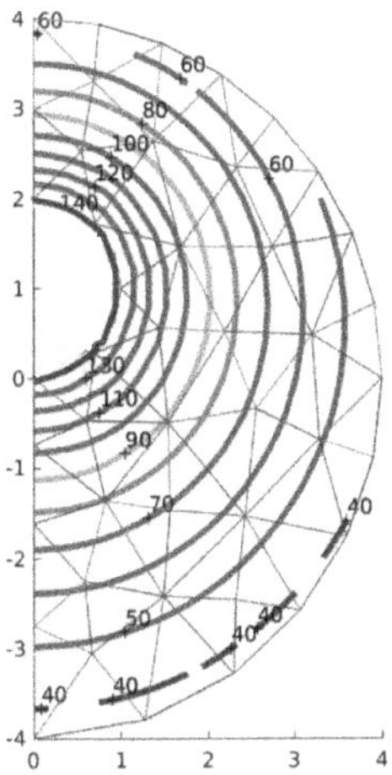

Fig. 12.13-10: Approximate contours of cylinder temperature.

```
msh_typ_nodes.txt                 msh_properties.txt    msc_ctrl_types.txt
1  85  64  82  66  65  81         2.    2.  0.  0.      6, 2, 4, 6
. . .                             0.    0.  0.  0.      8, 2, 4, 8
4 110  98  96   0   0   0         500.  0.  0.  0. <--  6, 2, 4, 6 <--
4  96  90  88   0   0   0         30.  1.5 0.0 0.0      3, 1, 3, 3
3  71  60  78  59  62  70 <--
```

Fig. 12.13-11: Data changes (arrow) to introduce an area of inward heat flux on a face.

scripts that read the standard input files and standard output files to produce a graphical output. The scripts *contour_result_on_mesh.m* and *contour_qp_flux_on_mesh.m* produced the contour plots given in Fig. 12.13-10.

It is not unusual for a planar part to have a heat source or convection region on part of its surface in addition to on its edges. The current application allows for such face elements, too. Let the previous conduction region of element 43 also have a normal heat flux of 500 W/cm^2. To include that normal heat source in the previous mesh, just append a type 3 element (77) that shares the same nodes as the conduction element (43). Only three lines change in the standard input files, as indicated in Fig. 12.13-11. The inflow heat flux element location is shown in Fig. 12.13-12 (plotted by script *color_selected_elements.m*) as lying on the face of conduction element 43. To include face convection on part or all of the planar area, it is changed in a similar fashion.

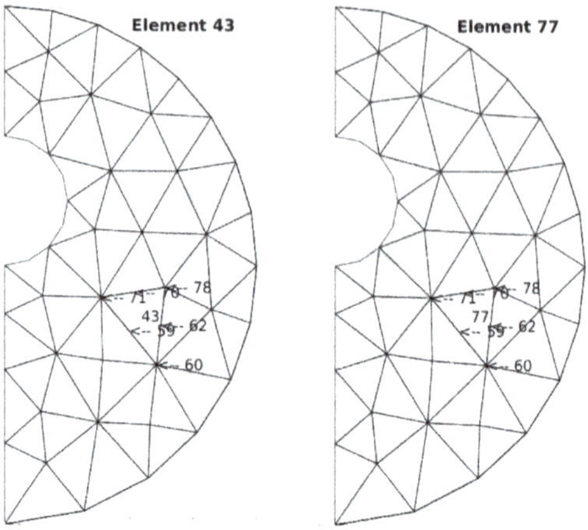

Fig. 12.13-12: Heat source face (77) shares nodes with conduction element (43).

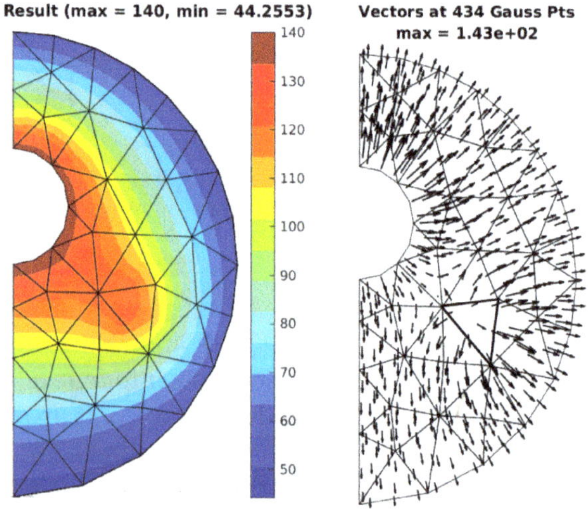

Fig. 12.13-13: New temperature (°C) and heat flux (W/m^2) from heat source (right).

That face heat flow warms up the temperature of its surrounding area and changes the overall heat flux magnitude and directions as illustrated by the approximate contours and new heat flux vectors in Fig. 12.13-13. Those figures should be compared to the prior results like Fig. 12.13-10. The change in the temperature along the symmetry plane (from script *result_on_const_x.m*) is shown in Fig. 12.13-14.

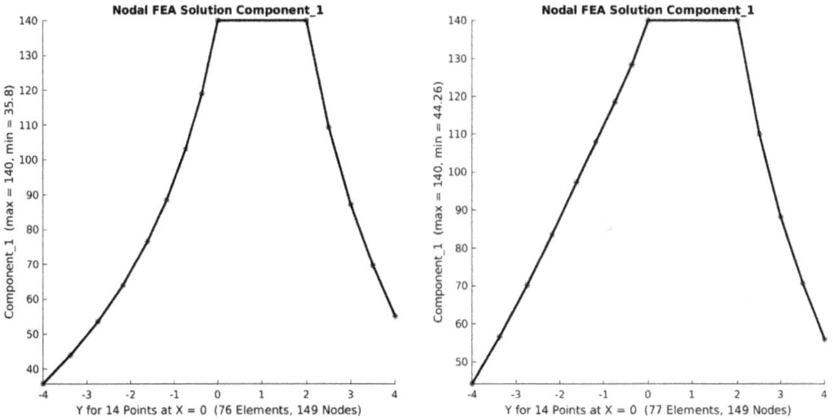

Fig. 12.13-14: Symmetry axis temperature before (left) and after normal face heat input.

Example 12.13-1 Given: The 8 × 8 cm isotropic square in Fig. 12.13-15 has an internal rate of heat generation of $Q = 6W/\text{cm}^3$. The material thermal conductivity of $k = 8\,W/\text{cm}^\circ\text{C}$. Determine the temperature distribution and reaction heat flows if the sides have a constant EBC temperature of $\theta = 5^\circ\text{C}$.

Solution: Use one-eighth symmetry, a unit thickness, and four right-angled linear triangular elements as follows. When all elements have their connectivity listed with the right-angled corner being second, all the element matrices (from Table 12.10-2) are the same with

$$\frac{k^e t^e}{4\,A^e}\begin{bmatrix} L_x^{e^2} & -L_x^{e^2} & 0 \\ -L_x^{e^2} & \left(L_x^{e^2} + L_y^{e^2}\right) & -L_y^{e^2} \\ 0 & -L_y^{e^2} & L_y^{e^2} \end{bmatrix}\begin{Bmatrix} \theta_1 \\ \theta_2 \\ \theta_3 \end{Bmatrix} = \frac{A^e t^e Q^e}{3}\begin{Bmatrix} 1 \\ 1 \\ 1 \end{Bmatrix}.$$

But here $L_x^e = L_y^e = L$, so

$$\rightarrow \frac{k^e t^e}{2}\begin{bmatrix} 1 & -1 & 0 \\ -1 & 2 & -1 \\ 0 & -1 & 1 \end{bmatrix}\begin{Bmatrix} \theta_1 \\ \theta_2 \\ \theta_3 \end{Bmatrix} = \frac{Q^e t^e L^2}{6}\begin{Bmatrix} 1 \\ 1 \\ 1 \end{Bmatrix}.$$

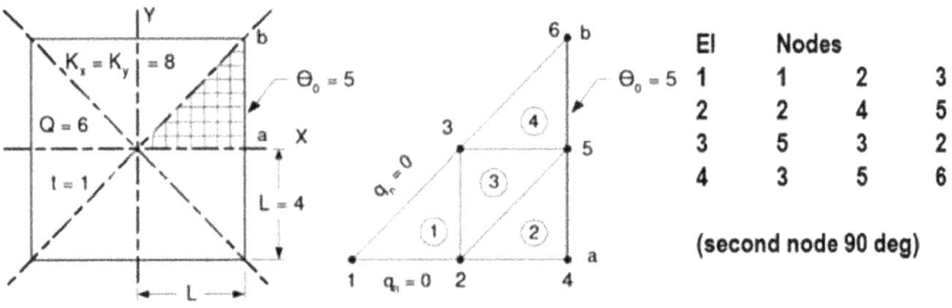

Fig. 12.13-15: One-eighth square with internal heat generation.

So numerically, all of the matrices are

$$\boldsymbol{S}^e = \begin{bmatrix} 4 & -4 & 0 \\ -4 & 8 & -4 \\ 0 & -4 & 4 \end{bmatrix} \text{W/°C and } \boldsymbol{c}^{e^T} = \begin{Bmatrix} 16 \\ 16 \\ 16 \end{Bmatrix} W.$$

Assembling the system conduction matrix gives

$$\begin{matrix} & \begin{matrix} 1 & 2 & 3 & 4 & 5 & 6 \end{matrix} & & \begin{matrix} 1 & 2 & 3 & 4 & 5 & 6 \end{matrix} \\ \boldsymbol{S} = & \begin{bmatrix} 4 & -4 & 0 & 0 & 0 & 0 \\ -4 & 8 & -4 & 0 & 0 & 0 \\ 0 & -4 & 4 & 0 & 0 & 0 \\ 0 & 0 & 0 & 0 & 0 & 0 \\ 0 & 0 & 0 & 0 & 0 & 0 \\ 0 & 0 & 0 & 0 & 0 & 0 \end{bmatrix} & + & \begin{bmatrix} 0 & 0 & 0 & 0 & 0 & 0 \\ 0 & 4 & 0 & -4 & 0 & 0 \\ 0 & 0 & 0 & 0 & 0 & 0 \\ 0 & -4 & 0 & 8 & -4 & 0 \\ 0 & 0 & 0 & -4 & 4 & 0 \\ 0 & 0 & 0 & 0 & 0 & 0 \end{bmatrix} \end{matrix}$$

$$+ \begin{bmatrix} 0 & 0 & 0 & 0 & 0 & 0 \\ 0 & 4 & -4 & 0 & 0 & 0 \\ 0 & -4 & 8 & 0 & -4 & 0 \\ 0 & 0 & 0 & 0 & 0 & 0 \\ 0 & 0 & -4 & 0 & 4 & 0 \\ 0 & 0 & 0 & 0 & 0 & 0 \end{bmatrix} + \begin{bmatrix} 0 & 0 & 0 & 0 & 0 & 0 \\ 0 & 0 & 0 & 0 & 0 & 0 \\ 0 & 0 & 4 & 0 & -4 & 0 \\ 0 & 0 & 0 & 0 & 0 & 0 \\ 0 & 0 & -4 & 0 & 8 & -4 \\ 0 & 0 & 0 & 0 & -4 & 4 \end{bmatrix}.$$

So

$$\boldsymbol{S} = \begin{bmatrix} 4 & -4 & 0 & 0 & 0 & 0 \\ -4 & (8+4+4) & (-4-4) & -4 & 0 & 0 \\ 0 & (-4-4) & (4+8+4) & 0 & (-4-4) & 0 \\ 0 & -4 & 0 & 8 & -4 & 0 \\ 0 & 0 & (-4-4) & -4 & (4+4+8) & -4 \\ 0 & 0 & 0 & 0 & -4 & 4 \end{bmatrix}$$

$$\boldsymbol{S} = \begin{bmatrix} 4 & -4 & 0 & 0 & 0 & 0 \\ -4 & 16 & -8 & -4 & 0 & 0 \\ 0 & -8 & 16 & 0 & -8 & 0 \\ 0 & -4 & 0 & 8 & -4 & 0 \\ 0 & 0 & -8 & -4 & 16 & -4 \\ 0 & 0 & 0 & 0 & -4 & 4 \end{bmatrix} \frac{W}{{}^\circ\mathrm{C}},$$

and assembling the heat source vectors gives

$$\boldsymbol{c_Q} = \begin{Bmatrix} 4 \\ 4 \\ 4 \\ 0 \\ 0 \\ 0 \end{Bmatrix} + \begin{Bmatrix} 0 \\ 4 \\ 0 \\ 4 \\ 4 \\ 0 \end{Bmatrix} + \begin{Bmatrix} 0 \\ 4 \\ 4 \\ 0 \\ 4 \\ 0 \end{Bmatrix} + \begin{Bmatrix} 0 \\ 0 \\ 4 \\ 0 \\ 4 \\ 4 \end{Bmatrix} = \begin{Bmatrix} 4 \\ 12 \\ 12 \\ 4 \\ 12 \\ 4 \end{Bmatrix} W,$$ and the reaction

terms are $$\mathbf{c_{NBC}} = \begin{Bmatrix} 0 \\ 0 \\ 0 \\ q_4 \\ q_5 \\ q_6 \end{Bmatrix} W.$$

The first three rows and columns are the independent ones, and columns 4, 5, and 6 are multiplied by the EBC value (5) and subtracted from the right-hand side to give

$$\mathbf{c_{EBC}} = -5\begin{Bmatrix} 0 & 0 & 0 \\ -4 + & 0 & +0 \\ 0 & -8 & 0 \end{Bmatrix} = \begin{Bmatrix} 0 \\ 20 \\ 40 \end{Bmatrix} W.$$

So the unique system equations for the unknown temperatures are from the first three rows and columns:

$$\begin{bmatrix} 4 & -4 & 0 \\ -4 & 16 & -8 \\ 0 & -8 & 16 \end{bmatrix}\begin{Bmatrix} \theta_1 \\ \theta_2 \\ \theta_3 \end{Bmatrix} = \begin{Bmatrix} 4 \\ 12 \\ 12 \end{Bmatrix} + \begin{Bmatrix} 0 \\ 20 \\ 40 \end{Bmatrix}, \rightarrow \begin{Bmatrix} \theta_1 \\ \theta_2 \\ \theta_3 \end{Bmatrix} = \begin{Bmatrix} 8.750 \\ 7.750 \\ 7.125 \end{Bmatrix} {}^\circ\mathrm{C}.$$

The nodal reactions (outward heat flows) are obtained from the last three rows of the system now that all temperatures are known:

$$\begin{bmatrix} 0 & -4 & 0 & 8 & -4 & 0 \\ 0 & 0 & -8 & -4 & 16 & -4 \\ 0 & 0 & 0 & 0 & -4 & 4 \end{bmatrix}\begin{Bmatrix} 8.750 \\ 7.750 \\ 7.125 \\ 5 \\ 5 \\ 5 \end{Bmatrix} = \begin{Bmatrix} 4 \\ 12 \\ 4 \end{Bmatrix} + \begin{Bmatrix} q_4 \\ q_5 \\ q_6 \end{Bmatrix}, \quad \begin{Bmatrix} q_4 \\ q_5 \\ q_6 \end{Bmatrix}$$

$$= \begin{Bmatrix} -15 \\ -29 \\ -4 \end{Bmatrix} W.$$

The sum of the reactions, $-48W$, equals the heat generated in the one-eighth model.

Example 12.13-2 Given: For the previous temperature calculation of Example 12.13-1, determine the gradient vectors and heat flux vectors in each element.

Solution: To determine the heat flux vectors, it is necessary to post-process each element. The post-processing steps are the same as in the prior one-dimensional examples; just the array sizes are bigger. This requires a loop over each element where the local solution results, local node coordinates, and element properties are gathered. The locations must be selected for doing the calculations. The guideline is to select the quadrature locations that would integrate the element conduction matrix. Here, that would be a one-point rule, $(r = 1/3,\ s = 1/3)$, which coincides with the geometric centroid of the element. For the linear elements, the temperature gradient, and thus the heat flux, are the same everywhere in an element. That means that the heat flux is discontinuous at the element interfaces (as it is for all C^0 elements). To obtain accurate results for the heat flux, a very fine mesh must be utilized.

For the first element, the element's node connections are [1 2 3], and the gathered temperatures are $\boldsymbol{\theta}^{e^T} = [8.750 \quad 7.750 \quad 7.125]$. At the first integration point $q = 1$ the interpolated physical coordinates are $x_q = \begin{bmatrix}1/3 & 1/3 & 1/3\end{bmatrix} \boldsymbol{x}^e = 1.333$. Likewise, $y_q = 0.667$. The gradient of the solution is $\boldsymbol{\nabla}\theta = \boldsymbol{B}^e(r_q, s_q)\boldsymbol{\theta}^e$ and at a point is

$$\boldsymbol{\nabla}\theta = \begin{Bmatrix} \partial\theta/\partial x \\ \partial\theta/\partial y \end{Bmatrix} = \frac{1}{2}\begin{bmatrix} -1 & 1 & 0 \\ -1 & 0 & 1 \end{bmatrix}\boldsymbol{\theta}^e = \begin{Bmatrix} -0.5000 \\ -0.8125 \end{Bmatrix} \frac{{}^\circ\mathrm{C}}{\mathrm{cm}}.$$

The heat flux at the point is defined by the Fourier Law $\vec{q} = \boldsymbol{q} = -\boldsymbol{\kappa}\boldsymbol{\nabla}\theta$, and here the constitutive matrix is diagonal with $k = 8\,W/\mathrm{cm}\,{}^\circ\mathrm{C}$ values. The heat flux vector is

$$\boldsymbol{q} = \begin{Bmatrix} 4.0000 \\ 6.5000 \end{Bmatrix} \frac{\mathrm{W}}{\mathrm{cm}^2}.$$

Example 12.13-3 Given: The conducting square in Fig. 12.13-16 has two adjacent edges subject to an inflow heat flux of $q_n = 2\,\mathrm{W/cm}^2$. The other two edges are held at constant temperature. Approximate the temperature distribution estimate using a single element.

Solution: For the conduction region, select a four-noded bilinear rectangle, with the nodes numbered CCW. For each NBC, select a compatible line element with two nodes. In this case, the line element connections are padded with zeros because Matlab requires all

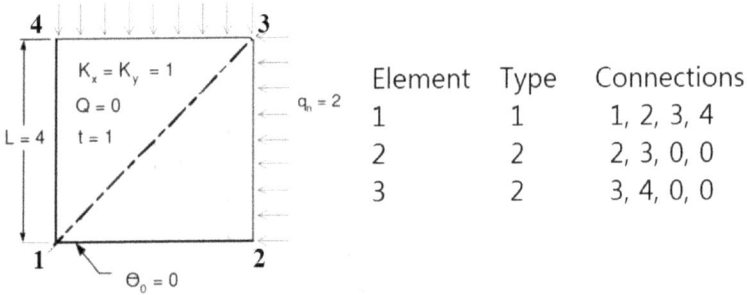

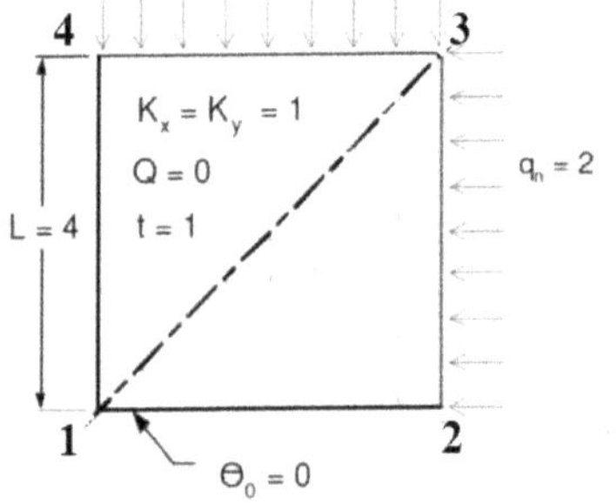

Element	Type	Connections
1	1	1, 2, 3, 4
2	2	2, 3, 0, 0
3	2	3, 4, 0, 0

Fig. 12.13-16: A square with two EBC and two NBC edges.

read arrays to have a constant number of columns. For general two-dimensional field problems, it is allowed to mix triangular (Type 1) and quadrilateral (Type 2) area conduction elements. Both of those have lines as their edges. A line can be subject to a Neumann BC with a known normal flux (Type 3) or to a Mixed NBC (Type 4). The conduction matrix is known (from Table 12.10-5) as follows:

$$\boldsymbol{S}^e = \int_A^e \boldsymbol{B}^{e^T} \boldsymbol{\kappa}^e \boldsymbol{B}^e \, dA = \frac{k_x^e \, t^e L_y^e}{6 \, L_x^e} \begin{bmatrix} 2 & -2 & -1 & 1 \\ -2 & 2 & 1 & -1 \\ -1 & 1 & 2 & -2 \\ 1 & -1 & -2 & 2 \end{bmatrix}$$

$$+ \frac{k_y^e \, t^e L_x^e}{6 \, L_y^e} \begin{bmatrix} 2 & 1 & -1 & -2 \\ 1 & 2 & -2 & -1 \\ -1 & -2 & 2 & 1 \\ -2 & -1 & 1 & 2 \end{bmatrix},$$

and for an isotropic material $k = K_x = K_y = 1W/\text{cm}\,^\circ\text{C}$ on a square $L = L_x = L_y = 4\,\text{cm}$ it simplifies to

$$\boldsymbol{S}^e = \frac{k \, t^e}{6} \begin{bmatrix} 4 & -1 & -2 & -1 \\ -1 & 4 & -1 & -2 \\ -2 & -1 & 4 & -1 \\ -1 & -2 & -1 & 4 \end{bmatrix} W/^\circ\text{C}.$$

On an edge with an NBC of the type that $-k\,\partial\Theta/\partial n = q_n$, the boundary source vector is

$$\boldsymbol{c}_{\boldsymbol{q}}^{\boldsymbol{b}} = \int_{L^b} \boldsymbol{H}^{\boldsymbol{b}^T}\, q_n\, t^b dL.$$

On the edge, the four area interpolations $\boldsymbol{H}^{\boldsymbol{e}}$ reduce to the two-line interpolations $\boldsymbol{H}^{\boldsymbol{b}}$:

$$\boldsymbol{H}^{\boldsymbol{e}}\,(r = 1,\, s) \Longrightarrow \boldsymbol{H}^{\boldsymbol{b}}\,(s) = \begin{Bmatrix} 1 - s \\ s \end{Bmatrix}.$$

That is the same integral developed previously for line elements with a constant source, namely

$$\boldsymbol{c}_{\boldsymbol{q}}^{\boldsymbol{b}} = \frac{q_n\, L^b\, t^b}{2} \begin{Bmatrix} 1 \\ 1 \end{Bmatrix} W$$

where the $L^b\, t^b$ is the area over which the heat flux per unit area enters the domain. Here, the thickness (normal to the area) of the edge is taken as unity. The system equations are, like before,

$$\boldsymbol{S}\,\boldsymbol{\Theta} = \boldsymbol{c}_{\mathbf{NBC}} + \boldsymbol{c}_{\mathbf{EBC}}.$$

The flux resultant, $\boldsymbol{c}_{\boldsymbol{q}}^{\boldsymbol{b}}$, over the two line elements are assembled to give the resultant NBC source

$$\boldsymbol{c}_{\mathbf{NBC}} = \frac{2\,(4)\,1}{2} \begin{Bmatrix} 0 \\ 1 \\ 1+1 \\ 1 \end{Bmatrix} W.$$

The sum of those coefficients shows that 16 units of heat entered the body. The reaction entries are not known until the Dirichlet BC DOFs are identified. Here, nodes 1, 2, and 4 have EBCs of $\Theta = 0°\text{C}$, so $\boldsymbol{c}_{\mathbf{EBC}}^T = \begin{bmatrix} R_1 & R_2 & 0 & R_4 \end{bmatrix}$ are the reaction heat flows to be determined. Thus,

$$\frac{1(4)}{6(4)}\begin{bmatrix} 4 & -1 & -2 & -1 \\ -1 & 4 & -1 & -2 \\ -2 & -1 & 4 & -1 \\ -1 & -2 & -1 & 4 \end{bmatrix}\begin{Bmatrix} \Theta_1 = 0 \\ \Theta_2 = 0 \\ \Theta_3 \\ \Theta_4 = 0 \end{Bmatrix} = 4\begin{Bmatrix} 0 \\ 1 \\ 2 \\ 1 \end{Bmatrix} + \begin{Bmatrix} R_1 \\ R_2 \\ 0 \\ R_4 \end{Bmatrix}.$$

Only row three is independent for finding the temperature. Moving the EBC terms to the right side

$$\frac{1}{6}[4]\{\Theta_3\} = \{8\} + \{0\} - \Theta_1\left\{\frac{-2}{6}\right\} - \Theta_2\left\{\frac{-1}{6}\right\} - \Theta_4\left\{\frac{-1}{6}\right\},$$

$$\Theta_3 = 12°\text{C}.$$

Now use the remaining rows to determine the reactions:

$$\frac{1(4)}{6(4)}\begin{bmatrix} 4 & -1 & -2 & -1 \\ -1 & 4 & -1 & -2 \\ -1 & -2 & -1 & 4 \end{bmatrix}\frac{W}{°\mathbf{C}}\begin{Bmatrix} 0 \\ 0 \\ 12 \\ 0 \end{Bmatrix}°\mathbf{C} = 4\begin{Bmatrix} 0 \\ 1 \\ 1 \end{Bmatrix}W + \begin{Bmatrix} R_1 \\ R_2 \\ R_4 \end{Bmatrix},$$

$$\begin{Bmatrix} R_1 \\ R_2 \\ R_4 \end{Bmatrix} = -\begin{Bmatrix} 4 \\ 6 \\ 6 \end{Bmatrix}W.$$

The sum of the reactions shows 16 W flowed out of the body at the Dirichlet BCs in order to balance the inflow.

Example 12.13-4 Given: Graph the previous temperature results in Example 12.13-3 along the diagonal 1-3.

Solution: First, the interior temperature values must be found. Of course, that is done by interpolating between the know temperatures. In unit coordinates $\Theta(r,\ s) = \boldsymbol{H}(r,\ s)\,\boldsymbol{\Theta}^e$. From the summary or Matlab interpolation scripts, the Q4 quadrilateral element interpolations are $\boldsymbol{H}(r,s) = [(1-r-s+rs)(r-rs)(rs)(s-rs)] = [H_1\ \ H_2\ \ H_3\ \ H_4]$. However, only Θ_3 is not zero so the temperature surface is approximated as $\Theta(r,\ s) = H_3\Theta_3 = rs\Theta_3 = 12\,r\,s$, which can be easily contoured by Matlab (the surface is a hyperbolic paraboloid). The diagonal line is given by $s = r$, so in that direction $\Theta_{\text{diag}} = 12r^2$. Thus the approximate temperature estimate increases quadratically from corner 1 to corner 3.

Example 12.13-5 Given: Let the conducting square in Fig. 12.13-16 have two adjacent edges subject to a convection heat flux of $q_n = -h\,A(u - u_\infty)\,W/\text{cm}^2$. Where $A = t^b L^b$ is the boundary surface area subjected to the convection along an edge. Develop the convection matrices for: (a) a straight edge and (b) a curved edge.

Solution: The matrix definition for a known normal heat flow (as it appears in the matrix form) changes to

$$\boldsymbol{c}_q^b = \int_\Gamma^b \boldsymbol{H}^{b^T}\, q_n\,(t^b d\Gamma) \rightarrow \boldsymbol{I}_h^b$$

$$= \int_\Gamma^b \boldsymbol{H}^{b^T}\left[-h\,A(\boldsymbol{H}^b\boldsymbol{\Theta}^b - \theta_\infty)\right]\left(t^b\frac{dL}{d\Gamma}d\Gamma\right) \rightarrow -\boldsymbol{S}_h^b\,\boldsymbol{\Theta}^b + \boldsymbol{c}_h^b$$

$$\boldsymbol{S}_h^b = \int_\Gamma^b \boldsymbol{H}^{b^T} h^b\, \boldsymbol{H}^b\left(t^b\frac{dL}{d\Gamma}d\Gamma\right) \text{ and } \boldsymbol{c}_h^b = \int_\Gamma^b \boldsymbol{H}^{b^T}\, h^b\theta_\infty\left(t^b\frac{dL}{d\Gamma}d\Gamma\right).$$

(a) For a straight-sided boundary with equal node spacing in unit coordinates, these become

$$\boldsymbol{S}_h^b = \int_0^1 \boldsymbol{H}^{b^T} h^b \boldsymbol{H}^b (t^b L^b d\mathrm{r}) \quad \boldsymbol{c}_h^b = \int_0^1 \boldsymbol{H}^{b^T} h^b \theta_\infty (t^b L^b d\mathrm{r}).$$

For the above two-noded linear edge, with constant coefficients they are (see Example 8.4-1):

$$\boldsymbol{S}_h^b = \frac{h^b t^b L^b}{6}\begin{bmatrix} 2 & 1 \\ 1 & 2 \end{bmatrix} \mathrm{W/^\circ C} \text{ and } \boldsymbol{c}_h^b = \frac{h^b \theta_\infty t^b L^b}{2}\begin{Bmatrix} 1 \\ 1 \end{Bmatrix} W.$$

(b) For a curved edge in two-dimensional space, the top row of the Jacobian matrix (the tangent vector components) gives the differential geometry relation that $\frac{dL}{dr} = \sqrt{\left(\frac{dx}{dr}\right)^2 + \left(\frac{dy}{dr}\right)^2}$, which generally requires numerical integration to make the convection source term

$$c_h^b = \int_0^1 \boldsymbol{H}^{b^T} h^b \theta_\infty t^b \sqrt{\left(\frac{dx}{dr}\right)^2 + \left(\frac{dy}{dr}\right)^2} dr$$

$$= \sum_{q=1}^{n_q} \boldsymbol{H}^{b^T}(r_q) h^b t^b \sqrt{\left(\frac{dx(r_q)}{dr}\right)^2 + \left(\frac{dy(r_q)}{dr}\right)^2} w_q,$$

and the boundary convection matrix

$$\boldsymbol{S}_h^b = \sum_{q=1}^{n_q} \boldsymbol{H}^{b^T}(r_q) h^b \theta_\infty t^b \boldsymbol{H}^b(r_q) \sqrt{\left(\frac{dx(r_q)}{dr}\right)^2 + \left(\frac{dy(r_q)}{dr}\right)^2} w_q.$$

Since the convection square matrix is post-multiplied by the unknown temperatures, it must be taken to the LHS and added to the conduction square matrix: $(\boldsymbol{S_k} + \boldsymbol{S_h})\,\boldsymbol{\Theta} = \boldsymbol{c}_{\mathbf{NBC}} + \boldsymbol{c_h}$.

12.14 Axisymmetric Fields

The governing equation, (12.2-2) can be transformed into cylindrical coordinates of (R, θ, Z). The gradient vector components are

$$\boldsymbol{\nabla} u = \begin{bmatrix} \frac{\partial u}{\partial R} & \frac{1}{r}\frac{\partial u}{\partial \theta} & \frac{\partial u}{\partial Z} \end{bmatrix}^{\boldsymbol{T}}, \tag{12.14-1}$$

and Fourier's Law for the heat flux vector remains the same. The diffusion term in (12.1-1) becomes

$$\boldsymbol{\nabla}\left([\boldsymbol{\kappa}]\,\boldsymbol{\nabla}^{\boldsymbol{T}} u\,(\mathrm{R}, \theta, Z, \tau)\right)$$
$$= \frac{1}{R}\frac{\partial}{\partial R}\left(R\kappa_{RR}\frac{\partial u}{\partial R}\right) + \frac{1}{R^2}\frac{\partial}{\partial \theta}\left(\kappa_{\theta\theta}\frac{\partial u}{\partial \theta}\right) + \frac{\partial}{\partial z}\left(\kappa_{zz}\frac{\partial u}{\partial Z}\right)$$

for an orthotropic material, and a differential volume is $dV = R\,dR\,d\theta\,dZ$. Then the solid is a body of revolution and the source terms and boundary conditions are independent of the angular position, θ, then $\partial/\partial\theta = 0$ and the problem becomes a two-dimensional axisymmetric study. For a model PDE of the form

$$\frac{1}{R}\frac{\partial}{\partial R}\left(R\,k_R\frac{\partial u}{\partial R}\right)+\frac{\partial}{\partial Z}\left(k_Z\frac{\partial u}{\partial Z}\right)+a\,u(R,\,Z)+Q\,(R,\,Z)=0$$

multiplying by the radius gives

$$\frac{\partial}{\partial R}\left(\{R\,k_R\}\frac{\partial u}{\partial R}\right)+\frac{\partial}{\partial Z}\left(\{Rk_Z\}\frac{\partial u}{\partial Z}\right)+\{R\,a\}\,u\,(R,\,Z)$$
$$+\{R\,Q\,(R,\,Z)=0. \qquad (12.14\text{-}2)$$

Comparing to the planar PDE

$$\frac{\partial}{\partial x}\left(k_x\frac{\partial u}{\partial x}\right)+\frac{\partial}{\partial y}\left(k_y\frac{\partial u}{\partial y}\right)+a\,u+Q\,(x,\,y)=0,$$

the axisymmetric model can be viewed as a planar model where the constant thickness form

$$I=\int_A u\,(x,\,y)\left[\frac{\partial}{\partial x}\left(k_x\frac{\partial u}{\partial x}\right)+\frac{\partial}{\partial y}\left(k_y\frac{\partial u}{\partial y}\right)+a\,(x,y)\,u+Q\,(x,\,y)\right]$$
$$t\,(x,\,y)\,dA=0$$

is simply replaced by the variable thickness of the volume of revolution, $t\,(x,y)=2\pi\,R$ to give

$$I=\int_A u\,(R,\,Z)$$
$$\left[\frac{\partial}{\partial R}\left(k_R\frac{\partial u}{\partial R}\right)+\frac{\partial}{\partial Z}\left(k_Z\frac{\partial u}{\partial Z}\right)+a\,(R,Z)\;u+Q\,(R,Z)\right]2\pi\,R\,dA=0. \qquad (12.14\text{-}3)$$

In other words, the planar analysis program can have a control integer, say *axisym*, which switches the evaluation of all of the element matrices to an axisymmetric analysis by branching to utilize the variable thickness (circumference) at every numerical integration point. This means that the prior integral matrix definitions are all simply multiplied by $2\pi\,R$, which usually means that the number of quadrature points must be increased by 1. In practice, it is inefficient to multiply by 2π millions of times while doing the numerical integration over a complicated mesh and then having them all cancel out after assembly of the system. For example, the only change in the source vector term, $\boldsymbol{c^e_Q}$, due to the volumetric rate of heat generation, Q, is

$$\boldsymbol{c}^e_Q \equiv \int_{\Omega^e} \boldsymbol{H}^{e^T} Q^e \, d\Omega = \int_{\mathrm{A}}^{e} \boldsymbol{H}^{e^T} Q^e \, R \, \mathrm{dA}. \tag{12.14-4}$$

Likewise, the only change from the two-dimensional diffusion matrix to the axisymmetric case (per radian) is including the radial position when conducting the numerical integration and increasing the number of quadrature points:

$$\boldsymbol{S}^e_\kappa = \int_{\Omega^e} \boldsymbol{B}^{e^T} \boldsymbol{\kappa}^e \boldsymbol{B}^e \, d\Omega = \int_{\mathrm{A}}^{e} \boldsymbol{B}^{e^T} \boldsymbol{\kappa}^e \boldsymbol{B}^e \, R \, d\mathrm{A}. \tag{12.14-5}$$

12.15 Three-Dimensional Fields

All of the planar problems discussed above are easily extended to three dimensions, and the supplied Matlab scripts will execute such problems just by changing the number of physical space dimensions to three ($n_s = 3$), utilizing the eight-node hexahedral (brick) element by setting the parametric element space to three and the number of nodes to eight ($n_p = 3$, $n_n = 8$), and selecting the correct number of integration points, which for brick elements is usually $2^3 = 8$ but maybe $3^3 = 27$. The size of the constitutive matrix, $\boldsymbol{E^e}$, and the operator matrix, $\boldsymbol{B^e}$, must be increased to three ($n_r = 3$) by adding

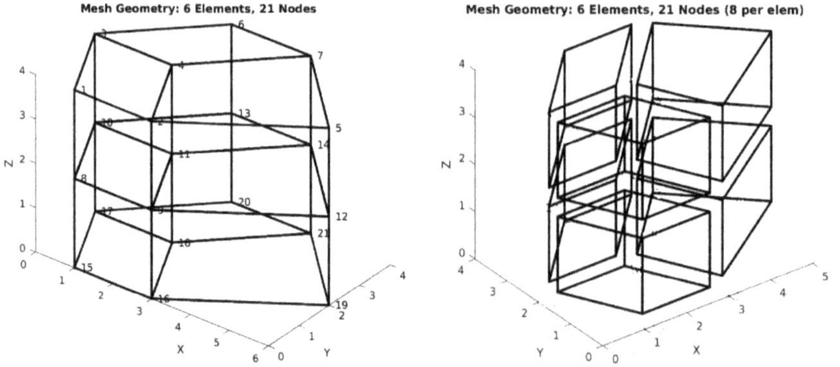

Fig. 12.15-1: Wireframe mesh for three-dimensional Poisson equation patch test.

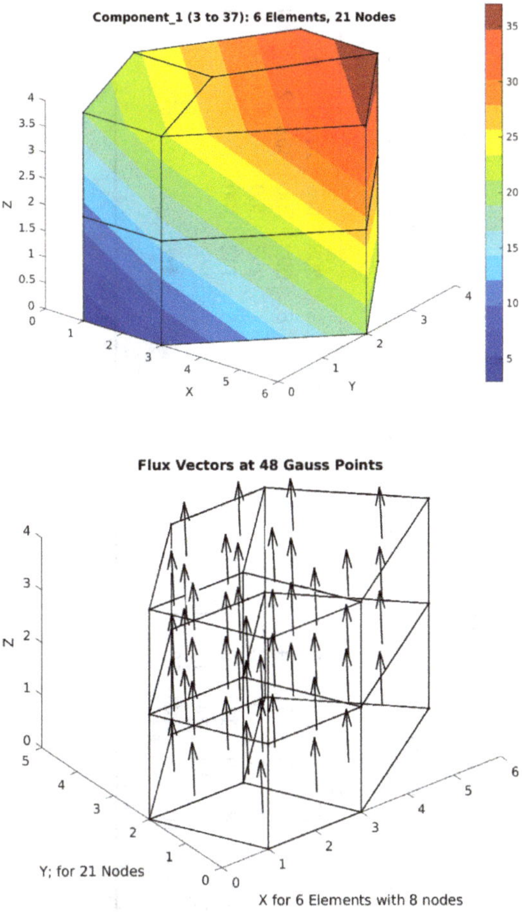

Fig. 12.15-2: Linear spatial solution and selected constant flux vectors from patch test.

the z derivative of the interpolations as its third row. Of course, additional elements can be added to the element library. However, most three-dimensional problems are better solved with commercial software simply because they have automatic solid element mesh generators and offer several good graphical post-processing.

As a minimal validation of the three-dimensional Poisson solver, a "patch test" was run with the mesh in Fig. 12.15-1 using six eight-noded trilinear hexahedral elements, enclosing node 11 with

Table 12.15-1: Brick elements selected inputs, node 11 result, gradient vector components.

Node	Bc	X	Y	Z	EBC/u	Element	Connection List								Elem	Pt	X	Y	Z	Gradient		
8	1	1	0	2	11	1	1	2	4	3	8	9	11	10	1	1	208	100	242	2	3	4
9	1	3	0	2	15	2	2	5	7	4	9	12	14	11	1	8	092	100	358	2	3	4
10	1	0	2	2	15	3	4	7	6	3	11	14	13	10	6	1	258	300	042	2	3	4
11	0	2	2	2	19	4	8	9	11	10	15	16	18	17	6	8	142	300	158	2	3	4
12	1	6	2	2	27	5	9	12	14	11	16	19	21	18								
13	1	2	4	2	25	6	10	11	14	13	17	18	21	20								
14	1	4	4	2	29																	

the only unknown to be determined, and using EBS at all exterior nodes that make the gradient vector components everywhere be constant with the components of (2, 3, 4). Thus, an assumed solution is $u(x, y, z) = 1 + 2x + 3y + 4z$. The center plane patch node coordinates, EBC values assigned, element connection list, and selected Gauss point locations and gradient values are listed in Table 12.15-1. The other two planes are two units above and below the tabulated values. The computed solution at node 11 is 19.0 as required by the assumed solution where $u(2, 2, 2) = 1 + 2*2 + 3*2 + 4*2 = 19$. The assumed constant gradient components were obtained at every quadrature point (see Fig. 12.15-2). All elements had the required constant gradient components of 2, 3, and 5.

12.16 Summary

$n_b \equiv$ Number of boundary segments	$n_d \equiv$ Number of system unknowns
$n_e \equiv$ Number of elements	$n_g \equiv$ Number of unknowns per node
$n_i \equiv$ Number of unknowns per element	$n_m \equiv$ Number of mesh nodes
$n_n \equiv$ Number of nodes per element	$n_p \equiv$ Dimension of parametric space
$n_q \equiv$ Number of total quadrature points	$n_s \equiv$ Dimension of physical space
b = boundary segment number	e = element number
$\subset$ = subset of a larger set	$\cup$ = union of two sets
Boundary, element, and system unknowns:	$\boldsymbol{\delta}^b \subset_b \boldsymbol{\delta}^e \subset_e \boldsymbol{\delta}$
Boolean extraction arrays:	$\boldsymbol{\delta}^b \equiv \boldsymbol{\beta}_b \boldsymbol{\delta}, \boldsymbol{\delta}^e \equiv \boldsymbol{\beta}_e \boldsymbol{\delta}$
Geometry:	
$\Gamma^b \subset \Omega^e \equiv$ Boundary segment	$\Omega^e \equiv$ Element domain
$\Omega = \cup_e \Omega^e \equiv$ Solution domain	$\Gamma = \cup_b \Gamma^b \equiv$ Domain boundary
Matrix multiplication:	$\boldsymbol{C} = \boldsymbol{A}\,\boldsymbol{B} \neq \boldsymbol{B}\,\boldsymbol{A}$, $C_{ij} \equiv \sum_k A_{ik} B_{kj}$
Transpose of a product:	$(\boldsymbol{A}\,\boldsymbol{B}\,\boldsymbol{C})^T = \boldsymbol{C}^T\,\boldsymbol{B}^T\,\boldsymbol{A}^T$

Jacobian matrix:

$$\begin{Bmatrix} \dfrac{\partial u}{\partial r} \\ \dfrac{\partial u}{\partial s} \\ \dfrac{\partial u}{\partial t} \end{Bmatrix} = \begin{bmatrix} \dfrac{\partial x}{\partial r} & \dfrac{\partial y}{\partial r} & \dfrac{\partial z}{\partial r} \\ \dfrac{\partial x}{\partial s} & \dfrac{\partial y}{\partial s} & \dfrac{\partial z}{\partial s} \\ \dfrac{\partial x}{\partial t} & \dfrac{\partial y}{\partial t} & \dfrac{\partial z}{\partial t} \end{bmatrix} \begin{Bmatrix} \dfrac{\partial u}{\partial x} \\ \dfrac{\partial u}{\partial y} \\ \dfrac{\partial u}{\partial z} \end{Bmatrix} \equiv [\boldsymbol{J}(r,\, s,\, t)] \begin{Bmatrix} \dfrac{\partial u}{\partial x} \\ \dfrac{\partial u}{\partial y} \\ \dfrac{\partial u}{\partial z} \end{Bmatrix}.$$

Calculation of element Jacobian: $\boldsymbol{J}^{\mathbf{e}}(r) = \dfrac{\partial \boldsymbol{H}(\boldsymbol{r})}{\partial r} \boldsymbol{x}^{\boldsymbol{e}}$.

Jacobian determinant:

$$J = |\,\boldsymbol{J}\,| = \begin{vmatrix} \dfrac{\partial x}{\partial r} & \dfrac{\partial y}{\partial r} & \dfrac{\partial z}{\partial r} \\ \dfrac{\partial x}{\partial s} & \dfrac{\partial y}{\partial s} & \dfrac{\partial z}{\partial s} \\ \dfrac{\partial x}{\partial t} & \dfrac{\partial y}{\partial t} & \dfrac{\partial z}{\partial t} \end{vmatrix}.$$

Differential volume relations: $d\Omega = |J(\boxdot)|\; d\boxdot$

$$dx = |J(r)\,|\,dr = \left| \frac{\partial x(r)}{\partial r} \right| dr$$

$$dA = dx\,dy = |J(r,\, s)|\; dr\,ds = \left| \frac{\partial x}{\partial r}\frac{\partial y(r,\, s)}{\partial s} - \frac{\partial y}{\partial r}\frac{\partial x(r,\, s)}{\partial s} \right| dr\,ds$$

$$dV = dx\,dy\,dz = |J(r,\, s,\, t)|\; dr\,ds\,dt.$$

Inverse Jacobian matrix: $\boldsymbol{\partial_\Omega}() = \boldsymbol{J}(\boxdot)^{-1}\, \boldsymbol{\partial}_{\boxdot}(\,)$.

$$\begin{Bmatrix} \dfrac{\partial u}{\partial x} \\ \dfrac{\partial u}{\partial y} \\ \dfrac{\partial u}{\partial z} \end{Bmatrix} = \begin{bmatrix} \dfrac{\partial x}{\partial r} & \dfrac{\partial y}{\partial r} & \dfrac{\partial z}{\partial r} \\ \dfrac{\partial x}{\partial s} & \dfrac{\partial y}{\partial s} & \dfrac{\partial z}{\partial s} \\ \dfrac{\partial x}{\partial t} & \dfrac{\partial y}{\partial t} & \dfrac{\partial z}{\partial t} \end{bmatrix}^{-1} \begin{Bmatrix} \dfrac{\partial u}{\partial r} \\ \dfrac{\partial u}{\partial s} \\ \dfrac{\partial u}{\partial t} \end{Bmatrix}.$$

$$\boldsymbol{J}^{-1} = \frac{1}{|\boldsymbol{J}|} \begin{bmatrix} \dfrac{\partial y}{\partial s} & -\dfrac{\partial y}{\partial r} \\ -\dfrac{\partial x}{\partial s} & \dfrac{\partial x}{\partial r} \end{bmatrix}, \quad |\boldsymbol{J}| = \left(\frac{\partial x}{\partial r}\frac{\partial y}{\partial s} - \frac{\partial y}{\partial r}\frac{\partial x}{\partial s} \right).$$

Integral transformations (two-dimensional):

$$\iint_{\Omega} f(x,\, y)\, dx\, dy = \iint_{\boxdot} f\left[x(r,\, s),\, y(r,s)\right] |\, J(r,\, s)| dr\, ds.$$

Green's theorem:

$$\begin{aligned}\iiint_V A\nabla^2 B\, dV &= \iint_S A\vec{\nabla} B \cdot \vec{n} dS - \iiint_V \vec{\nabla} A \cdot \vec{\nabla} B\, dV \\ &= \iint_S A\frac{\partial B}{\partial n} dS - \iiint_V \vec{\nabla} A \cdot \vec{\nabla} B\, dV.\end{aligned}$$

Symmetry plane NatBC: $\partial u/\partial n \equiv 0$.

Model ordinary differential equation:

$$\frac{\partial}{\partial x}\left(k_x \frac{\partial u}{\partial x}\right) + \frac{\partial}{\partial y}\left(k_y \frac{\partial u}{\partial y}\right) + T\, u + Q(x,\, y) = \rho c_p \frac{\partial u}{\partial \tau}.$$

Equivalent integral form:

$$\begin{aligned}&\int_{\Gamma^b} u \left(k_{nn}\frac{\partial u}{\partial n}\right) d\Gamma - \int_{\Omega}\left(\frac{\partial u}{\partial x}\left(k_x\frac{\partial u}{\partial x}\right) + \frac{\partial u}{\partial y}\left(k_y \frac{\partial u}{\partial y}\right)\right) d\Omega \\ &\quad - \int_{\Omega} u\, T\, u\, d\Omega - \int_{\Omega} u\, Q\, d\Omega - \int_{\Omega} u\, \rho c_p\, u\, d\Omega = 0.\end{aligned}$$

Conduction, convection, advection, and source matrices:

$$\boldsymbol{S}^e_{\kappa} = \int_{\Omega} \vec{\nabla} \boldsymbol{H}^{\boldsymbol{T}} \boldsymbol{\kappa}\, \vec{\nabla} \boldsymbol{H} d\Omega, \quad \boldsymbol{A}^e_v = \int_{\Omega^e} \boldsymbol{H}^{\boldsymbol{e}^T} m^e v^e \boldsymbol{B}^{\boldsymbol{e}}\, d\Omega$$

$$\boldsymbol{M}^e_h = \int_{\Omega^e} \boldsymbol{H}^{\boldsymbol{e}^T} h^e \boldsymbol{H}^{\boldsymbol{e}}\, d\Omega, \quad \boldsymbol{M}^e_{\rho} = \int_{\Omega^e} \boldsymbol{H}^{\boldsymbol{e}^T} \rho^e c^e_p \boldsymbol{H}^{\boldsymbol{e}}\, d\Omega,$$

$$\boldsymbol{c}^e_Q = \int_{\Omega^e} \boldsymbol{H}^{\boldsymbol{e}^T} Q^e\, d\Omega,\; \boldsymbol{c}^b_{NBC} = \int_{\Gamma^b} \boldsymbol{H}^{\boldsymbol{b}^T} \left(k_{nn}\frac{\partial u}{\partial n}\right)^b d\Gamma,$$

$$\boldsymbol{c}^b_q = \int_{\Gamma^b} \boldsymbol{H}^{\boldsymbol{b}^T} q_n d\Gamma.$$

Transient matrix system: $[\boldsymbol{S}_{\boldsymbol{k}} + \boldsymbol{A}_{\boldsymbol{v}} + \boldsymbol{M}_{\boldsymbol{h}}]\, \boldsymbol{u}(\tau) + [\boldsymbol{M}_{\boldsymbol{\rho}}]\, \dot{\boldsymbol{u}}(\tau) = \boldsymbol{c}(\tau)$.

Steady-state matrix system: $\dot{\boldsymbol{u}}(\tau) = \mathbf{0}$: $[\boldsymbol{S_k} + \boldsymbol{A_v} + \boldsymbol{M_h}]\,\boldsymbol{u} = \boldsymbol{c}$.

Triangle geometric constants: $2A^e = a_1 + a_2 + a_3 = b_2c_3 - b_3c_2$

$$a_i = x_jy_k - x_ky_j,\ b_i = y_j - y_k,\ c_i = x_k - x_j,\ \ ijk \to 123 \to 231 \to 312$$

$$a_1 = x_2y_3 - x_3y_2,\ a_2 = x_3y_1 - x_1y_3,\ a_3 = x_1y_2 - x_2y_1$$

$$b_1 = y_2 - y_3,\ b_2 = y_3 - y_1,\ b_3 = y_1 - y_2,$$

$$c_1 = x_3 - x_2,\ c_2 = x_1 - x_3,\ c_3 = x_2 - x_1.$$

Linear triangle conduction and volumetric source matrices:

$$\boldsymbol{S}^e_\kappa = \frac{t^e}{4\,A^e}\left[k^e_x\begin{bmatrix} b_1b_1 & b_1b_2 & b_1b_3 \\ b_2b_1 & b_2b_2 & b_3b_3 \\ b_3b_1 & b_3b_2 & b_3b_3 \end{bmatrix} + k^e_y\begin{bmatrix} c_1c_1 & c_1c_2 & c_1c_3 \\ c_2c_1 & c_2c_2 & c_2c_3 \\ c_3c_1 & c_3c_2 & c_3c_3 \end{bmatrix}\right],$$

$$\boldsymbol{c}^e_Q = \frac{Q^eA^et^e}{3}\begin{Bmatrix} 1 \\ 1 \\ 1 \end{Bmatrix}.$$

Linear triangle face and edge convection matrices (and normal flux matrices, $h^e \to q^e_n$):

$$\boldsymbol{M}^e_h = \frac{h^eA^e}{12}\begin{bmatrix} 2 & 1 & 1 \\ 1 & 2 & 1 \\ 1 & 1 & 2 \end{bmatrix}, \quad \boldsymbol{c}^b_h = \frac{h^b\,t^b\,L^b}{2}\begin{Bmatrix} 1 \\ 1 \end{Bmatrix}.$$

Linear rectangle conduction and volumetric source matrices:

$$\boldsymbol{S}^e_\kappa = \frac{k^e_x\,t^e L^e_y}{6\,L^e_x}\begin{bmatrix} 2 & -2 & -1 & 1 \\ -2 & 2 & 1 & -1 \\ -1 & 1 & 2 & -2 \\ 1 & -1 & -2 & 2 \end{bmatrix} + \frac{k^e_yt^eL^e_x}{6L^e_y}\begin{bmatrix} 2 & 1 & -1 & -2 \\ 1 & 2 & -2 & -1 \\ -1 & -2 & 2 & 1 \\ -2 & -1 & 1 & 2 \end{bmatrix},$$

$$\boldsymbol{c}^e_Q = \frac{Q^eA^et^e}{4}\begin{Bmatrix} 1 \\ 1 \\ 1 \\ 1 \end{Bmatrix}.$$

Linear rectangle face and edge convection matrices (and normal flux matrices, $h^e \to q_n^e$):

$$\boldsymbol{M}_h^e = \frac{h^e L_x^e L_y^e}{36} \begin{bmatrix} 4 & 2 & 1 & 2 \\ 2 & 4 & 2 & 1 \\ 1 & 2 & 4 & 2 \\ 2 & 1 & 2 & 4 \end{bmatrix}, \quad \boldsymbol{c}_h^b = \frac{h^b t^b L^b}{2} \begin{Bmatrix} 1 \\ 1 \end{Bmatrix}.$$

12.17 Review

1. In heat transfer, the heat flux is defined by: _____.

   (a) The thermal conductivity (b) The integral of the temperature (c) Hooke's law
   (d) Fourier's law (e) The temperature difference (f) Poisson's ratio
   (g) The temperature gradient (h) The heat flow (i) None of these
   (j) (a) and (g) (k) (a), (d), and (g)

2. In heat transfer, the heat flow is _____.

   (a) The area integral of the normal heat flux (b) The area integral of the temperature
   (c) The volume integral of the heat flux (d) Zero across insulated surfaces
   (e) Zero at specified temperatures (f) (a) and (d)

3. In a bar thermal analysis, what is the sum of the terms in the element convection square matrix?
4. In a thermal analysis, the default Neumann BC on the exterior surface is: _____.

   (a) Zero normal heat flux (b) Zero normal displacement (c) Zero stresses
   (d) Zero rotation (e) None of these (f) All of these

5. Which boundary conditions are satisfied weakly? _____.
   (a) Dirichlet (b) Neumann (c) Both

6. At a point on a plane of thermal symmetry, which items are zero? _____.

   (a) Tangential displacements (b) Normal displacement (c) Tangential heatflux
   (d) Temperature (e) Normal heat flux (f) Tangential rotations
   (g) Normal rotations (h) All of the above (i) None of the above

7. Can a mesh with a mixture of six-noded triangles, eight-noded quadrilaterals, and nine-noded quadrilaterals be a compatible mixture of element types? If yes, explain why.
8. What happens to a finite element solution if you fail to apply the EBCs to the matrix form?
9. If you are calculating a Poisson analysis with an eight-noded quadrilateral element, how many quadrature points do you need in each parametric direction? _____.
10. In a two-dimensional torsional stress analysis of a straight shaft, the primary unknown is: _____.
    (a) Torque (b) Twist angle (c) Stress function
    (d) Shear stress (e) Shear modulus (f) None of the above

11. In an FEA torsional stress analysis of a straight shaft, what is the shear stress at a sharp re-entrant corner? _____
    (a) Zero (b) Value of the stress function (c) Integral of the stress function
    (d) Infinite (e) None of the above

12. In an FEA torsional stress analysis of a straight shaft, what is the shear stress at a sharp exterior corner? _____
    (a) Zero (b) Value of the stress function (c) Integral of the stress function
    (d) Infinite (e) None of the above

13. In an FEA torsional stress analysis of a straight shaft, what is the applied torque proportional to? _____.
    (a) Value of the stress function (b) Integral of the stress function (c) Stress function gradient
    (d) The length (e) None of the above

14. In a solid thermal analysis, what is the sum of the terms in the element conduction matrix? _____.
15. The angle at which a temperature contour intersects a homogeneous material Insulated boundary should always be _____.

    (a) Tangent to the boundary
    (b) Perpendicular to the boundary
    (c) Proportional to the conductivity
    (d) Proportional to the convection coefficient

16. A symmetry plane divides mirror images of the _____.

    (a) Geometric shape
    (b) Distribution of material properties
    (c) Dirichlet boundary conditions
    (d) External loadings
    (e) All of the above
    (f) None of the above

17. Beginning with knowledge of the governing differential equation, list the major steps or phases of a finite element analysis (in order of occurrence).

Chapter 13

Elasticity

13.1 Introduction

The subject of elasticity deals with the stress analysis applications where the component returns to its original size and shape when loads act on the component. The finite element method has proven to be a very practical process for any elasticity analysis. The vast majority of finite element elasticity models utilize the displacements as the primary unknowns. A general solid analysis requires three displacement components that lead to six stress components. An elasticity analysis involves four major topics: the displacement components, the six strain components obtained from the gradients of the displacement components (known in solid mechanics as the strain–displacement relation), and the experimental material property knowledge that relates the strain components to the stress components. It is more common to state the material stress–strain law which is the inverse of the experimental relation. After the displacements are known, they are post-processed to give the strains and stresses. Once the strains and stresses are known, they must be compared to an experimentally established material failure criterion.

All stress analysis involves a solid object. Historically, many mathematical simplifications have been developed to model common special shapes in order to avoid actual solid stress analysis. They include bending of curved three-dimensional shells, axisymmetric solids, two-dimensional plane–stress (where a plane is stress-free as in

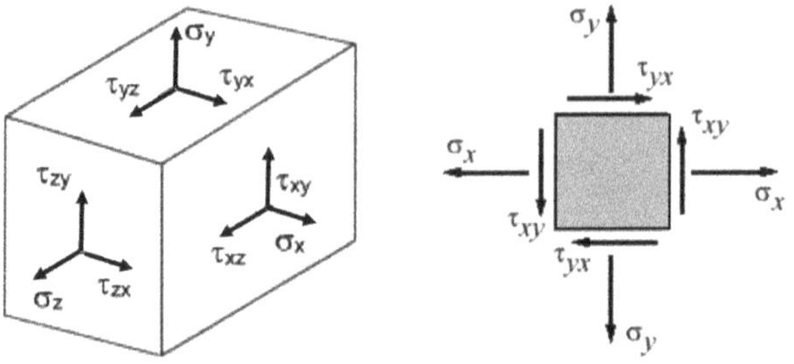

Fig. 13.1-1: Plane–stress is a special case of solid stress analysis.

Fig. 13.1-1), two-dimensional plane–strain (where a plane is strain-free), bending of two-dimensional flat plates, two-dimensional torsion of non-circular shafts, one-dimensional torsion of circular shafts, bending of one-dimensional beams, and finally one-dimensional axial bars. All of those special cases have a different set of governing differential equations. However, they can all be solved by a single finite element approach.

Today, it is practical to conduct a three-dimensional stress analysis, but it is not always the most accurate, or the most efficient approach. For example, in certain cases, thousands of solid elements approximating a straight beam can be less accurate than tens of beam elements. Whatever element type is used in an analysis, all finite element study results should be independently validated by some handbook solution, and/or some simplified mathematical model, in an attempt to set upper and lower bounds for the answer of the actual problem being solved.

Early in human history people built with post, simple beams, and arches. One of the first published studies of structures was that of Galileo in 1638 where he analyzed axial loads and the bending of cantilever beams (see Fig. 13.1-2). His analysis was incorrect, but it represents the beginning of engineers' understanding of the mathematical analysis of structures. In 1678, Robert Hooke published material studies that established the linear proportionality between material strains and stresses. That relation was used as the foundation upon which the mechanics of elastic structures was built. His work is often called Hooke's law or the material constitutive law. Sir Isaac Newton published his laws governing dynamics and equilibrium in 1687. With those foundations, Jacob Bernoulli almost correctly

Fig. 13.1-2: Bar and bending tests by Galileo, 1638.

solved for the deflection of a cantilever beam in 1705. Leonard Euler correctly formulated the differential equations for beam equilibrium and solved them in 1736. In 1744, Euler published the first book on variational calculus (which later played a large part in finite element analysis). By 1750, the basic mechanics (materials and differential equations) for treating the equilibrium and dynamics of all elastic structures were known.

Thus, the governing differential and integral formulations for the equilibrium of three-dimensional solids were known for about 200 years before the advent of digital computers and the finite element method made it practical for novice engineers to solve such systems. Before the appearance of digital computers in the 1950s, two- and three-dimensional limited numerical approximations were obtained by finite difference relaxation methods. Some analytical solutions were obtained for simple shapes like rectangles, circles, and triangles. Several of the one-dimensional simplifications for bars, shafts, and beams were treated earlier.

The governing differential equations of elasticity problems can be converted to corresponding integral forms by using the method of weighted residuals, and in particular Galerkin's method. Likewise, the variational calculus of Euler and the Principle of Virtual Work can give the equivalent integral as can the work–energy approach known as the theorem of minimum total potential energy (MTPE).

Those methods, and the Galerkin method, give identical forms of the element matrices.

Thus, the relatively simpler theorem of MTPE is used here for the finite element formulation of the displacement-based stress analysis of elastic bodies. The total potential energy, Π, is defined as the strain energy (potential energy), U, stored internal to a body minus the mechanical work, W, done by externally applied sources:

$$\Pi = U - W. \tag{13.1-1}$$

The theorem states: The displacement field that satisfies the essential displacement boundary conditions, and renders stationary the total potential energy, is the unique displacement field that corresponds to the state of static equilibrium. Stationary points are minimum (stable) points, maximum (unstable) points, or inflection (neutral) points. For elastic solids, it can be shown that the stationary state is the stable minimum state, thus herein it is referred to as the minimum principle. Therefore, if δ represents all of the displacement components, then the equation of static equilibrium is

$$\frac{\partial \Pi}{\partial \delta} = \mathbf{0}. \tag{13.1-2}$$

This gives one equation per displacement component that must be satisfied for the elastic body to be in equilibrium. The displacements must also satisfy the essential boundary conditions (EBCs), and the above equations also yield the reactions needed for system equilibrium, developed at the EBC locations.

13.2 Linear Springs

Before considering the general case, a review of how these topics were introduced in introductory physics courses. The "linear spring" is usually introduced with the EBC pre-applied by fixing one end against displacement. That reduces a two-degree-of-freedom (DOF) to a one-DOF analysis, as noted in Fig. 13.2-1. The spring has an axial stiffness of k. The unrestrained end has an axial force, F, that causes an axial displacement, δ. If the system is in equilibrium, what is the relation between these three features of the linear spring?

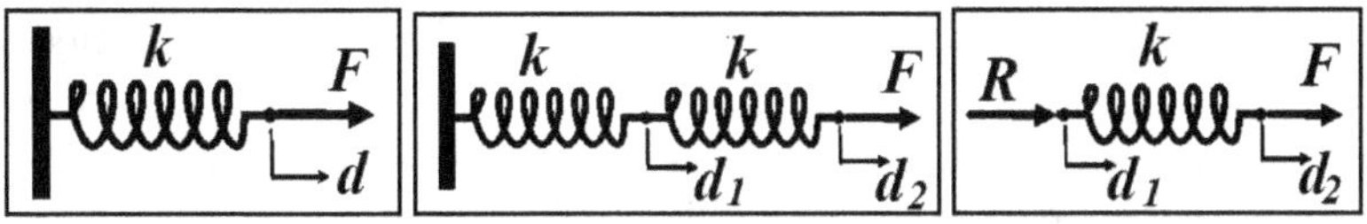

Fig. 13.2-1: Linear spring systems.

Recall that the strain (potential) energy of a linear spring is $U = k\,\delta^2/2$. The mechanical work due to the external force is defined as the product of the force and the displacement component in the direction of the force. In this case, they are parallel so the mechanical work is

$$W = \delta\, F.$$

In general, they are not parallel and the work is the scalar (dot) product of the force vector and the displacement vector:

$$W = \vec{\boldsymbol{\delta}} \cdot \vec{F} = \boldsymbol{\delta}^T\ \boldsymbol{F} = \delta_x F_x + \delta_y F_y + \delta_z F_z. \tag{13.2-1}$$

Let the x-axis lie along the spring endpoints. Then the total potential energy is

$$\Pi(\delta_x) = \mathrm{U} - \mathrm{W} = k\,\delta_x^2/2 - \delta_x F_x.$$

Calculus teaches that to find a stationary point of a function $y(x)$ it is necessary to set its derivative to zero, $dy/dx = 0$, and solve that equation for the value of x that corresponds to the stationary point. To determine what type of stationary point, it is necessary to evaluate the second derivative, d^2y/dx^2, at the point. If the second derivative is positive, it defines a minimum point, if negative, it defines a maximum point, and a zero value defines a neutral point. The Total Potential Energy is defined as a function of each and every displacement unknown in the system. Here, δ_x is the only displacement associated with the spring. Therefore, stationary equilibrium for the spring requires

$$\frac{\partial \Pi}{\partial \delta_x} = \quad 0 = 2\,k\,\delta_x/2\ -F_x.$$

This gives the equilibrium equation as

$$\delta_x = F_x/k \quad \text{or} \quad F_x = k\,\delta_x.$$

Physics courses usually state the second form. The deformed state minimizes the Total Potential Energy as is seen by taking its second derivative: $d^2\Pi/d\delta_x{}^2 = k$, which is always positive.

Next, consider two identical springs joined in series. The mechanical work is still the same since there is no *external* force applied to the intermediate node, $W = 0\delta_1 + F\,\delta_2$. There are equal and opposite *internal* forces at that point. They are the reaction forces on the springs needed to have each spring in equilibrium as well as having the assembly of springs in equilibrium. The net displacement of the end where the external load is applied is $(\delta_2 - \delta_1)$, so the scalar strain energy of the assembly of springs is

$$U = \frac{1}{2}k\delta_1^2 + \frac{1}{2}k(\delta_2 - \delta_1)^2 = \frac{k}{2}(2\delta_1^2 - 2\delta_1\delta_2 + \delta_2^2),$$

and the total potential energy becomes

$$\Pi = \frac{k}{2}(2\delta_1^2 - 2\delta_1\delta_2 + \delta_2^2) - (0\delta_1 + F\,\delta_2).$$

To reach equilibrium, this quantity must be minimized with respect to each and every one of the displacement DOFs:

$$\frac{\partial\Pi}{\partial\delta_1} = \frac{k}{2}(4\delta_1 - 2\delta_2) - (0),$$
$$\frac{\partial\Pi}{\partial\delta_2} = \frac{k}{2}(-2\delta_1 + 2\delta_2) - (F).$$

In matrix format the displacement equations of equilibrium are

$$k\begin{bmatrix} 2 & -1 \\ -1 & 1 \end{bmatrix}\begin{Bmatrix} \delta_1 \\ \delta_2 \end{Bmatrix} = \begin{Bmatrix} 0 \\ F \end{Bmatrix}.$$

The leftmost node satisfied in advance the EBC of specifying a known displacement (0 here), and these two displacement components will minimize the total potential energy (iff the square matrix is non-singular), and thus these displacements will correspond to the state of static equilibrium. Multiplying by the inverse of the square matrix:

$$\begin{Bmatrix} \delta_1 \\ \delta_2 \end{Bmatrix} = \frac{1}{k}\begin{bmatrix} 1 & 1 \\ 1 & 2 \end{bmatrix}\begin{Bmatrix} 0 \\ F \end{Bmatrix} = \frac{F}{k}\begin{Bmatrix} 1 \\ 2 \end{Bmatrix}.$$

The left spring has the same displacement as it did in the previous case, $\delta_1 = F/k$, and the right spring has a displacement that is twice as large $\delta_2 = 2F/k$. This makes sense because the external load,

F, is simply transmitted through the first spring to the second spring, which in turn transmits it to rigid support wall.

Often the system reactions are needed, and sometimes the reactions on some or all of the elements are needed. Since the EBC was applied in advance, there is no equation available to compute the system reaction, but by requiring that each spring is in equilibrium the internal reaction force(s) can be obtained since now all of the displacements are known. Let the reaction force on the left node of the right spring be R, which is assumed to be in the positive direction. The individual spring's total potential energy is

$$\Pi = \frac{1}{2}k\,(\delta_2 - \delta_1)^2 - (R\delta_1 + F\,\delta_2),$$

which gives element equilibrium equations

$$\frac{\partial \Pi}{\partial \delta_1} = 0 = \frac{k}{2}\,(2\delta_1 - 2\delta_2) - (R),$$
$$\frac{\partial \Pi}{\partial \delta_2} = 0 = \frac{k}{2}\,(-2\delta_1 + 2\delta_2) - (F),$$

and substituting all of the known displacements into the first element equilibrium equation gives

$$0 = \frac{k}{2}\,(2F/k - 4F/k) - (R) = -F - R,$$

which gives the expected (from Newton's laws) result that $R = -F$.

13.3 Mechanical Work

To begin generalizing and automating the above process to any elastic system, it is necessary to consider additional types of external forces. A viscous fluid, and other sources like electromagnetic surface eddy currents, can apply an external force per unit area to adjacent solid surfaces. These are called "surface tractions", and they are denoted in vector and matrix forms by $\vec{\boldsymbol{T}} \leftrightarrow \boldsymbol{T}$, respectively. In this application, the number of displacement DOFs at a point, n_g, is the same as the number of spatial dimensions, $n_g = 3 = n_s$. The differential force at a point on the surface area dS becomes $\overrightarrow{\boldsymbol{dF}} = \vec{\boldsymbol{T}}\,dS$.

When a point on the surface, S, is subjected to a displacement, the scalar work done by the traction vector is

$$dW_T = \vec{\boldsymbol{\delta}} \cdot \vec{\boldsymbol{T}}\, dS = \boldsymbol{\delta}^T \boldsymbol{T}\, dS,$$

so that the total work done by all surface tractions is

$$W_T = \int_S \boldsymbol{\delta}^T \boldsymbol{T}\, dS. \tag{13.3-1}$$

Likewise, external translational acceleration and/or rotational velocities and accelerations, and other sources like the effects of external magnetic fields acting on electric currents flowing through a body, will cause forces per unit volume to occur inside an object. These are called "body forces", and they are denoted in vector and matrix forms by $\vec{\boldsymbol{f}} \leftrightarrow \boldsymbol{f}$, respectively, and the differential force acting on a differential volume is $\overrightarrow{\boldsymbol{dF}} = \vec{\boldsymbol{f}}\, dV$. When the differential volume is subjected to a displacement, the scalar work done by the body force vector is

$$dW_f = \vec{\boldsymbol{\delta}} \cdot \vec{\boldsymbol{f}}\, dV = \boldsymbol{\delta}^T \boldsymbol{f}\, dV,$$

so the total work done by body forces is

$$W_f = \int_V \boldsymbol{\delta}^T \boldsymbol{f}\, dV. \tag{13.3-2}$$

Finally, recognizing that more than one point can have an external point load and that the work done by each must be included, the general definition of external mechanical work is

$$W = \int_V \boldsymbol{\delta}^T \boldsymbol{f}\, dV + \int_S \boldsymbol{\delta}^T \boldsymbol{T}\, dS + \sum_{k=1}^{k=n_P} \boldsymbol{\delta}_k^T \boldsymbol{F}_k. \tag{13.3-3}$$

13.4 Displacements and Mechanical Strains

Here, the definitions for a solid are given, while the common simplified special cases of plane–stress, plane–strain, and axisymmetric solids will be discussed later. To generalize the strain energy definition, it will be defined for the full three-dimensional case so all of the simplifications, like plane–stress case in Fig. 13.1-1, are automatically included. The governing matrix relations to be developed in this chapter retain their symbolic forms in all elasticity applications. They simply change size when one of the simplifications is invoked. The starting point is the $n_g = 3$ displacement components in the x-, y-, and z-directions at a point:

$$\vec{u} \leftrightarrow \boldsymbol{u} = \left\{ \begin{array}{c} u(x,\, y,\, z) \\ v(x,\, y,\, z) \\ w(x,\, y,\, z) \end{array} \right\}. \qquad (13.4\text{-}1)$$

The differential of the x-component of the displacement vector is

$$d\boldsymbol{u}\,(x,\, y, z) = \frac{\partial u}{\partial x} dx + \frac{\partial u}{\partial y} dy + \frac{\partial u}{\partial z} dz.$$

The differential of the displacement vector can be written in matrix form as

$$d\boldsymbol{u} = \left\{ \begin{array}{c} du(x,\, y,\, z) \\ dv(x,\, y,\, z) \\ dw(x,\, y,\, z) \end{array} \right\} = \begin{bmatrix} \frac{\partial u}{\partial x} & \frac{\partial u}{\partial y} & \frac{\partial u}{\partial z} \\ \frac{\partial v}{\partial x} & \frac{\partial v}{\partial y} & \frac{\partial v}{\partial z} \\ \frac{\partial w}{\partial x} & \frac{\partial w}{\partial y} & \frac{\partial w}{\partial z} \end{bmatrix} \left\{ \begin{array}{c} dx \\ dy \\ dz \end{array} \right\},$$

Note that the square matrix containing the partial derivatives of the displacement components can be written as the sum of three square matrices as

$$\begin{bmatrix} \frac{\partial u}{\partial x} & 0 & 0 \\ 0 & \frac{\partial v}{\partial y} & 0 \\ 0 & 0 & \frac{\partial w}{\partial z} \end{bmatrix} + \frac{1}{2} \begin{bmatrix} 0 & \frac{\partial u}{\partial y} + \frac{\partial v}{\partial x} & \frac{\partial u}{\partial z} + \frac{\partial w}{\partial x} \\ \frac{\partial v}{\partial x} + \frac{\partial u}{\partial y} & 0 & \frac{\partial v}{\partial z} + \frac{\partial w}{\partial y} \\ \frac{\partial w}{\partial x} + \frac{\partial u}{\partial z} & \frac{\partial w}{\partial y} + \frac{\partial v}{\partial z} & 0 \end{bmatrix}$$

$$+ \frac{1}{2} \begin{bmatrix} 0 & \frac{\partial u}{\partial y} - \frac{\partial v}{\partial x} & \frac{\partial u}{\partial z} - \frac{\partial w}{\partial x} \\ \frac{\partial v}{\partial x} - \frac{\partial u}{\partial y} & 0 & \frac{\partial v}{\partial z} - \frac{\partial w}{\partial y} \\ \frac{\partial w}{\partial x} - \frac{\partial u}{\partial z} & \frac{\partial w}{\partial y} - \frac{\partial v}{\partial z} & 0 \end{bmatrix}.$$

These three groups of combinations of the displacement gradients have geometrical interpretations and physical interpretations. The geometrical shapes for both the plane–stress and the plane–strain simplifications of a planar rectangular differential element are shown in Fig. 13.4-1.

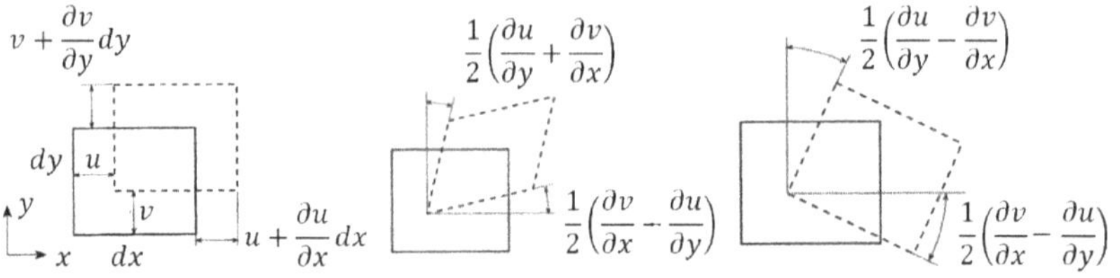

Fig. 13.4-1: Decomposition of the planar displacement gradient components.

The first matrix partition represents a displacement change of the faces of that element in directions normal to their original positions (left part of the figure). Those diagonal components are known as the "normal strains":

$$\varepsilon_x=\frac{\partial u}{\partial x},\qquad \varepsilon_y=\frac{\partial v}{\partial y},\qquad \varepsilon_z=\frac{\partial w}{\partial z}. \tag{13.4-2}$$

Normal strains change the volume of the differential element but not its shape. The differential element goes from one rectangle to another.

The second matrix of displacement gradient component combinations changes the shape (middle of Fig. 13.4-1) by distorting the rectangle into a parallelogram, without changing its area. This second symmetric matrix contains components of what mathematicians call the shear strain tensor. However, engineers choose to define the terms inside the matrix brackets as the (engineering) shear strains:

$$\gamma_{xy}=\frac{\partial u}{\partial y}+\frac{\partial v}{\partial x}=\gamma_{yx},\quad \gamma_{xz}=\frac{\partial u}{\partial z}+\frac{\partial w}{\partial x}=\gamma_{zx},\quad \gamma_{yz}=\frac{\partial v}{\partial z}+\frac{\partial w}{\partial y}=\gamma_{zy}. \tag{13.4-3}$$

The omission of the one-half term for the engineering shear strains simply means that the rules for rotating the stresses (Mohr's circle) and the engineering strains from one coordinate system to another are different. That contrasts with the tensor formulations where the stress tensor and the strain tensor (and any other second-order tensor) have the same rotational transformation.

The third matrix corresponds to a rigid body rotation (right part of the figure) of the differential element. That rotation does not change its volume and does not change its shape. In other words, the third combination of displacement components has no effect on the material contained within the differential element and therefore will not be further considered.

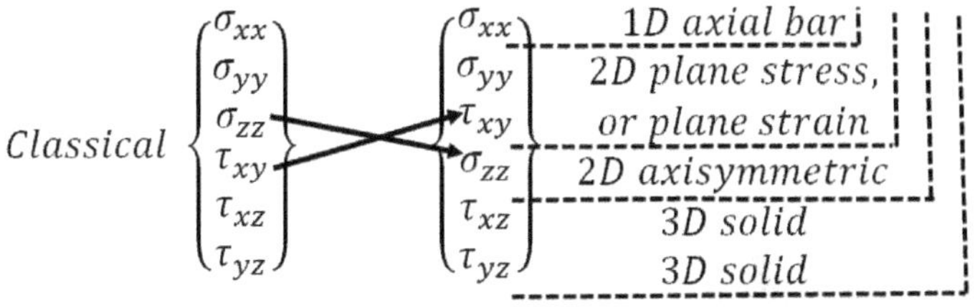

Fig. 13.4-2: Stress component order in provided Matlab scripts.

Most finite element elasticity studies use a matrix formulation that represents the strain and stress components as column vectors. This is called the Voigt representation and contrasts with the tensor representation. In matrix notation, the n_r material strain components are usually ordered as

$$\boldsymbol{\varepsilon}^T = \left[\, \varepsilon_x \; \varepsilon_y \;\; \varepsilon_z \; \gamma_{xy} \;\; \gamma_{xz} \; \gamma_{yz} \,\right]. \tag{13.4-4}$$

As implied by the comparison of the planar elements in Figs. 13.4-1 and 13.1-1, the n_r stress components are correspondingly ordered as

$$\boldsymbol{\sigma}^T = \left[\, \sigma_x \; \sigma_y \;\; \sigma_z \; \tau_{xy} \;\; \tau_{xz} \; \tau_{yz} \,\right]. \tag{13.4-5}$$

When a single source program is used to solve multiple classes of stress analysis, then it is not unusual to find the positions of τ_{xy} and σ_z interchanged. That is the order utilized in the stress analysis Matlab scripts provided here. That application-dependent ordering of the stress components is shown in Fig. 13.4-2.

13.5 Strain Energy

The potential energy stored internally in the body is determined by referring to the left-hand sides of Figs. 13.1-1 and 13.4-1. The body is initially stress-free and the normal stress σ_x is gradually applied to the differential face area of $dA = dy\, dz$ to create a normal differential force $dF_x = \sigma_x\, dy\, dz$. The perpendicular displacement is

$$[(u + \partial u/\partial x\, dx) - u] = \partial u/\partial x\, dx = \varepsilon_x\, dx,$$

which makes the work done by that normal stress (the area under the force-displacement curve)

$$dU_x = \frac{1}{2}(0 + \sigma_x)\, dy\, dz\, \varepsilon_x dx = \frac{1}{2}\sigma_x \varepsilon_x\, dx\, dy\, dz = \frac{1}{2}\sigma_x \varepsilon_x\, dV.$$

Likewise, the differential work done by the three normal stresses is

$$dU_n = \frac{1}{2}\left(\sigma_x \varepsilon_x + \sigma_y \varepsilon_y + \sigma_z \varepsilon_z\right) dV.$$

The vertical shear stress τ_{xy} acts on the same differential area, $dA = dy\,dz$, and causes a vertical differential force of $dF_{xy} = \tau_{xy}\,dy\,dz$. Its displacement is a little less clear. Recall that for differential rotations the quantity

$$\frac{1}{2}\left(\frac{\partial u}{\partial y} + \frac{\partial v}{\partial x}\right) = d\theta_z$$

is a differential rotation measured in radians. That rotation of the horizontal length dx through that angle moves the front face vertically an (arc) distance of

$$\frac{1}{2}\left(\frac{\partial u}{\partial y} + \frac{\partial v}{\partial x}\right) dx = \frac{1}{2}\gamma_{xy}\,dx,$$

which contributes the differential work

$$dU_{xy1} = \frac{1}{2}\left(0 + \tau_{xy}\right) dy\,dz\,\frac{1}{2}\gamma_{xy}\,dx = \frac{1}{4}\tau_{xy}\gamma_{xy}\,dx\,dy\,dz = \frac{1}{4}\tau_{xy}\gamma_{xy}\,dV.$$

Of course, there is symmetry in the shear stress and shear strain (for moment equilibrium) so $\tau_{xy} = \tau_{yx}$ and $\gamma_{xy} = \gamma_{yx}$, which means that the horizontal shear stress component does exactly the same amount of work giving the total τ_{xy} work contribution to be

$$dU_{xy} = \frac{1}{2}\tau_{xy}\gamma_{xy}\,dV.$$

Summing all of the six stress component contributions gives the strain energy density

$$\begin{aligned} dU &= \frac{1}{2}\left(\sigma_x \varepsilon_x + \sigma_y \varepsilon_y + \sigma_z \varepsilon_z + \tau_{xy}\gamma_{xy} + \tau_{xz}\gamma_{xz} + \tau_{yz}\gamma_{yz}\right) dV \\ &= \frac{1}{2}\boldsymbol{\sigma}^T \boldsymbol{\varepsilon}\,dV = \frac{1}{2}\boldsymbol{\varepsilon}^T \boldsymbol{\sigma}\,dV, \end{aligned}$$

and the total strain energy is

$$U = \frac{1}{2}\int_V \boldsymbol{\sigma}^T \boldsymbol{\varepsilon}\,dV. \qquad (13.5\text{-}1)$$

Half of the scalar product of the stresses times the strains, $\boldsymbol{\sigma}^T\boldsymbol{\varepsilon}/2$, at a point is called the "strain-energy density".

13.6 Material Properties

Next it is necessary to consider the material(s) from which the solid to be studied is made because the material governs the interaction of the strains and stress components. Hooke published (1678) his experiments that found a linear relation between strain and stress, which were extended by Poisson in 1811. The corrected relationship is still called Hooke's law, or the material "constitutive relation". For example, the relation between the normal strain in the x-direction and the stress components, for an isotropic material, with initial thermal strain is

$$\varepsilon_x = [\sigma_x - \upsilon(\sigma_y - \sigma_z)]/E + \alpha_x \Delta T,$$

where E is the material's elastic modulus (the slope of a strain–stress diagram), υ denotes the material's Poisson ratio (the ratio of $\varepsilon_y/\varepsilon_x$ and $\varepsilon_z/\varepsilon_x$), α_x is the coefficient of thermal expansion of the material, and ΔT is the temperature increase from the material's stress-free state. The experiments on natural materials placed bounds on Poisson's ratio of $0 \leq \upsilon \leq 0.5$ with the upper bound corresponding to "incompressible materials", like natural rubber. However, modern materials science can produce man-made materials that violate those classic lower and upper bounds.

The experimental x-y shear strain to shear stress relation, for an isotropic material *only*, is

$$\gamma_{xy} = \gamma_{yx} = \frac{2\,(1+\upsilon)}{E}\tau_{xy} = \frac{1}{G}\tau_{xy}, \quad G = \frac{E}{2\,(1+\upsilon)},$$

etc., where G is the material's shear modulus. In theory, G is not an independent material property. However, in practice it is sometimes useful to treat the shear modulus as independent. Some finite element codes will accept the input of a shear modulus but warn you that it is not consistent with the values of υ and E.

All of Hooke's law strain–stress relationships can be concisely written in matrix form. For a general anisotropic (directionally dependent) material, with initial thermal strains, the matrix form is

$$\boldsymbol{\varepsilon} = \boldsymbol{E}\boldsymbol{\sigma} + \varepsilon_0, \quad \boldsymbol{E} = \boldsymbol{E}^T, \quad |\boldsymbol{E}| >, \quad \varepsilon_T = \boldsymbol{\alpha}\,\Delta T \subset \varepsilon_0,$$
$$\boldsymbol{\alpha}^T = \left[\, \alpha_x\; \alpha_y \;\; \alpha_z\; \alpha_{xy} \;\; \alpha_{xz}\; \alpha_{yz} \,\right], \tag{13.6-1}$$

where the 6×6 "compliance matrix" relates the stresses to the strains. The $\boldsymbol{E}$ matrix is symmetric and positive definite. The inverse of the compliance matrix is the 6 × 6 "elasticity matrix", $\boldsymbol{E} = \boldsymbol{E}^{-1}$. For an isotropic solid,

$$\boldsymbol{E} = \frac{1}{E}\begin{bmatrix} 1 & -v & -v & 0 & 0 & 0 \\ -v & 1 & -v & 0 & 0 & 0 \\ -v & -v & 1 & 0 & 0 & 0 \\ 0 & 0 & 0 & 2(1+v) & 0 & 0 \\ 0 & 0 & 0 & 0 & 2(1+v) & 0 \\ 0 & 0 & 0 & 0 & 0 & 2(1+v) \end{bmatrix}.$$

If it is necessary to formulate a new material, then several sets of experimental data, subject to the constraints of (13.6-1), are entered into the compliance matrix. Those data are manipulated to render the compliance matrix symmetric and positive definite. Then, it is numerically inverted to yield the numerical values of the elasticity matrix for that specific material.

The relationship of the stresses in terms of the strains is obtained by inverting the compliance matrix and multiplying both sides of (13.6-1) by it as follows:

$$\boldsymbol{\sigma} = \boldsymbol{E}\varepsilon - \boldsymbol{E}\varepsilon_0, \quad \boldsymbol{E} = \boldsymbol{E}^{-1}\varepsilon_T = \boldsymbol{\alpha}\,\Delta T \subset \varepsilon_0. \tag{13.6-2}$$

Of course, the inverse relation can also be written in a (messy) scalar format. For example, for an isotropic material (properties independent of direction) with an initial thermal strain,

$$\sigma_x = \frac{E}{(1+v)(1-2v)}\left[(1-v)\,\varepsilon_x + v\,(\varepsilon_y + \varepsilon_z)\right] - \frac{E\alpha\Delta T}{(1-2v)}, \quad \tau_{xy} = \tau_{yx} = G\gamma_{xy},$$

but the matrix form is always consistent, even for the most general anisotropic materials. For an isotropic solid, the matrix form of Hooke's law is

$$\begin{Bmatrix} \sigma_x \\ \sigma_y \\ \sigma_z \\ \tau_{xy} \\ \tau_{xz} \\ \tau_{yz} \end{Bmatrix} = \frac{E}{(1+v)(1-2v)}\begin{bmatrix} a & v & v & 0 & 0 & 0 \\ v & a & v & 0 & 0 & 0 \\ v & v & a & 0 & 0 & 0 \\ 0 & 0 & 0 & b & 0 & 0 \\ 0 & 0 & 0 & 0 & b & 0 \\ 0 & 0 & 0 & 0 & 0 & b \end{bmatrix}\begin{Bmatrix} \varepsilon_x \\ \varepsilon_y \\ \varepsilon_z \\ \gamma_{xy} \\ \gamma_{xz} \\ \gamma_{yz} \end{Bmatrix} - \frac{E\alpha\Delta T}{(1-2v)}\begin{Bmatrix} 1 \\ 1 \\ 1 \\ 0 \\ 0 \\ 0 \end{Bmatrix}. \tag{13.6-3}$$

```
function [E_e] = E_elastic_solid (E, nu, G)
% * * * * * * * * * * * * * * * * * * * * * * * * * * * * * * * *
%         SOLID_STRESS CONSTITUTIVE MATRIX DEFINITION
%        STRESS COMPONENT ORDER: XX, YY, XY, ZZ, XZ, YZ
% * * * * * * * * * * * * * * * * * * * * * * * * * * * * * * * *
% E   = Young's modulus of elasticity
% G   = shear modulus (not independent)
% nu  = Poisson's ratio
% E_e = constitutive matrix
% n_r = number of rows in B and E matrices = 6

if ( nargin == 2 )                              ; % classic definition
  G  = 0.5 * E / (1 + nu)                                ; % in theory
end                                            ; % if special material
c_1 = E * (1 - nu) / (1 + nu) / (1 - nu - nu)          ; % constant
c_2 = c_1 * nu / (1 - nu)                               ; % constant

E_e = zeros (6, 6)                                      ; % largely 0
E_e(1, 1) = c_1 ; E_e(2, 1) = c_2 ; E_e(4, 1) = c_2 ; % normals
E_e(1, 2) = c_2 ; E_e(2, 2) = c_1 ; E_e(4, 2) = c_2 ; % normals
E_e(1, 4) = c_2 ; E_e(2, 4) = c_2 ; E_e(4, 4) = c_1 ; % normals
E_e(3, 3) = G   ; E_e(5, 5) = G   ; E_e(6, 6) = G    ; % shears
% end E_solid_stress
```

Fig. 13.6-1: Constitutive arrays for solid elasticity analysis.

$$a = (1 - \upsilon), \quad b = (1 - 2\upsilon)/2.$$

For the most general anisotropic material, both the elasticity matrix, $\boldsymbol{E}$, and the compliance matrix, $\boldsymbol{E}$, are completely full matrices. The reader is warned that for incompressible materials, with $\upsilon = 0.5$, the above classical theory gives division by zero! In that case, an advanced constitutive law that includes the hydrostatic pressure, $p = (\sigma_x + \sigma_y + \sigma_z)/3$, must be utilized; or advanced finite element numerical tricks (like reduced integration) must be employed to get correct results. Likewise, if a man-made material has $\upsilon > 0.5$, then that causes negative stiffnesses, and advanced material theories and/or numerical tricks must again be invoked to get correct answers. Equation (13.6-3) is implemented in Fig. 13.6-1.

13.7 Interpolating Displacement Vectors:

The previous chapters dealt with interpolating primary unknowns which were scalar quantities, $n_g = 1$. Now those approaches must be extended to interpolate the three displacement vector components, $n_g = 3$, that govern the elasticity formulations. The x-component of displacement was earlier interpolated for use in axial bars. The same matrix form is used here, but the interpolation functions are simply formulated in a higher-dimension space. That is done using the same interpolation functions for all three displacement components within each element:

$$\begin{aligned} u(x,\ y,\ z) &= \boldsymbol{H}(x,\ y,\ z)\,\boldsymbol{u}^{\mathbf{e}}, \\ v(x,\ y,\ z) &= \boldsymbol{H}(x,\ y,\ z)\,\boldsymbol{v}^{\mathbf{e}}, \\ w(x,\ y,\ z) &= \boldsymbol{H}(x,\ y,\ z)\,\boldsymbol{w}^{\mathbf{e}}. \end{aligned} \tag{13.7-1}$$

The analysis requires placing the displacement vector at each node connected to the element to define the element DOFs. The ordering used here is number the u, v, w values at the first element node, then those at the second node, and so on. The element displacement DOFs are

$$\boldsymbol{\delta}^{\mathbf{e}^T} = [u_1, v_1, w_1, u_2, \ldots, \ldots, u_{n_n}, v_{n_n}, w_{n_n}]^e, \tag{13.7-2}$$

and likewise numbering all of the system displacements gives the vector of system unknowns:

$$\boldsymbol{\delta}^T = [u_1, v_1, w_1, u_2, v_2, \ldots, \ldots, u_{n_m}, v_{n_m}, w_{n_m}]. \tag{13.7-3}$$

It is common in the finite element literature to write the interpolation of the displacement vector at a point in an element using the symbol $\boldsymbol{N}(x,\ y,\ z)$, namely

$$\begin{Bmatrix} u(x,\ y,\ z) \\ v(x,\ y,\ z) \\ w(x,\ y,\ z) \end{Bmatrix} = \boldsymbol{u}\,(x,\ y,\ z) \equiv \boldsymbol{N}(x,\ y,\ z)\boldsymbol{\delta}^{\mathbf{e}} \tag{13.7-4}$$

$$n_g \times 1 = (n_g \times n_i)\,(n_i \times 1).$$

Here, n_g is the number of generalized unknowns per node, the number of independent element equations is $n_i = n_g n_n$ for an element with n_n nodes per element. The first three columns of the rectangular interpolation matrix $\boldsymbol{N}\,(x,\ y,\ z)$ use only the three displacements of the element's first node. Likewise, the $k-$th node is only associated with three columns, ending with column *3k*. Therefore, the rectangular $\boldsymbol{N}\,(x,\ y,\ z)$ can be partitioned into, and programmed as, a sequence of $n_g \times n_g$ sparse matrices associated with each element node.

The first row of (13.7-4) uses only x-displacement components:

$$u(x, y, z) = H_1(x, y, z)\, u_1^e + 0 + 0 + H_2(x, y, z)\, u_2^e + 0 + 0 \\ + \cdots + H_{n_n}(x, y, z)\, u_{n_n}^e + 0 + 0,$$

and two-thirds of the other two rows are zero. Therefore, a typical partition of the rectangular $\boldsymbol{N}(x, y, z)$ contains a scalar interpolation function, $H_k(x, y, z)$, and zeros in each row. In this three-dimensional case,

$$\boldsymbol{N}(x, y, z) = [\boldsymbol{N}_1|\boldsymbol{N}_2|\cdots|\boldsymbol{N}_{n_n}],$$

$$\boldsymbol{N}_k(x, y, z) = \begin{bmatrix} H_k(x, y, z) & 0 & 0 \\ 0 & H_k(x, y, z) & 0 \\ 0 & 0 & H_k(x, y, z) \end{bmatrix} = H_k[\boldsymbol{I}]. \tag{13.7-5}$$

This approach forces the displacement vector to be continuous at the interface between two materials with different structural properties. That is the physically correct behavior for stress analysis. However, the reader is warned that in electromagnetic applications this vector continuity approach cannot be used. That is because vectors like the electric field intensity, $\vec{E}$, magnetic field intensity, $\vec{H}$, and the magnetic vector potential, $\vec{A}$, have either their normal or their tangential vector component discontinuous at a material interface with different electrical or magnetic properties. Then the interpolations must be based on vectors on the element edges and faces. These are called "edge-based elements" or "vector elements" in contrast to the procedure covered here which are referred to in electrical engineering as "node-based elements". In electrical engineering, such vector interpolations are denoted as $\vec{N}(r, s, t)$.

It was shown earlier that the element interpolations in a domain reduce to a boundary interpolation set when a face or edge or node of the element falls on the boundary of the domain. For example, assume that a constant z-coordinate face, Γ^b, of the element falls on the boundary, Γ. Then the displacement interpolation of the surface displacements, $\boldsymbol{N}^b$, is just a degeneration (subset) of the element interpolation:

$$\boldsymbol{N}^b(x, y) \subset_b \boldsymbol{N}(x, y, z), \quad \text{for } \Gamma^b \quad \text{on } \Gamma. \tag{13.7-6}$$

13.8 Mechanical Work in Matrix Form

Having converted the displacements into matrix forms in (13.7-4) and (13.7-6), the mechanical work definition of (13.3-3) can now be written in terms of the element displacement DOFs, and thereby define element and system load vectors. Begin with the mechanical work definition for any elastic system:

$$W = \int_V \boldsymbol{\delta}^T \boldsymbol{f}\, dV + \int_S \boldsymbol{\delta}^T \boldsymbol{T}\, dS + \sum_{k=1}^{k=n_P} \boldsymbol{\delta}_k^T \boldsymbol{F}_k.$$

The external point load work summation can be replaced as with a scalar product of the system displacements, $\boldsymbol{\delta}$, and a system point load vector, $\boldsymbol{F}$, that is zero except where point loads are input at a node:

$$\sum_{k=1}^{k=n_P} \boldsymbol{\delta}_k^T \boldsymbol{F}_k = \boldsymbol{\delta}^T\ \boldsymbol{F} = \boldsymbol{F}^T \boldsymbol{\delta}. \tag{13.8-1}$$

Having divided the elastic domain and its surface with a mesh, the volume integral of any quantity becomes the sum of the integrals of that quantity in the element:

$$\int_V \_dV = \sum_{e=1}^{n_e} \int_V^e \_\ dV.$$

Therefore, the work done by body forces becomes

$$\int_V \boldsymbol{\delta}^T \boldsymbol{f}\, dV = \sum_{e=1}^{n_e} \int_V^e (\boldsymbol{N}(x,\, y,\, z)\boldsymbol{\delta}^e)^T \boldsymbol{f}(x,\, y,\, z) dV$$

$$= \sum_{e=1}^{n_e} \boldsymbol{\delta}^{e^T} \int_V^e \boldsymbol{N}^T(x,\, y,\, z)\boldsymbol{f}(x,\, y,\, z) dV \equiv \sum_{e=1}^{n_e} \boldsymbol{\delta}^{e^T} \boldsymbol{c}_f^e.$$

This defines the resultant element nodal load resultants due to body forces:

$$\boldsymbol{c}_f^e \equiv \int_V^e \boldsymbol{N}^T(x,\, y,\, z)\boldsymbol{f}(x,\, y,\, z) dV. \tag{13.8-2}$$

$$(n_i \times 1)\ =\ (n_i \times n_g)(n_g \times 1).$$

The remaining contribution to the external work due to surface tractions, $\int_S \boldsymbol{\delta}^T \boldsymbol{T}\, dS$, is also split by the mesh generation to sum over the boundary segments having a non-zero traction:

$$\int_S \boldsymbol{\delta}^T \boldsymbol{T}\, dS = \sum_{b=1}^{n_b} \int_\Gamma^b \left(\boldsymbol{N}^b(x,\, y)\, \boldsymbol{\delta}^b\right)^T \boldsymbol{T}(x,\, y) dS$$

$$= \sum_{b=1}^{n_b} \boldsymbol{\delta}^{b^T} \int_\Gamma^b \boldsymbol{N}^{b^T}(x,\, y) \boldsymbol{T}(x,\, y\,) dS \equiv \sum_{b=1}^{n_b} \boldsymbol{\delta}^{b^T} \boldsymbol{c}_T^b.$$

This defines the resultant boundary segment nodal load resultants due to tractions:

$$\boldsymbol{c}_T^b \equiv \int_\Gamma^b \boldsymbol{N}^{b^T}(x,\, y)\, \boldsymbol{T}(x,\, y) dS \qquad (13.8\text{-}3)$$

$$\left(n_g n_{nb} \times 1\right) \; = \; \left(n_g n_{nb} \times n_g\right) \left(n_g \times 1\right).$$

where n_b is the number of boundary segments and $1 \leq n_{nb} \leq n_n$ is the number of nodes on the segment.

When each set of element displacements, $\boldsymbol{\delta}^e$, are identified, using the element node connection list, with their positions in the system displacement vector, $\boldsymbol{\delta}$, then scattering all of the body force node resultants gives the assembled system-level body force resultant:

$$\sum_{e=1}^{n_e} \boldsymbol{\delta}^{e^T} \boldsymbol{c}_f^e = \boldsymbol{\delta}^T \boldsymbol{c}_f.$$

When each set of boundary displacements, $\boldsymbol{\delta}^b$, is identified, using the boundary node connection list, with its positions in the system displacement vector, $\boldsymbol{\delta}$, then scattering all of the surface traction node resultants gives the assembled system-level traction resultant:

$$\sum_{b=1}^{n_b} \boldsymbol{\delta}^{b^T} \boldsymbol{c}_T^b = \boldsymbol{\delta}^T \boldsymbol{c}_T.$$

Some authors like to introduce an "assembly symbol", A, to emphasize that the system level body force resultant, $\boldsymbol{c}_f$, is the assembly (scattering) of all of the element level body force resultants, $\boldsymbol{c}_f^e$, and that the system level surface traction resultant, $\boldsymbol{c}_T$, is the assembly (scattering) of all of the boundary segment level traction resultants, $\boldsymbol{c}_T^b$:

$$\boldsymbol{c}_f = A_e\, \boldsymbol{c}_f^e \qquad \text{and} \qquad \boldsymbol{c}_T = A_b\, \boldsymbol{c}_T^b \qquad (13.8\text{-}4)$$

$$\left(n_g n_m \times 1\right) \Leftarrow_+ \left(n_i \times 1\right) \qquad \left(n_g n_m \times 1\right) \Leftarrow_+ \left(n_i \times 1\right).$$

Here, the number of system equations is $n_d = n_g n_m$, for a mesh with n_m nodes. Finally, the external work is found to be the scalar product of the system displacement vector and a set of assembled force vectors:

$$W = \boldsymbol{\delta}^T \boldsymbol{c}_f + \boldsymbol{\delta}^T \boldsymbol{c}_T + \boldsymbol{\delta}^T \boldsymbol{F} \equiv \boldsymbol{\delta}^T \boldsymbol{c}. \tag{13.8-5}$$

Here $\boldsymbol{c}$ denotes the system resultant forces to which the initial strain forces will be added.

13.9 The Strain–Displacement Matrix

Next the six strains within an element, $\boldsymbol{\varepsilon}$, also need to be defined in terms of the element displacements, $\boldsymbol{\delta^e}$. This leads to a larger rectangular matrix, usually denoted in the finite element literature as $\boldsymbol{B^e}(x, y, z)$, which is known as the strain–displacement matrix. It has six rows and $n_i = n_n n_g$ columns that correspond to the element displacements. Recall that each component can be interpolated using the scalar forms in (13.7-1). From the geometric definitions of Section 13.4, the six strain components are

$$\varepsilon_x = \frac{\partial u}{\partial x} = \frac{\partial \boldsymbol{H}(x, y, z)}{\partial x} \boldsymbol{u^e}, \quad \varepsilon_y = \frac{\partial v}{\partial y} = \frac{\partial \boldsymbol{H}(x, y, z)}{\partial y} \boldsymbol{v^e},$$

$$\varepsilon_z = \frac{\partial w}{\partial z} = \frac{\partial \boldsymbol{H}(x, y, z)}{\partial z} \boldsymbol{w^e},$$

$$\gamma_{xy} = \frac{\partial u}{\partial y} + \frac{\partial v}{\partial x} = \frac{\partial \boldsymbol{H}(x, y, z)}{\partial y} \boldsymbol{u^e} + \frac{\partial \boldsymbol{H}(x, y, z)}{\partial x} \boldsymbol{v^e},$$

$$\gamma_{xz} = \frac{\partial u}{\partial z} + \frac{\partial w}{\partial x} = \frac{\partial \boldsymbol{H}(x, y, z)}{\partial z} \boldsymbol{u^e} + \frac{\partial \boldsymbol{H}(x, y, z)}{\partial x} \boldsymbol{w^e},$$

$$\gamma_{yz} = \frac{\partial v}{\partial z} + \frac{\partial w}{\partial y} = \frac{\partial \boldsymbol{H}(x, y, z)}{\partial z} \boldsymbol{v^e} + \frac{\partial \boldsymbol{H}(x, y, z)}{\partial y} \boldsymbol{w^e}.$$

These can be re-arranged into the matrix format

$$\begin{Bmatrix} \varepsilon_x \\ \varepsilon_y \\ \varepsilon_z \\ \gamma_{xy} \\ \gamma_{xz} \\ \gamma_{yz} \end{Bmatrix}^e = \boldsymbol{\varepsilon^e} = \boldsymbol{B^e}(x, y, z)\boldsymbol{\delta^e} \tag{13.9-1}$$

$$(n_r \times 1) = (n_r \times n_i)\,(n_i \times 1).$$

The first row has triplet entries of

$$\varepsilon_x = \frac{\partial H_1}{\partial x} u_1^e + 0 + 0 + \frac{\partial H_2}{\partial x} u_2^e + 0 + 0 + \cdots + \frac{\partial H_{n_n}}{\partial x} u_{n_n}^e + 0 + 0,$$

and the last row has triplet entries of

$$\gamma_{yz} = 0 + \frac{\partial H_1}{\partial z} v_1^e + \frac{\partial H_1}{\partial y} w_1^e + \cdots + 0 + \frac{\partial H_1}{\partial z} v_{n_n}^e + \frac{\partial H_1}{\partial y} w_{n_n}^e.$$

Like the vector interpolations, the rectangular $\boldsymbol{B^e}$ strain–displacement matrix can be partitioned into, and programmed as, rectangular nodal contributions $\boldsymbol{B^e}(x, y, z) = \left[B_1^e | B_2^e | \cdots | B_{n_n}^e\right]$, with a typical classic definition partition (with $n_r = 6$ rows of strains and $n_g = 3$ displacement component columns) being

$$\boldsymbol{B_k^e} = \begin{bmatrix} H_{k,x} & 0 & 0 \\ 0 & H_{k,y} & 0 \\ 0 & 0 & H_{k,z} \\ H_{k,y} & H_{k,x} & 0 \\ H_{k,z} & 0 & H_{k,x} \\ 0 & H_{k,z} & H_{k,y} \end{bmatrix}, \quad H_{k,x} = \partial H_k / \partial x \; H_{k,y} = \partial H_k / \partial y.$$

$$(n_r \times n_g) \tag{13.9-2}$$

All five options for the strain–displacement choices listed in Fig. 13.4-2 are included in the single script *B_matrix_elastic.m* in the functions library.

13.10 Stiffness Matrix

The strain energy of (13.5-1) defines the stiffness matrix of an elastic system by relating its integrand to the unknown displacements:

$$\begin{aligned} U &= \frac{1}{2} \int_V \boldsymbol{\sigma}^T \boldsymbol{\varepsilon} \, dV = \frac{1}{2} \sum_{e=1}^{n_e} \int_V^e \boldsymbol{\sigma}^{e^T} \boldsymbol{\varepsilon}^e dV \\ &= \frac{1}{2} \sum_{e=1}^{n_e} \int_V^e \left(\boldsymbol{E^e} \boldsymbol{\varepsilon}^e\right)^T \boldsymbol{\varepsilon}^e dV \\ &= \frac{1}{2} \sum_{e=1}^{n_e} \int_V^e \boldsymbol{\varepsilon}^{e^T} \boldsymbol{E}^{e^T} \boldsymbol{\varepsilon}^e \, dV = \frac{1}{2} \sum_{e=1}^{n_e} \int_V^e \left(\boldsymbol{B^e} \boldsymbol{\delta}^e\right)^T \boldsymbol{E}^e \left(\boldsymbol{B^e} \boldsymbol{\delta}^e\right) dV \\ &= \frac{1}{2} \sum_{e=1}^{n_e} \boldsymbol{\delta}^{e\,T} \left[\int_V^e \boldsymbol{B}^{e^T} \boldsymbol{E^e} \boldsymbol{B}^e \, dV\right] \boldsymbol{\delta}^e = \frac{1}{2} \sum_{e=1}^{n_e} \boldsymbol{\delta}^{e\,T} [\boldsymbol{S}^e] \boldsymbol{\delta}^e. \end{aligned}$$

So that the element stiffness matrix is defined as

$$\begin{aligned} \boldsymbol{S}^e &= \int_V^e \boldsymbol{B}^{e^T} \boldsymbol{E}^e \, \boldsymbol{B}^e \, dV \\ (n_i \times n_i) &= (n_i \times n_r)\,(n_r \times n_r)\,(n_r \times n_i). \end{aligned} \tag{13.10-1}$$

13.11 Work Done by Initial Strains*

When any initial strain is present, its name implies the fact that it is constant from the beginning of an imposed mechanical strain (and stress) to the end of that strain. Therefore, the work that it does differs from (13.5-1) by a factor of two and is

$$W_0 = \int_V \boldsymbol{\sigma}^T \boldsymbol{\varepsilon_0} \, dV,$$

$$\begin{aligned} W_0 &= \int_V \boldsymbol{\sigma}^T \boldsymbol{\varepsilon_0} \, dV = \sum_{e=1}^{n_e} \int_V^e \boldsymbol{\sigma}^{e^T} \boldsymbol{\varepsilon}_0^e \, dV \\ &= \sum_{e=1}^{n_e} \int_V^e (\boldsymbol{B}^e \boldsymbol{\delta}^e)^T \, \boldsymbol{E}^e \, \boldsymbol{\varepsilon}_0^e \, dV. \end{aligned} \tag{13.11-1}$$

This defines the element initial strain resultant force vector as

$$\begin{aligned} W_0 &= \sum_{e=1}^{n_e} \boldsymbol{\delta}^{e^T} \boldsymbol{c}_0^e \quad \text{with}\, \boldsymbol{c}_0^e = \int_V^e \boldsymbol{B}^{e^T} \boldsymbol{E}^e \, \boldsymbol{\varepsilon}_0^e \, dV \\ (n_i \times 1) &= (n_i \times n_r)\,(n_r \times n_r)\,(n_r \times 1). \end{aligned} \tag{13.11-2}$$

13.12 Matrix Equilibrium Equations

Having converted all of the work and strain energy contributions in their interpolated matrix forms, the matrix equations of equilibrium are

$$\boldsymbol{S}\,\boldsymbol{\delta} = \boldsymbol{c_0} + \boldsymbol{c_P} + \boldsymbol{c_T} + \boldsymbol{c_X} + \boldsymbol{c_{NBC}} \equiv \boldsymbol{c}. \tag{13.12-1}$$

Here, all of the element and boundary contributions are assembled into the large system matrices by direct scattering of the rows and columns, or (in theory) by the direct Boolean algebra:

$$\boldsymbol{S} = \sum_{e=1}^{n_e} \boldsymbol{\beta}^{e^T} [\boldsymbol{S}^e] \boldsymbol{\beta}^e, \; \boldsymbol{c_X} = \sum_{e=1}^{n_e} \boldsymbol{\beta}^{e^T} \boldsymbol{c}_{\boldsymbol{X}}^e, \; \boldsymbol{c_T} = \sum_{b=1}^{n_b} \boldsymbol{\beta}^{b^T} \boldsymbol{c}_{\boldsymbol{T}}^b.$$

13.13 Kinetic Energy and Dynamics*

Later in the examination of the dynamics of solids it is necessary to include the kinetic energy converted to the same matrix notation. The displacement components at any time, τ, at any point in an element are

$$\begin{Bmatrix} u(x,\, y,\, z, \tau) \\ v(x,\, y,\, z, \tau) \\ w(x,\, y,\, z, \tau) \end{Bmatrix} = \boldsymbol{u}\,(x,\, y,\, z, \tau) \equiv \boldsymbol{N}(x,\, y,\, z)\boldsymbol{\delta}^{\boldsymbol{e}}(\tau). \qquad (13.13\text{-}1)$$

The velocity is

$$\dot{u} = \frac{\partial \boldsymbol{u}(x,\, y,\, z, \tau)}{\partial \tau} \equiv \boldsymbol{N}(x,\, y,\, z)\frac{\partial \boldsymbol{\delta}^{\boldsymbol{e}}(\tau)}{\partial \tau} \equiv \boldsymbol{N}(x,\, y,\, z)\dot{\delta^e}, \quad (13.13\text{-}2)$$

where a dot above a term denotes its partial derivative with respect to time. The kinetic energy of a point mass is one-half the mass times the velocity squared. For a material of mass density of ρ, the kinetic energy of an element volume is

$$\begin{aligned} KE^e &= \frac{1}{2}\int_{V^e} \dot{u}\cdot\dot{u}\,\rho\, dV = \frac{1}{2}\int_{V^e} \dot{u}^T \rho\, \dot{u}\, dV \\ &= \frac{1}{2}\int_{V^e} \left(\boldsymbol{N}(x,\, y,\, z)\dot{\delta^e}\right)^T \rho \left(\boldsymbol{N}(x,\, y,\, z)\dot{\delta^e}\right) dV \\ KE^e &= \frac{1}{2}\dot{\delta^e}^T \left[\int_{V^e} \boldsymbol{N}\,(x,\, y,\, z)^T \rho^e \boldsymbol{N}\,(x,\, y,\, z) dV\right]\dot{\delta^e} \\ &\equiv \frac{1}{2}\dot{\delta^e}^T \boldsymbol{m}^{\boldsymbol{e}}\dot{\delta^e}. \end{aligned} \qquad (13.13\text{-}3)$$

This defines the square symmetric element mass matrix, which is the same size as the element stiffness matrix:

$$\boldsymbol{m}^{\boldsymbol{e}} \equiv \int_{V^e} \boldsymbol{N}(x,\, y,\, z)^T \rho^e \boldsymbol{N}(x,\, y,\, z) dV. \qquad (13.13\text{-}4)$$

The total system mass matrix, $\boldsymbol{M}$, is assembled in exactly the same way as the system stiffness matrix. When the system acceleration, $\ddot{\delta}$, is included, the equilibrium equation in (13.13-1) becomes (without dampening) the matrix equation of motion:

$$\boldsymbol{M}\,\ddot{\delta}\,(\tau) + \boldsymbol{S}\,\boldsymbol{\delta}\,(\tau) = \boldsymbol{c}\,(\tau),$$

which is also subject to the initial conditions on $\dot{\delta}(0)$ and $\ddot{\delta}(0)$ at time $\tau = 0$. Of course, damping proportional to the velocity, say $\boldsymbol{D}$, is usually present and the equations of motion are

$$\boldsymbol{M}\,\ddot{\delta}\,(\tau) + \boldsymbol{D}\;\dot{\delta}(\tau) + \boldsymbol{S}\,\boldsymbol{\delta}\,(\tau) = \boldsymbol{c}(\tau). \tag{13.13-5}$$

Since damping can be very difficult to define accurately, it is commonly assumed to be the sum of a portion, α, of the mass matrix and a portion, β, of the stiffness matrix, as follows:

$$\boldsymbol{D} \approx \alpha \boldsymbol{S} + \beta\,\boldsymbol{M}. \tag{13.13-6}$$

Of course, the dynamic equations of motion must have the Dirichlet boundary conditions enforced and be modified to satisfy the initial conditions before a unique time history can be simulated.

13.14 Plane–stress and Plane–strain

The finite element method easily models three-dimensional solids including the most general anisotropic and non-homogeneous materials, with general loadings and boundary conditions. The provided Matlab scripts can execute such models, but mainly with the external support of a three-dimensional mesh generator. However, here the three most common two-dimensional model simplifications will be emphasized, mainly because of the educational aspects of two-dimensional graphical displays of the results.

The plane–stress simplification in Fig. 13.1-1 is the most common of all planar simplifications and is taught to most aerospace, civil, and mechanical engineers in required courses in solid mechanics. Plane–stress analysis approximates a very thin solid $(t \ll L)$ where its bounding z-planes are free of stress $(\sigma_z = \tau_{xz} = \tau_{yz} = 0)$, but the normal strain is not zero, $\varepsilon_z \neq 0$. The normal strain can be recovered, including the effects of an initial thermal strain, in post-processing calculations from $\varepsilon_z = \alpha \Delta T - \upsilon\left(\sigma_x + \sigma_y\right)/E$. The active displacements at all points are the x- and y-components of the displacement vector, $\boldsymbol{u}^T = \left[u(x,\,y)\;v(x,\,y)\right]$. The retained stress and strain components needed for the plane–stress analysis (see Fig. 13.4-2) are $\boldsymbol{\sigma}^T = \left[\sigma_x\;\sigma_y\;\tau_{xz}\right]$ and $\boldsymbol{\varepsilon}^T = \left[\varepsilon_x\;\varepsilon_y\;\gamma_{xy}\right]$.

In the software provided, the strains (and stresses) are ordered as in Fig. 13.4-2. The algorithm for filling the full $\boldsymbol{B}^e$ matrix for plane–stress or plane–strain applications is shown in *B_planar_elastic.m* in Fig. 13.14-1. The strains are related to the stresses through the reduced Hooke law:

```
function [B] = B_planar_elastic (DGH, n_n)
% * * * * * * * * * * * * * * * * * * * * * * * * * * *
%      ELASTICITY STRAIN-DISPLACEMENT RELATIONS  (B)
%  For plane-stress or plane-strain: n_g = 2, n_r = 3
% * * * * * * * * * * * * * * * * * * * * * * * * * * *
% B   = strain-displacement matrix    (n_r, n_n * n_g)
% DGH = global derivatives of H       (n_s, n_n * n_g)
% n_g = number of displacements per node
% n_n = number of nodes per element
%       Stress and strain order is: xx, yy, xy

n_g = 2 ; n_r = 3     ; % for planar stress
n_i = n_n * n_g       ; % number of element dof
B = zeros (n_r, n_i) ; % initialize strain-displacement

for J = 1:n_n ; % loop over nodes ==>> ==>> ===>> ===>>
  K = n_g * (J - 1) + 1     ; % u-column contribution
  L = K + 1                 ; % v-column contribution
  B (1, K) = DGH (1, J)     ; % du/dx for normal xx
  B (3, K) = DGH (2, J)     ; % du/dy for shear  xy
  B (2, L) = DGH (2, J)     ; % dv/dy for normal yy
  B (3, L) = DGH (1, J)     ; % dv/dx for shear  xy
end ; % for J nodes of element  <<=== <<=== <<=== <<===
% end B_planar_elastic
```

Fig. 13.14-1: Strain–displacement matrix for plane–stress or –strain.

```
function [E_e] = E_plane_stress (E, nu, G)
% * * * * * * * * * * * * * * * * * * * * * * * * * * *
%      PLANE STRESS CONSTITUTIVE MATRIX DEFINITION
%          STRESS COMPONENT ORDER: XX, YY, XY
% * * * * * * * * * * * * * * * * * * * * * * * * * * *
% E   = Young's modulus of elasticity
% G   = shear modulus (not independent)
% nu  = Poisson's ratio
% E_e = constitutive matrix
% n_r = number of rows in B and E matrices = 3

if ( nargin == 2 )                    ; % classic definition
  G  = 0.5 * E / (1 + nu)                      ; % in theory
end                                  ; % if special material
c_1 = E / (1 - nu^2) ; c_2 = c_1 * nu          ; % constants

E_e = zeros (3, 3)                             ; % largely 0
E_e(1, 1) = c_1 ; E_e(2, 1) = c_2 ;              ; % normals
E_e(1, 2) = c_2 ; E_e(2, 2) = c_1 ;              ; % normals
E_e(3, 3) = G                                      ; % shear
% end E_plane_stress
```

Fig. 13.14-2: Constitutive arrays for plane–stress analysis.

$$\begin{Bmatrix} \sigma_x \\ \sigma_y \\ \tau_{xy} \end{Bmatrix} = \frac{E}{1-\upsilon^2} \begin{bmatrix} 1 & \upsilon & 0 \\ \upsilon & 1 & 0 \\ 0 & 0 & (1-\upsilon)/2 \end{bmatrix} \begin{Bmatrix} \varepsilon_x \\ \varepsilon_y \\ \gamma_{xy} \end{Bmatrix} - \frac{E\alpha\Delta T}{1-\upsilon} \begin{Bmatrix} 1 \\ 1 \\ 0 \end{Bmatrix}. \tag{13.14-1}$$

The Matlab script to form the material E matrix for plane–stress is shown in Fig. 13.14-2.

After any finite element stress analysis is completed, the stresses and/or strains are substituted into the appropriate material-dependent failure criteria to determine if any point in the material has yielded or "failed" and thus violates the assumptions that justified a linear analysis. The reader is simply reminded that just computing the displacements, strains, and stresses *does not* complete any elasticity analysis.

For two-dimensional problems, the differential volume is $dV = \int_A^e t^e(x, y)dA$, where t^e is the local thickness of the planar section, A^e. Usually, the thickness is constant in each element. If the thickness is the same constant in all elements, and there are no external point loads, then it cancels out since it appears in every integral. Many commercial finite element systems, and the application scripts supplied here, allow the plane–stress elements to have different thicknesses. When the elements do not have the same constant thickness, the analysis is called a 2.5-dimensional analysis. It approximates a three-dimensional part and can be used in a preliminary analysis to guide the local mesh control needed in the actual three-dimensional study. Alternately, it can be considered as a useful validation check of a prior three-dimensional analysis.

Usually, the stresses in a 2.5-dimensional model are accurate, except in the immediate region adjacent to changes in the element thicknesses. If the thickness is to be allowed to continuously vary, then it is usually input at the element nodes and interpolated to give the local thickness, $t^e(x, y)$. A variable thickness element clearly requires the stiffness matrix to be evaluated by numerical integration with an appropriately higher number of integration points. If the thickness is continuously varying, then it can be input as an additional fake coordinate and is simple to gather to the nodes of each element for interpolation. If only a constant thickness program is available, the upper and lower bounds on displacements and

```
function [E_e] = E_plane_strain (E, nu, G)
% * * * * * * * * * * * * * * * * * * * * * * * * * * * *
%      PLANE STRAIN CONSTITUTIVE MATRIX DEFINITION
%          STRESS COMPONENT ORDER: XX, YY, XY
% * * * * * * * * * * * * * * * * * * * * * * * * * * * *
% E   = Young's modulus of elasticity
% G   = shear modulus (not independent)
% nu  = Poisson's ratio
% E_e = constitutive matrix
% n_r = number of rows in B and E matrices = 3

if ( nargin == 2 )                ; % classic definition
  G  = 0.5 * E / (1 + nu)                 ; % in theory
end                              ; % if special material
c_1 = E / (1 + nu) / (1 - nu - nu)        ; % constant
c_2 = c_1 * nu ; c3 = c1 * (1 - nu)       ; % constant

E_e = zeros (3, 3)                        ; % largely 0
E_e(1, 1) = c_3 ; E_e(2, 1) = c_2 ;         ; % normals
E_e(1, 2) = c_2 ; E_e(2, 2) = c_3 ;         ; % normals
E_e(3, 3) = G                                ; % shear
% end E_plane_strain
```

Fig. 13.14-3: Constitutive arrays for plane–strain analysis.

stresses can be estimated by running one model with the minimum thickness and a second with the maximum thickness. The Matlab script to form the material $\boldsymbol{E}$ matrix for plane–strain is shown in Fig. 13.14-3.

13.15 Plane–Stress Q10 Application

In undergraduate mechanics of materials, the two-dimensional applications usually consider the special case of plane–stress analysis. Here, to illustrate the versatility of the Matlab plane–stress script provided, it is applied here to the U-clamp in Fig. 13.15-1. Approximations of that part are a combination of straight beam theory and curved beam theory. The normal stress in straight beam varies linearly through the thickness and is maximum at the surfaces. Normal stress in a curved beam increases hyperbolically as the radius decreases, and the largest normal stress is expected at the innermost material in section a-a.

Here the material is aluminum with an elastic modulus, and Poisson's ratio of $E = 68{,}900\,\text{MPa}$, and $\nu = 0.33$. The clamp is loaded at its ends by two equal and opposite forces of $P = 8{,}550\,\text{N}$. The clamp has the inverted T cross-section shown in Fig. 13.15-1,

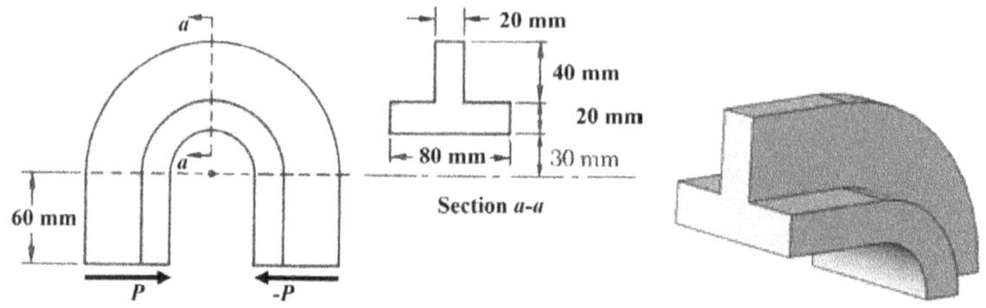

Fig. 13.15-1: U-clamp geometry (circular beam plus cantilever beams).

with its outer web 20 mm wide and 40 mm deep, and the inner flange is 80 mm wide and 20 mm deep. The inner surface of the section has a radius of 30 mm.

Commercial finite element systems, like SolidWorks Simulation from Dassault Systems used here, make it easy to solve such problems. However, any such simulation should be validated, or bound, by other methods. Beam theory, constant thickness plane–stress, and variable thickness plane–stress models are used here as comparison solutions.

First, some peak stresses and deflections will be predicted from the mechanics of materials. An analytic curved beam approximation shows a hyperbolic curve variation of the circumferential strain between the outer low strain and the higher inner strain. It estimates the maximum circumferential stress and maximum von Mises stress as about 50 MPa at the point where the inner arc crosses the axis of symmetry (node 1 on elements 1 and 2). Curved beam theory also yields a radial stress along the symmetry line that vanishes at the inner and outer radii. However, the radial stress can be large on the interior of the beam. That radial stress has a step increase where the thickness decreases at the junction of the flange and the web sections. The shear stress is zero along the symmetry axis, so the von Mises effective stress is a combination of the circumferential and radial stresses. A plot of the curve beam theory stresses along the symmetry line is shown in Fig. 13.15-2 and will be compared to the plane–stress and three-dimensional solid finite element estimates.

The outward deflection where the load P is applied is obtained from mechanics theory using Castigliano's theorem. That deflection consists of four contributions: the shear force P, and its variable moment acting on the curved section, the rigid body rotation of the straight section due to the slope at the end of the curved portion, and

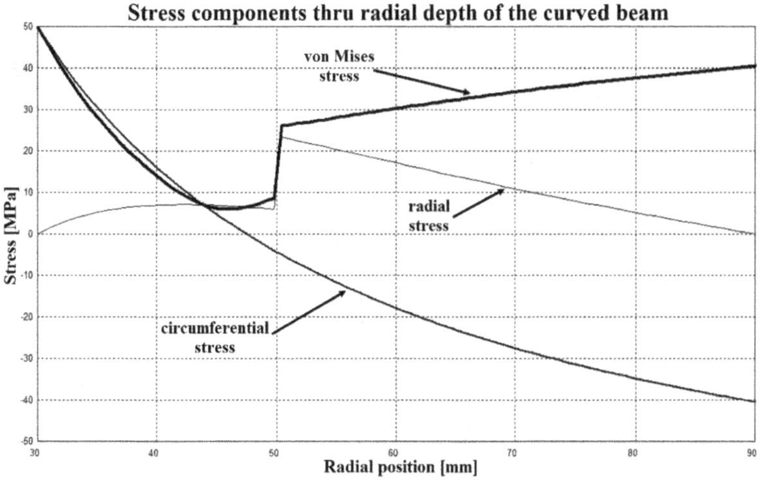

Fig. 13.15-2: Curved beam theory symmetry line (section a-a) stresses.

the outward deflection of the straight section acting as a cantilever beam at the end of the curved portion. Using half symmetry, the curved portion end deflection and slope are estimated as 0.0481 mm and 0.0014 radians, respectively. The rotation due to the slope contributes an end deflection of 0.0838 mm, and the cantilever bending deflection is 0.01395 mm giving a total estimated deflection relative to the centerline of 0.146 mm.

Half symmetry plane–stress models are used, and will be compared to the above curved beam estimates and to a quarter symmetry solid model. All approaches are tabulated in what follows for comparison. The problem is modeled as a plane–stress system with the Matlab library provided. First, constant minimum and maximum thicknesses were run as likely bounds on the solution, and then portions of the mesh were assigned either of the two thicknesses. It should be noted that averaged stress plots along a thickness change or a material change line are not conservative, in general.

For this part, stresses depend only on the shape of the part. The displacements always depend on the material properties. The meshes are shown in Fig. 13.15-3. The script accepts T6 or $Q9$ area quadratic elements and the $L3$ curved line element; while SolidWorks only utilizes the quadratic ten-noded tetrahedra. The initial crude mesh sizes

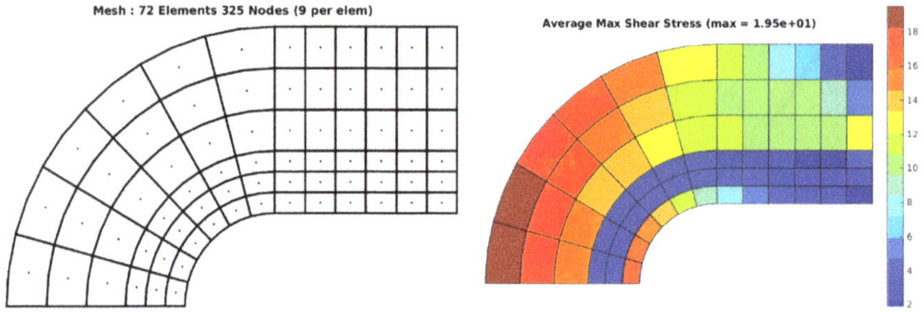

Fig. 13.15-3: Meshes: two and a half-dimensional plane–stress bi-quadratic quads, three-dimensional quadratic tetrahedrons.

are about the same and both types are easily refined with automatic mesh generators.

The bottom horizontal edge (plane) is a symmetry restraint with zero vertical displacements. The vertical edges (plane) of the right-most elements carry the opening (vertical) force, P (and $P/2$). The loaded nodes are shown in the right-hand side of Fig. 13.15-3. Those script nodes are identified by input files *msh_ebc.txt* and *msh_pt_loads.txt*, respectively. Any FEA must have enough restraints sufficient to prevent rigid body translations and rotations. Otherwise, the system stiffness matrix is singular and no solution can be obtained. The above restraint prevents translation in the y-direction and rotation about the z-axis (normal to the page). However, a translation in the x-direction can occur and must be prevented. Therefore, the x-displacement at the inner radius node was set to zero. That means that all x-displacements are relative to that point. Since no loads are applied in the x-direction, the reaction force recovered at that point will be zero. Of course, the vertical reaction forces at the restrained nodes will sum to be equal and opposite to the vertical loads applied at the end of the clamp. For the solid model, the vertical symmetry plane has no normal displacement. That eliminates the z-axis rigid body translation, and rigid body rotations about the x- and the y-axes.

To account for the two different plane–stress thickness regions, two different element types were input (via data file *msh_typ_nodes.txt*). That means that only two sets of properties were required. Those property sets are the elastic modulus, Poisson's ratio, and the element thickness. Those two property lines were input via *msh_properties.txt*. The first three innermost element layers (in Fig. 13.15-3) were defined as type 2 elements and were assigned the maximum thickness. The amplified nodal displacement vectors are shown in Fig. 13.15-4, and the deformed shapes in Fig. 13.15-5. The maximum deflection is at the top corner. The plane–stress 2.5-dimensional estimate is 0.255 mm, while the full three-dimensional result is about 0.292 mm.

The peak radial and von Mises stresses (see Fig. 13.15-2) are expected to occur along the horizontal symmetry line (plane), with the maximum at the inner radius. For a ductile material like this one, failure would be predicted by either the von Mises (effective) stress, or the maximum shear stress (half the Intensity). For the 2.5-dimensional model, node averaging of stresses along the thickness change line is questionable, thus the averages in each element over

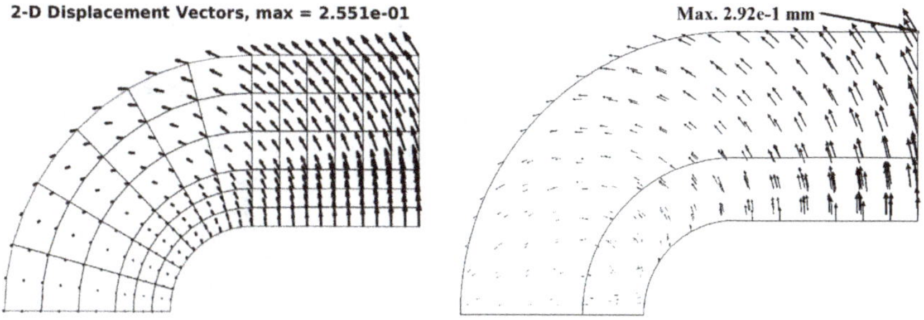

Fig. 13.15-4: 2.5-dimensional and three-dimensional amplified nodal displacement vectors (mm).

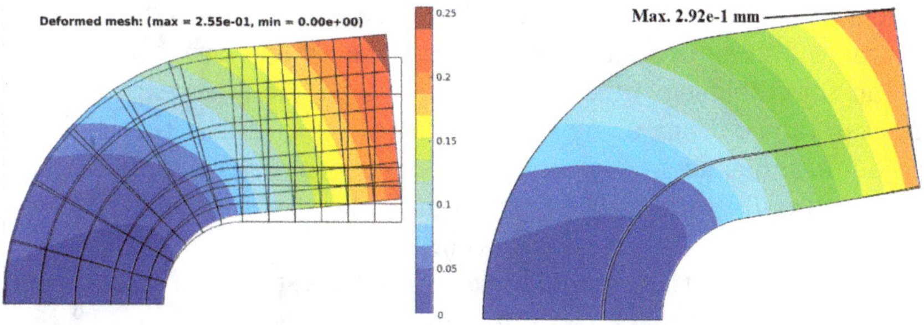

Fig. 13.15-5: Amplified 2.5-dimensional and three-dimensional deformed shapes (mm).

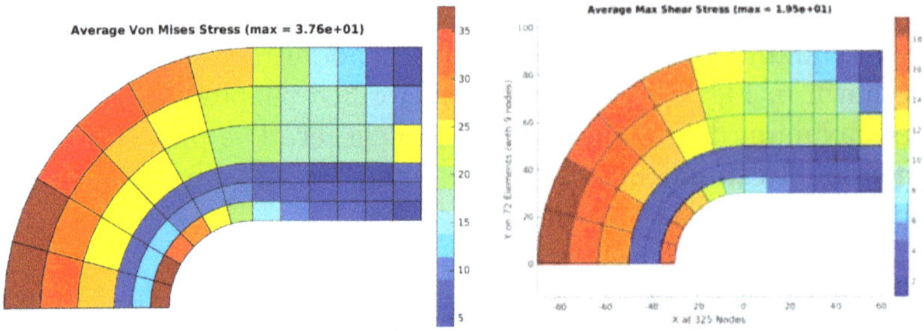

Fig. 13.15-6: 2.5-Dimensional element averaged von Mises stress (left) and max two-dimensional shear stress.

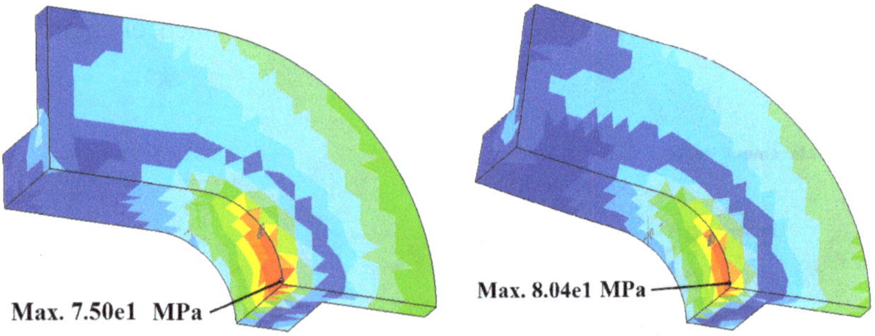

Fig. 13.15-7: Three-dimensional element averaged von Mises stress (left) and twice the max three-dimensional shear stress.

its nine integration points are shown first in Figs. 13.15-6 for Von Mises and two-dimensional maximum shear stress, respectively. The regions of peak values are about the same. The corresponding solid element averages are given in Fig. 13.15-7. Generally, the average stress values at the nodes model the physical stresses better. The averages for the two and a half-dimensional model are in Fig. 13.15-8 and the solid element averages are in Fig. 13.15-9. As expected, the largest values occur along the inner and outer arcs of the U-clamp. The inner thickness region (inner three-element layers) was originally designed quite wide to hopefully reduce the stresses there. However, the peak von Mises stress still occurs there.

Curved beam theory predicts that the largest normal stress occurs on the horizontal plane (SY) at the smallest radius. In Fig. 13.15-2, it is denoted as the circumferential stress. The 2.5-dimensional and three-dimensional circumferential stresses are shown in Fig. 13.15-10.

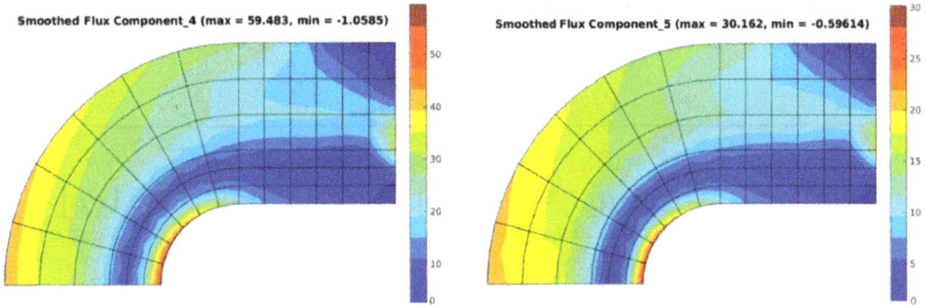

Fig. 13.15-8: 2.5-Dimensional smoothed nodal von Mises and maximum two-dimensional shear stress (MPa).

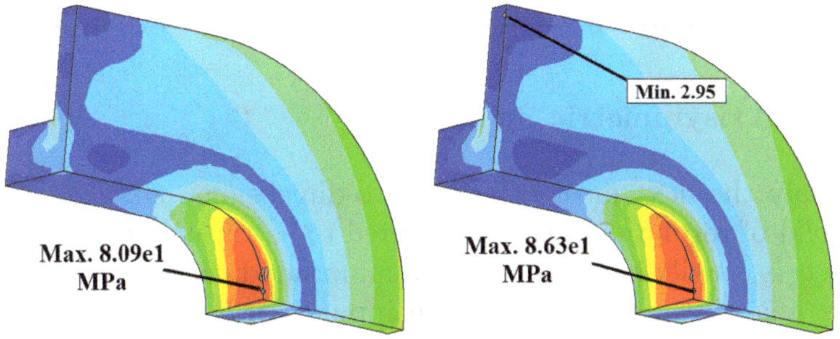

Fig. 13.15-9: Three-dimensional smoothed nodal von Mises (left) and Intensity stresses (MPa).

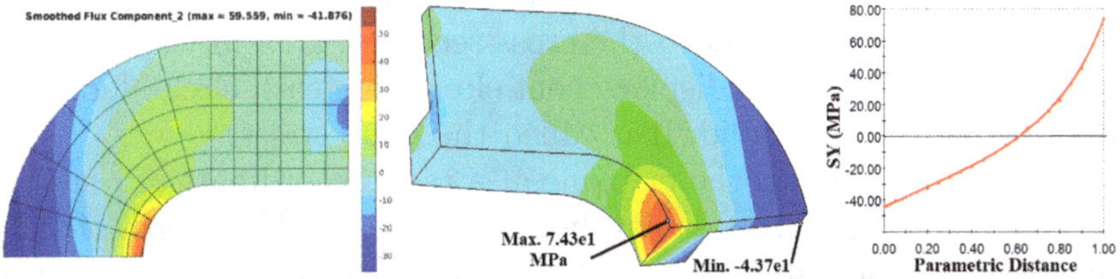

Fig. 13.15-10: 2.5-Dimensional (left), three-dimensional SY normal stress on centerline of horizontal plane (MPa).

In addition to the von Mises equivalent stress and the maximum shear stress, we are also interested in the two principal normal stresses, $P1$ and $P3$. They define the regions of maximum tension and maximum compressive stresses, but they are not displayed here.

The results of the bounding and validation estimates are summarized here:

Method	*U*max [mm]	Von Mises [MPa]	MaxShear [MPa]	*Sx* [MPa]
Theory	0.146	50.0	—	—
2D, 20 mm	0.369	131.7	64.7	76.6
2D, 80 mm	0.094	36.0	18.0	19.1
2.5D	0.221	51.9	25.5	30.7
3D	0.261	80.9	43.2	74.3

13.16 Axisymmetric Solid

Probably the next most common two-dimensional simplification is the solid of revolution and it is referred to as axisymmetric analysis. Since it is usually implemented as a minor modification of the plane–stress analysis and uses the same input coordinate data with the x-axis taken as the radial r-direction and the y-axis treated as the z-axis of revolution, the active displacements at all points are the r- and z-components of the displacement vector, $\boldsymbol{u}^T = \left[u(r,\, z)\; v(r,\, z)\right]$. In the plane that is revolved to form the volume of revolution the two normal stresses, σ_r and σ_z, and the one shear stress, τ_{rz}, are present. A new stress, σ_θ, normal to the cross-sectional area in the rz-plane occurs due to the radial displacement elongating each circumferential fiber of the revolved solid. It is called the hoop stress.

Consider a point in the rz-plane at a radial coordinate of r shown in Fig. 13.16-1. Before a radial displacement of u, the length of that revolved fiber of material is $L = 2\pi r$, after the displacement it moves to position $(r + u)$ with a length of $L' = 2\pi(r + u)$, which causes a circumferential normal strain of

$$\varepsilon_\theta = (L^{'} - L)/L = (2\pi(r + u) - 2\pi r)/2\pi r = u/r, \qquad (13.16\text{-}1)$$

which is called the hoop strain. It is important to note that the hoop strain is the only strain considered herein that depends on

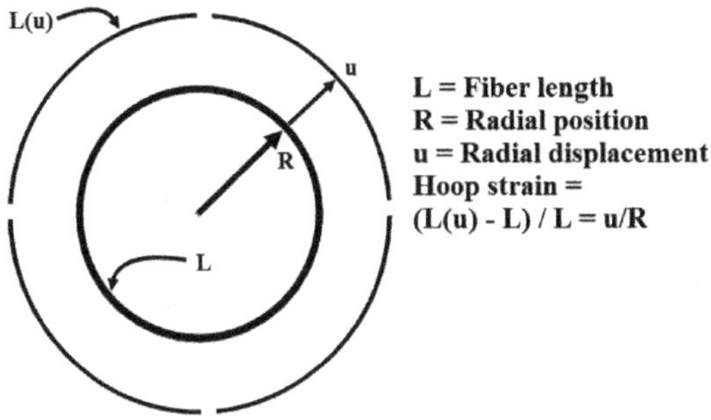

Fig. 13.16-1: Hoop strain caused by a radial displacement.

a displacement component rather than a displacement gradient. The hoop strain has an indeterminate form that goes to zero at $r = 0$. However, numerically trying to evaluate the hoop strain on the axis of revolution causes division by zero, and should be avoided. Thus, when using numerical integration to form the stiffness matrix, only rules that have points inside the element should be used. Usually the hoop strain is added to the end of the prior three strains: $\boldsymbol{\varepsilon}^T = [\varepsilon_r\ \varepsilon_z\ \gamma_{rz}\ \varepsilon_\theta]$ and the corresponding stress components (see Fig. 13.4-2) become $\boldsymbol{\sigma}^T = [\sigma_r\ \sigma_z\ \tau_{rz}\ \sigma_\theta]$.

The axisymmetric stress version adds one additional row to the definitions of the strains, as shown in *B_axisym_elastic.m* in Fig. 13.16-2, and the stresses, in (13.16-2), and the script, in Fig. 13.16-3. The axisymmetric Hooke law is

$$\begin{Bmatrix} \sigma_r \\ \sigma_z \\ \tau_{rz} \\ \sigma_\theta \end{Bmatrix} = \frac{E}{(1+v)(1-2v)} \begin{bmatrix} a & \nu & 0 & \nu \\ \nu & a & 0 & \nu \\ 0 & 0 & b & 0 \\ \nu & \nu & 0 & a \end{bmatrix} \begin{Bmatrix} \varepsilon_r \\ \varepsilon_z \\ \gamma_{rz} \\ \varepsilon_\theta \end{Bmatrix} - \frac{E\alpha\Delta T}{(1-2v)} \begin{Bmatrix} 1 \\ 1 \\ 0 \\ 1 \end{Bmatrix} \tag{13.16-2}$$

$$a = (1-v), \quad b = (1-2v)/2.$$

It is common to encounter plane–stress or axisymmetric solids that are orthotropic. Such property values are usually specified in the principal material axis directions. Denote those orthogonal directions by (n, s, t), with $n{-}s$ being the major plane and t being perpendicular

```
function [B] = B_axisym_elastic (DGH, n_n, H, R)
% * * * * * * * * * * * * * * * * * * * * * * * * * * * *
%      ELASTICITY STRAIN-DISPLACEMENT RELATIONS  (B)
%        For axisymmetric solid: n_g = 2, n_r = 4
% * * * * * * * * * * * * * * * * * * * * * * * * * * * *
% B   = strain-displacement matrix   (n_r, n_n * n_g)
% DGH = global derivatives of H      (n_s, n_n * n_g)
% H   = element interpolation matrix (n_n * n_g)
% n_g = number of displacements per node
% n_n = number of nodes per element
% n_r = number of strains (rows in B)
% R   = axisymmetric radius at the point
%       Stress and strain order is: xx, yy, xy, zz

n_g = 2 ; n_r = 4    ; % for axisymmetric stress
n_i = n_n * n_g      ; % number of element dof
B = zeros (n_r, n_i) ; % initialize strain-displacement

for J = 1:n_n ; % loop over nodes ==>> ==>> ===>> ===>>
  K = n_g * (J - 1) + 1     ; % u-column contribution
  L = K + 1                 ; % v-column contribution
  B (1, K) = DGH (1, J)     ; % du/dx for normal xx
  B (3, K) = DGH (2, J)     ; % du/dy for shear  xy
  B (2, L) = DGH (2, J)     ; % dv/dy for normal yy
  B (3, L) = DGH (1, J)     ; % dv/dx for shear  xy
  if ( R <= 0 )
    error ('zero radius in B_axisym_elastic')
  end ; % if division by zero
  B (4, K) = H (J) / R      ; % u/R hoop strain zz
end ; % for J nodes of element <<=== <<=== <<=== <<===
% end B_axisym_elastic
```

Fig. 13.16-2: Strain–displacement matrix for axisymmetric stress model.

to them. Then the strain–stress relation for an axisymmetric solid is again $\boldsymbol{\varepsilon} = \boldsymbol{E\sigma} + \boldsymbol{\alpha}\,\Delta T$:

$$\begin{Bmatrix} \varepsilon_{nn} \\ \varepsilon_{ss} \\ \varepsilon_{tt} \\ \gamma_{ns} \end{Bmatrix} = \begin{bmatrix} 1/E_n & -\upsilon_{sn}/E_s & -\upsilon_{tn}/E_t & 0 \\ -\upsilon_{ns}/E_n & 1/E_s & -\upsilon_{ts}/E_t & 0 \\ -\upsilon_{nt}/E_n & -\upsilon_{st}/E_s & 1/E_t & 0 \\ 0 & 0 & 0 & 1/G_{ns} \end{bmatrix} \begin{Bmatrix} \sigma_{nn} \\ \sigma_{ss} \\ \sigma_{tt} \\ \tau_{ns} \end{Bmatrix} + \Delta T \begin{Bmatrix} \alpha_n \\ \alpha_s \\ \alpha_t \\ 0 \end{Bmatrix}. \quad (13.16\text{-}3)$$

```
function [E_e] = E_axisym_stress (E, nu, G)
% * * * * * * * * * * * * * * * * * * * * * * * * * * * * * * *
%      AXISYMMETRIC STRESS CONSTITUTIVE MATRIX DEFINITION
%             STRESS COMPONENT ORDER: XX, YY, XY, ZZ
% * * * * * * * * * * * * * * * * * * * * * * * * * * * * * * *
% E   = Young's modulus of elasticity
% G   = shear modulus (not independent)
% nu  = Poisson's ratio
% E_e = constitutive matrix
% n_r = number of rows in B and E matrices = 4

if ( nargin == 2 )                          ; % classic definition
  G  = 0.5 * E / (1 + nu)                          ; % in theory
end                                        ; % if special material
c_1 = E / (1 + nu) / (1 - nu - nu)                  ; % constant
c_2 = c_1 * nu ; c3 = c1 * (1 - nu)                 ; % constant

E_e = zeros (4, 4)                                  ; % largely 0
E_e(1, 1) = c_3 ; E_e(2, 1) = c_2 ; E_e(4, 1) = c_2 ; % normals
E_e(1, 2) = c_2 ; E_e(2, 2) = c_3 ; E_e(4, 2) = c_2 ; % normals
E_e(3, 3) = G                                           ; % shear
E_e(1, 4) = c_2 ; E_e(2, 4) = c_2 ; E_e(4, 4) = c_3 ; % normals
% end E_axisym_stress
```

Fig. 13.16-3: Constitutive arrays for axisymmetric stress analysis.

Here, Poisson's ratios are denoted as $\upsilon_{ij} = \varepsilon_j/\varepsilon_i$, where i is the load direction and j is one of the two perpendicular contraction directions. For the case of a "transversely isotropic" material, it is isotropic in the $n - s$ plane but not isotropic in the t-direction. For that material, $E_n = E_s$ and $\upsilon_{ns} = \upsilon_{sn}$. Only seven of the material constants are independent due to the theory of elasticity relationship:

$$E_j \upsilon_{ij} = E_i \upsilon_{ji}. \tag{13.16-4}$$

13.17 Discussion

All of the finite element stress analysis programs are essentially the same except for minor differences in the post-processing. The majority of any applications system consists of reading and checking the data, creating and assembling *application-dependent* elements, enforcing the EBCs, solving the equilibrium equations, displaying and saving the generalized displacements, and completing any *application-dependent* post-processing of the elements. Note that mainly the generation and post-processing of the *application-dependent* elements is what changes. The other 95% of the coding is unchanged. There may be additional calculations for an error estimator, but they are not required. Also, there are usually several off-line features such as resources to graphically display the results of importance.

All of the planar problems discussed above are easily extended to three dimensions, and the supplied Matlab scripts will execute such problems just by changing the number of physical space dimensions to three ($n_s = 3$), utilizing the eight-noded hexahedral (brick) element by setting the parametric element space to three and the number of nodes to eight ($n_p = 3$, $n_n = 8$), and selecting the correct number of integration points, which is usually $2^3 = 8$ but maybe 27. The size of the constitutive matrix, $\boldsymbol{E}^e$, and the operator matrix, $\boldsymbol{B}^e$, must be increased to six ($n_r = 6$) by adding three more strain–displacement relations. Of course, additional elements can be added to the element library. However, most three-dimension problems are better solved with commercial software simply because they have automatic solid element mesh generators and offer several good graphical post-processing tools.

To illustrate those points again, the discussion of three-dimensional solid stress analysis will be limited to one of the simplest implementations. The linear four-noded tetrahedron element (here called the pyramid $P4$ to avoid confusion with triangular element shorthand) was the first solid element. It is relatively easy to create it with an automatic mesh generator. But it gives only constant stresses within its volume and is no longer recommended unless a very large number of tetrahedra are used (compared to the number of higher-order elements they replace). The 10-node tetrahedra ($P10$) are commonly used since they can be obtained from the same automatic mesh generators as the $P4$ elements. However, they are only interpolating the displacements with complete quadratics, and thus give only linearly changing stress estimates.

The hexahedra element family is considered to be a better choice for solid stress analysis because they have higher-order interior interpolation functions than do the tetrahedral elements having the same number of edge nodes. They are more difficult to create with an automatic mesh generator and that restricts their widespread use.

13.18 Symmetry and Cyclic-symmetry*

These topics were introduced earlier, but they become even more useful when dealing with solid parts that have planes of symmetry, anti-symmetry, or cyclic symmetry. Figures 8.1-1 and 10.13-1 showed applications where one- and two-dimensional symmetry conditions can occur for a scalar application. Based on operation counts for solving linear systems, each symmetry, anti-symmetry, or cyclic symmetry plane used in the model reduces the execution time by about a factor of eight. In other words, they speed up the equation solution by a factor of 8^n, where n is the effective number of planes.

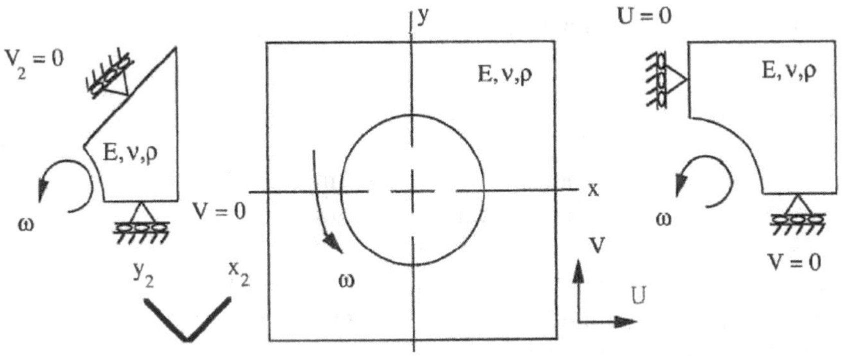

Fig. 13.18-1: Centrifugal (angular velocity) loading square with a circular hole.

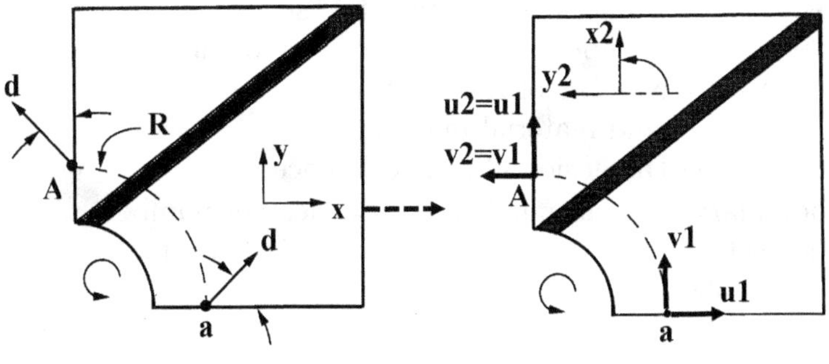

Fig. 13.18-2: Cyclic symmetry planes of an angular velocity loading of a two-material square.

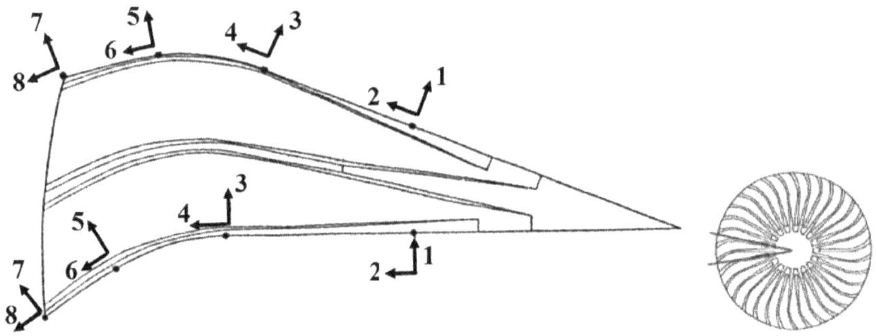

Fig. 13.18-3: Cyclic symmetry surfaces of spinning turbine blades.

Figures 13.18-1–13.18-3 illustrate some symmetry planes and some cyclic symmetry surfaces.

13.19 Summary

$n\_b \longleftrightarrow n_b \equiv$ Number of boundary segments
$n\_d \longleftrightarrow n_d \equiv$ Number of system unknowns $= n\_g \times n\_m$
$n\_e \longleftrightarrow n_e \equiv$ Number of elements
$n\_g \longleftrightarrow n_g \equiv$ Number of generalized DOF per node
$n\_i \longleftrightarrow n_i \equiv$ Number of unknowns per element $= n\_g \times n\_n$
$n\_m \longleftrightarrow n_m \equiv$ Number of mesh nodes
$n\_n \longleftrightarrow n_n \equiv$ Number of nodes per element or segment
$n\_P \longleftrightarrow n_P \equiv$ Number of point loads
$n\_p \longleftrightarrow n_p \equiv$ Dimension of parametric space
$n\_q \longleftrightarrow n_q \equiv$ Number of total quadrature points
$n\_r \longleftrightarrow n_r \equiv$ Number of rows in the $\boldsymbol{B}^e$ matrix (and material matrix)
$n\_s \longleftrightarrow n_s \equiv$ Dimension of physical space

$b =$ boundary segment number	$e =$ element number
$\subset =$ subset	$\cup =$ union of sets
Boundary, element, and system unknowns:	$\boldsymbol{\delta}^b \subset_b \boldsymbol{\delta}^e \subset_e \boldsymbol{\delta}$
Geometry:	
$\Omega^e \equiv$ Element domain	$\Omega = \cup_e \Omega^e \equiv$ Solution domain
$\Gamma^b \subset \Omega^e \equiv$ Boundary segment	$\Gamma = \cup_b \Gamma^b \equiv$ Domain boundary

Element coordinates:	$\boldsymbol{x}^e \equiv \begin{bmatrix} x_1 & y_1 & z_1 \\ \vdots & \vdots & \vdots \\ x_{n_m} & y_{n_m} & z_{n_m} \end{bmatrix}^e$
Geometry mapping:	$\boldsymbol{x}(r) = \boldsymbol{G}(r)\boldsymbol{x}^e, \boldsymbol{H}(r) \ \leq \boldsymbol{G}(r) \geq \boldsymbol{H}(r)$. $\partial x(r)/\partial r = [\partial \boldsymbol{G}(r)/\partial r]\, \boldsymbol{x}^e \equiv \boldsymbol{J}^e$.
Displacement interpolation:	$\boldsymbol{u}(\boldsymbol{x}) = \boldsymbol{N}(r)\, \boldsymbol{\delta}^e = \boldsymbol{u}(\boldsymbol{x})^{\boldsymbol{T}} = \boldsymbol{\delta}^{e^{\boldsymbol{T}}} \boldsymbol{N}(r)^{\boldsymbol{T}}$.
Local gradient:	$\partial \boldsymbol{u}(r)/\partial r = [\partial \boldsymbol{N}(r)/\partial r]\, \boldsymbol{\delta}^e$.
Geometric Jacobian:	$\boldsymbol{J}^e = [\partial \boldsymbol{G}(r)/\partial r]\, \boldsymbol{x}^e$.
Physical gradient:	$\partial u(x)/\partial x = (\partial u(r)/\partial r)(\partial r/\partial x)$. $\partial u(x)/\partial x = (\partial u(r)/\partial r)\, (\partial x/\partial r)^{-1}$. $\partial u(x)/\partial x = (\partial x/\partial r)^{-1}\, [\partial \boldsymbol{H}(r)/\partial r]\, \boldsymbol{u}^e$, etc.
Strain–Displacement matrix:	$\boldsymbol{B}^e(\boldsymbol{r}),\ \boldsymbol{\varepsilon}\,(\boldsymbol{r}) \equiv \boldsymbol{B}^e\,(\boldsymbol{r})\, \boldsymbol{\delta}^e$.
Mechanical work:	$W = \int_V \boldsymbol{\delta}^T \boldsymbol{f}\, dV + \int_S \boldsymbol{\delta}^T \boldsymbol{T}\, dS + \sum_{k=1}^{k=n_P} \boldsymbol{\delta}_k^T \boldsymbol{F}_k$.
Engineering strain components:	$\boldsymbol{\varepsilon}^T = \left[\varepsilon_x\, \varepsilon_y\ \ \varepsilon_z\, \gamma_{xy}\ \ \gamma_{xz}\, \gamma_{yz} \right]$.
Stress components:	$\boldsymbol{\sigma}^T = \left[\sigma_x\, \sigma_y\ \ \sigma_z\, \tau_{xy}\ \ \tau_{xz}\, \tau_{yz} \right]$.
Principal axis thermal expansion coeff.:	$\boldsymbol{\alpha}^T = \left[\alpha_x\, \alpha_y\ \ \alpha_z\, \alpha_{xy}\ \ \alpha_{xz}\, \alpha_{yz} \right]$.
Principal orthotropic CTE:	$\boldsymbol{\alpha}^T = [\alpha_x\ \ \alpha_y\ \ \alpha_z\ \ 0\ \ 0\ \ 0]$.
Isotropic thermal expansion coeff.	$\boldsymbol{\alpha}^T = \alpha \left[\, 1\,1\,1\ \ 0\,0\,0 \,\right]$.
Mechanical strain–stress relation:	$\boldsymbol{\varepsilon} = \boldsymbol{E}\boldsymbol{\sigma} + \boldsymbol{\alpha}\, \Delta T, \quad \boldsymbol{E} = \boldsymbol{E}^T, \quad \lvert \boldsymbol{E} \rvert >$.

Mechanical stress–strain relation: $\boldsymbol{\sigma} = \boldsymbol{E}\varepsilon - \boldsymbol{E}\boldsymbol{\alpha}\,\Delta T, \quad \boldsymbol{E} = \boldsymbol{E}^{-1}.$

Strain energy:
$$U = \frac{1}{2}\int_V \boldsymbol{\sigma}^T \varepsilon\, dV = \frac{1}{2}\int_V \varepsilon^T \boldsymbol{\sigma}\, dV = \frac{1}{2}\int_V \varepsilon^T \boldsymbol{E}\varepsilon\, dV.$$

Work of initial strains, ε_0: $W_0 = \int_V \boldsymbol{\sigma}^T \varepsilon_0\, dV = \int_V \varepsilon^T \boldsymbol{E}\varepsilon_0\, dV,$
$\varepsilon_T = \boldsymbol{\alpha}\ \Delta T \subset \varepsilon_0.$

Element strain energy: $U^e = \frac{1}{2}\boldsymbol{\delta}^{\boldsymbol{e}^T}\left[\boldsymbol{K}^e\right]\boldsymbol{\delta}^{\boldsymbol{e}}.$

Stiffness matrix: $\boldsymbol{K}^e = \int_\Omega^e \boldsymbol{B}^{e^T}\boldsymbol{E}^e\boldsymbol{B}^e\, d\Omega^e.$

Stress tensor:
$$\boldsymbol{\sigma}^{\boldsymbol{T}} = \begin{bmatrix} \sigma_x & \sigma_y & \sigma_z & \tau_{xy} & \tau_{xz} & \tau_{yz} \end{bmatrix}$$
$$\Leftrightarrow [\boldsymbol{\sigma}] = \begin{bmatrix} \sigma_{xx} & \tau_{xy} & \tau_{xz} \\ \tau_{xy} & \sigma_{yy} & \tau_{yz} \\ \tau_{xz} & \tau_{yz} & \sigma_{zz} \end{bmatrix}.$$

Principal stresses: $\left|[\boldsymbol{\sigma}] - \lambda_k\,[\boldsymbol{I}]\right| = 0,\ k = 1, \ldots, n_s$ and
$\sigma_1 > \sigma_2 > \sigma_3.$

Hydrostatic pressure: $p = (\sigma_1 + \sigma_2 + \sigma_3)/3 = (\sigma_{xx} + \sigma_{yy} + \sigma_{zz})/3.$

Experimental yield stresses: σ_t tensile, σ_c compressive, $\kappa \equiv \sigma_c/\sigma_t$ ratio

Von Mises criterion:
$$\sigma_E = \tfrac{1}{\sqrt{2}}\sqrt{\left(\sigma_1 - \sigma_2\right)^2 + \left(\sigma_1 - \sigma_3\right)^2 + \left(\sigma_2 - \sigma_3\right)^2}.$$
$$\sigma_E = \tfrac{1}{\sqrt{2}}\sqrt{\begin{matrix}\left(\sigma_{yy} - \sigma_{xx}\right)^2 + \left(\sigma_{zz} - \sigma_{xx}\right)^2 \\ + \left(\sigma_{zz} - \sigma_{yy}\right)^2 + 6\left(\tau_{xy}^2 + \tau_{xz}^2 + \tau_{yz}^2\right)\end{matrix}}.$$

Burzynski criterion:
$$\sigma_B = \left[3p\,(\kappa - 1) + \sqrt{9p^2\,(\kappa - 1)^2 + 4\kappa\sigma_E^2}\right]/2\kappa,$$
$\sigma_B\,(\kappa = 1) = \sigma_E.$

Ductile material failure criterion: $\sigma_E \geq \sigma_t$ or $\sigma_B \geq \sigma_t$.

Effective (non) stress: Absolute maximum shear stress: $\tau_{\max} = (\sigma_1 - \sigma_3)/2$.

Linear axial bar stiffness: $\boldsymbol{S}^e = \frac{E^e A^e}{L^e} \begin{bmatrix} 1 & -1 \\ -1 & 1 \end{bmatrix}$.

Quadratic axial bar stiffness: $\boldsymbol{S}^e = \frac{E^e A^e}{3L^e} \begin{bmatrix} 7 & -8 & 1 \\ -8 & 16 & -8 \\ 1 & -8 & 7 \end{bmatrix}$.

Cubic axial bar stiffness: $\boldsymbol{S}^e = \frac{E^e A^e}{40L^e} \begin{bmatrix} 148 & -189 & 54 & -13 \\ -189 & 432 & -297 & 54 \\ 54 & -297 & 432 & -189 \\ -13 & 54 & -189 & 148 \end{bmatrix}$.

Line loads for linear, quadratic, and cubic bars:

$$\boldsymbol{c}_{\boldsymbol{w}}^{\boldsymbol{e}} = \frac{w^e L^e}{2} \begin{Bmatrix} 1 \\ 1 \end{Bmatrix}, \quad \boldsymbol{c}_{\boldsymbol{w}}^{\boldsymbol{e}} = \frac{w^e L^e}{6} \begin{Bmatrix} 1 \\ 4 \\ 1 \end{Bmatrix}, \quad \boldsymbol{c}_{\boldsymbol{w}}^{\boldsymbol{e}} = \frac{w^e L^e}{8} \begin{Bmatrix} 1 \\ 3 \\ 3 \\ 1 \end{Bmatrix}.$$

Thermal loads for linear, quadratic, and cubic bars:

$$\boldsymbol{c}_{\boldsymbol{\alpha}}^{\boldsymbol{e}} = E^e A^e \alpha^e \Delta T^e \begin{Bmatrix} -1 \\ 1 \end{Bmatrix}, \quad \boldsymbol{c}_{\boldsymbol{\alpha}}^{\boldsymbol{e}} = E^e A^e \alpha^e \Delta T^e \begin{Bmatrix} -1 \\ 0 \\ 1 \end{Bmatrix},$$

$$\boldsymbol{c}_{\boldsymbol{\alpha}}^{\boldsymbol{e}} = E^e A^e \alpha^e \Delta T^e \begin{Bmatrix} -1 \\ 0 \\ 0 \\ 1 \end{Bmatrix}.$$

Strain–displacement relation, $\boldsymbol{\varepsilon}^{\boldsymbol{e}} = \boldsymbol{B}^{\boldsymbol{e}}(x,\, y,\, z)\, \boldsymbol{\delta}^{\boldsymbol{e}}$, for elastic solid:

$$\begin{Bmatrix} \varepsilon_x \\ \varepsilon_y \\ \varepsilon_z \\ \gamma_{xy} \\ \gamma_{xz} \\ \gamma_{yz} \end{Bmatrix}^e, \boldsymbol{B}^{\boldsymbol{e}}(x,\, y,\, z) = \left[\boldsymbol{B}_{\boldsymbol{1}}^{\boldsymbol{e}} \vdots \boldsymbol{B}_{\boldsymbol{2}}^{\boldsymbol{e}} \vdots \cdots \boldsymbol{B}_{n_n}^{\boldsymbol{e}}\right], \boldsymbol{B}_{\boldsymbol{k}}^{\boldsymbol{e}} = \begin{bmatrix} H_{k,x} & 0 & 0 \\ 0 & H_{k,y} & 0 \\ 0 & 0 & H_{k,z} \\ H_{k,y} & H_{k,x} & 0 \\ H_{k,z} & 0 & H_{k,x} \\ 0 & H_{k,z} & H_{k,y} \end{bmatrix}$$

$(n_r \times n_i) \qquad\qquad (n_r \times n_g).$

Strain–displacement relation, $\boldsymbol{\varepsilon}^{\boldsymbol{e}} = \boldsymbol{B}^{\boldsymbol{e}}(x,\, y)\boldsymbol{\delta}^{\boldsymbol{e}}$, for plane–stress and plane–strain:

$$\begin{Bmatrix} \varepsilon_x \\ \varepsilon_y \\ \gamma_{xy} \end{Bmatrix}^e, \ \boldsymbol{B}_{\boldsymbol{k}}^{\boldsymbol{e}}(x,\, y) = \begin{bmatrix} H_{k,x} & 0 \\ 0 & H_{k,y} \\ H_{k,y} & H_{k,x} \end{bmatrix}.$$

Constant strain triangle (CST) version (T3):

$$2A^e = x_1^e\,(y_2^e - y_3^e) + x_2^e\,(y_3^e - y_1^e) + x_3^e\,(y_1^e - y_2^e)$$

$$a_i^e = x_j^e y_k^e - x_k^e y_j^e,\ b_i^e = y_j^e - y_k^e,\ \ c_i^e = x_k^e - x_j^e, \quad 2A^e = a_1^e + a_2^e + a_3^e,$$

specifically,

$$\begin{array}{lll} a_1 = x_2 y_3 - x_3 y_2, & a_2 = x_3 y_1 - x_1 y_3, & a_3 = x_1 y_2 - x_2 y_1 \\ b_1 = y_2 - y_3, & b_2 = y_3 - y_1, & b_3 = y_1 - y_2 \\ c_1 = x_3 - x_2, & c_2 = x_1 - x_3, & c_3 = x_2 - x_1 \end{array}$$

$$\boldsymbol{B}_{\boldsymbol{k}}^{\boldsymbol{e}} = \frac{1}{2A^e} \begin{bmatrix} b_k & 0 \\ 0 & c_k \\ c_k & b_k \end{bmatrix}.$$

Strain–displacement relation, $\boldsymbol{\varepsilon}^{\boldsymbol{e}} = \boldsymbol{B}^{\boldsymbol{e}}(x,\, y)\boldsymbol{\delta}^{\boldsymbol{e}}$, for axisymmetric stress:

$$\begin{Bmatrix} \varepsilon_R \\ \varepsilon_y \\ \gamma_{Ry} \\ \varepsilon_\theta \end{Bmatrix}^e, \ \boldsymbol{B}_{\boldsymbol{k}}^{\boldsymbol{e}}(x,\, y) = \begin{bmatrix} H_{k,x} & 0 \\ 0 & H_{k,y} \\ H_{k,y} & H_{k,x} \\ H_k/R & 0 \end{bmatrix}.$$

Linear triangle (CST) version (T3):

$$H_i\,(x,\,y) = \frac{a_i^e + b_i^e x + c_i^e y}{2A^e},\quad \boldsymbol{B}_i^{e}\,(x,y) = \begin{bmatrix} \dfrac{b_i}{2A^e} & 0 \\ 0 & \dfrac{c_i}{2A^e} \\ \dfrac{c_i}{2A^e} & \dfrac{b_i}{2A^e} \\ H_i\,(x,y)/R\,(x,y) & 0 \end{bmatrix},$$

$$R\,(x,y) = \sum_{i=1}^{3} H_i(x,\,y)R_i^e.$$

Constitutive law, isotropic plane–stress:

$$\begin{Bmatrix} \sigma_x \\ \sigma_y \\ \tau_{xy} \end{Bmatrix} = \frac{E}{1-\upsilon^2}\begin{bmatrix} 1 & \upsilon & 0 \\ \upsilon & 1 & 0 \\ 0 & 0 & (1-\upsilon)/2 \end{bmatrix}\begin{Bmatrix} \varepsilon_x \\ \varepsilon_y \\ \gamma_{xy} \end{Bmatrix} - \frac{E\alpha\Delta T}{1-\upsilon}\begin{Bmatrix} 1 \\ 1 \\ 0 \end{Bmatrix}.$$

Constitutive law, anisotropic plane–stress

$$\begin{Bmatrix} \varepsilon_{nn} \\ \varepsilon_{ss} \\ \varepsilon_{tt} \\ \gamma_{ns} \end{Bmatrix} = \begin{bmatrix} 1/E_n & -\upsilon_{sn}/E_s & -\upsilon_{tn}/E_t & 0 \\ -\upsilon_{ns}/E_n & 1/E_s & -\upsilon_{ts}/E_t & 0 \\ -\upsilon_{nt}/E_n & -\upsilon_{st}/E_s & 1/E_t & 0 \\ 0 & 0 & 0 & 1/G_{ns} \end{bmatrix}\begin{Bmatrix} \sigma_{nn} \\ \sigma_{ss} \\ \sigma_{tt} \\ \tau_{ns} \end{Bmatrix} + \Delta T\begin{Bmatrix} \alpha_n \\ \alpha_s \\ \alpha_t \\ 0 \end{Bmatrix}.$$

Constitutive law, isotropic plane–strain:

$$\begin{Bmatrix} \sigma_x \\ \sigma_y \\ \tau_{xy} \end{Bmatrix} = \frac{E}{(1+\upsilon)\,(1-2\upsilon)}\begin{bmatrix} a & \upsilon & 0 \\ \upsilon & a & 0 \\ 0 & 0 & b \end{bmatrix}\begin{Bmatrix} \varepsilon_x \\ \varepsilon_y \\ \gamma_{xy} \end{Bmatrix} - \frac{E\alpha\Delta T}{1-\upsilon}\begin{Bmatrix} 1 \\ 1 \\ 0 \end{Bmatrix}$$

$$a = (1-\upsilon),\quad b = (1-2\upsilon)/2.$$

Constitutive law, isotropic axisymmetric stress:

$$\begin{Bmatrix} \sigma_r \\ \sigma_z \\ \tau_{rz} \\ \sigma_\theta \end{Bmatrix} = \frac{E}{(1+\upsilon)(1-2\upsilon)} \begin{bmatrix} a & \nu & 0 & \nu \\ \nu & a & 0 & \nu \\ 0 & 0 & b & 0 \\ \nu & \nu & 0 & a \end{bmatrix} \begin{Bmatrix} \varepsilon_r \\ \varepsilon_z \\ \gamma_{rz} \\ \varepsilon_\theta \end{Bmatrix} - \frac{E\alpha\Delta T}{(1-2\upsilon)} \begin{Bmatrix} 1 \\ 1 \\ 0 \\ 1 \end{Bmatrix}$$

$$a = (1-\upsilon), \quad b = (1-2\upsilon)/2, \quad \upsilon \neq 0.5.$$

Constitutive law, isotropic solid stress:

$$\begin{Bmatrix} \sigma_x \\ \sigma_y \\ \sigma_z \\ \tau_{xy} \\ \tau_{xz} \\ \tau_{yz} \end{Bmatrix} = \frac{E}{(1+\upsilon)(1-2\upsilon)} \begin{bmatrix} a & \upsilon & \upsilon & 0 & 0 & 0 \\ \upsilon & a & \upsilon & 0 & 0 & 0 \\ \upsilon & \upsilon & a & 0 & 0 & 0 \\ 0 & 0 & 0 & b & 0 & 0 \\ 0 & 0 & 0 & 0 & b & 0 \\ 0 & 0 & 0 & 0 & 0 & b \end{bmatrix} \begin{Bmatrix} \varepsilon_x \\ \varepsilon_y \\ \varepsilon_z \\ \gamma_{xy} \\ \gamma_{xz} \\ \gamma_{yz} \end{Bmatrix}$$

$$- \frac{E\alpha\Delta T}{(1-2\upsilon)} \begin{Bmatrix} 1 \\ 1 \\ 1 \\ 0 \\ 0 \\ 0 \end{Bmatrix}$$

$$a = (1-\upsilon), \quad b = (1-2\upsilon)/2, \quad \upsilon \neq 0.5.$$

13.20 Review

1. What are the primary uses of the geometric Jacobian in a typical element?
2. In a structural analysis, what is the sum of the terms in the resultant element force vector due only to the body weight? _____.
3. What is the sum of the terms in the element Lagrangian interpolation matrix, $\boldsymbol{H}^e$?_____.
4. Geometry mapping from a parametric space to physical space is done with the _____.

(a) Determinant of the Jacobian
(b) Inverse of the Jacobian matrix
(c) Jacobian matrix
(d) Interpolation functions
(e) Derivatives of interpolation functions
(f) Parametric derivatives

5. The physical differential volume is related to the parametric volume by the _____.

   (a) Determinant of the Jacobian
   (b) Inverse of the Jacobian matrix
   (c) Jacobian matrix
   (d) Interpolation functions
   (e) Derivatives of interpolation functions
   (f) Parametric derivatives

6. When is the Jacobian matrix square and when does it have a rectangular form?
7. What are the basic concepts for isoparametric elements?
8. Identify the nature of the following items using S to denote scalars, V to denote vectors:

   Mass _____ Weight _____ Work _____ Energy _____ Displacement _____.
   Velocity _____ Temperature _____ Heat flux _____ Poisson's ratio _____ Acceleration _____.

9. A material that is the same at all points is _____.

   (a) Homogeneous
   (b) Non-homogeneous
   (c) Isotropic
   (d) Anisotropic
   (e) Orthotropic

10. In a structural analysis, what is the sum of the terms in the element stiffness matrix?
11. The physical partial derivative of a displacement, du/dx, is obtained from the Parametric partial derivative, du/dr, of a quantity (when one-to-one) by: _____.

    (a) Adding the Jacobian determinate
    (b) Pre-multiplied by Jacobian inverse
    (c) Pre-multiplied by the Jacobian matrix
    (d) Adding the interpolation functions
    (e) Post-multiplied by the Jacobian matrix
    (f) Post-multiplied by Jacobian inverse

12. In stress analysis, the default Neumann BC at a point on the exterior surface is: _____.

    (a) Zero heat flux (b) Zero displacement (c) Zero stresses
    (d) Zero temperature (e) None of these (f) All of these

13. Which boundary conditions are satisfied weakly? _____.

    (a) Dirichlet (b) Neumann (c) Both

14. At a point on a plane of structural symmetry, which items are zero? _____.

    (a) Tangential displacements (b) Normal displacement (c) Tangential heat flux
    (d) Temperature (e) Normal rotations (f) Tangential rotations
    (g) Both (a) and (f) (h) All of the above (i) None of the above

15. A material that is the same in all directions is _____.

    (a) Homogeneous (b) Non-homogeneous (c) Isotropic
    (d) Anisotropic (e) Orthotropic

16. What are the basic concepts for isoparametric elements?
17. If you are calculating a plane–stress analysis with an eight-noded quadrilateral element:
    (a) How many unknowns are at each node? _____
    (b) How many stresses are there in any element? _____
    (c) What is the size of the element strain–displacement matrix, $\boldsymbol{B}^e$? _____

18. If you are calculating a plane–strain analysis with an eight-noded quadrilateral element:
    (a) How many unknowns are at each node? _____
    (b) How many stresses are there in any element? _____
    (c) What is the size of the element strain–displacement matrix, $\boldsymbol{B}^e$? _____

19. If you are calculating an axisymmetric stress analysis with an eight-noded quadrilateral element:
    (a) How many unknowns are at each node? _____
    (b) How many stresses are there in any element? _____

(c) What is the size of the element strain–displacement matrix, $\boldsymbol{B}^e$? _____

20. In a continuum solid structural analysis, what is the sum of the terms in the element mass matrix?_____
21. The stress intensity (INT), which is twice the maximum shear stress, predicts material failure when it reaches the: _____

(a) Ultimate stress (b) Endurance stress (c) Yield stress (d) None of these

22. A straight-sided plane–stress six-noded triangle has a parabolic (three-noded) edge with pressure components p_x and p_y as input data at those three nodes. Set up the integral to form the corresponding resultant force vector, in terms of those data.
23. Name three material failure criteria and indicate which you would use for a ductile material.
24. Denote the number of physical strain components by n_r, the number of unknowns per node as n_g, the number of nodes per element by n_n, and the number of quadrature points by n_q:

(a) How many rows does the element operator matrix $\boldsymbol{B}^e(x, y)$ have?
(b) How many columns does the element operator matrix $\boldsymbol{B}^e(x, y)$ have?
(c) How many rows does the material constitutive matrix $\boldsymbol{E}^e$ have?

26. A symmetry plane divides mirror images of the _____.

(a) Geometric shape
(b) Distribution of material properties
(c) Dirichlet boundary conditions
(d) External loadings
(e) All of the above
(f) None of the above

27. What are the number of rows and columns in the element strain–displacement matrix, $\boldsymbol{B}^e$, for:

(a) An axial bar _____.
(b) A plane–stress three-noded triangle _____.
(c) A plane–strain four-noded quadrilateral _____.
(d) An axisymmetric six-noded triangle _____.
(e) A solid 20-noded brick element _____.

Chapter 14

Eigenanalysis

14.1 Introduction

Another common type of analysis problem is where a coefficient in the governing differential equation, λ, is an unknown global constant to be determined, called an eigenvalue. There is a group of solutions to such a differential equation. This class of analysis is called an eigenproblem from the German word *eigen* meaning belonging distinctly to a group. Eigenproblem solutions require much more computation effort than solving a linear system of equations.

Mechanical engineers approach eigenproblems with two extremely different goals. The most common is to avoid exciting the resonate (natural) frequency of a system that can drive it to destruction. That involves determining the natural frequencies of surrounding structures and/or equipment to verify that their frequencies are not too close to the resonate frequency in question.

At the other extreme, obtaining an optimal design goal can require changing the shape and materials of a system to reach a specific frequency of response. One such example is designing expensive audio systems. Acoustical vibrations determine where the acoustical pressure (sound) changes with the natural frequencies of the shape of a closed volume. Today, automobile companies conduct extensive acoustical studies for each automobile passenger compartment in order to design high-quality sound systems. Electromagnetic waveguides involve eigenproblem solutions to design radar systems, microwave ovens, and several other electrical components. The surface elevations of shallow bodies of water, like harbors, are subjected to periodic excitations by the moon. Tidal studies are called Seiche motion studies and are governed by eigenproblem solutions. Those problems, and others, are described by the scalar Helmholtz differential equation:

$$k\,\nabla^2 u(x,\,y,\,t)+\lambda\,u(x,\,y,\,t)=0 \tag{14.1-1}$$

which is solved using a group for multiple eigenvalues, λ_n, and a corresponding set of solution eigenvectors to define the group of solutions. Another common application leading to an eigenproblem analysis is the vibration of elastic solids where the eigenvalues and their corresponding deflected mode shapes are to be determined. In theory, a continuous system has an infinite number of eigenvalues, and a finite element approximation of a system has as many eigenvalues as there are degrees of freedom (after enforcing the essential boundary condition (EBC)). Most applications are interested in the first few or the last few eigenvalues and eigenvectors. There are efficient algorithms for both approaches.

For waveguides and other applications, the eigenvalue can be a complex number, but for elastic vibrations, it is a non-negative number. For elastic vibrations, a positive value corresponds to the square of the natural frequency of vibration, $\lambda = \omega^2$, and a zero value corresponds to a rigid body (non-vibrating) motion. There are at most six rigid-body motions of a solid. Theoretically, a vibration analysis should not yield a negative eigenvalue, $\lambda < 0$, but numerical errors can produce them as an approximation of a rigid body motion.

A practical finite element eigenproblem study can involve tens of thousands of unknowns after a few boundary conditions are imposed, but the engineer is usually interested in less than ten of its eigenvalues and eigenvectors. The eigenvectors of interest are usually just examined as plotted mode shapes. For example, in linear buckling theory, only the single smallest eigenvalue is useful and its plotted buckled mode shape can imply where additional supports will increase its buckling capacity.

Here, the examples are presented utilizing Matlab and some specific features of that environment need to be noted. Matlab provides the two functions *eig* and *eigs* for eigenproblem solutions. The finite element method provides two matrix arguments, say $\boldsymbol{K}$ and $\boldsymbol{M}$, that (after EBCs) are real, symmetric, and non-negative and define the problem as solving

$$[\boldsymbol{K} - \lambda_j \boldsymbol{M}]\, \boldsymbol{\delta_j} = 0, \quad j = 1, 2, \ldots$$

For a "small" numbers of degrees of freedom the function call $[\boldsymbol{V}, \boldsymbol{\Lambda}] = eig\,(\boldsymbol{K}, \boldsymbol{M})$ returns two square matrices where each eigenvector, $\boldsymbol{\delta_j}$, as the jth column of the first square matrix, $\boldsymbol{V}$, and the corresponding eigenvalue, λ_j, is placed in the jth row diagonal term of the matrix $\boldsymbol{\Lambda}$. In other words, the returned row number, j, of any eigenvector, λ_j, is also the column number of its corresponding eigenvector, $\boldsymbol{\delta_j}$. The eigenvalues can be conveniently placed in a vector, with the same row numbers, by using the Matlab function diag as $\boldsymbol{\lambda} = \text{diag}\,(\boldsymbol{\Lambda})$.

In finite element applications, the eigenvalues, $\boldsymbol{\lambda}$, can be complex numbers, but for common vibration problems they are positive real numbers that are the square of the natural frequency, or zero for rigid body motions (a maximum of six). Numerical round-off errors can make the theoretical positive number have a tiny complex part. Thus, the safe thing to do is to use the Matlab function *real* to transform $\boldsymbol{\omega}^2 = \boldsymbol{\lambda} = \text{real}(\boldsymbol{\lambda})$ in vibration studies.

However, the Matlab eigenvalues, $\boldsymbol{\lambda}$, are NOT always in a sequential order either increasing or decreasing. For a buckling study, only the smallest eigenvalue is needed. That can be extracted by using the Matlab function *min*. But it is also necessary to extract its eigenvector that shows the buckled shape of the structure. That can be done using the extended *min* function that returns two arguments:

$$[\lambda_1,\, row_1] = min\,(\boldsymbol{\lambda}),$$

where the smallest eigenvalue λ_1 was found in row row_1 of the vector $\boldsymbol{\lambda}$ and where the corresponding eigenvector column can be extracted by next using the row number as a column number and setting $\boldsymbol{\delta_1} = \boldsymbol{V}(:, row_1)$.

For a medium-sized problem, say where you want three λ_j out of 20 degrees of freedom, you need to find those three smallest values in the vector $\boldsymbol{\lambda}$. That is done using the extended Matlab function *sort* as follows:

$$[\boldsymbol{\lambda}_{\text{new}}, \boldsymbol{Order}] = sort\,(\boldsymbol{\lambda}),$$

where the vector $\boldsymbol{\lambda}_{\text{new}}$ contains all of the eigenvalue in ascending order such that the smallest eigenvalue is $\lambda_{\text{new}}\,(1) = \lambda_{\text{small}}$, and where the vector subscript $\boldsymbol{Order}$ gives the row number where the new sorted value was found in the original random list of eigenvalues. The vector subscript $\boldsymbol{Order}$ is very important since it is the key to finding the eigenvector that corresponds to a particular eigenvalue. For example, the smallest eigenvalue and its eigenvector are $\lambda_{\text{new}}(1)$, and $\boldsymbol{\delta}_1 = \boldsymbol{V}(:, \boldsymbol{Order}\,(1))$ and the fifth pair is $\lambda_{\text{new}}(5)$ and $\boldsymbol{\delta}_5 = \boldsymbol{V}(:, \boldsymbol{Order}\,(5))$.

For very large problems where the analysts need only a small number of the smallest eigenvalues, as in mechanical vibrations, or a small number of the largest eigenvalue, then the call to the Matlab function *eigs* provides the much more efficient eigenvalue control with:

$$[\boldsymbol{V}, \boldsymbol{\Lambda}] = eigs\,(\boldsymbol{K},\ \boldsymbol{M},\ n',\ sm'),$$

where the number n is the number of the eigenvalues required, and the string "*sm*", requests the smallest eigenvalues. This choice requires the least dynamic memory since $\boldsymbol{\Lambda}$ is a small $n \times n$ matrix and $\boldsymbol{V}$ is a rectangular matrix with only n columns. However, the eigenvalues on the diagonal of $\boldsymbol{\Lambda}$ are still usually in a random order and it is still necessary to sort them and to use the $\boldsymbol{Order}$ subscripts to extract the proper eigenvectors.

There are times when the largest eigenvalue of a finite element matrix is required. For example, in time history solutions the time step size limit for a stable solution depends on the inverse of the largest eigenvalue of the system. The *eigs* function defaults to giving the largest eigenvalues. Iron's Bound Theorem provides bounds on the extreme eigenvalues by using the corresponding element matrices (as they are built for assembly):

$$\lambda^e_{\text{min}} \le \lambda_{\text{min}} \le \lambda_{\text{max}} \le \lambda^e_{\text{max}}. \tag{14.1-2}$$

This means that the largest eigenvalue in the system is less that the largest eigenvalue of its smallest element.

14.2 Finite Element Eigenproblems

When a differential equation having an unknown global constant is solved by the finite element method, the global constant factors out all of the element matrices and appears in the assembled governing matrix system. The typical form of the matrix system becomes the "general eigenproblem":

$$[\boldsymbol{K} - \lambda \boldsymbol{M}]\,\boldsymbol{\delta} = \mathbf{0}, \tag{14.2-1}$$

where $\boldsymbol{K}$ is typically a stiffness matrix or conduction matrix, $\boldsymbol{M}$ is typically a generalized mass matrix or a literal mass matrix for vibration problems, $\boldsymbol{\delta}$ corresponds to the nodal values of the primary unknowns (displacements, acoustical pressure, water elevation, etc.), and λ is the global unknown constant to be determined.

The consistent finite element theory creates a full symmetric element mass matrix. Based on prior finite difference methods which always create a diagonal mass matrix, some users prefer to diagonalize the consistent mass matrix by using a diagonal matrix constructed from scaling up the original diagonal so the sum of the new diagonal equals the total mass. Some numerical experiments have shown improved numerical accuracy for both eigenvalue and time history solutions when the average of the consistent mass matrix and its diagonalized form are employed (the averaged mass matrix).

Recall that the integral form introduces the non-essential boundary conditions (NBCs) into the element matrices which are assembled into the system matrices. The EBCs must have been enforced such that $\boldsymbol{\delta}$ represents only the free unknowns in (14.2-1). Usually, the EBCs specify zero for the known nodal values.

Equation (14.2-1) represents a matrix set of linear homogeneous equations. For those equations to have a non-zero solution the determinant of the square matrix in the brackets must vanish. That is,

$$\det[\boldsymbol{K} - \lambda \boldsymbol{M}] = |\boldsymbol{K} - \lambda \boldsymbol{M}| = 0. \tag{14.2-2}$$

That condition leads to a group of solutions (eigenproblems) equal in number to the number of free unknowns in $\boldsymbol{\delta}$ after the EBCs have been enforced:

$$[\boldsymbol{K} - \lambda_j \boldsymbol{M}]\,\boldsymbol{\delta}_j = 0, \quad j = 1, 2, \ldots, \tag{14.2-3}$$

where the λ_j are the eigenvalue corresponding to the eigenvector $\boldsymbol{\delta}_j$. The usual convention is to normalize the eigenvector so that the absolute value of its largest term is unity.

For vibration studies, the eigenvalue is the square of the natural frequency; $\lambda = \omega^2$. When calculated by a finite element approximation, the frequency (in radians per second) ω_n is more accurate than the next higher frequency, ω_{n+1}. As more degrees of freedom are added, each natural frequency estimate becomes more accurate. Generally, engineers are interested in a small number (≤ 10) of natural frequencies. Solutions should continue to use an increased number of degrees until the highest desired eigenvalue is unchanged to a desired number of significant figures after additional degrees of freedom are included in the model.

For solid vibrations, a non-zero EBC or a non-zero forcing term must be enforced before reaching the form of (14.2-1). Those conditions are imposed on a static solution to determine the stress state they cause. That solid stress state is used in turn to calculate the additional element "geometric stiffness matrix" which is assembled into the system geometric stiffness matrix, say $\boldsymbol{K_G}$, (also known as the initial stress matrix) that is added to the original structural stiffness matrix to yield the net system stiffness matrix, $\boldsymbol{K}$, in (14.2-1). That process is known as including stress stiffening effects on the vibration problem.

For structural buckling problems, the system geometric stiffness matrix is the second matrix in (14.2-1) and λ becomes the unknown "buckling load factor", BLF, which can be positive or negative:

$$[\boldsymbol{K} - BLF\, \boldsymbol{K_G}]\, \boldsymbol{\delta} = \mathbf{0}. \tag{14.2-4}$$

In that case, the system degrees of freedom, $\boldsymbol{\delta}$, represent the (normalized) structural displacements in the (linearized) buckled shape.

14.3 Spring-mass Systems

Most engineers are introduced to vibrations through the simple harmonic motion (SHM) of a system of massless linear springs jointed at their ends by point masses, as shown in Fig. 14.3-1. That system, before the EBC, has three displacement degrees of freedom, $\boldsymbol{\delta}$. Thus, the point masses have a system diagonal mass matrix of

$$\boldsymbol{M} = \begin{bmatrix} 0 & 0 & 0 \\ 0 & m_1 & 0 \\ 0 & 0 & m_2 \end{bmatrix}.$$

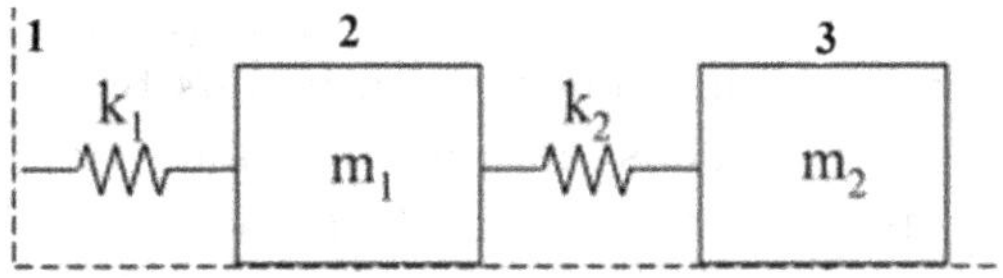

Fig. 14.3-1: A two DOF spring-mass system.

Recall that each linear spring element has a stiffness matrix of $\boldsymbol{k^e} = k\begin{bmatrix} 1 & -1 \\ -1 & 1 \end{bmatrix}$, so the assembled stiffness matrix in the equations of motion, $\left[\boldsymbol{K} - \omega^2\,\boldsymbol{M}\right]\boldsymbol{\delta} = \boldsymbol{0}$, before EBC is

$$\boldsymbol{K} = \begin{bmatrix} k_1 & -k_1 & 0 \\ -k_1 & (k_1 + k_2) & -k_2 \\ 0 & -k_2 & k_2 \end{bmatrix}.$$

Enforcing the EBC such that the displacement (and velocity and acceleration) of the first node is zero eliminates the first row and column of the two system matrices and yields the eigenproblem to be solved for the two vibration frequencies of the spring-mass system as

$$\left| \begin{bmatrix} (k_1 + k_2) & -k_2 \\ -k_2 & -k_2 \end{bmatrix} - \omega^2 \begin{bmatrix} m_1 & 0 \\ 0 & m_2 \end{bmatrix} \right| = 0.$$

Of course, the simplest spring-mass system is that of a single massless spring and a single point mass. Then the determinant of the matrix system reduces to $\left|k_1 - \omega^2 m_1\right| = 0$, which gives the single degree of freedom result where its natural frequency (in rad. per sec.) is

$$\omega = \sqrt{\mathrm{k}}/\mathrm{m}. \tag{14.3-1}$$

However, when continuous (continuum) solutions are modeled, then the elastic body is no longer massless and its spatial distribution of mass must be considered as must the spatial distribution of its elastic properties. That requires using differential equations to represent the equation of motion. Even then, occasional engineering approximations will introduce point masses and/or point springs into the resulting matrix system. The supplied function library provides tools to define (input) and assemble point masses and/or point stiffnesses (springs) into the matrix systems. Those data are stored in text file *msh_mass_pt.txt* and/or *msh_stiff_pt.txt* and are read by functions *get_and_add_pt_mass.m*, etc.

There are handbook analytic solutions for the natural frequencies for the most common homogeneous continuous bars, beams, shafts, membranes, plates, and shells for numerous boundary conditions and including point spring supports and local point masses. The finite element method allows for the fast modeling of the vibration of any elastic solid. Every user should validate any finite element result with a second calculation and handbooks provide one useful check for that task.

Example 14.3-1 Given: A vertical axial bar of length L and area A has an elastic modulus of E and a mass density of ρ is fixed at one end. The other end is connected to equipment considered to be a point mass of value M. Approximate the natural frequency of this system including and neglecting the equipment mass.

Solution: Use a two-noded bar element with

$$\boldsymbol{K}^e = \frac{EA}{L}\begin{bmatrix} 1 & -1 \\ -1 & 1 \end{bmatrix}, \ \boldsymbol{m}^e = \frac{\rho AL}{6}\begin{bmatrix} 2 & 1 \\ 1 & 2 \end{bmatrix}, \ \boldsymbol{m}^p = M\begin{bmatrix} 0 & 0 \\ 0 & 1 \end{bmatrix}.$$

An elastic bar behaves the same as a linear spring. Denote the usual bar "axial stiffness" as $k = EA/L$ and its total bar mass as $m = \rho AL$, and assemble the line element and point element matrices to form the system natural frequency relation:

$$\left| k\begin{bmatrix} 1 & -1 \\ -1 & 1 \end{bmatrix} - \omega_j^2\left(\frac{m}{6}\begin{bmatrix} 2 & 1 \\ 1 & 2 \end{bmatrix} + M\begin{bmatrix} 0 & 0 \\ 0 & 1 \end{bmatrix}\right)\right| = 0.$$

Applying the EBC reduces this to a single DOF problem:

$$\left| k\,[1] - \omega_1^2\left(\frac{m}{6}\,[2] + M\,[1]\right)\right| = 0.$$

The first (and only available) natural frequency is $\omega = \sqrt{k}/(M + m/3)$, rad/sec. This shows that increasing the end mass decreases the frequency. Had the elastic bar been treated as a massless spring ($m = 0$), this would be the exact frequency. For an elastic bar without an end mass this becomes $\omega = \sqrt{3}\sqrt{k/m}$. Compared to the exact frequency of $\omega = \pi/2\sqrt{k/m}$ the single linear element estimate is in error by about 10.4%.

14.4 Vibrating String

The differential equation of the transverse motion of an elastic string, without bending resistance, damping, or external transverse loads is

$$T\frac{\partial v^2}{\partial x^2} - \rho\frac{\partial v^2}{\partial t^2} = 0, \tag{14.4-1}$$

where $v\,(x,\,t)$ is the transverse displacement of the string with a tension of T, and a mass density per unit length of ρ, and t denotes time. Later, when time histories are studied in detail this will be referred to as a wave equation. This PDE is of the hyperbolic class. From physics, it is known that strings (and most elastic bodies) vibrate with SHM. Applying that assumption here, define a separation of variables

$$v\,(x,\,t) = v_o\,(x)\sin\,(\omega t), \tag{14.4-2}$$

where $v_o\,(x)$ is a "mode shape" defining the shape of the string along the x-direction as it changes between positive and negative values that change with a frequency of ω. The second time derivative of $v\,(x,\,t)$ is

$$\frac{\partial v^2}{dt^2} = -\omega^2 v_o\,(x)\sin\,(\omega t) = -\omega^2\,v\,(x,\,t).$$

The assumption of SHM changes the hyperbolic PDE over time and space into an elliptic ODE in space:

$$T\frac{dv^2}{dx^2} + \rho\omega^2 v = 0. \tag{14.4-3}$$

When the ODE has an unknown global constant (ω^2) multiplying the solution value, it is called a scalar Helmholtz equation. This has the usual EBC and NBC options to define a unique solution. For a guitar string, the usual EBCs are that both ends have zero transverse displacements. Use of the Galerkin method and integration by parts (the introduction of the NBCs) gives the governing integral form

$$I = \left[v\left(T\frac{dv}{dx}\right)\right]_0^L - \int_0^L \frac{dv}{dx}\left(T\frac{dv}{dx}\right)dx + \int_0^L v\,(x)\,\rho\,\omega^2\,v(x)dx = 0. \tag{14.4-4}$$

Next, introduce a finite element mesh and the usual element interpolations that in each element

$$v(x) = \boldsymbol{H}(r)\, \boldsymbol{v^e} = (\boldsymbol{H}(r)\, \boldsymbol{v^e})^{\boldsymbol{T}} = \boldsymbol{v^e}^{\boldsymbol{T}} \boldsymbol{H}(r)^{\boldsymbol{T}}$$

Noting that the frequency, ω, is an unknown global constant, it is pulled outside the spatial integral and will also be pulled outside the governing matrix system: $\left[\boldsymbol{K} - \omega^2 \boldsymbol{M}\right]\{\boldsymbol{v}\} = \boldsymbol{c_{NBC}}$. When the EBCs of $v\,(0) = 0 = v(L)$ are enforced, the rows in $\boldsymbol{c_{NBC}}$ associated with the remaining free DOFs are zero and the reduced problem is the same as (14.2-2). The typical element stiffness and consistent mass matrices are

$$\boldsymbol{K^e} = \int_{L^e} \frac{d\boldsymbol{H}(r)}{dx}^T T^e \frac{d\boldsymbol{H}(r)}{dx}\, dx, \ \boldsymbol{M^e} = \int_{L^e} \boldsymbol{H}(r)^T \rho^e \boldsymbol{H}(r) dx. \tag{14.4-5}$$

For constant properties and the Jacobian, the closed-form matrices for the two-noded and three-noded line elements are

$$\boldsymbol{K^e} = \frac{T^e}{L^e}\begin{bmatrix} 1 & -1 \\ -1 & 1 \end{bmatrix}, \quad \boldsymbol{M^e} = \frac{\rho^e L^e}{6}\begin{bmatrix} 2 & 1 \\ 1 & 2 \end{bmatrix}, \tag{14.4-6}$$

$$\boldsymbol{K^e} = \frac{T^e}{3L^e}\begin{bmatrix} 7 & -8 & 1 \\ -8 & 16 & -8 \\ 1 & -8 & 7 \end{bmatrix}, \quad \boldsymbol{M^e} = \frac{\rho^e L^e}{30}\begin{bmatrix} 4 & 2 & -1 \\ 2 & 16 & 2 \\ -1 & 2 & 4 \end{bmatrix}, \tag{14.4-7}$$

respectively. The resulting vibration shapes (mode shapes) come in sets that are either symmetric or anti-symmetric with respect to the center of the string.

Note that the assumptions imply that the string has slope continuity along its entire length (with unknown values at the support points). That observation suggests that using Hermite elements will give more accurate eigenvalues and more physically realistic mode shape plots. For the two-node cubic Hermite element the nodal unknowns are the string deflection and its slope $\boldsymbol{v^e}^T = [v_1\ \theta_1\ v_2\ \theta_2]$, where θ denotes the slope of the string. The element matrices are

$$\boldsymbol{K}^e = \frac{T^e}{30\,L^e}\begin{bmatrix} 36 & 3L^e & -36 & 3L^e \\ 3L^e & 4L^{e^2} & -3L & -L^{e^2} \\ -36 & -3L^e & 36 & -3L^e \\ 3L^e & -L^{e^2} & -3L & 4L^{e^2} \end{bmatrix},$$

$$\boldsymbol{M}^e = \frac{\rho^e L^e}{420}\begin{bmatrix} 156 & 22L^e & 54 & -13L^e \\ 22L^e & 4L^{e^2} & 13L^e & -3L^{e^2} \\ 54 & 13L^e & 156 & -22L^e \\ -13L^e & -3L^{e^2} & -22L^e & 4L^{e^2} \end{bmatrix}. \tag{14.4-8}$$

Similarly, if the three-noded quintic element is used to solve Eq. (14.4-1), then the matrices are

$$\boldsymbol{K}^e = \frac{T^e}{630\,L^e}\begin{bmatrix} 1{,}668 & 39L & -1{,}536 & 240L & -132 & -9L \\ 39L & -28L^2 & -48L & -8L^2 & 9L & -5L^2 \\ -1{,}536 & -48L & 3{,}072 & 0 & -1{,}536 & 48L \\ 240L & -8L^2 & 0 & 256L^2 & -240L & -8L^2 \\ -132 & 9L & -1{,}536 & -240L & 1{,}668 & -39L \\ -9L & -5L^2 & 48L & -8L^2 & -39L & 28L^2 \end{bmatrix},$$

$$\boldsymbol{M}^e = \frac{\rho AL}{13{,}860}\begin{bmatrix} 2{,}092 & 114L & 880 & -160L & 262 & -29L \\ 114L & 8L^2 & 88L & -12L^2 & 29L & -3L^2 \\ 880 & 88L & 5{,}632 & 0 & 880 & -88L \\ -160L & -12L^2 & 0 & 128L^2 & 160L & -12L^2 \\ 262 & 29L & 880 & 160L & 2{,}092 & -114L \\ -29L & -3L^2 & -88L & -12L^2 & -114L & 8L^2 \end{bmatrix}. \tag{14.4-9}$$

The disadvantage of that approach is that the eigenproblem is twice as large as the one using Lagrange interpolation and the same number of nodes. But it should give results more accurately than a Lagrange element solution with twice as many nodes (without interior supports).

Example 14.4-1 Given: A guitar string is needed for a musical instrument. The string has both ends fixed, a mass per unit length of ρ, and has a constant tension of T. Determine how the tension of the string affects the first natural frequency of the string.

Solution: The first symmetric mode is the fundamental one. Approximate it using a single quadratic line element, with both ends fixed. Then $L^e = L$ and the system (and element) stiffness and mass matrices are

$$\left(\frac{T}{3L}\begin{bmatrix} 7 & -8 & 1 \\ -8 & 16 & -8 \\ 1 & -8 & 7 \end{bmatrix} - \omega^2\frac{\rho L}{30}\begin{bmatrix} 4 & 2 & -1 \\ 2 & 16 & 2 \\ -1 & 2 & 4 \end{bmatrix}\right)\begin{Bmatrix} v_1 \\ v_2 \\ v_3 \end{Bmatrix} = \begin{Bmatrix} -c(0)_{\text{NBC}} \\ 0 \\ c(L)_{\text{NBC}} \end{Bmatrix}$$

Enforcing the two EBCs gives

$$\left(\frac{T}{L}[16] - \omega^2\frac{\rho L}{10}[16]\right)\{v_2\} = \{0\}.$$

For a non-trivial solution, $v_2 \neq 0$, the determinant of the square matrix in the brackets must vanish. That happens only for specific values of ω_k, $1 \leq k \leq n_d$ that are equal in number to the number of free DOFs in the mesh. Here, there is only one so

$$\omega_1^2 = 10T/\rho L^2, \quad \omega_1 = 3.1623\sqrt{T}/\rho L^2$$

The exact solution for the kth mode is $\omega_k = k\,\pi\sqrt{T}/\rho L^2$, rad/sec where odd values of k are symmetric modes and even values are non-symmetric. The answer to the given question is that the frequency of the string vibration increases with the square root of its tension.

Here, the single quadratic element has only 0.66% error in the first natural frequency. The first mode shape is a half-sine curve, the amplitude of which is normalized to unity. The half-sine mode shape is approximated spatially by a parabolic segment in a single element model.

Example 14.4-2 Given: Write a Matlab script to find the first three frequencies of the tensioned string using a uniform mesh with two quadratic Lagrangian line elements where $T = 6e5\,N$, $L = 2\,\text{m}$, and $\rho = 0.0234\,\text{kg/m}$.

Solution: Figure 14.4-1 details all of the required calculations (but it does not list the computed mode shapes. The coordinates and properties are set manually and (14.4-7) is inserted to build the element matrices once since they are the same for each element. The loop over each element defines the element connection list manually and uses it to assemble the two elements. The EBCs eliminate the first and fifth DOFs, so only rows and columns 2 through 4 of the two square matrices are passed to the Matlab function *eig.m* which returns the mode shapes (as columns of a square matrix, and the square of the natural frequencies (ω_k^2) as the diagonal elements of a second square matrix. Then the square root gives the three actual frequencies, which are compared to the exact values. (The script *String_vib_L3.m* is included in the Applications Library.) The first frequency is accurate to 0.4%, the second is accurate to 0.6%, and the third has significantly increased to 20%. The execution of the script lists the mode shapes as

Node	Mode 1	Mode 2	Mode 3
1	0.0000	0.0000	0.0000
2	0.7068	–1.0000	0.4068
3	1.0000	0.0000	–1.0000
4	0.7068	1.0000	0.4068
5	0.0000	0.0000	0.0000

where the zero boundary displacements were added to the two ends so the complete (normalized) mode shapes can be plotted, as shown in Fig. 14.4-2. There, the dashed line is the exact mode shape. Note that the first two modes with low-frequency error have small changes in slope between the two elements. However, the third mode has a large change in slope error between the elements. The odd mode numbers are symmetric and should have a zero slope at the center point. A refined mesh of several small elements would reduce the change in slope between elements. Even though the differential equation order does not require the use of C1 elements, it is known from the analytic solutions that the slope of the tensioned string should be continuous. Thus, Hermite elements would give more accurate frequencies. This fact is illustrated in Fig. 14.4-3

```
function [] = String_vib_w_L3() % vibration of a string
% T U_xx = rho U_tt,        SHM: T U_xx = -omega^2 rho U
%         x_1=0   x_2     x_3     x_4     x_5= L
%    T <==*------(1)------*------(2)------*==> T
% Fixed   U_1     U_2     U_3     U_4     U_5 Fixed
% Connectivity :   e       i       j      k          % L3
% (for n_e = 2)    1       1       2      3          % L3
%                  2       3       4      5          % L3
n_e = 2 ; n_g = 1 ; n_n = 3 ; n_m = 5 ;      % constants
n_i = n_n*n_g ; n_d = n_g*n_m ;      % elem & system DOFs
L = 2. ; T = 6e5 ; rho = 0.0234      ; % given m, N, kg/m
L_e = L / n_e                            ; % element length
K_e =  T * [ 7, -8,  1, ; ...      %       stiffness L3
            -8, 16, -8, ; ...      %
             1, -8,  7 ] / (3*L_e) ;
M_e = rho *L_e*[4, 2, -1 ; ...     %            mass L3
                2, 16, 2 ; ...     %
               -1,  2, 4 ] / 30    ;
% Assemble two 3x3 element sq matrices into a n_d x n_d
S=zeros (n_d, n_d);  M=zeros (n_d, n_d)    ; % allocate
for k = 1:n_e                          ; % loop over elements
 rows = [1:n_n] + (k - 1)*(n_n - 1)     ; % connectivity
 S (rows, rows) = S (rows, rows) + K_e ; % add to stiff
 M (rows, rows) = M (rows, rows) + M_e ;  % add to mass
end                                      ; % for element k

%  Solve for eigenvalues and eigenvectors, general form
[Vec, Diag] = eig(S(2:4, 2:4), M(2:4m 2:4));% partition
% Vec = eigenvector cols,   Diag = eigenvalue^2 on diag
fprintf ('String natural frequencies \n')      % heading
exact = pi() * sqrt(T/(rho*L^2))       ; % exact constant
V_abs = max (abs (Vec))            ; % relative amplitude
for k = 1:n_d-2         ; % loop over DOFs less two EBCs
  omega = sqrt(real(Diag (k, k)))       ; % natural freq
  true  = k * exact                ; % exact natural freq
  fprintf ('%i, FEA = %8.3e, Exact = % 8.3e \n', ...
             k, omega, true)                % pretty print
end                                ; % for all active DOF
% end of String_vib_w_L3                  % Running gives:
%   String natural frequencies
%   1, FEA = 7.984e+03, Exact =  7.954e+03
%   2, FEA = 1.601e+04, Exact =  1.591e+04
%   3, FEA = 2.873e+04, Exact =  2.386e+04
```

Fig. 14.4-1: Tensioned string eigenvalue–eigenvector calculations.

```
function Torsion_Vib_BHA_L3                    % Revised 4/5/17
%  Drill string torsionial vibration with end BHA inertia
% v = Angle of twist per unit length,     G = shear modulus,
% rho = mass density, t=time, J_e= shaft polar mass inertia
%       x1=0  x2   x3   x4   x5=L Exact_freq1 = 2.41 rad/sec
% Fixed *---(1)---*----(2)----*  BHA_lumped_J
%        v1   v2   v3   v4    v5  Exact_freq2 = 7.93 rad/sec
% Connectivity list: [1  2  3; 3  4  5] for L3_C0
%.........................................................
n_e = 2                   ; % number of elements
n_n = 3                   ; % number of nodes per element
n_i = 3                   ; % number of DOF per element
n_d = 5                   ; % system degrees of freedom (DOF)

% specific problem: Thomson Ex 56.2 drill string & BHA
L   = 5000. ; L_e = L / n_e  ; % domain, element length, ft
G   = 1.728e9                    ; % shear modulus, lb/ft^2
rho = 15.22                     ; % mass density, slug/ft^3
J_e = 9.4e-4 ; J_BHA = 29.3      ; % string and BHA inertia
Free = [ 2 3 4 5]             ; % vector subscript after EBC

%     Constant quadratic element square matrices
K_e = G * J_e * [ 7, -8,  1, ; ...
                 -8, 16, -8, ; ...
                  1, -8,  7 ] / (3*L_e) ; % stiffness L3_C0
M_e = J_e*rho*L_e*[4, 2, -1 ; ...
                   2, 16, 2 ; ...
                  -1,  2, 4 ] / 30        ; % inertia L3_C0

%        Assemble two n_i by n_i square matrix terms
S = zeros (n_d, n_d) ;   M = zeros (n_d, n_d)   ; % allocate
for k = 1:n_e     ; % loop over elements ===> ===> ===> ===>
  rows = [1:n_n] + (k - 1)*(n_n - 1)    ; % get connectivity
  S (rows, rows) = S (rows, rows) + K_e    ; % add stiffness
  M (rows, rows) = M (rows, rows) + M_e     ; % add inertia
```

Fig. 14.4-2: Torsional frequencies for a shaft with end-point inertia.

where the quintic Hermite polynomial was used to create the stiffness and mass matrices in (14.4-9) and to solve for the first four natural frequencies by using a single three-noded element. Figure 14.4-4 shows the increased accuracy in the fourth mode shape when two quintic elements are employed.

When a structure has symmetric geometry, materials, and boundary conditions, it is common to be able to use only half the structure. Using the zero slope natural boundary condition at the center point yields only the odd-numbered symmetric modes. Repeating the half model with a zero displacement at the center point yields only the even-numbered anti-symmetric modes. Combining the two solution sets gives the full range of symmetric and anti-symmetric modes.

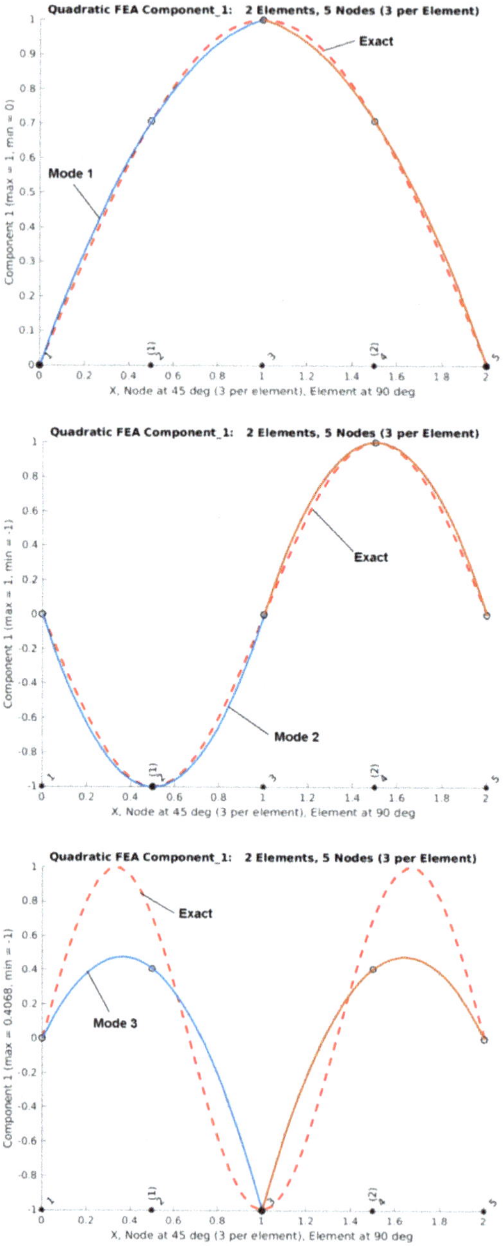

Fig. 14.4-3: Three tensioned string modes (dashed) with two L3 approximations.

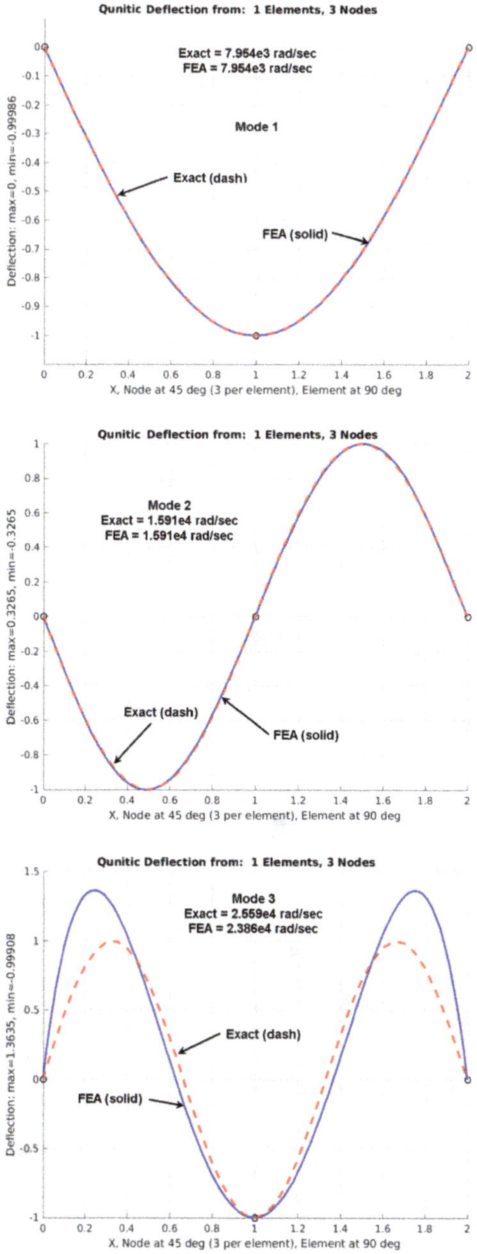

Fig. 14.4-4: Three modes of tensioned string from one quintic element.

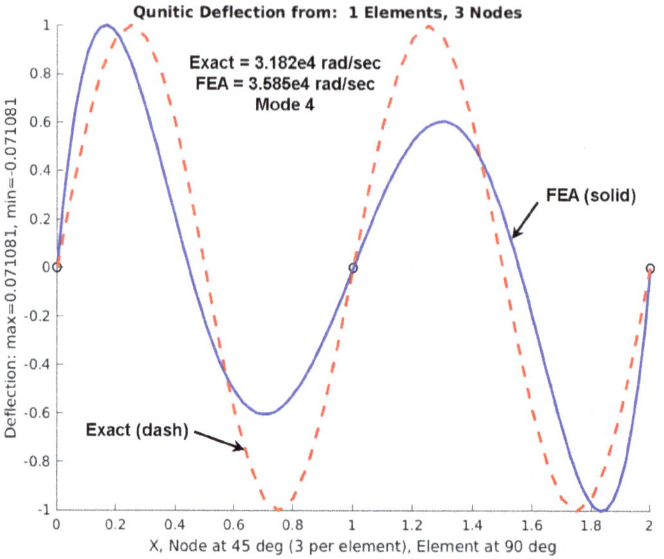

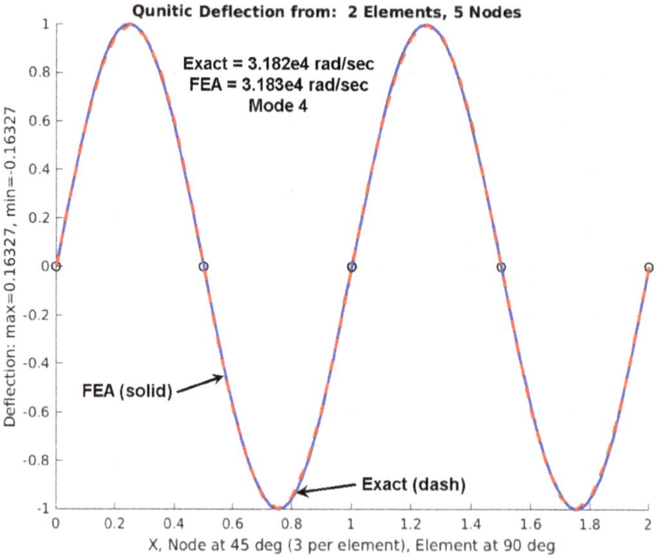

Fig. 14.4-5: Fourth string mode with one (top) and two quintic elements.

Example 14.4-3 Given: Use a quadratic line element fixed at one end, with an averaged mass matrix, to approximate the first two frequencies of axial vibration, and compare them to the exact values of $\pi/2$ and $3\pi/2$ times $\sqrt{EA}/\text{mL}$.

Solution: The stiffness and averaged mass matrices are given in the summary. The system is

$$\left(\frac{E^e A^e}{3L^e}\begin{bmatrix} 7 & -8 & 1 \\ -8 & 16 & -8 \\ 1 & -8 & 7 \end{bmatrix} - \lambda_j \frac{m^e}{60}\begin{bmatrix} 9 & 2 & -1 \\ 2 & 36 & 2 \\ -1 & 2 & 9 \end{bmatrix}\right) \boldsymbol{u}_j^e = \begin{Bmatrix} -c(0)_{\text{NBC}} \\ 0 \\ 0 \end{Bmatrix}.$$

Enforcing the EBC at node 1 reduces the problem to two DOFs. The general eigenproblem is

$$\left|\frac{E^e A^e}{3L^e}\begin{bmatrix} 16 & -8 \\ -8 & 7 \end{bmatrix} - \lambda_j \frac{m^e}{60}\begin{bmatrix} 36 & 2 \\ 2 & 9 \end{bmatrix}\right| = 0.$$

Solving gives the characteristic equation

$$0 = [240\, EA^2 - 107 EA\, \text{mL}\, \lambda + 4L^2 m^2\, \lambda^2]/45\, L^2.$$

Calculating the two roots gives

$$\begin{aligned}\lambda_1 = \omega_1^2 &= \left(107 - \sqrt{7609}\right) EA/(8\,\text{mL}) \to \omega_1 \\ &= 1.5720\sqrt{EA}/\text{mL} \;\; \text{rad/sec}\end{aligned}$$

$$\lambda_2 = \omega_2^2 = \left(107 + \sqrt{7609}\right) EA/(8\,\text{mL}) \to \omega_2 = 4.9273\sqrt{EA}/\text{mL}.$$

This gives the first two frequency errors of 0.08% and 4.56%, respectively. Changing the interpretation of the coefficients to torsional shafts, this corresponds to the free vibration of a fixed-free shaft.

14.5 Torsional Vibrations

The equation of motion of a vibrating torsional shaft or drill string is of the same form as the transverse string vibration:

$$GJ\frac{\partial^2\theta}{\partial x^2} - \rho J\frac{\partial^2\theta}{\partial t^2} = 0, \qquad (14.5\text{-}1)$$

where G is the material shear modulus, J is the cross-section polar moment of inertia, ρ is the mass density per unit length, and θ is the (small) angle of twist of the shaft. The rotational inertia of the shaft cross-section is defined as $I = \rho J$. By analogy to all of the stiffness matrices in Section 14.4, the torsional stiffness matrix always includes the term $GJ/L \equiv k_t$ (divided by a number). That term is known as the torsional stiffness of the shaft and many problems supply that number to describe a shaft segment of length L.

It is common for equipment to be attached to a vibrating system. If the mass, or rotational inertia, of the equipment is large, then the usual practice is to treat the equipment as a point mass and attach it to a node at an element interface. That is, the point mass (or inertia) is added to the diagonal of the system mass matrix at the node where the equipment is located.

For a very long oil well drill string, the end "bottom hole assembly" (BHA) is relatively short but has a very large rotational inertia. In the spring-mass simplified models this type of vibration is called the rotational pendulum. Thus, it is often treated as a point source of rotational inertia, say I_L that is placed on the diagonal of the rotational inertia matrix at the free end node. That physical argument is justified by considering the secondary boundary condition in (14.4-4) at L:

$$\left[\theta\left(GJ\frac{d\theta}{dx}\right)\right]_L \equiv \theta_L\,\tau_L,$$

where τ_L is the external torque applied to the end of the shaft. The BHA is being considered as a rotating planar rigid body. From Newton's law the torque applied to a rotating rigid disk at its center of mass is

$$\tau_{\text{disk}} = \rho J_{\text{disk}}\frac{\partial^2\theta}{\partial t^2} = I_{\text{disk}}\frac{\partial^2\theta}{\partial t^2}.$$

But, for SHM at a frequency ω, Newton's law gives: $\tau_{disk} = -\omega^2 I_{\text{disk}}\theta_{\text{disk}}$. An equal and opposite torque is applied to the shaft from the disk, $\tau_L = -\tau_{\text{disk}}$. Therefore, the system analogous to (14.3-4) becomes

$$\theta_{\text{disk}}\left(\omega^2 I_{\text{disk}}\theta_{\text{disk}}\right) - 0 - \boldsymbol{\theta}^T\boldsymbol{K}\boldsymbol{\theta} + \omega^2\boldsymbol{\theta}^T\boldsymbol{M}\boldsymbol{\theta} = \mathbf{0},$$

which shows that the planar disk inertia, I_{disk}. is simply placed on the diagonal of the inertia matrix, $\boldsymbol{M}$, at the (end) node where the disk is attached to the shaft, as expected.

Example 14.5-1 Given: Create a Matlab script to determine the natural frequencies of torsional vibration of a circular vertical shaft, fixed at the top, and having a large point inertia at its end.

Solution: The script, *Torsional_Vib_BHA_L3.m*, is shown in Fig. 14.5-1 where it manually sets data from a published study that has an exact analytic solution. It utilizes two three-noded quadratic line elements in a mesh with five nodes. Again, the Matlab *eig* function is used to solve the eigenproblem equations. The first torsional frequency is overestimated by only 0.4%.

14.6 Beam Vibrations

The transverse vibration, v, of a beam yields the same matrix eigenproblem even though it begins a differential equation of motion containing fourth-order spatial derivatives:

$$EI\frac{\partial^4 v}{\partial x^4} - \rho A\frac{\partial^2 v}{\partial t^2} = 0, \tag{14.6-1}$$

where A and I are the area and moment of inertia of the cross-section, E and ρ are the elastic modulus and mass density of the material so $\rho A = m$ is the mass per unit length. The bending stiffness matrix (from 9.4-2) and consistent mass matrix (9.4-5) are

$$\begin{aligned}\boldsymbol{K}^e &= \int_{L^e} \frac{d^2\boldsymbol{H}(x)}{dx^2}^T E^e I^e \frac{d^2\boldsymbol{H}(x)}{dx^2}\,dx,\\ \boldsymbol{M}^e &= \int_{L^e} \boldsymbol{H}(x)^T \rho^e A^e \boldsymbol{H}(x)\,dx.\end{aligned} \tag{14.6-2}$$

In Chapter 9, these matrices for the classic two-noded cubic beam are

$$\boldsymbol{K}^e = \frac{EI}{L^3}\begin{bmatrix} 14 & 6L & -12 & 6L \\ 6L & 4L^2 & -6L & 2L^2 \\ -12 & -6L & 12 & -6L \\ 6L & 2L^2 & -6L & 4L^2 \end{bmatrix},$$

$$\boldsymbol{M}^e = \frac{\rho AL}{420}\begin{bmatrix} 156 & 22L & 54 & -13L \\ 22L & 4L^2 & 13L & -3L^2 \\ 54 & 13L & 156 & -22L \\ -13L & -3L^2 & -22L & 4L^2 \end{bmatrix}, \tag{14.6-3}$$

and for the three-noded quintic beam they are

$$\boldsymbol{K}^e = \frac{EI}{35L^3}\begin{bmatrix} 5{,}092 & 1{,}138L & -3{,}584 & 1{,}920L & -1{,}508 & 242L \\ 1{,}138L & 332L^2 & -896L & 320L^2 & -242L & 38L^2 \\ -3{,}584 & -896L & 7{,}168 & 0 & -3{,}584 & 896L \\ 1{,}920L & 320L^2 & 0 & 1{,}280L^2 & -1{,}920L & 320L^2 \\ -1{,}508 & -242L & -3{,}584 & -1{,}920L & 5{,}092 & -1{,}138L \\ 242L & 38L^2 & 896L & 320L^2 & -1{,}138L & 332L^2 \end{bmatrix},$$

and

$$\boldsymbol{M}^e = \frac{\rho AL}{13{,}860}\begin{bmatrix} 2{,}092 & 114L & 880 & -160L & 262 & -29L \\ 114L & 8L^2 & 88L & -12L^2 & 29L & -3L^2 \\ 880 & 88L & 5{,}632 & 0 & 880 & -88L \\ -160L & -12L^2 & 0 & 128L^2 & 160L & -12L^2 \\ 262 & 29L & 880 & 160L & 2{,}092 & -114L \\ -29L & -3L^2 & -88L & -12L^2 & -114L & 8L^2 \end{bmatrix}. \tag{14.6-4}$$

Figure 14.6-1 shows a cantilever beam with an elastic spring support at the end point. If the point spring stiffness is zero, then the system becomes a standard cantilever and if the spring stiffness is infinite, the system becomes a propped cantilever. For all intermediate values of the stiffness this is called an elastic support. Such a

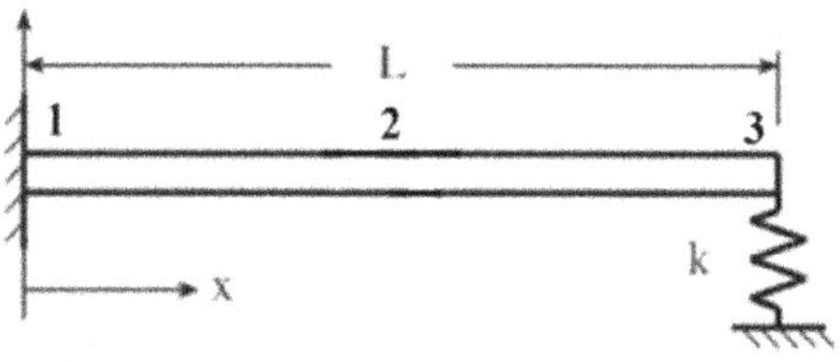

Fig. 14.6-1: Beam with a vertical spring support.

```
function Cantilever_beam_spr_freq_L3   % w/wo spring
%    -d2/dx2 (E I d2u/dx2) = rho d2u/dt2
% Four beam natural frequencies and mode shapes
% for quintic L3_C1 element with vertical end spring
%   NODES:  1------2------3 -->r
%   DOF:     1,2     3,4     5,6
Free = [3 4 5 6]          ; % free DOF after fixed EBC
EI = 1. ; rho = 1. ; L = 1. ; L_2 = L^2 ; m = rho*L ;
k = EI / L^3 ; k_5 = 500*k; % beam & spring stiffness

S = (k / 35) * ...        % beam bending stiffness L3_C0
  [5092     1138*L  -3584    1920*L    -1508     242*L   ;
   1138*L   332*L_2 -896*L   320*L_2   -242*L    38*L_2  ;
  -3584    -896*L    7168     0        -3584     896*L   ;
   1920*L   320*L_2   0      1280*L_2 -1920*L   320*L_2  ;
  -1508    -242*L   -3584   -1920*L     5092    -1138*L  ;
   242*L    38*L_2   896*L   320*L_2  -1138*L   332*L_2];
M = (m / 13860) * ...            % beam mass matrix L3_C0
  [2092     114*L    880    -160*L     262      -29*L    ;
   114*L    8*L_2    88*L   -12*L_2    29*L     -3*L_2   ;
   880      88*L     5632    0         880      -88*L    ;
  -160*L   -12*L_2    0      128*L_2   160*L    -12*L_2  ;
   262      29*L     880     160*L     2092     -114*L   ;
  -29*L    -3*L_2   -88*L   -12*L_2   -114*L    8*L_2] ;

stiff_pt = 1    ; % turn on(1)/off vert spring at DOF 5
if (stiff_pt == 1); S(5,5) = S(5,5) + k_5  ; % add k_5
 fprintf('Beam frequencies with end spring rad/s \n');
else ;
 fprintf ('Beam frequencies with free end rad/s \n') ;
end                   ; % now solve system after EBCs
[Vec_eig, D] = eigs(S(Free,Free),M(Free,Free),4,'sm');
RadPS = sqrt(real(diag(D)))        ; % freq in rad/sec

disp(RadPS); fprintf('Modes 1-4 \n'); DOF=zeros(6,4) ;
Big = max(abs(Vec_eig(1:2:3, :)))    ; % scale factors
for k =1:4; Vec_eig (:,k) = Vec_eig(:,k)/Big(k); end ;
DOF (Free, 1:4) = Vec_eig         % show values to plot
```

Fig. 14.6-2: Natural frequencies of a cantilever with a transverse spring.

system could also have an end point rotational spring to control the end rotation of the beam. Recall that the ratio $k_b \equiv EI/L^3$ is known as the bending stiffness of a beam of span L. The analytic solution for the system in Fig. 14.6-1 depends on the ratio of the spring stiffness to the bending stiffness, say R$\equiv k/k_b$. A Matlab script to find the frequencies of the beam in Fig. 14.6-1 is given in Fig. 14.6-2, and the

```
Beam frequencies with free end, rad/s
    3.5160
   22.1578
   63.3466
  281.5963

Modes 1-4:
         0          0          0          0
         0          0          0          0
    0.3396     0.6938     0.0304     0.2134
    1.1630    -0.4619    -4.6174     1.1355
    1.0000    -1.0000     1.0000     1.0000
    1.3765    -4.7792     7.8409    22.6260

Beam frequencies with end spring, rad/s
   14.9787
   45.0988
   88.9748
  299.3957

Modes 1-4:
         0          0          0          0
         0          0          0          0
    1.0000    -0.6486    -0.1159     0.1903
    1.1965     7.1361    -2.5252     0.9619
    0.1177     1.0000     1.0000     1.0000
   -3.6965    -4.4572     3.3741    21.3334
```

Fig. 14.6-3: Comparing cantilever modes with and without an end spring.

results of the script are in Fig. 14.6-3. That figure shows that as the spring value gets very large, the frequency approaches that of a propped cantilever, as expected.

14.7 Membrane Vibration

There are many applications that use thin membranes of various shapes. A vibrating or pressurized membrane with zero displacement on its boundary, of any shape, corresponds to the shape of a soap bubble. The Matlab logo is one example that is very similar to the amplitude of the vibration of an L-shaped membrane (with the displacements enlarged). A membrane is a thin tensioned material undergoing transverse small displacements without bending resistance. Many membranes require a vibration analysis. For a global uniform membrane tension per unit length on the boundary, T, the two-dimensional equation of motion is

$$T\,\nabla^2 v\,(x,\,y) + \rho h \frac{\partial^2 v(x,\,y)}{\partial t^2} = 0, \tag{14.7-1}$$

where $v(x,\,y)$ is the transverse displacement, ρ is the material mass density, h is the membrane thickness, so ρh is the mass per unit area.

The first term is the same as that for isotropic heat conduction and gives a membrane stiffness matrix, Section 10.7, of

$$\boldsymbol{K}^e = \int_A^e \boldsymbol{B}^{e^T} T \boldsymbol{B}^e \, dA = \int_A^e \begin{bmatrix} \partial \boldsymbol{H}/\partial x \\ \partial \boldsymbol{H}/\partial y \end{bmatrix}^{e^T} T \begin{bmatrix} \partial \boldsymbol{H}/\partial x \\ \partial \boldsymbol{H}/\partial y \end{bmatrix}^{e} dA. \tag{14.7-2}$$

The membrane of thickness, h, also has a mass per unit area, $m = \rho h$, and the corresponding consistent mass matrix of

$$\boldsymbol{M}^e = \int_A^e \boldsymbol{H}^{e^T} \rho^e h^e \boldsymbol{H}^e \, dA, \tag{14.7-3}$$

which assembles into the vibration eigenproblem

$$\left[\boldsymbol{K} - \omega_j^2 \boldsymbol{M}\right] \boldsymbol{\delta}_j = 0.$$

The form of those element matrices were developed in Chapter 10.

The vibration of a flat L-shaped membrane to date has no analytic solution and requires a numerical solution. Very accurate theoretical upper and lower bounds for the natural frequencies of the first 10 modes have been published. Consider an L-shaped membrane made up of three-unit square sub-regions. That membrane is very similar to the one that serves as the Matlab logo.

Note that any L-shaped membrane has a singular point at the re-entrant corner. For static solutions, the radial gradient of the

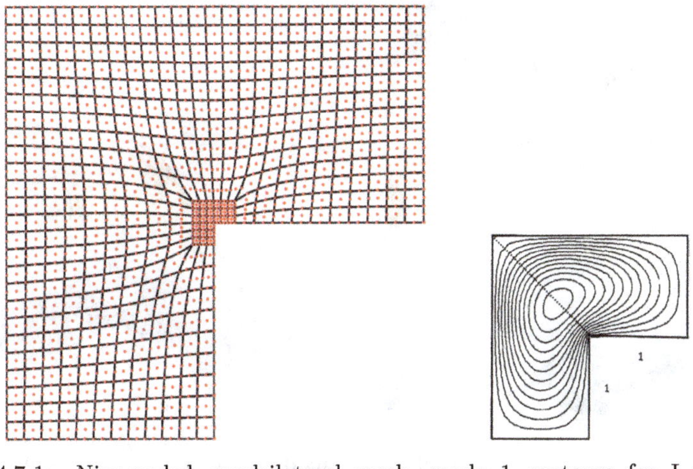

Fig. 14.7-1: Nine-noded quadrilateral mesh, mode 1 contours for L-shaped membrane.

deflected shape at that corner is theoretically infinite and no finite element solution with a uniform mesh will ever reach the theoretical solution. Not only does the asymptotic analytic solution have an infinite gradient, but that gradient changes rapidly with the angle from the first exterior edge to the second edge. These two facts mean that ideally the mesh should be manually controlled to make the elements smaller as they radially approach any singular point, but the mesh should have several elements sharing one vertex at the singular point.

In the early days of finite element solutions, when the available memory was very very small, a special type of "singularity elements"

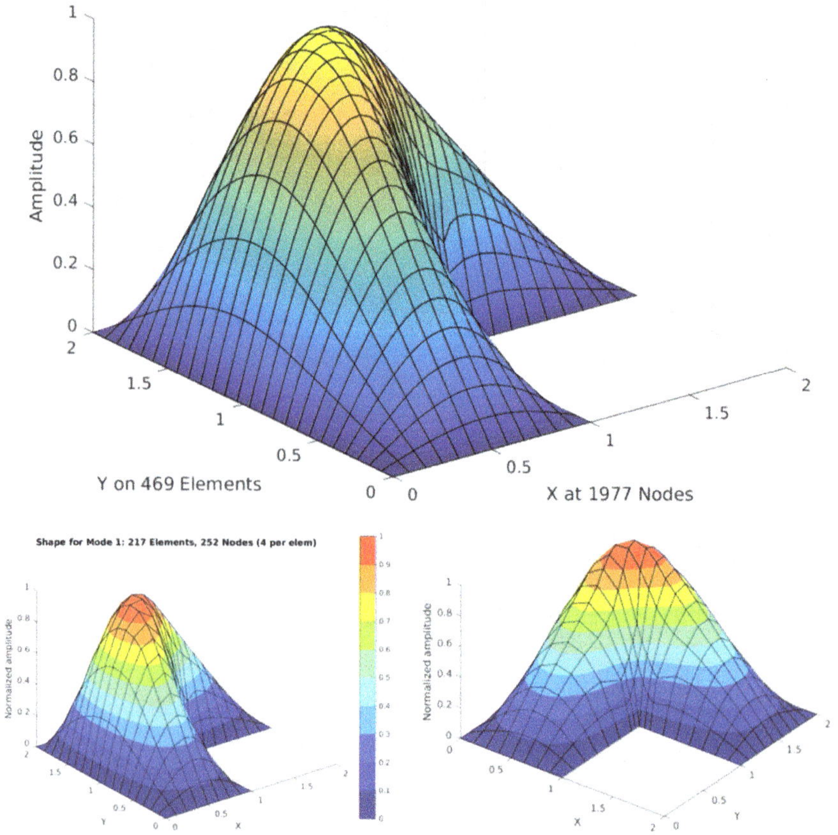

Fig. 14.7-2: L-shaped membrane first mode of vibration with Q9 and Q4 elements.

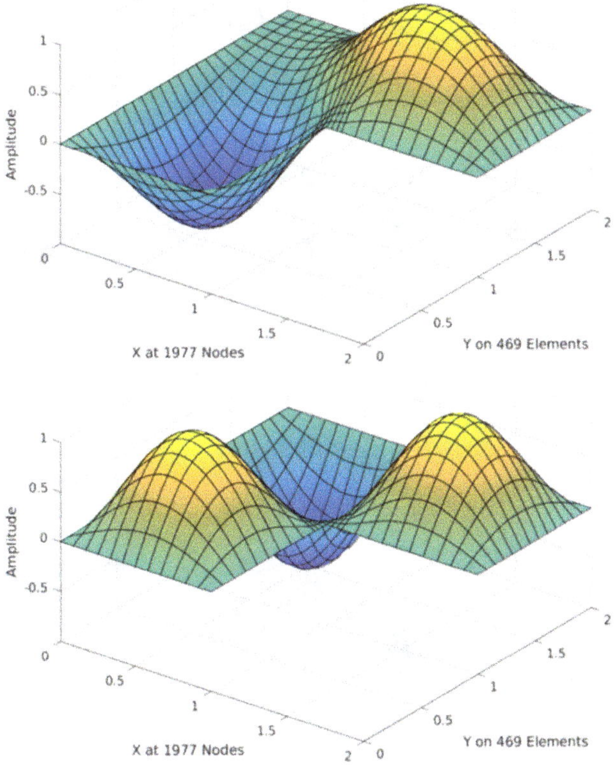

Fig. 14.7-3: Second and third mode shapes of the L-shaped membrane (Q9).

were developed to include in the mesh at singular points. Today, with adaptive mesh generation it is up to the user to create a reasonable mesh refinement at any re-entrant corner. (For adaptive error analysis solutions the user must also limit the size of the smallest element at a re-entrant corner to prevent all new elements being placed there in the attempt to calculate an infinite gradient.)

For a regular shape, like an L-shaped membrane, symmetric and anti-symmetric modes may negate the presence of a re-entrant corner. For example, it will be seen that the third mode of the L-shaped membrane has the same mode shape (with +, −, + signs) in each of the three square sub-regions. Thus, the interior vertical and horizontal lines passing through the corner have zero displacement amplitudes. In other words, it is exactly like computing the first mode of a square with no re-entrant corner.

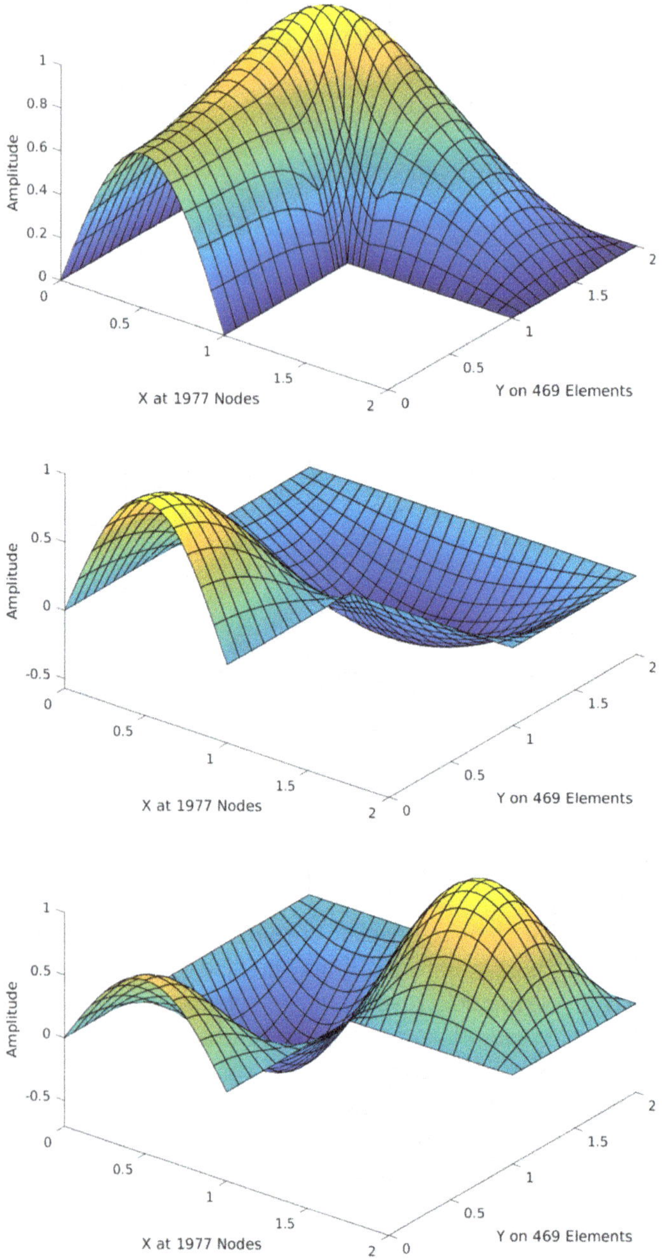

Fig. 14.7-4: First three symmetric modes of half of a U-shaped membrane.

Figure 14.7-1 shows a mesh of nine-noded bi-quadratic quadrilaterals and 1,977 degrees of freedom (nodes) that were used to model the L-shaped membrane and the anti-symmetric modes of a U-shaped membrane. Figure 14.7-2 shows the mode 1 shape (top) obtained with the above mesh; while the bottom shows the shape from bi-linear four-noded quadrilateral elements with only 252 DOF. The two first mode frequency estimates differ by less than 4%. The top view angle, like the one of the Matlab logo, hides the re-entrant corner. The second and third modes are in Fig. 14.7-3. The symmetric modes of a U-shaped membrane are obtained by imposing zero slope along $y = 0$, as seen in Fig. 14.7-4.

The calculations were done by the script *Membrane_vibration.m*, which is in the Application Library. It accepts a membrane of any shape meshed with any element in the provided library. The elements are numerically integrated to alloy for curved membranes and variable Jacobian elements. To produce the mode shape plots invokes the script *mode_shape_surface.m*, which is in the general function library.

14.8 Structural Buckling*

There are two major categories leading to the sudden failure of a mechanical component: structural instability, which is often called buckling, and brittle material failure. Buckling failure is primarily characterized by a sudden, and usually catastrophic, loss of structural stiffness that usually renders the structure unusable. The buckling estimate is computed from a finite element eigenproblem solution. Slender or thin-walled components under compressive stress are susceptible to buckling. Buckling studies are much more sensitive to the component restraints than a normal stress analysis. A buckling mode describes the deformed shape the structure assumes (but not the direction) when it buckles, but (like a vibration mode) says nothing about the numerical values of the displacements or stresses. The numerical values may be displayed, but are only relative and are usually scaled to have a maximum absolute value of one.

Undergraduate linear buckling studies usually focus on the buckling of columns (beams) using the Euler theory. The ideal estimates depend heavily on the EBCs (end constraints) and handbooks give the solution for ideal beams with various end, and mid-span, constraints. Many of those critical column buckling loads can be written as $P_{cr} = k\,\pi^2 EI/L^2$, where k represents the effects of the Dirichlet BCs. The five most common EBC constants for an ideal beam are shown in Fig. 14.8-1.

This section addresses the finite element implementation of the common linear theory of buckling, which like the Euler theory of column buckling, tends to overestimate the load case necessary to cause buckling. An accurate buckling estimate depends heavily on the geometry of the model. For example, here a beam is assumed to be a perfect straight line when the axial load is applied. Furthermore, it is also assumed that the axial load acts exactly through the centroid of the cross-section of the beam. Otherwise, the loading becomes eccentric causing a transverse moment to be applied as well as the axial load. If the part has small irregularities that have been omitted, they can drastically reduce the actual buckling load.

When a constant axial load acts along the entire beam, say N_B, it factors out of the element initial stress (geometric stiffness) matrices and the assembly process to appear as a constant in the system matrices. The goal is to find the scaling up or down of the applied load that causes linear buckling. That scale factor is called the "buckling load factor (BLF)" and replacing N_B with $BLF \times N_B$ leads to a buckling eigenproblem to determine the value of BLF (see Table 14.8-1).

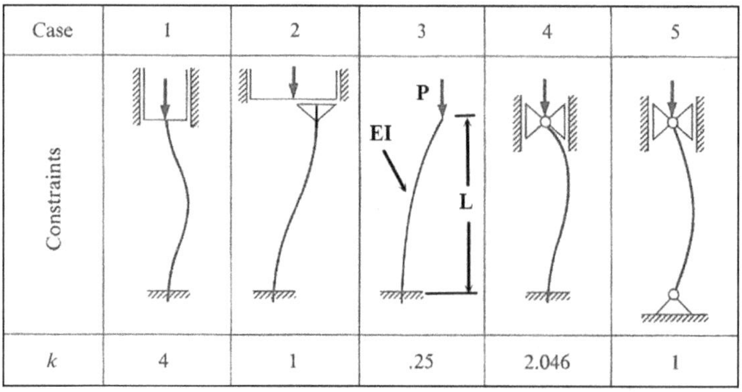

Fig. 14.8-1: Restraints influence the critical buckling load, $P_{cr} = k\,\pi^2 EI/\pi^2$.

For a general structure with a set of loads (called a load case), the system geometric stiffness matrix depends on the stress in each element. That means that it depends on all of the assembled loads, say F_{ref}. In general, a linear static analysis is completed and the deflections are determined from the system equilibrium using the elastic stiffness matrix and any foundation stiffness matrix: $[\boldsymbol{K_E} + \boldsymbol{K_k}]\{\boldsymbol{v}\} = \{\boldsymbol{F}_{\text{ref}}\}$. Those displacements are post-processed to determine the stresses in each element. Then each element's geometric stiffness matrix is calculated from those stresses. The element stresses, and thus its geometric stiffness matrix, is directly proportional to the resultant system load, so as the loads are scaled by the buckling factor, the system geometric stiffness matrix increases by the same amount

$$\boldsymbol{F} \to BLF\, \boldsymbol{F}_{\text{ref}}, \quad \boldsymbol{K_N} \to BLF\, \boldsymbol{K}_{\text{ref}}.$$

The scaling value, *BLF*, that renders the combined system stiffness to have a zero determinant (that is to become unstable) is the increase (or decrease) of all of the applied loads that will cause the structure to buckle. That critical value is calculated from a buckling eigenproblem using the previous matrices plus the geometric stiffness matrix based on the current load case:

$$|\boldsymbol{K_E} + \boldsymbol{K_k} - BLF\, \boldsymbol{K}_{\text{ref}}\,| = 0. \tag{14.8-1}$$

That equation is solved for the value of the *BLF*. Then the system load case that would theoretically cause buckling is $BLF\ \boldsymbol{F}_{\text{ref}}$. The solution of the eigenproblem also yields the relative buckled

Table 14.8-1: Interpretation of the buckling load factor.

Value	**Status**	**Note**
$\lvert BLF\rvert > 1$	Buckling not predicted	The applied loads are less than the theoretical critical loads
$\lvert BLF\rvert \leq 1$	Buckling predicted	The applied loads exceed the theoretical critical loads
$BFL < 0$	Buckling possible	Buckling occurs if the directions of the applied loads are reversed

mode shape (eigenvector), $\boldsymbol{v_{BF}}$. The magnitude of the buckling mode shape displacements are arbitrary and most commercial software normalizes them to range from 0 to 1.

For straight beams with an axial load, several of the above steps are skipped because each element's axial stress and its geometric stiffness matrix are known by inspection. The eigenvalue BLF is the ratio of the buckling load case to the applied load case. The following table gives the interpretation of possible values for the buckling factor.

In theory, there are as many buckling modes as there are DOFs in a structure. Due to the limitations of linear buckling theory, only the first buckling mode is of practical importance. Structural buckling is usually instantaneous and catastrophic. A Factor of Safety of four is often applied to linear buckling estimates. There are commercial finite element systems that can solve the more accurate nonlinear post-buckling behavior of structures.

The estimated Euler buckling force can be unrealistically large as the length of the member decreases. A linear buckling calculation implies that the compression load-deflection relation, and thus the material compression stress–strain relation, are linear. That is true only up to where the stress reaches the material compressive yield stress, say S_{yc}. In other words, the critical compressive stress, $\sigma_{cr} = P_{cr}/A$, caused by the critical force, P_{cr}, must also be considered. To do that the critical stress relation must be re-written in terms of the cross-sectional area. That is done by using the geometric "radius of gyration", r_g, defined as $I \equiv A r_g^2$. Then for typical boundary conditions

$$P_{cr} = k\pi^2 EI/L^2 = k\pi^2 E(A r_g^2)/L^2 = k\pi^2 EA/(L/r_g)^2,$$

where the ratio L/r_g is known as the "slenderness ratio" of the cross-section. It is evaluated at the location of the smallest I found on any plane perpendicular to the axis of the load. The critical compressive stress is $\sigma_{cr} = P_{cr}/A = k\pi^2 E/(L/r_g)^2 \leq S_{yc}$. Once the critical stress exceeds half of the yield stress, other empirical theories, such as the Johnson theory in Fig. 14.8-2, are used.

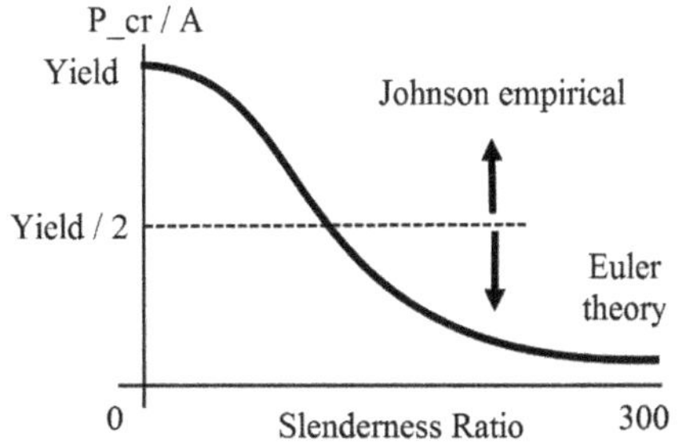

Fig. 14.8-2: Euler and Johnson buckling curves for three Dirichlet BC.

Example 14.8-1 Given: Case 1 of Fig. 14.8-1 represents a fixed–fixed beam-column of length $2L$ which has an unknown lateral displacement at center (L) along with a zero slope. Use a single cubic beam element, of length L, to estimate the axial buckling force.

Solution: The governing ODE and matrix forms are

$$\frac{d^2}{dx^2}\left[EI\,\frac{d^2v}{dx^2}\right] - N\frac{d^2v}{dx^2} = q\,(x) \rightarrow [\boldsymbol{S_{EI}}]\,\{\boldsymbol{\delta}\} + [\boldsymbol{S_N}]\,\{\boldsymbol{\delta}\} = \{\boldsymbol{c_q}\}.$$

For no load, $q = 0$, and constant coefficients (EI, N) in all elements (here one) the unknown axial tension force, N, changes sign and factors out as an unknown global constant (buckling load), converting this into an eigenproblem:

$$|[\boldsymbol{S_{EI}}] - N\,[\boldsymbol{S^*_N}]| = 0.$$

For a cubic beam member, the matrices are (see summary of Chapter 10)

$$\left[\frac{EI^e}{L^3}\begin{bmatrix} 12 & 6L & -12 & 6L \\ 6L & 4L^2 & -6L & 2L^2 \\ -12 & -6L & 12 & -6L \\ 6L & 2L^2 & -6L & 4L^2 \end{bmatrix} - \frac{N}{30L}\begin{bmatrix} 36 & 3L & -36 & 3L \\ 3L & 4L^2 & -3L & -L^2 \\ -36 & -3L & 36 & -3L \\ 3L & -L^2 & -3L & 4L^2 \end{bmatrix}\right]$$

$$\begin{Bmatrix} v_1 \\ \theta_1 \\ v_2 \\ \theta_2 \end{Bmatrix} = \{\boldsymbol{c_q}\},$$

and applying the three Dirichlet conditions that $\theta_1 = 0 = v_2 = \theta_2$ leaves only the transverse displacement

$$\left[\frac{EI^e}{L^3}[12] - \frac{N}{30\,L}[36]\right]\{v_1\} = \{0\},$$

But N is a global unknown so $\left[\frac{EI^e}{L^3}[12] - \frac{N}{30\,L}[36]\right] \equiv 0$ and the estimated buckling force is $N = 10\,EI/L^2$. The exact horizontally symmetric buckling force is $N_{\text{exact}} = \pi^2\,EI/L^2$ and there is a 1.3% error in the buckling force.

Example 14.8-2 Given: Case 4 of Fig. 14.8-1 represents the anti-symmetric case for the above fixed–fixed beam-column of length $2L$. The only change from Example 14.8-1 is that the center point has an unknown slope along with a zero lateral displacement. Use a single cubic beam element, of length L, to estimate the axial buckling force. Approximate the buckling force for that case.

Solution: For a cubic beam member, the matrices are (see Summary 10)

$$\left[\frac{EI^e}{L^3}\begin{bmatrix} 12 & 6L & -12 & 6L \\ 6L & 4L^2 & -6L & 2L^2 \\ -12 & -6L & 12 & -6L \\ 6L & 2L^2 & -6L & 4L^2 \end{bmatrix} - \frac{N}{30L}\begin{bmatrix} 36 & 3L & -36 & 3L \\ 3L & 4L^2 & -3L & -L^2 \\ -36 & -3L & 36 & -3L \\ 3L & -L^2 & -3L & 4L^2 \end{bmatrix}\right]$$

$$\begin{Bmatrix} v_1 \\ \theta_1 \\ v_2 \\ \theta_2 \end{Bmatrix} = \{\boldsymbol{c_q}\}.$$

Applying the three Dirichlet conditions, $v_1 = 0 = v_2 = \theta_2$, leaves the center point-slope, θ_1:

$$\left[\frac{EI^e}{L^3}[4L^2] - \frac{N}{30\,L}[4L^2]\right]\{\theta_1\} = \{0\}.$$

But N is a global unknown so $\left[\frac{EI^e}{L^3}[4L^2] - \frac{N}{30\,L}[4L^2]\right] \equiv 0$ and $N = 30\,EI/L^2$. The exact horizontally symmetric buckling force is $N_{\text{exact}} = 4\pi^2\,EI/L^2$ and there is a 32% error in the buckling force in this second mode. Usually, buckling occurs catastrophically at the lowest (first) buckling mode (force).

Since the beam model used the Euler beam theory, this result corresponds to the Euler buckling theory (presented in mechanics of materials course) which grossly over estimates the buckling force as the column gets shorter.

Example 14.8-3 Given: A fixed–pinned beam (case 4 of Fig. 14.8-1) has an axial compression load of P. Determine the approximate value of P that causes the beam to buckle.

Solution: A single cubic beam has only one DOF, but could give an upper bound on the buckling load (try it). A six-DOF model will give a better estimate. That can be a three-noded mesh with either two cubic beam elements or a single quintic element. They would both have the middle and end slope as DOF, along with the middle transverse deflection to define the mode shape.

The elastic stiffness, geometric stiffness, and mass matrices for the quintic beam (L3_C1) were given in (9.5-2). For a single quintic element model, the two stiffnesses and matrices are

$$\boldsymbol{K_E} = \frac{EI}{35L^3} \begin{bmatrix} 5{,}092 & 1{,}138L & -3{,}584 & 1{,}920L & -1{,}508 & 242L \\ 1{,}138L & 332L^2 & -896L & 320L^2 & -242L & 38L^2 \\ -3{,}584 & -896L & 7{,}168 & 0 & -3{,}584 & 896L \\ 1{,}920L & 320L^2 & 0 & 1{,}280L^2 & -1{,}920L & 320L^2 \\ -1{,}508 & -242L & -3{,}584 & -1{,}920L & 5{,}092 & -1{,}138L \\ 242L & 38L^2 & 896L & 320L^2 & -1{,}138L & 332L^2 \end{bmatrix}$$

$$\boldsymbol{K_N} = \frac{-P}{630L} \begin{bmatrix} 1{,}668 & 39L & -1{,}536 & 240L & -132 & -9L \\ 39L & 28L^2 & -48L & -8L^2 & 9L & -5L^2 \\ -1{,}536 & -48L & 3{,}072 & 0 & -1{,}536 & 48L \\ 240L & -8L^2 & 0 & 256L^2 & -240L & -8L^2 \\ -132 & 9L & -1{,}536 & -240L & 1{,}668 & -39L \\ -9L & -5L^2 & 48L & -8L^2 & -39L & 28L^2 \end{bmatrix},$$

corresponding to the DOF

$$\boldsymbol{v}^{\boldsymbol{T}} = \left[\, v_1\ \theta_1\ v_2\ \theta_2\ v_3\ \theta_3 \,\right] = \left[\, 0\ 0\ v_2\ \theta_2\ 0\ \theta_3 \,\right],$$

so that only DOFs 3, 4, and 6 are free. Substituting those three rows and columns into the eigenproblem and multiplying by the coefficient of $\boldsymbol{K_E}$ gives

$$\left| \begin{bmatrix} 7{,}168 & 0 & 896\,L \\ 0 & 1{,}280\,L^2 & 320\,L^2 \\ 896\,L & 320\,L^2 & 332\,L^2 \end{bmatrix} - \frac{P}{630\,L}\frac{35\,L^3}{EI} \begin{bmatrix} 3{,}072 & 0 & 48\,L \\ 0 & 256\,L^2 & -8\,L^2 \\ 48\,L & -8\,L^2 & 28\,L^2 \end{bmatrix} \right| = 0.$$

Defining the eigenvalue as $\lambda \equiv P_{cr}L^2/18\,EI$, setting the determinant to zero, yields a cubic characteristic equation $-81\,\lambda^3 + 1575\,\lambda^2 - 6020\,\lambda + 4900 = 0$. Computing the roots of that polynomial gives: $\lambda_3 = 14.6546$, $\lambda_2 = 3.6628$, and $\lambda_1 = 1.1270$. The smallest eigenvalue corresponds to the first, and most critical, buckling load. Therefore, the estimated buckling load is $P_1 = 18 \times \lambda_1 EI/L^2 = 20.286\,EI/L^2$, where EI/L^2 is known as the beam stiffness The buckled mode shape is given in Fig. 14.8-5. The exact coefficient is 20.187. The quintic beam-column element gave an error of 0.5%. Repeating this calculation with two cubic beam elements gives a 2.5% error.

Example 14.8-4 Given: Describe how the Example 14.8-3 changes if a transverse spring is present as in Fig. 14.8-3.

Solution: Only the active elastic stiffness matrix changes by adding the spring stiffness to the diagonal location in $\boldsymbol{K_E}$ corresponding to the node to which the spring is attached:

$$\boldsymbol{K_E} = \frac{EI}{35\,L^3} \begin{bmatrix} 7{,}168 & 0 & 896\,L \\ 0 & 1{,}280\,L^2 & 320\,L^2 \\ 896\,L & 320\,L^2 & 332\,L^2 \end{bmatrix} + \begin{bmatrix} k & 0 & 0 \\ 0 & 0 & 0 \\ 0 & 0 & 0 \end{bmatrix},$$

which makes the first coefficient in the left matrix, after defining λ, depend on the ratio of the spring axial stiffness to the transverse

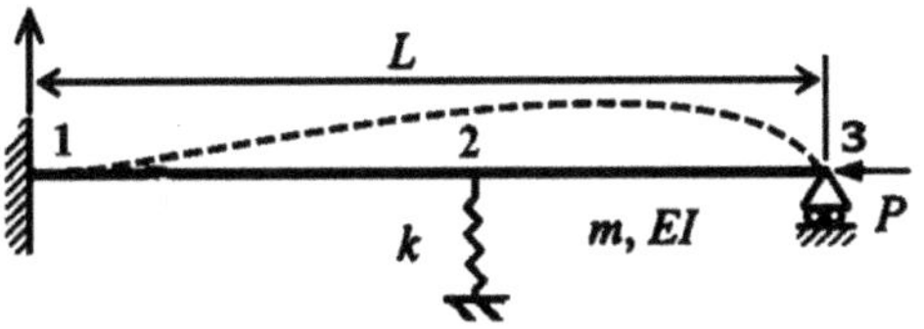

Fig. 14.8-3: Beam-column with axial load and vertical spring.

beam stiffness, EI/L^3:

$$\left(7{,}168 + 35\,k\,L^3/EI\right) = \left(7{,}168 + 35\,k/k_{\text{beam}}\right).$$

Increasing the sprint stiffness will slightly increase the critical buckling force. The spring makes the algebra get much worse, but has no noticeable effect on how the numerical calculations are done after the spring stiffness is scattered to the proper diagonal location.

Note that the limit of $k \to \infty$ makes the spring act as a second pin support at the mid-span. That also cuts the free span length in half, significantly increases the bending stiffness, and then the spring significantly increases the force required to buckle the column.

Example 14.8-5 Given: The constant EA truss in Fig. 14.8-4 has the connection list [1 2, 3 1] and a previous analysis showed that the inclined member is force- (and stress-) free and the vertical (first) carries an axial force of $N = -P$. Repeat the truss analysis with the addition of the initial stress (geometric) stiffnesses to determine the value of P required to cause the truss to buckle (in its original plane).

Solution: The elastic stiffness matrix of a truss member must be rotated from its horizontal position. The direction angles of the first (vertical) and second (inclined) members are $C_x = 90°$, $C_y = |, 0$, and

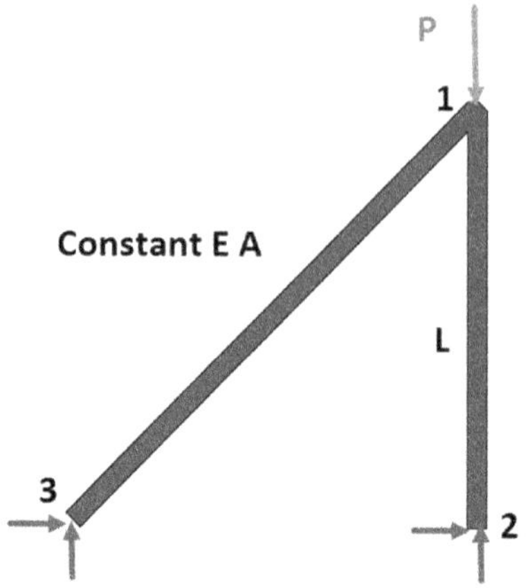

Fig. 14.8-4: Simple truss with a potential buckling load.

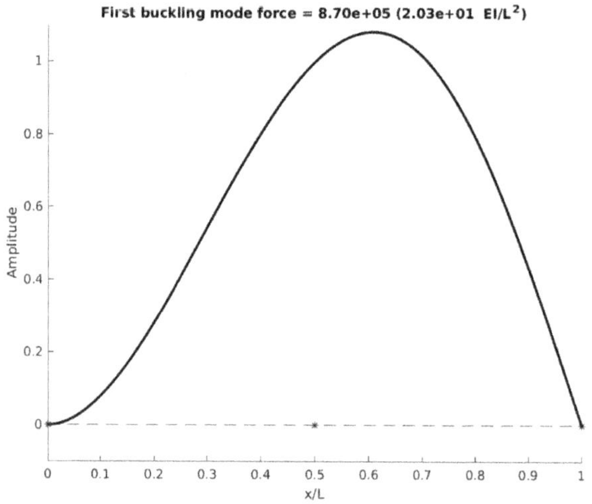

Fig. 14.8-5: Quintic buckled mode shape estimate of fixed–pinned column.

$C_x = 45°, C_y = 45°$, respectively. Thus, their respective transformation sub-matrices are

$$\boldsymbol{t}^{e=1}(\theta) = \begin{bmatrix} 0 & 1 & 0 & 0 \\ -1 & 0 & 0 & 0 \end{bmatrix}, \quad \boldsymbol{t}^{e=2}(\theta) = \frac{1}{\sqrt{2}} \begin{bmatrix} 1 & 1 & 0 & 0 \\ -1 & 1 & 0 & 0 \end{bmatrix},$$

$$[\boldsymbol{T}(\theta)] = \begin{bmatrix} \boldsymbol{t}(\theta) & \mathbf{0} \\ \mathbf{0} & \boldsymbol{t}(\theta) \end{bmatrix}$$

and the original and transformed elastic stiffness matrices,

$$\boldsymbol{S^e_G} = [\boldsymbol{T}(\theta)]^{\boldsymbol{T}}\, \boldsymbol{S^e_L}\, [\boldsymbol{T}(\theta)],$$

are

$$\boldsymbol{S^e_E} = \frac{E^e A^e}{L^e}\begin{bmatrix} 1 & 0 & -1 & 0 \\ 0 & 0 & 0 & 0 \\ -1 & 0 & 1 & 0 \\ 0 & 0 & 0 & 0 \end{bmatrix},$$

DOF

$$\boldsymbol{S^{e=1}_E} = \frac{E\,A}{L}\begin{bmatrix} 1 & 2 & 3 & 4 \\ 0 & 0 & 0 & 0 \\ 0 & 1 & 0 & -1 \\ 0 & 0 & 0 & 0 \\ 0 & -1 & 0 & 1 \end{bmatrix},$$

$$\boldsymbol{S^{e=2}_E} = \frac{E\,A}{(\sqrt{2}L)}\frac{1}{2}\begin{bmatrix} 5 & 6 & 1 & 2 \\ 1 & 1 & -1 & -1 \\ 1 & 1 & -1 & -1 \\ -1 & -1 & 1 & 1 \\ -1 & -1 & 1 & 1 \end{bmatrix}.$$

The initial stress (geometric) stiffness matrix transforms in the same manner:
DOF

$$\boldsymbol{S^e_i} = \frac{N}{L}\begin{bmatrix} 0 & 0 & 0 & 0 \\ 0 & 1 & 0 & -1 \\ 0 & 0 & 0 & 0 \\ 0 & -1 & 0 & 1 \end{bmatrix}, \quad \boldsymbol{S^{e=1}_i} = \frac{-P}{L}\begin{bmatrix} 1 & 2 & 3 & 4 \\ 1 & 0 & -1 & 0 \\ 0 & 0 & 0 & 0 \\ -1 & 0 & 0 & 0 \\ 1 & 0 & 0 & 0 \end{bmatrix},$$

$$\boldsymbol{S^{e=2}_i} = \boldsymbol{0}.$$

The structure has six DOFs, but only the first two are free, so only those partitions need to be assembled:

$$\left[\left(\frac{EA}{L}\begin{bmatrix}0 & 0\\0 & 1\end{bmatrix}+\frac{EA}{2\sqrt{2}\,L}\begin{bmatrix}1 & 1\\1 & 1\end{bmatrix}\right)-P\left(\frac{1}{L}\begin{bmatrix}1 & 0\\0 & 0\end{bmatrix}\right)\right]\begin{Bmatrix}u_1\\u_2\end{Bmatrix}=\begin{Bmatrix}0\\0\end{Bmatrix}.$$

The critical buckling force causes the determinant to vanish:

$$\begin{vmatrix}\left(\frac{EA}{2\sqrt{2}\,L}-\frac{P_{crit}}{L}\right) & \frac{EA}{2\sqrt{2}\,L}\\ \frac{EA}{2\sqrt{2}\,L} & (1+2\sqrt{2})\frac{EA}{2\sqrt{2}\,L}\end{vmatrix}=0$$

$$=\frac{EA}{2\sqrt{2}\,L}\left|\begin{bmatrix}(1-2\sqrt{2}\,P_{crit}/EA) & 1\\ 1 & (1+2\sqrt{2})\end{bmatrix}\right|.$$

Evaluating the determinant gives the critical load of

$$P_{crit}=EA\left(2\sqrt{2}-1\right)/7=0.261\,EA,$$

which is the same value obtained from the mechanics of materials.

Example 14.8-6 Given: Write a Matlab script to implement the calculations given in Example 14.8-3, and to plot the buckled mode shape.

Solution: Such a script is in Fig. 14.8-6. The mechanics calculations take about a dozen lines. After the EBCs are enforced, only the mid-span displacement, mid-span rotation, and the end-point rotation remain free (DOFs 3, 4, 6). Those three rows and columns from the elastic stiffness and the geometric matrices are passed as input arguments to the Matlab function *eig* which returns three critical BLF values and their corresponding buckled mode shapes. The three BLF are extracted from the returned square matrix into a vector using the Matlab function *diag*. That was done because *eig* does NOT always return the eigenvalues in increasing order. The Matlab *abs min* function combination was used to find which eigenvalue was the smallest and to grab that value. The location of the smallest eigenvalue was then used to extract the column from the eigenvector square matrix which corresponds to the lowest buckling mode shape. (Note, the higher buckling modes are not important so an algorithm that finds and returns only the lowest

```
% Beam buckling load and mode shape for a single quintic
%                  fixed-pinned L3_C1 element
%   DOF:  1,2    3,4    5,6 ROLLER PIN
%   FIXED: *-------*-------* <=== P          (Theory 20.19 EI/L^2)
L = 10.0; E = 70.e9; I = 61.3e-6; Free = [3 4 6]  ; % model data
EIL2 = E*I/L^2; K_e = EIL2/(35*L)           ; % beam & L3 stiffness
K = [7168,        0,    896*L ;                    % bending matrix
        0, 1280*L^2, 320*L^2 ;
    896*L,  320*L^2, 332*L^2] * K_e                ; % free DOF only
G = [3072,        0,    48*L ;                    % geometric matrix
        0, 256*L^2, -8*L^2 ;
     48*L,  -8*L^2, 28*L^2] / (630*L)              ; % free DOF only

[Modes, BFsq] = eig (K, G)            ; % solve for buckling load
BFs = diag(BFsq)               ; % Buckling Factors (NOT in order)
[B_n, L_n] = min((abs(BFs)))          ; % min force value & where
fprintf('Buckling force estimate %7.2e \n', B_n)   ; % eigenvalue
fprintf('Use force  %7.2e \n', B_n/4)                     ; % safer

DOF(1:6)=0; DOF(Free) = Modes(:, L_n)   ; % buckling mode to plot
Big = max(abs(DOF(1:2:5))); DOF = DOF/Big           ; % scale mode
x = zeros (100,1); y = zeros (100,1)         ; % allocate plot pts
for k = 1:101; % beam points in parametric space --> --> --> -->
  r = (k-1)/100         ; % 0 <= r <= 1 from Hermite_1D_C1_library
  r2 = r^2 ; r3 = r^3 ; r4 = r^4 ; r5 = r^5             ; % constants
  H=[(1-23*r2+66*r3-68*r4+24*r5) (r-6*r2+13*r3-12*r4+4*r5)*L ...
     (16*r2-32*r3+16*r4 )        (-8*r2+32*r3-40*r4+16*r5)*L ...
     (7*r2-34*r3+52*r4-24*r5)    (-r2+5*r3-8*r4+4*r5)*L] ;
  y(k) = H * DOF' ; x(k) = r               ; % mode amplitude & x/L
end ; % for k points on beam ,-- <-- <-- <-- <-- <-- <-- <-- <--
clf; hold on; grid on; axis([0, 1, -0.1, 1.1]);       % clear plot
xlabel('x/L'); ylabel('Amplitude'); ratio=B_n/EIL2;% plot labels
title(['First buckling mode force = ', num2str(B_n,'%7.2e'), ...
       ' (', num2str(ratio,'%7.2e'),'  EI/L^2)'])        ; % title
plot (x, y, 'b-'); xb=[0,0.5,1]; yb=[0,0,0]; % modes & beam info
plot(xb,yb,'k--'); plot(xb,yb,'k*')     ; % show beam line & nodes
p_text = 'Beam_buckle_shape'; print('-dpng',p_text); % save plot
n_text = ['Created png file ', p_text]          ; % add extension
fprintf (1,'%s', n_text); fprintf (1, ' \n');       ; % tell user
```

Fig. 14.8-6: Linear buckling load and mode shape for a fixed–pinned beam.

eigenvalue is the most efficient way to do buckling studies.) The lowest BLF is printed, along with that value reduced by a Factor of Safety (FOS) of four. Then the retained buckling mode is plotted and saved.

The larger lower section of the figure primarily addresses the scaled magnitude of the fifth-degree polynomial used to calculate the critical load. To list or graph the mode shape the full system displacement vector must be restored by inserting the three free buckled displacement components in with the prior three EBC values. The magnitudes of the components of the buckling mode displacement are only relative, so they are scaled to have a maximum non-dimensional value of one. Then the six-element DOFs are interpolated at many points along the fifth-degree polynomial to display the exact curve of the approximate buckled mode shape. The location of the three-element nodes and a dashed line representing the original column centerline are optionally added to provide a more informative graph.

14.9 Beam Frequency with an Axial Load*

To determine the natural frequencies of a structure subjected to an axial load the eigenproblem is $|(\boldsymbol{K_E} + \boldsymbol{K_N}) - \omega^2 \boldsymbol{M}| = 0$, where $\boldsymbol{K_E}$ is the usual elastic stiffness matrix, $\boldsymbol{K_N}$ is the geometric stiffness matrix associated with the axial load, $\boldsymbol{N}$, and $\boldsymbol{M}$ is the usual mass matrix. When the axial load is a constant, say N_B, then it factors out of each element geometric stiffness matrix and becomes a global constant:

$$|(\boldsymbol{K_E} + N_B \boldsymbol{K_n}) - \omega^2 \boldsymbol{M}| = 0, \tag{14.9-1}$$

where the unit initial stress matrix, $\mathrm{K_n}$, is formed with a unit positive load. This equation shows that any axial load, $\mathrm{N_B}$, has an influence on the natural frequency, ω. In general, a tensile force (+) increases the natural frequency while a compression force (–) lowers the natural frequency.

One of the most common applications of this state is finding the natural frequencies of turbine blades in jet engines. Their high rotational speed imposes a tension centripetal force on the blades that increases with radial position. A static solution at a fixed rotational speed defines the element stresses that in turn define the element geometric (initial stress) matrix. Then the eigenproblem is solved to compute the blade frequencies at each rotational speed of the engine.

This eigenproblem is easily solved numerically. There are several published analytic solutions for a beam-column with various EBCs. Still, a single finite element can give an important insight into how the primary variables impact the resulting natural frequency. Consider finding the natural frequency of a fixed–pinned column (case 4) subjected to an axial tension force, P. A single cubic beam element model has only the single end rotation, θ_2, as its one free DOF. Substituting that term from the cubic beam matrices, from (9.5-1), and

(9.5-3), into the third row of the system matrix (14.9-1) gives:

$$\left| \frac{EI}{L^3}\left[4L^2\right] + \frac{P}{L}\left[\frac{2\,L^2}{15}\right] - \omega^2 \rho AL\left[\frac{4\,L^2}{420}\right] \right| = 0,$$

dividing all terms by EI/L gives

$$4 + \frac{PL^2}{EI}\frac{2}{15} - \omega^2\frac{\rho AL^4}{EI} = 0,$$

so, the natural frequency squared is

$$\omega^2 = 420\frac{EI}{\rho AL^4}\left\{1 + \frac{1}{30}\frac{PL^2}{EI}\right\} = 420\frac{EI}{m\,L^3}\left\{1 + \frac{1}{30}\frac{P}{L}\frac{L^3}{EI}\right\},$$

where $m = \rho AL$ is the mass of the beam, EI/L^3 is the beam elastic stiffness, and P/L is the beam geometric stiffness. The frequency is

$$\omega = 20.49\sqrt{\frac{EI}{m\,L^3}}\sqrt{1 + \frac{1}{30}\frac{P}{L}\frac{L^3}{EI}}.$$

The last re-arranged term is the general form that the exact analytic solution takes for various EBCs (that generate their corresponding n_1 and n_2 values):

$$\omega \equiv n_1\sqrt{\frac{EI}{m\,L^3}}\sqrt{1 + \frac{1}{n_2}\frac{P}{L}\frac{L^3}{EI}}. \tag{14.9-2}$$

For example, in a pinned–pinned single span beam the ith frequency has $n_1 = \pi\, i^2/2$, $n_2 = \pi^2 i^2$. That general form shows that when the axial load is tension ($P > 0$), the natural frequency is increased. Conversely, when the load is compressive ($P < 0$), the natural frequency is reduced. The lower limit is when the frequency goes to zero, which corresponds to the column buckling (losing its stiffness): $P_{cr} = -n_2 EI/L^2$. The theoretical relation between the square of the frequency and the axial load is linear and is shown for compression loads in Fig. 14.9-1.

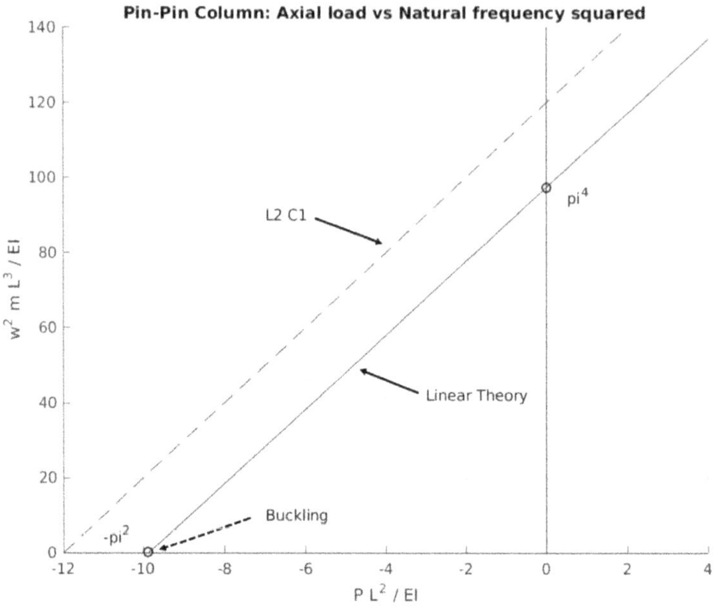

Fig. 14.9-1: Square of column frequency is proportional to axial load.

If the above single cubic element is changed to a pinned–pinned pair of EBCs, then it has two DOFs and thus two natural frequencies:

$$\omega_1 = 10.954\sqrt{\frac{EI}{m\,L^3}}\sqrt{1+\frac{1}{12}\frac{P}{L}\frac{L^3}{EI}},$$

$$\omega_2 = 50.200\sqrt{\frac{EI}{m\,L^3}}\sqrt{1+\frac{1}{60}\frac{P}{L}\frac{L^3}{EI}},$$

and setting $\omega_1 = 0$ gives a buckling load estimate of $P_1 = -12\,EI/L^2$ which is about 27% higher than the exact value of $-\pi^2 EI/L^2$.

Example 14.9-1 Given: Write a Matlab script to determine the natural frequencies of the quintic fixed–pinned beam-column (case 4 of Fig. 14.8-1) in Example 14.8-1 with an axial tension load of P.

Solution: Only the quintic beam element mass matrix is needed in addition to the elastic stiffness and geometric stiffness given in

```
%  Natural frequency of a beam column via one quintic
%            L3_C1 pinned-pinned element
%        NODES:  1------2------3 <<=== P
%        DOF:    1,2     3,4     5,6  ; % Four frequencies
         Free = [2      3 4       6]  ; % free after 0 EBC
EI = 1. ; rho = 1. ; L = 1. ; L_2 = L^2 ; m = rho*L  ;
k = EI / L^3 ; P = -1    ; % beam stiffness, axial load

S = (k / 35) * ...        % beam bending stiffness L3_C0
  [5092     1138*L  -3584   1920*L    -1508    242*L    ;
   1138*L  332*L_2 -896*L  320*L_2   -242*L    38*L_2   ;
  -3584    -896*L   7168      0      -3584     896*L    ;
   1920*L  320*L_2   0     1280*L_2 -1920*L   320*L_2  ;
  -1508    -242*L  -3584  -1920*L     5092    -1138*L   ;
   242*L    38*L_2  896*L  320*L_2  -1138*L   332*L_2];
M = (m / 13860) * ...             % beam mass matrix L3_C0
   [2092     114*L    880    -160*L      262     -29*L   ;
    114*L    8*L_2    88*L   -12*L_2     29*L    -3*L_2  ;
    880      88*L     5632     0         880     -88*L   ;
   -160*L  -12*L_2     0     128*L_2    160*L   -12*L_2 ;
    262      29*L     880     160*L     2092     -114*L  ;
   -29*L   -3*L_2   -88*L   -12*L_2   -114*L     8*L_2] ;
%                   Geometric stiffness matrix, due to P
G = (P / 630) * ...    % beam geometric stiffness L3_C0
   [1668/L   39     -1536/L   240     -132/L   -9      ;
    39        28*L  -48       -8*L     9       -5*L    ;
   -1536/L  -48      3072/L   0       -1536/L   48     ;
    240     -8*L     0        256*L   -240     -8*L    ;
   -132/L    9      -1536/L  -240      1668/L  -39     ;
   -9       -5*L     48       -8*L    -39       28*L]  ;
K = S(Free,Free) + G(Free,Free)      ; % total stiffness

[Vec_eig, D_vals] = eig (K, M(Free,Free))      ; % solve
RadPS = sqrt(real(diag(D_vals)))      ; % freq in rad/sec
fprintf('Mode 1-4 frequencies \n')      ; % print header
disp(RadPS)                         ; % show first four freq
Big = max(abs(Vec_eig(2, 1)))           ; % scale mid displ
DOF = zeros(6, 1)                     ; % set up plot storage
DOF (Free) = Vec_eig(:, 1) / Big          % mode 1 to plot
```

Fig. 14.9-2: Frequencies of beam-column with axial load.

that example. The determinate is

$$\left| \frac{EI}{35L^3} \begin{bmatrix} 7{,}168 & 0 & 896L \\ 0 & 1{,}280L^2 & 320L^2 \\ 896L & 320L^2 & 332L^2 \end{bmatrix} + \frac{P}{630L} \begin{bmatrix} 3{,}072 & 0 & 48L \\ 0 & 256L^2 & -8L^2 \\ 48L & -8L^2 & 28L^2 \end{bmatrix} \right|$$

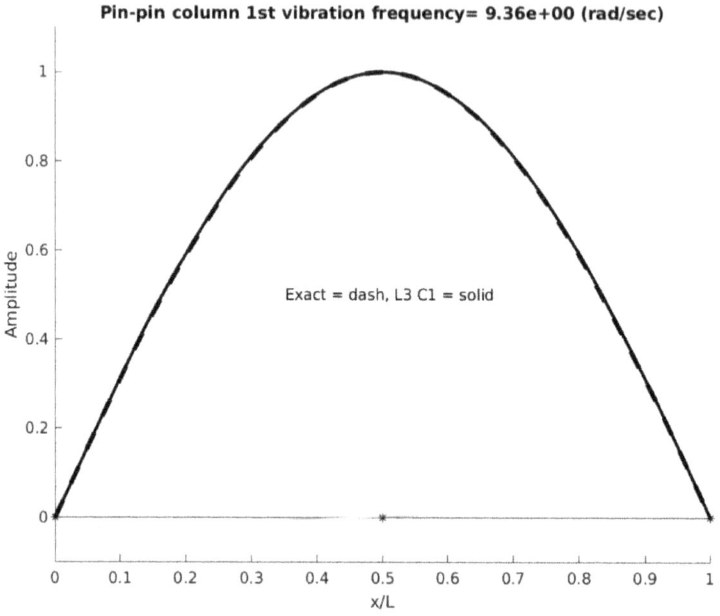

Fig. 14.9-3: Column exact and L3_C1 first mode shape.

$$-\omega^2 \frac{\rho A L^4}{EI} \begin{bmatrix} 5{,}632 & 0 & -88L \\ 0 & 128L^2 & -12L^2 \\ -88L & -12L^2 & 8L^2 \end{bmatrix} \Bigg| = 0.$$

The Matlab solution script, *Beam_Col_Freq_L3.m*, is shown in Fig. 14.9-2, with the omission of the trailing mode shape plot details for a unit property beam. Figure 14.9-3 shows the first vibrational mode shape approximation and the exact sine curve shape.

14.10 Plane–Frame Modes and Frequencies*

Chapter 10 presented the planar stiffness and mass matrices for the classic cubic beam element and the more useful quintic beam element. Those matrices are also repeated in the summary of this chapter. The vibration analysis of a frame basically just replaces the linear equation solver with a call to the eigenvalue solver. Since the planar frame has three DOFs per node, the main new effort is plotting the true cubic of quintic vibration modes (or the lowest buckling mode).

14.11 Modes and Frequencies of Two-Dimensional Continua

The natural frequency calculations for plane–stress, plane–strain, and axisymmetric solids are almost identical. Thus, the plane–stress case will be demonstrated here. The definitions for elastic stiffness matrix and the consistent mass matrices were given in (11.11-1) and (11.14-4), respectively:

$$\boldsymbol{S}^e = \int_V^e \boldsymbol{B}^{e^T} \boldsymbol{E}^e \boldsymbol{B}^e dV \quad \boldsymbol{M}^e \equiv \int_V^e \boldsymbol{N}^T \rho^e \boldsymbol{N}\, dV. \qquad (14.11\text{-}1)$$

Note that the mass array used vector interpolation $\boldsymbol{N}$ instead of the scalar interpolation $\boldsymbol{H}$ used for the generalized mass matrices for scalar one-dimensional arrays. The total mass (and its generalized mass matrix from $\boldsymbol{H}$) occur in each space-dimension. In other words, the provided script for plane–stress or plane–strain integrates a generalized mass matrix and then scatters a copy to the x-direction degrees of freedom, and the y-direction, rather than integrate the same terms twice.

Plane–stress and plane–strain applications have the same strain–displacement matrices, $\boldsymbol{B}^e$, but their constitutive matrices, $\boldsymbol{E}^e$, have different entries. The axisymmetric solids have one more row in their $\boldsymbol{B}^e$ and $\boldsymbol{E}^e$ matrices. For planar solids, the differential volume is $dV = t^e\, dA$ for an element thickness of t^e, and for the axisymmetric solid it is $dV = 2\pi\, R\, dA$. In the example script used here, numerical integration is used to formulate the element matrices for curved quadratic triangular (T6) elements.

Empirical studies have shown that alternate forms of the mass matrix are available. Special exact integration rules that use the nodes as quadrature points produce a diagonal mass matrix. The same diagonal matrix, $\boldsymbol{M}^e_{\text{diag}} = \lceil \boldsymbol{M}^e \rfloor$, can be obtained by scaling up the diagonal of the consistent mass matrix:

$$\boldsymbol{M}^e_{\text{diag}} = \text{diag}\,(\boldsymbol{M}^e) \times \text{sum}\,(\boldsymbol{M}^e)/\text{sum}(\text{diag}\,(\boldsymbol{M}^e)), \qquad (14.11\text{-}2)$$

```
================ Begin Application Remarks ===================
In-plane vibrations of a deep cantilever shear beam (sq. plate)
Mesh 20 x 20 = 400 T6 numerically integrated elements. Plate is
10 x 10 x 0.01 m, E = 2e11 N/m^2, nu = 0.3, rho = 8e3 Kg/m^3
Theoretical freq., Hz: 1-52.404 2-125.69 3-140.78 4-222.54
================= End Application Remarks ====================
```

Fig. 14.11-1: Description of planar vibration validation problem.

to preserve the total of mass present. For elements including rotary inertia, like beams, the sums are split to retain the proper units for different degrees of freedom. Numerical studies of natural frequency calculations have shown that the average of the above two forms improve the rate of convergence of the frequencies and their mode shapes. For planar problems, the first few mode shapes tend to show a bending response in the longest direction, then an extension in the longest direction or a shear distortion in the shortest direction. Real structures usually have hundreds of mode shapes and they are difficult to interpret unless you do that daily. The provided application script *Plane_Stress_T6_freq_sm.m* illustrates most of the finite element concepts covered in this book. It uses numerically integrated isoparametric (curved) triangles to build the model and the Matlab function *eigs* to extract a small number of modes. It also uses the Matlab function *sort* to place them in increasing order. The requested numbers of eigenvalues are listed. The corresponding eigenvectors can optionally be listed, but usually they are optionally processed into a plot file.

There are few analytical benchmarks for planar shapes. The planar vibration script was compared against one listed in Fig. 14.11-1 and the numerical eigenvalue results in Fig. 14.11-2 compare better than usual. The system has 882 DOFs (before the EBCs and 840 after). Therefore, the system had 840 natural frequencies but only the first five were extracted. The errors in the first four frequencies are only 0.05%, 0.04%, 0.20%, and 0.72%, respectively. The first five-mode shapes (eigenvectors) are shown in Fig. 14.11-3.

14.12 Principal Stresses*

At any point in a stressed solid, there are three mutually orthogonal planes where the shear stresses vanish and only the normal

```
NOTE: Rigid body motions give zero frequencies

Eigenvalue 1 = 1.0853e+05
Natural frequency, Hz (rad/sec)  1 5.24309e+01 (3.29433e+02)

Eigenvalue 2 = 6.2416e+05
Natural frequency, Hz (rad/sec)  2 1.25738e+02 (7.90037e+02)

Eigenvalue 3 = 7.8570e+05
Natural frequency, Hz (rad/sec)  3 1.41074e+02 (8.86396e+02)

Eigenvalue 4 = 1.9834e+06
Natural frequency, Hz (rad/sec)  4 2.24143e+02 (1.40833e+03)

Eigenvalue 5 = 2.3093e+06
Natural frequency, Hz (rad/sec)  5 2.41860e+02 (1.51965e+03)

Created png file mode_shape_1_2d
Created png file mode_shape_2_2d
Created png file mode_shape_3_2d
Created png file mode_shape_4_2d
Created png file mode_shape_5_2d
```

Fig. 14.11-2: Planar vibration numerical validation results.

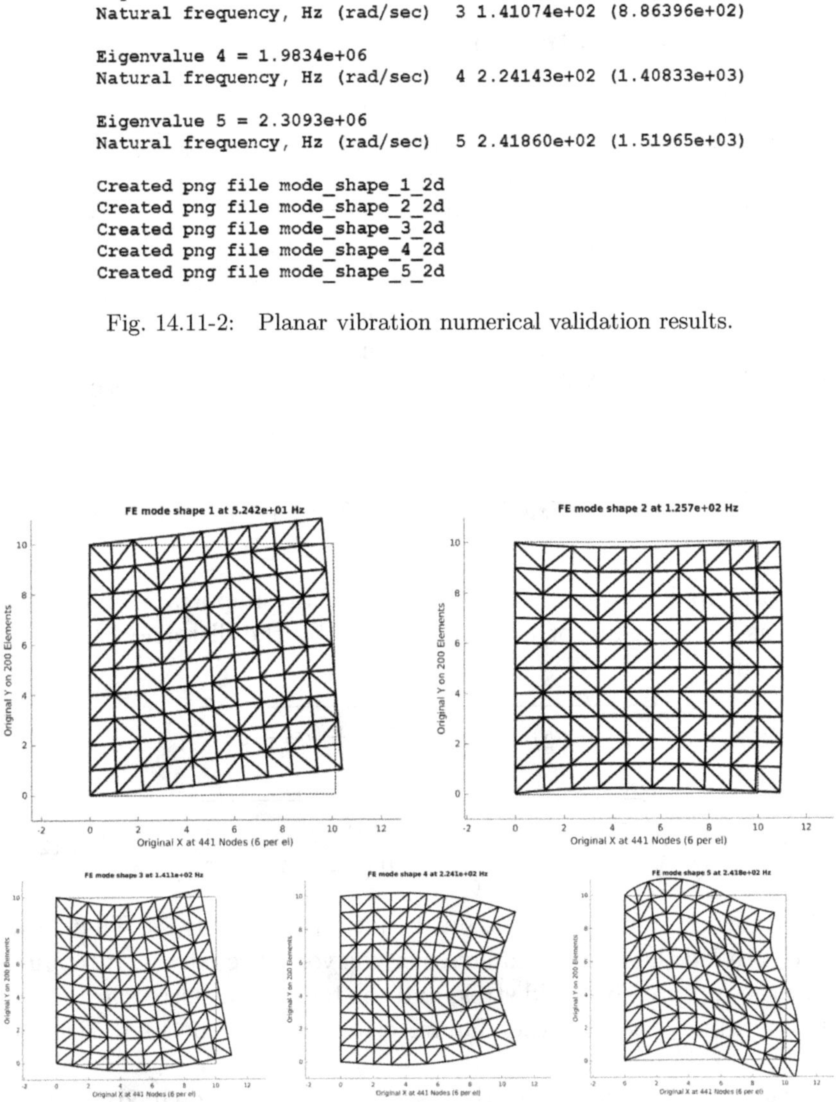

Fig. 14.11-3: First five modes of a planar deep cantilever vibration problem.

stresses remain. Those three normal stresses are called the principal stresses. The principal stresses are utilized to define the most common failure criteria theories for most materials. Therefore, their calculation is usually obtained at each quadrature point in a stress analysis. The principal stresses are found from a small **3** $\times$ **3** classic eigenproblem:

$$\left|[\boldsymbol{\sigma}] - \lambda_k [\boldsymbol{I}]\right| = 0, \quad k = 1, \ldots, n_s, \tag{14.12-1}$$

where $[\boldsymbol{I}]$ is the identity matrix, $[\boldsymbol{\sigma}]$ is the symmetric second-order stress tensor, λ_k, is a real principal stress value giving the algebraic maximum stress, $\lambda_1 = \sigma_1$, the minimum stress $\lambda_2 = \sigma_2$, and for three-dimensional solids, $\lambda_3 = \sigma_3$ is the intermediate stress. (This process is valid for any other second-order symmetric tensor, such as the moment of inertia tensor.) The principle stresses (in reverse order) are obtained from the Matlab function *eig*, with only $[\boldsymbol{\sigma}]$ as the single argument. Finite element formulations often use the Voigt stress notation as a condensed form of the stress tensor:

$$\boldsymbol{\sigma}^T = \begin{bmatrix} \sigma_x \, \sigma_y & \sigma_z \, \tau_{xy} & \tau_{xz} \, \tau_{yz} \end{bmatrix} \Leftrightarrow [\boldsymbol{\sigma}] = \begin{bmatrix} \sigma_{xx} & \tau_{xy} & \tau_{xz} \\ \tau_{xy} & \sigma_{yy} & \tau_{yz} \\ \tau_{xz} & \tau_{yz} & \sigma_{zz} \end{bmatrix}.$$

The principal stresses define other physically important quantities, such as the measure of material failure, by the distortional energy criterion:

$$\sigma_E = \frac{1}{\sqrt{2}} \sqrt{(\sigma_1 - \sigma_2)^2 + (\sigma_1 - \sigma_3)^2 + (\sigma_2 - \sigma_3)^2}, \tag{14.12-2}$$

$$\sigma_E = \frac{1}{\sqrt{2}} \sqrt{\begin{array}{l} (\sigma_{yy} - \sigma_{xx})^2 + (\sigma_{zz} - \sigma_{xx})^2 \\ \quad + (\sigma_{zz} - \sigma_{yy})^2 + 6\left(\tau_{xy}^2 + \tau_{xz}^2 + \tau_{yz}^2\right) \end{array}}, \tag{14.12-3}$$

which has the units of stress, but is not a physical stress. That measure is called the Equivalent stress or the von Mises stress. It requires that the compressive yield stress and the tensile yield stress are equal. If they differ, then another failure criterion must be used, like the Burzynski criterion.

Another terminology is the "stress intensity", defined as $\sigma_I = \sigma_1 - \sigma_2 = 2\tau_{\max}$, where $\tau_{\max}$ is the absolute maximum shear stress on any three-dimensional plane in the solid at that point. There is also a simple mathematical upper bound for the maximum shear stress: $\tau_{\text{limit}} = \sigma_E/\sqrt{3}$. For plane–stress, the maximum plane shear stress is

$$\tau_{\text{plane}} = \sqrt{\frac{(\sigma_x - \sigma_y)^2}{2} + \tau_{xy}^2} \leq \tau_{\text{yield}} = \frac{1}{2}\sigma_y. \tag{14.12-4}$$

But, if the thickness of the planar part is not very small, the absolute maximum shear stress can lie in a different plane and has to be found from the above three-dimensional intensity.

For a ductile material, its tensile yield stress, σ_Y, is compared to the σ_E value to see if it has failed based on distortional energy at the point. Material failure is declared when $\sigma_E \geq \sigma_Y$. That is checked because in a uniaxial tension test of material failure

$$\sigma_{\text{test}} = \frac{1}{\sqrt{2}}\sqrt{(\sigma_y - 0)^2 + (\sigma_y - 0)^2 + (0 - 0)^2} = \frac{\sqrt{2}}{\sqrt{2}}\sigma_{\text{yield}} = \sigma_{\text{yield}}.$$

The yield stress of a ductile material is also compared to the stress intensity because in a uniaxial test of material failure the maximum shear stress is $\tau_{\max} = \sigma_Y/2$ and the Intensity is $\sigma_{\text{test}} = \sigma_Y - 0 = 2\tau_{\max}$.

Example 14.12-1 Given: The stress at a point is

$$\boldsymbol{\sigma}^T = \begin{bmatrix} 1 & 1 & 4 & -3 & \sqrt{2} & -\sqrt{2} \end{bmatrix} \Leftrightarrow [\boldsymbol{\sigma}] = \begin{bmatrix} 1 & -3 & \sqrt{2} \\ -3 & 1 & -\sqrt{2} \\ \sqrt{2} & -\sqrt{2} & 4 \end{bmatrix} \text{MPa.}$$

Develop a Matlab script to determine the principal stresses, the intensity, and the equivalent stress.

Solution: The script in Fig. 14.12-1 gives principal stresses of $\sigma(1:3) = [6,\ 2,\ -2]$ MPa, an intensity of 8 MPa (and thus a maximum shear stress of 4 MPa), and an equivalent stress of $\sigma_E = 6.93$ MPa and a shear stress upper bound of 4 MPa.

```
function eigen_stress        % Principal stresses at a point
Stress=[1 -3 sqrt(2); -3 1 -sqrt(2); sqrt(2) -sqrt(2) 4]
[values] = eig(Stress)                ; % assending eigenvalues
P = values (3:-1:1)             % desending principal stresses
S_I = P(1) - P(3)                           % stress intensity
Tau = S_I / 2                            % maximum shear stress
c = (P(1) - P(2))^2 + (P(1) - P(3))^2 + (P(2) - P(3))^2;
S_E = sqrt (c) / sqrt(2)                    % Von MIses stress
Limit = S_E / sqrt(3)              % shear stress upper limit
% end eigen_stress
```

Fig. 14.12-1: Computing ductile material failure criteria.

Example 14.12-2 Given: The stress at a point is

$$\sigma^T \Leftrightarrow [\sigma] = \begin{bmatrix} 20 & 10 & 0 \\ 10 & 10 & 0 \\ 0 & 0 & 0 \end{bmatrix} \text{ksi}$$

Determine the in-plane maximum shear stress, the absolute maximum shear stress, the shear stress limit, and compare the first two.

Solution: Modifying the Stress row in the script in Fig. 14.14-1 gives principal stresses of $\sigma(1:3) = [26.2, 3.82, 0]$ ksi, and the three-dimensional intensity gives the absolute maximum shear stress as $\tau_{\text{max}} = 13.1\,\text{ksi}$, and the upper bound on the shear stress is 14.1 ksi. The maximum in-plane shear stress approximation gives $\tau_{\text{plane}} = 11.2$ ksi, which is about 18% low.

14.13 Mohr's Circle for Principal Stresses*

In mechanics of materials, the Principal Stresses are found by rotating the planes on which the stresses act to find the orientation that has no shear stresses, just the three normal stresses. Historically, that process of solving the rotation equations was done graphically using three circles known as Mohr's circle(s), in Fig. 14.13-1. For more than 100 years engineers have used it as a practical way

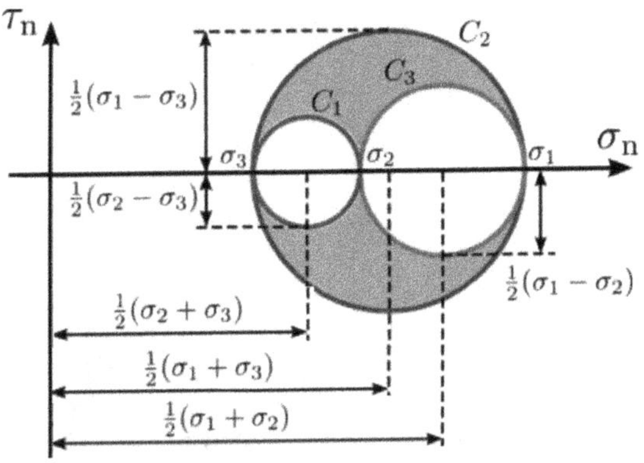

Fig. 14.13-1: Mohr's circles of stress from stress tensor eigenvalues.

to graphically represent the principal normal stresses and to interpret the general three-dimensional stress state on any plane at a point.

Figure 14.13-2 (top) shows a Mohr's circle of three-dimensional stress with the above stress terminology denoted with additional lines denoting the scalar upper bound on the shear stress (actually a point on the shear stress axis) and the scalar value of the Von Mises effective stress (not an actual normal stress, but is compared to them). In the top part of that figure, the data

$$\boldsymbol{\sigma}^T = \begin{bmatrix} 40 & 20 & -15 & 10 & 20 & -5 \end{bmatrix} \text{ksi}$$

gives a Von Mises stress greater than the maximum principal stress.

The bottom image shows where a change in the sign of one stress value

$$\boldsymbol{\sigma}^T = \begin{bmatrix} 40 & 20 & 15 & 10 & 20 & -5 \end{bmatrix} \text{ksi}$$

gives an effective stress that is less than the maximum principal stress. Today, it is still a useful visualization tool, but it is now constructed from the computed eigenvalues, as shown in Fig. 14.13-1.

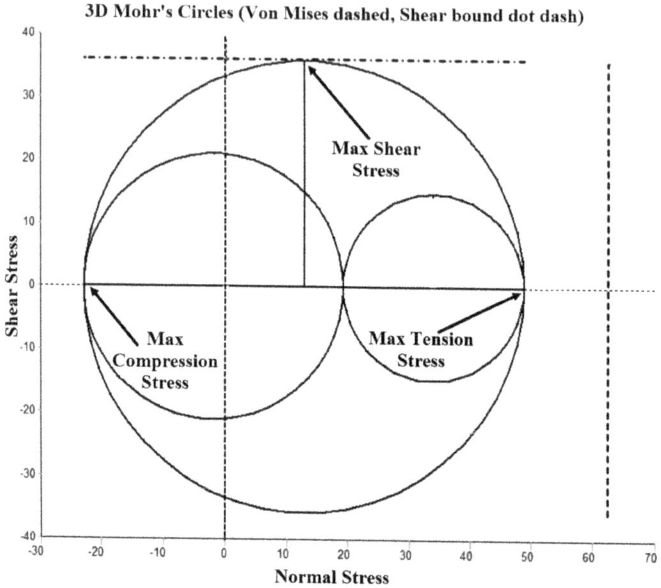

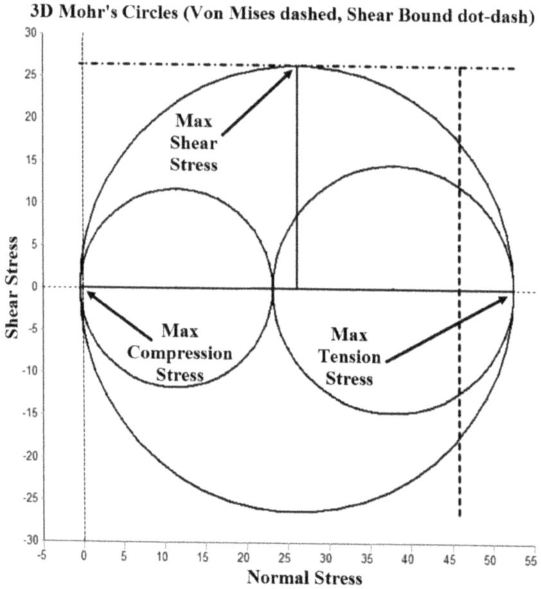

Fig. 14.13-2: Mohr's circles where $\sigma_E > \sigma_1$ (top) and $\sigma_E < \sigma_1$.

14.14 Summary

PDE Eigenvalue
Form: $\nabla^2 u(x, y, t) + \lambda\, u(x, y, t) = 0.$
Interpolation: $u(x) = \boldsymbol{H}(r)\, \boldsymbol{u^e}.$
Matrix form: $\det\, [\boldsymbol{K}+\lambda\, \boldsymbol{M}] = |\boldsymbol{K}+\lambda \boldsymbol{M}| = 0.$
Eigen-group: $[\mathrm{K}+\lambda_{\mathrm{j}}\, \mathrm{M}]\, \delta_j\; = 0,\;\; j = 1,\, 2,\, \ldots$
Iron's Bound
Theorem: $\lambda^e_{\text{min}} \leq \lambda_{\text{min}} \leq \lambda_{\text{max}} \leq \lambda^e_{\text{max.}}$
Vibration: $\lambda = \omega^2$, ω real.
Rigid body
motion: $\omega = 0.$
Spring-mass: $\omega = \sqrt{k}/\text{m}.$
Stiffnesses: $\boldsymbol{K_E}$ = elastic, $\boldsymbol{K_k}$ = foundation stiffness,
$\boldsymbol{K_G}$ = geometric stiffness.
Buckling: $[\boldsymbol{K_E} + \boldsymbol{K_k} + BLF\, \boldsymbol{K_G}]\, \boldsymbol{\delta} = \boldsymbol{0}.$
Beam-Column: $|\,(\boldsymbol{K_E} + N_B \boldsymbol{K_n}) - \omega^2\, \boldsymbol{M}| =,\; \boldsymbol{K_G} = N_B \boldsymbol{K_n}.$
Principle
stresses: $\sigma_1 > \sigma_2 > \sigma_3.$
Hydrostatic
pressure: $p = (\sigma_1 + \sigma_2 + \sigma_3)\, /3.$
Experimental
yield stresses: σ_t tensile, σ_c compressive, $\kappa \equiv \sigma_c/\sigma_t$ ratio.
Von Mises criterion:

$$\sigma_E = \frac{1}{\sqrt{2}} \sqrt{(\sigma_1 - \sigma_2)^2 + (\sigma_1 - \sigma_3)^2 + (\sigma_2 - \sigma_3)^2}.$$

Burzynski criterion:

$$\sigma_B = \left[3p\,(\kappa - 1) + \sqrt{9p^2\,(\kappa - 1)^2 + 4\kappa\sigma_E^2} \right] /2\kappa,$$

$$\sigma_B\,(\kappa = 1) \equiv \sigma_E.$$

Ductile material
failure criterion: $\sigma_E \geq \sigma_t$ or $\sigma_B \geq \sigma_t.$

Lagrange linear line element stiffness matrix:

$$\boldsymbol{K^e_{bar}} = \frac{E^e A^e}{L^e} \begin{bmatrix} 1 & -1 \\ -1 & 1 \end{bmatrix}, \boldsymbol{K^e_{\text{shaft}}} = \frac{G^e J^e}{L^e} \begin{bmatrix} 1 & -1 \\ -1 & 1 \end{bmatrix},$$

$$\boldsymbol{K^e_{\text{spring}}} = k^e \begin{bmatrix} 1 & -1 \\ -1 & 1 \end{bmatrix}.$$

Lagrange quadratic line element stiffness matrix:

$$\boldsymbol{K}^{\boldsymbol{e}}_{\text{bar}} = \frac{E^e A^e}{3\,L^e}\begin{bmatrix} 7 & -8 & 1 \\ -8 & 16 & -8 \\ 1 & -8 & 7 \end{bmatrix}.$$

Lagrange cubic line element stiffness matrix:

$$\boldsymbol{K}^{\boldsymbol{e}}_{\text{bar}} = \frac{E^e A^e}{40L^e}\begin{bmatrix} 148 & -189 & 54 & -13 \\ -189 & 432 & -297 & 54 \\ 54 & -297 & 432 & -189 \\ -13 & 54 & -189 & 148 \end{bmatrix}.$$

Lagrange linear line element consistent mass matrix:

$$\boldsymbol{M}^{\boldsymbol{e}} = \frac{m^e}{6}\begin{bmatrix} 2 & 1 \\ 1 & 2 \end{bmatrix}.$$

Lagrange quadratic line element consistent mass:

$$\boldsymbol{M}^{\boldsymbol{e}} = \frac{m^e}{30}\begin{bmatrix} 4 & 2 & -1 \\ 2 & 16 & 2 \\ -1 & 2 & 4 \end{bmatrix}.$$

Lagrange cubic line element consistent mass matrix:

$$\boldsymbol{M}^{\boldsymbol{e}} = \frac{m^e}{1,680}\begin{bmatrix} 128 & 99 & -36 & 19 \\ 99 & 648 & -81 & -36 \\ -36 & -81 & 648 & 99 \\ 19 & -36 & 99 & 128 \end{bmatrix}.$$

Lagrange linear triangle consistent mass matrix:

$$\boldsymbol{M}^{\boldsymbol{e}}_{\boldsymbol{x}} = \frac{m^e}{12}\begin{bmatrix} 2 & 1 & 1 \\ 1 & 2 & 1 \\ 1 & 1 & 2 \end{bmatrix} = \boldsymbol{M}^{\boldsymbol{e}}_{\boldsymbol{y}}.$$

$$\boldsymbol{M}^{\boldsymbol{e}}\,(\boldsymbol{Odd},\,\boldsymbol{Odd}) = \boldsymbol{M}^{\boldsymbol{e}}_{\boldsymbol{x}},\ \boldsymbol{M}^{\boldsymbol{e}}\,(\boldsymbol{Even},\,\boldsymbol{Even}) = \boldsymbol{M}^{\boldsymbol{e}}_{\boldsymbol{y}}.$$

Lagrange linear line element averaged mass matrix:

$$\boldsymbol{M}^e = \frac{m^e}{12}\begin{bmatrix} 5 & 1 \\ 1 & 5 \end{bmatrix}.$$

Lagrange quadratic line averaged mass:

$$\boldsymbol{M}^e = \frac{m^e}{60}\begin{bmatrix} 9 & 2 & -1 \\ 2 & 36 & 2 \\ -1 & 2 & 9 \end{bmatrix}.$$

Lagrange cubic line averaged mass matrix:

$$\boldsymbol{M}^e = \frac{m^e}{325,920}\begin{bmatrix} 25{,}856 & 9{,}603 & -3{,}492 & 1{,}843 \\ 9{,}603 & 13{,}0896 & -7{,}857 & -3{,}492 \\ -3{,}492 & -7{,}857 & 130{,}896 & 9{,}603 \\ 1{,}843 & -3{,}492 & 9{,}603 & 25{,}856 \end{bmatrix}.$$

Lagrange linear triangle averaged mass matrix:

$$\boldsymbol{M}^e_{\boldsymbol{x}} = \frac{m^e}{24}\begin{bmatrix} 6 & 1 & 1 \\ 1 & 6 & 1 \\ 1 & 1 & 6 \end{bmatrix} = \boldsymbol{M}^e_{\boldsymbol{y}}$$

$$\boldsymbol{M}^e\,(\boldsymbol{Odd},\ \boldsymbol{Odd}) = \boldsymbol{M}^e_{\boldsymbol{x}},\ \boldsymbol{M}^e\,(\boldsymbol{Even},\ \boldsymbol{Even}) = \boldsymbol{M}^e_{\boldsymbol{y}}.$$

Lagrange linear line element diagonalized mass matrix:

$$\boldsymbol{M}^e = \frac{m^e}{2}\begin{bmatrix} 1 & 0 \\ 0 & 1 \end{bmatrix}.$$

Lagrange quadratic line diagonalized mass:

$$\boldsymbol{M}^e = \frac{m^e}{6}\begin{bmatrix} 1 & 0 & 0 \\ 0 & 4 & 0 \\ 0 & 0 & 1 \end{bmatrix}.$$

Lagrange cubic line element diagonalized mass matrix:

$$\boldsymbol{M}^e = \frac{m^e}{194}\begin{bmatrix} 16 & 0 & 0 & 0 \\ 0 & 81 & 0 & 0 \\ 0 & 0 & 81 & 0 \\ 0 & 0 & 0 & 16 \end{bmatrix}.$$

Lagrange linear triangle diagonalized mass matrix:

$$\boldsymbol{M}_{\boldsymbol{x}}^{\boldsymbol{e}} = \frac{m^e}{3}\begin{bmatrix} 1 & 0 & 0 \\ 0 & 1 & 0 \\ 0 & 0 & 1 \end{bmatrix} = \boldsymbol{M}_{\boldsymbol{y}}^{\boldsymbol{e}},$$

$$\boldsymbol{M}^{\boldsymbol{e}}\,(\boldsymbol{Odd},\ \boldsymbol{Odd}) = \boldsymbol{M}_{\boldsymbol{x}}^{\boldsymbol{e}},\ \boldsymbol{M}^{\boldsymbol{e}}\,(\boldsymbol{Even},\ \boldsymbol{Even}) = \boldsymbol{M}_{\boldsymbol{y}}^{\boldsymbol{e}}.$$

14.15 Review

1. What are the primary uses of the geometric Jacobian in a typical element?
2. In a structural analysis, what is the sum of the terms in the element mass square matrix?
3. The mass matrix of a classic cubic beam involves the integral of a cubic interpolation matrix times itself. How many Gaussian quadrature points are required to integrate the mass matrix for a constant mass density?
4. On a symmetric stress analysis plane, the proper boundary condition is that the: _____.

   (a) Displacement in the plane is zero
   (b) Zero displacement normal to the plane
   (c) Rotation vector normal to the plane is zero
   (d) Zero rotation vector tangent to plane
   (e) All of the above

5. A horizontal three-noded bar element is fixed at both ends. Obtain its first natural frequency for axial vibration.
6. The natural frequency calculation of a solid: _____.

   (a) Requires the stiffness matrix
   (b) Requires the mass matrix
   (c) Requires known supports
   (d) Requires known forces
   (e) Is an eigenvalue problem
   (f) (a), and (b), and (e)

7. A symmetry plane divides mirror images of the _____.

   (a) Geometric shape
   (b) Distribution of material properties
   (c) Dirichlet boundary conditions
   (d) External loadings
   (e) All of the above
   (f) None of the above

8. What natural frequency corresponds to a rigid body motion?
9. How can you change the finite element model to remove the mode shape kink in Fig. 14.4-2?
10. The stress components at a point are

$$[\sigma] = \begin{bmatrix} \sigma_{xx} & \tau_{xy} & \tau_{xz} \\ \tau_{xy} & \sigma_{yy} & \tau_{yz} \\ \tau_{xz} & \tau_{yz} & \sigma_{zz} \end{bmatrix} = \begin{bmatrix} 40 & 10 & -5 \\ 10 & 20 & 20 \\ -5 & 20 & -15 \end{bmatrix} \text{ MPa.}$$

    Determine the Principle Stresses at the point, and the stress intensity.

Chapter 15

Transient and Dynamic Solutions

15.1 Introduction to Transient Systems

The general linear model equation is extended into the transient domain by including the first time derivative of the solution:

$$-D(x,\,t)\frac{\partial^2 T(x,\,t)}{\partial x^2}+A(x,\,t)\frac{\partial T(x,\,t)}{\partial x}+C(x,\,t)\,T(x,\,t)+F(x,\,t)$$
$$=G(x,\,t)\frac{\partial T(x,\,t)}{\partial t}. \qquad (15.1\text{-}1)$$

Including time can be done using higher-dimensional space–time interpolations, or extent the previous methods to use a separation of variables approach. That is, let the interpolated nodal degrees of freedom (DOFs) be time-dependent, with the space interpolations unchanged:

$$T(x,\,y,\,z,t)\equiv \boldsymbol{H}(x,\,y,\,z)\,\boldsymbol{T}^{e}(t), \qquad (15.1\text{-}2)$$

and have the time derivative

$$\frac{\partial T(x,\,y,\,z,t)}{\partial t}\equiv \boldsymbol{H}(x,\,y,\,z)\frac{\partial \boldsymbol{T}^{e}(t)}{\partial t}\equiv \boldsymbol{H}(x,\,y,\,z)\dot{T}^{e}(t).$$

To obtain the integral form, as in Section 12.4, multiply the PDE by $T\,(x,t)$. Then a new integral appears:

$$\int_\Omega T\,G\,(x,\,t)\,\partial T/\partial t d\Omega \Rightarrow \sum_{e=1}^{n_e}\boldsymbol{T}^{e^T}\left[\int_\Omega^e \boldsymbol{H}^{e^T}G^e\boldsymbol{H}^e\,d\Omega\right]\dot{T}^e$$
$$=\sum_{e=1}^{n_e}\boldsymbol{T}^{e^T}\,[\boldsymbol{M}^e]\,\dot{T}^e,$$

with

$$\boldsymbol{M}^e = \int_{\Omega}^{e} \boldsymbol{H}(x)^T G(x,\, t)\, \boldsymbol{H}(x)\, d\Omega. \tag{15.1-3}$$

In transient heat transfer the unknown, T, is temperature and the time coefficient, G, is the product of the material's mass density and its specific heat at constant pressure, $G \equiv \rho c_p$. Then, the new square matrix coupled with the solution velocity, $\dot{T}^e$, is called the heat capacity matrix.

This PDE and other first-order time-dependent scalar field problems solved by using finite elements in space usually lead to a matrix ordinary differential equation in time of the form

$$[\boldsymbol{K}]\, \{\boldsymbol{T}(t)\} + [\boldsymbol{M}]\, \{\dot{\boldsymbol{T}}(t)\} = \{\boldsymbol{c}(t)\},\ \dot{\{\}} = \frac{\partial}{\partial t}\{\}, \tag{15.1-4}$$

where the first three terms in the PDE contribute a square conduction matrix to $[\boldsymbol{K}]$, the time derivative term in the PDF contributes the square capacity matrix, $[\boldsymbol{M}]$, and the source term F contributes to the source vector $\{\boldsymbol{c}(t)\}$.

This matrix ODE is subject to the initial condition (IC), $\{\boldsymbol{T}(0)\} = \boldsymbol{T}_{\boldsymbol{IC}}$, and the time-dependent Dirichlet essential boundary conditions (EBCs), $\boldsymbol{T}_{\boldsymbol{EBC}}(t)$. After the matrix system has been modified to include the EBCs, by adding $\boldsymbol{c}_{\boldsymbol{EBC}}(t)$ to $\boldsymbol{c}(t)$, only the time history values of the remaining free DOFs remain to be computed. Here the approach is simplified by assuming that the Dirichlet conditions are time-independent.

Many engineering applications involve sharp transients or nonlinear responses, $[\boldsymbol{K}] = [\boldsymbol{K}(\{\boldsymbol{T}(t)\})]$. Such applications require a direct time integration to obtain the solution time history. Some direct methods require an estimate of the initial time rate of change of the solution. It is often approximated as zero, but it can be found from the IC as

$$\{\dot{\boldsymbol{T}}(0)\} = [\boldsymbol{M}]^{-1} \left(\{\boldsymbol{c}\,(0)\} - [\boldsymbol{K}]\, \{\boldsymbol{T}\,(0)\}\right), \tag{15.1-5}$$

where the capacitance matrix, $[\boldsymbol{M}]$, can be approximated by its scaled diagonal.

After any EBCs are applied, the original system will be reduced in size to, say

$$[\boldsymbol{K}]\,\{\boldsymbol{T}(t)\} + [\boldsymbol{M}]\,\{\dot{\boldsymbol{T}}(t)\} = \{\boldsymbol{c}(t)\} - \{\boldsymbol{c_{EBC}}(t)\} \equiv \{\boldsymbol{p}(t)\}, \quad (15.1\text{-}6)$$

where $\{\mathbf{c_{EBC}}(t)\}$ comes from any non-zero EBC multiplying the columns of the larger original matrices. There are hundreds of algorithms for integrating this system in time. These include using finite differences in time, finite elements in time, or even space–time finite elements. Since many engineering applications involve discontinuous changes at certain points in time, single-step methods are more likely to capture and respond accurately to the discontinuity. If it is known that the driving source terms $\{\boldsymbol{c}(t)\}$, and the EBC $\{\mathbf{c_{EBC}}(t)\}$, are continuous in time then multi-step methods, like the Runge–Kutta four-step method, become more efficient.

Most temporal integration schemes use finite differences in time or finite elements in time to derive the algorithm using constant increments of time, say Δt, to define time as $t_n = t_0 + n\,\Delta t$ at time step number n. Most of the algorithms form a static linear system to be solved at each time step as

$$[\boldsymbol{S}(\Delta t, \beta, \boldsymbol{K}, \boldsymbol{M})]\,\{\boldsymbol{T}\}_n = \left\{\boldsymbol{F}(\beta, t_n, t_{n-1}, \boldsymbol{K},\ \boldsymbol{M},\ \boldsymbol{c}, \{\boldsymbol{T}\}_{n-1})\right\}, \quad (15.1\text{-}7)$$

where β is an algorithm constant. In this form, the left square matrix is constant if it is not nonlinear and if the time step, Δt, is constant. Assembling the linear system matrix $[\boldsymbol{S}]$ is computationally expensive and obtaining its inverse or factorization is very expensive. Thus, it is desirable to do those operations only once or twice. The right-hand column changes with every time step and the result at time step n is

$$\{\boldsymbol{T}\}_n = [\boldsymbol{S}(\Delta t, \beta, \boldsymbol{K}, \boldsymbol{M})]^{-1}\,\{\boldsymbol{F}\}_n. \quad (15.1\text{-}8)$$

15.2 Generalized Trapezoidal Algorithms

The popular generalized trapezoidal one-step method in time leads to an updated square matrix defined as

$$[\boldsymbol{S}] = ([\boldsymbol{M}]\,/\Delta t + \beta\,[\boldsymbol{K}])\,, \quad (15.2\text{-}1)$$

and the source vector updated at every time step is

$$\{\boldsymbol{f}\}_n = ([\boldsymbol{M}]/\Delta t + (\beta - 1)[\boldsymbol{K}])\{\boldsymbol{T}\}_{n-1} + (1-\beta)\{\boldsymbol{p}\}_{n-1} + \beta\{\boldsymbol{p}\}_n . \tag{15.2-2}$$

These combine to give a linear matrix system to be solved at every time step:

$$[\boldsymbol{S}]\{\boldsymbol{T}\}_n = \{\boldsymbol{f}\}_n . \tag{15.2-3}$$

Note that so long as the time step Δt is kept constant, the computationally expensive assembly and factorization (or inversion) of the linear system square matrix $[\boldsymbol{S}]$ only needs to be done once. This contrasts to the source vector $\{\boldsymbol{f}\}_n$ which must be updated at every time step. The forward- and backward-substitution of $\{\boldsymbol{f}\}_n$ into a factorization of $[\boldsymbol{S}]$ is relatively cheap and fast. The time step is usually smallest at the start of the transient solution. As a steady-state solution is approached, a large time step could be used, but often is not used. If the time step is changed, then the last solution from the prior small time step is used as the IC for the larger time step.

The common choices for the algorithm constant β are

$\beta = 0$ the conditionally stable forward difference (Euler) method.
$\beta = \frac{1}{2}$ the unconditionally stable trapezoidal (Crank–Nicolson) method.
$\beta = \frac{2}{3}$ the unconditionally stable Galerkin-in-time method.
$\beta = 1$ the unconditionally stable backward difference method.

The above four algorithms are all single-step methods since they only require storing the results from the last time step. They minimize the memory requirements and were developed when computers had extremely small amounts of memory, but their main asset is that they deal well with sudden changes in the source term or the EBCs. There are many other algorithms that lead to a linear system to be solved at each time step.

When the solution in time is known to be smooth, then multiple-step methods can lead to more efficient transient solutions. Of course, they require more memory in order to save the solution from each of the time steps needed to formulate the multi-step algorithm.

15.3 One-Dimensional Transient Responses

The transient one-dimensional heat conduction equation for the temperature, $T(x,t)$, is

$$K\,A\frac{\partial^2 T}{\partial\, x^2} = \rho\, c_p\, A\frac{\partial \mathrm{T}}{\partial \mathrm{t}}, \tag{15.3-1}$$

which is subject to the initial temperature distribution $T\,(x,\,0) = T_0(x)$ and EBCs like $T\,(0,t) = V_0(t)$ and/or $T\,(L,t) = V_L(t)$ at the ends of the domain. For an element with constant properties, the conduction matrix is linear line

$$\boldsymbol{S}^e = \int_{L^e} \frac{d\boldsymbol{H}(r)}{dx}^T K^e\,(x)\,\frac{d\boldsymbol{H}(r)}{dx}\,A\,(x)\,dx = \frac{K^e A^e}{L^e}\begin{bmatrix} 1 & -1 \\ -1 & 1 \end{bmatrix}, \tag{15.3-2}$$

and the element heat capacity matrix is

$$\boldsymbol{M}^e = \int_{L^e} \boldsymbol{H}\,(r)^T \rho^e c_p^e\,(x)\boldsymbol{H}\,(r)\,dx = \frac{\rho^e c_p^e L^e}{6}\begin{bmatrix} 2 & 1 \\ 1 & 2 \end{bmatrix}. \tag{15.3-3}$$

For a constant volumetric rate of heat generation, the element source vector is

$$\boldsymbol{c}_{\boldsymbol{Q}}^e = \int_{L^e} \boldsymbol{H}(r)^T Q^e\,(x) A\,(x)\,dx = \frac{Q^e A^e L^e}{2}\begin{Bmatrix} 1 \\ 1 \end{Bmatrix}. \tag{15.3-4}$$

Consider a system with three equal elements in the domain $L = 3L^e$. Then the assembled matrix system for the three elements, with a constant source, Q, gives

$$[\boldsymbol{S}]\,\{\boldsymbol{T}(t)\} + [\boldsymbol{M}]\,\{\dot{\boldsymbol{T}}(t)\} = \{\boldsymbol{c_Q}(t)\}\,,$$

where

$$[\boldsymbol{S}] = \frac{K^e A^e}{L^e}\begin{bmatrix} 1 & -1 & 0 & 0 \\ -1 & 2 & -1 & 0 \\ 0 & -1 & -1 & 0 \\ 0 & 0 & -1 & 1 \end{bmatrix}, \quad [\boldsymbol{M}] = \frac{\rho^e c_p^e L^e}{6}\begin{bmatrix} 2 & 1 & 0 & 0 \\ 1 & 4 & 1 & 0 \\ 0 & 1 & 4 & 1 \\ 0 & 0 & 1 & 2 \end{bmatrix},$$

$$\boldsymbol{c_Q} = \frac{Q^e A^e L^e}{2}\begin{bmatrix} 1 & 2 & 2 & 1 \end{bmatrix}^T. \tag{15.3-5}$$

For the conditionally stable Euler method, $\beta = 0$, the finite difference approximation in time is

$$\{\dot{\boldsymbol{T}}(t)\} = \frac{\partial \boldsymbol{T}}{\partial t} \approx \frac{\boldsymbol{T}_{t+\Delta t} - \boldsymbol{T}_t}{\Delta t} = \frac{\boldsymbol{T}_{n+1} - \boldsymbol{T}_n}{\Delta t},$$

so at the time $(t + \Delta t)$ the four equations become $[\boldsymbol{S}]\{\boldsymbol{T}_{n+1}\} + [\boldsymbol{M}]\left\{\frac{\boldsymbol{T}_{n+1} - \boldsymbol{T}_n}{\Delta t}\right\} = \{\boldsymbol{c}_{\boldsymbol{Q}}(t_{n+1})\}$, or

$$[\boldsymbol{S}]\{\boldsymbol{T}_{n+1}\} + [\boldsymbol{M}]\left\{\frac{\boldsymbol{T}_{n+1}}{\Delta t}\right\} = \{\boldsymbol{c}_{\boldsymbol{Q}}(t_{n+1})\} + [\boldsymbol{M}]\left\{\frac{\boldsymbol{T}_n}{\Delta t}\right\},$$

which is

$$\left[\frac{K^e A^e}{L^e}\begin{bmatrix} 1 & -1 & 0 & 0 \\ -1 & 2 & -1 & 0 \\ 0 & -1 & 2 & -1 \\ 0 & 0 & -1 & 1 \end{bmatrix} + \frac{\rho^e c_p^e L^e}{6\Delta t}\begin{bmatrix} 2 & 1 & 0 & 0 \\ 1 & 4 & 1 & 0 \\ 0 & 1 & 4 & 1 \\ 0 & 0 & 1 & 2 \end{bmatrix}\right]\begin{Bmatrix} T_1 \\ T_2 \\ T_3 \\ T_4 \end{Bmatrix}_{(t+\Delta t)}$$

$$= \frac{Q^e A^e L^e}{2}\begin{Bmatrix} 1 \\ 2 \\ 2 \\ 1 \end{Bmatrix}_{(t+\Delta t)} + \frac{\rho^e c_p^e L^e}{6\Delta t}\begin{bmatrix} 2 & 1 & 0 & 0 \\ 1 & 4 & 1 & 0 \\ 0 & 1 & 4 & 1 \\ 0 & 0 & 1 & 2 \end{bmatrix}\begin{Bmatrix} T_1 \\ T_2 \\ T_3 \\ T_4 \end{Bmatrix}_{(t)}. \tag{15.3-6}$$

At the first time step $(n = 0, t = 0)$ the IC, say $T = T_0$, will be applied to start the time history. Thereafter, the EBCs, $T_{\text{EBC}}(t+\Delta t)$, will be applied at every time step to the first and last node. Thus, the restrained DOF numbers are Fixed = [1, 4], and the other equation numbers, Free = [2, 3], are to be solved for at each time step. If the EBCs vary with time, then

$$\frac{\partial T_1}{\partial t} = \frac{\partial V_0}{\partial t}, \quad \text{and} \quad \frac{\partial T_4}{\partial t} = \frac{\partial V_L}{\partial t}.$$

Assume that the IC is that all nodes are at a constant temperature of T_0. Then the free rows and columns at $t = 0$, $(n = 0)$, and the effects of the EBCs (moved to right) give the equations for first step in the time history for the free DOFs:

$$\left[\frac{K^eA^e}{L^e}\begin{bmatrix}2 & -1\\ -1 & 2\end{bmatrix}+\frac{\rho^e c_p^e L^e}{6\Delta t}\begin{bmatrix}4 & 1\\ 1 & 4\end{bmatrix}\right]\begin{Bmatrix}T_2\\ T_3\end{Bmatrix}_{(1)}$$

$$=\frac{Q^eA^eL^e}{2}\begin{Bmatrix}2\\ 2\end{Bmatrix}_{(1)}+\frac{\rho^e c_p^e L^e}{6\Delta t}\begin{bmatrix}4 & 1\\ 1 & 4\end{bmatrix}\begin{Bmatrix}T_0\\ T_0\end{Bmatrix}_{(0)}.$$

$$-V_0(0)\frac{K^eA^e}{L^e}\begin{Bmatrix}-1\\ 0\end{Bmatrix}+\frac{\partial V_0(0)}{\partial t}\frac{\rho^e c_p^e L^e}{6\Delta t}\begin{Bmatrix}1\\ 0\end{Bmatrix}$$

$$-V_L(0)\frac{K^eA^e}{L^e}\begin{Bmatrix}0\\ -1\end{Bmatrix}+\frac{\partial V_L(0)}{\partial t}\frac{\rho^e c_p^e L^e}{6\Delta t}\begin{Bmatrix}1\\ 0\end{Bmatrix}. \qquad (15.3\text{-}7)$$

Multiplying the RHS by the inverse of the square matrix gives the next free values, $\boldsymbol{T}\,(Free)$.

Note that the ICs define a steady state condition so that the initial reactions at nodes 1 and 4 would be recovered as described previously. Now that all four temperatures are known at the end of step $n = 1$, the **Fixed** rows can be optionally used to recover the new reactions at this step. In other words, the reactions are also transient and can be recovered. The next set of free equations, including the updated EBCs, $V_0\,(\Delta t)$ and $V_L\,(\Delta t)$, become

$$\left[\frac{K^eA^e}{L^e}\begin{bmatrix}2 & -1\\ -1 & 2\end{bmatrix}+\frac{\rho^e c_p^e L^e}{6\Delta t}\begin{bmatrix}4 & 1\\ 1 & 4\end{bmatrix}\right]\begin{Bmatrix}T_2\\ T_3\end{Bmatrix}_{(2)}$$

$$=\frac{Q^eA^eL^e}{2}\begin{Bmatrix}2\\ 2\end{Bmatrix}_{(2)}+\frac{\rho^e c_p^e L^e}{6\Delta t}\begin{bmatrix}4 & 1\\ 1 & 4\end{bmatrix}\begin{Bmatrix}T_2\\ T_3\end{Bmatrix}_{(1)}$$

$$-V_0(\Delta t)\frac{K^eA^e}{L^e}\begin{Bmatrix}-1\\ 0\end{Bmatrix}+\frac{1}{6}\frac{\partial V_0(\Delta t)}{\partial t}\frac{\rho^e c_p^e L^e}{\Delta t}\begin{Bmatrix}1\\ 0\end{Bmatrix}$$

$$-V_L(\Delta t)\frac{K^eA^e}{L^e}\begin{Bmatrix}0\\ -1\end{Bmatrix}+\frac{1}{6}\frac{\partial V_L(\Delta t)}{\partial t}\frac{\rho^e c_p^e L^e}{\Delta t}\begin{Bmatrix}1\\ 0\end{Bmatrix},$$

and so forth until $n_{\max}$ has been reached.

To present a numerical example of the time-stepping process, let the initial temperature at all nodes be $T_0 = 0$, and thereafter the EBCs are constant with values of $V_0 = 10$ and $V_L = 20$, and the material is heat source-free ($Q^e = 0$). Then dividing the remaining matrices by $K^e A^e / L^e$, define a new constant

$$\alpha = \frac{\rho^e c_p^e (L^e)^2}{\Delta t\, K^e A^e}.$$

Note that as the time step gets smaller, this constant gets bigger. The backward difference method is unconditionally stable, but it loses accuracy with each additional time step. You should rerun a study with a smaller time step until the two results are in agreement over the time interval of interest.

The starting step for $\begin{Bmatrix} T_2 \\ T_3 \end{Bmatrix}_{(1)}$ for no heat source and constant EBCs simplifies to

$$\left[\begin{bmatrix} 2 & -1 \\ -1 & 2 \end{bmatrix} + \frac{\alpha}{6}\begin{bmatrix} 4 & 1 \\ 1 & 4 \end{bmatrix}\right]\begin{Bmatrix} T_2 \\ T_3 \end{Bmatrix}_{(1)}$$

$$= \begin{Bmatrix} 0 \\ 0 \end{Bmatrix} + \frac{\alpha}{6}\begin{bmatrix} 4 & 1 \\ 1 & 4 \end{bmatrix}\begin{Bmatrix} T_0 \\ T_0 \end{Bmatrix}_{(0)} - V_0\begin{Bmatrix} -1 \\ 0 \end{Bmatrix} + \frac{\alpha}{6}\begin{Bmatrix} 0 \\ 0 \end{Bmatrix} - V_L\begin{Bmatrix} 0 \\ -1 \end{Bmatrix} + \frac{\alpha}{6}\begin{Bmatrix} 0 \\ 0 \end{Bmatrix},$$

are

$$\left[\begin{bmatrix} 2 & -1 \\ -1 & 2 \end{bmatrix} + \frac{\alpha}{6}\begin{bmatrix} 4 & 1 \\ 1 & 4 \end{bmatrix}\right]\begin{Bmatrix} T_2 \\ T_3 \end{Bmatrix}_{(n+1)} = \frac{\alpha}{6}\begin{bmatrix} 4 & 1 \\ 1 & 4 \end{bmatrix}\begin{Bmatrix} T_2 \\ T_3 \end{Bmatrix}_{(n)} - V_0\begin{Bmatrix} -1 \\ 0 \end{Bmatrix} - V_L\begin{Bmatrix} 0 \\ -1 \end{Bmatrix}.$$

Since $Q^e = 0$ the previous solutions showed that the steady-state solution will be a straight line between the constant essential boundary values of V_0 and V_L. The results of such a study with $a = 8$ and 10-time steps are shown in Fig.15.3-1 and the portion of the Matlab script that computed the time histories is given in Fig.15.3-2.

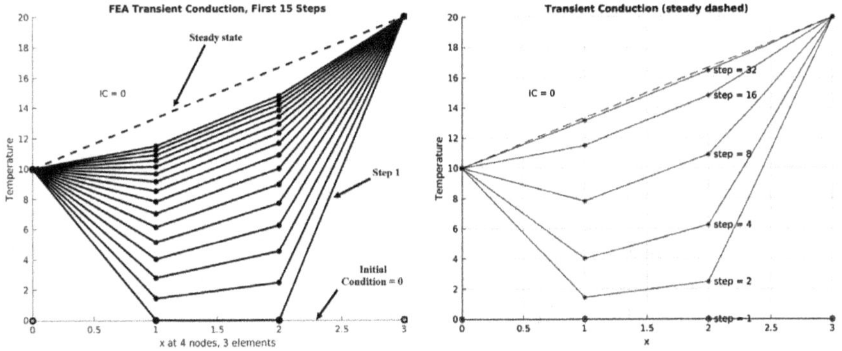

Fig. 15.3-1: Node temperatures for early steps after the ICs.

```
function [] = Example_Transients ()
% Time stepping example of a transient conducting bar
% EBC:  V_0 1          2          3          4 V_L
%           .***(1)***.***(2)***.***(3)***.        Q=0
% ICs:      T_0        T_0        T_0        T_0
%
I_C = 0 ; T_0 = I_C*[1; 1]      ; % Initial Conditions
V_0 = 10 ; V_L = 20                    ; % Constant EBC
x=[0 1 2 3]'                            ; % Coordinates
a = 8.0                    ; % Bigger for smallet Del_T
n_steps = 10                   ; % Number of time steps

T = zeros (2, n_steps) ; % Allocate Free temperatures
K = [2   -1; -1  2]    ; % Assembled conduction matrix
M = [4  1;  1  4]*a/6   ; % Assembled capacity matrix
Q = [0 ; 0]                 ; % Assembled source vector
S = K + M           ; % New linear system at each time
S_inv = inv(S)   ; % Invert only once (constant Del_T)
BC_1 = V_0*[-1;0]; BC_4 = V_L*[0;-1]; % c_EBC vectors
c = M*T_0 - BC_1 - BC_4              ; % first c(t=Del_T)
T(:,1) = S_inv * c ; % solve for first history result

for n = 2:n_steps  ; % March through later time steps
  c = M*T(:, n-1)-BC_1-BC_4 ; % update the RHS source
  T(:,n) = S_inv * c ; % solve for T at this new time
end ; % for each step after the first

% Restore EBC to graph mesh values through time
```

Fig. 15.3-2: Computing the transient node temperatures.

15.4 Two-Dimensional Transient Responses

To illustrate two-dimensional transient responses, consider the one-eighth symmetry model of the cross-section of a square electrical conductor. It is initially at a constant temperature. When the current is turned on, the rate of heat generation per unit volume becomes a constant $Q = i\, R^2$ where i is the current flow and R is the electrical resistance of the material. As shown in Fig. 15.4-1, it is modeled with four linear triangles, $T3$, and six nodal points. The temperature of the interior three nodes will vary with time until their steady-state values are reached. The steady-state solution was given as Example 12.14-1.

A typical Matlab script for running the generalized trapezoidal transient integration, *gen_trap_history.m*, and portions of it are given in Figs. 15.4-2(a) and 15.4-2(b). The first part of the illustrated calculation allocates the needed memory and extracts the independent DOF. Those steps could actually be done in the calling program. Here they serve as reminders that the presence of EBCs influences the transient solution as well. The second part of the calculations is quite compact when done in matrix notation. If the EBC were time-dependent, then a minor extension would allow for that requirement. The presence of any EBC over time means that the reactions at those DOFs will change with time. That optional calculation is included in the illustrated script.

The output from a transient solution can be listed, but that is not very practical; so the time history is usually saved to a file (binary is best) to be post-processed by graphing the time history of selected DOFs, contouring the mesh results, or making mesh carpet plots at selected times, etc. A typical listing of transient temperatures and reaction heat flows is given in Fig, 15.4-3; while time history

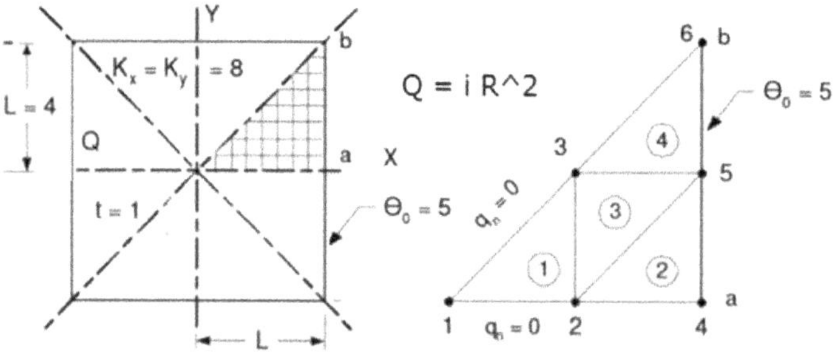

Fig. 15.4-1: Cross-section of an electrical conductor.

```
function [R_u, React, time] = gen_trap_history (S, M, ...
               C_Q, beta, n_steps, delta_t, ...
               ic_value, Fixed, bc_value, Free) % =============
% Define generalized trapezoidal time integration data
% for solution results R(t) from Initial Condition state
%      [beta * S + M / delta_t] * R_new = C_rhs
% C_rhs = [(beta - 1)S + M / delta_t] * R_old
%       + (1 - beta)C_old + beta C_new, here C_old=C_new
% beta = 1/2 Crank-Nicolson method, beta = 2/3 Galerkin in time
% beta = 0   Foward difference,    beta = 1 Backward difference
% n_steps = number of times steps,  delta_t = size of time step
% time = actual time values,            R_u = solution history

n_bc   = size (Fixed, 2)           ; % number of essentrial BC
n_d    = size (C_Q, 1)               ; % number of system DOF
n_unkn = n_d - n_bc                    ; % number of unknowns
time = [0:1:n_steps] * delta_t         ; % actual time values

% Allocate time history storage, inset initial condition
S_uu = zeros (n_unkn, n_unkn)          ; % allocate conduction
M_uu = zeros (n_unkn, n_unkn)            ; % allocate capacity
C_Qu = zeros (n_unkn, 1)                   ; % allocate source
C_bcu= zeros (n_unkn, 1)               ; % allocate EBC source
C_old= zeros (n_unkn, 1)              ; % allocate time source
R_u  = zeros (n_unkn, n_steps+1)     ; % allocate time history
R_bc = ones  (n_bc, 1) * bc_value    ; % known BC temperatures
React= zeros (n_bc, n_steps)     ; % optional reaction history
R_u  = zeros (n_unkn, n_steps+1)     ; % allocate time history
R_u (:, 1) = ic_value              ; % insert initial condition

%  Extract the unknown equations active in the time history
%      M_uu * R_u_dot + S_uu * R_u = C_Qu(t) + C_bcu(t)
M_uu = M (Free, Free)                        ; % free capacity
S_uu = S (Free, Free)                      ; % free conduction
S_ub = S (Free, Fixed)                      ; % coupled to EBC
S_bb = S (Fixed, Fixed)                            ; % optional
C_Qu = C_Q (Free)                              ; % free source
```

Fig. 15.4-2(a): Preparing for a transient integration of the finite element matrices.

graphs of the temperature at three DOFs are seen in Fig. 15.4-4. From those time history graphs, it is seen that for most of the time steps there are only small changes at a point as the steady-state solution is approached.

For two-dimensional solutions, carpet plots of the temperatures at one or more time steps can be informative, especially when the number of DOFs reaches practical levels. Figure 15.4-5 shows a group of temperature surfaces at different times. There the mesh has been increased to 64 elements. The script, *hidden_result_time_1248.m*, accepts a beginning time step number (here first = 1) and an integer constant (here mult = 4) that defines the next time step as a multiple of the prior one (here time step numbers 1, 4, 16, 64) to view how the solution changes in the beginning and how it approaches the steady-state values.

```
%  Form matrices for linear system S_hat * R_u(time) = F(time)
%     that will be solved at each time step for R_u
% [beta * S + M / delta_t] * R_new = C_rhs
% C_rhs = [(beta - 1)S + M / delta_t] * R_old + C_Qu + C_bc
S_hat = beta * S_uu + M_uu / delta_t         ; % constant in time
S_inv = inv (S_hat)                               ; % invert once
% Square matrix terms for RHS:   F = C_Qu + C_bc + S_RHS*R_u_old
S_RHS = S_hat - S_uu                         ; % constant in time

% Time marching solution, for constant data and delta_t
R_u (:, 1) = ic_value                  ; % insert initial condition
for k = 2:1:n_steps+1; % march to next time ---> ---> ----> --->
  % source from prior time step
  C_old = S_RHS * R_u (:, k-1)                      ; % prior time
  % update the effective source terms
  C_bc = -S_ub * R_bc                     ; % if EBC time dependent
  F = C_Qu + C_bc + C_old                         ; % at this time
  % Backsubstitute current effective source for current solution
  R_u (:, k) = S_inv * F                               ; % answer
  % Recover optional reaction heat flow at EBC equations
  React (:, k) = S_ub' * R_u (:, k) + S_bb * R_bc - C_Q (Fixed);
end % for all time steps <--- <--- <--- <--- <--- <--- <--- <---
% end gen_trap_history
```

Fig. 15.4-2(b): Time stepping the independent DOF and recovering the reactions.

Example 15.4-1 Given: Prior example 12.13-1 gave the steady-state solution for a conducting square area with a uniform rate of internal heat generation. Use the Crank–Nicolson method to compute the early transient part of that solution.

Solution: The 6×6 conduction matrix, $[\boldsymbol{S}]$, and the 6×1 source vector, $\{\boldsymbol{c}\}$, were developed in that example. The transient solution requires the assembled element capacity matrix (see Table 4.10-1):

$$\boldsymbol{m}^e = \int_A^e \boldsymbol{H}^T \rho c_p \boldsymbol{H}\, dA = \frac{\rho^e c_p^e A^e}{12} \begin{bmatrix} 2 & 1 & 1 \\ 1 & 2 & 1 \\ 1 & 1 & 2 \end{bmatrix}.$$

Setting the material properties $\rho c_p = 1$, setting the IC at all nodes at $T = 5$, and using the same EBCs as the steady-state case, the time-stepping algorithm in Fig. 15.4-1 gives the time history for the three free DOFs shown in Fig. 15.4-3. Clearly, all of the free DOFs have nearly reached their steady-state values after 2 s.

The reactions at the EBC also vary with time and since they depend on the temperature gradient, they more quickly approach their steady-state values. The early details for the time histories of the temperatures and the reactions are listed in Fig. 15.4-4.

```
% ---------------------------------------------------------
% Time history solution for 1/8 symmetry square with
% constant heat generation Q=6 to steady state        6
% connections: (1)  1  2  3      Kx=Ky=8             /  |
%              (2)  2  4  5      right EBC=5      3----5
%              (3)  3  5  6      right L=4      / |  / |
%              (4)  5  3  2                    1---2/---4
% ---------------------------------------------------------
% ic_value = 5, bc_value = 5, beta = 0.5
Fixed = [ 4     5     6]; Free   = [ 1     2     3]
Current   time step = 2.50e-02

Time history solution results at above 'Free' DOF
Step, Time,          Solution at DOF  1  2  3
   1, 0.0000e+00,  5.0000e+00  5.0000e+00  5.0000e+00
   2, 2.5000e-02,  5.1150e+00  5.2009e+00  5.1950e+00
   3, 5.0000e-02,  5.2737e+00  5.3791e+00  5.3568e+00
   4, 7.5000e-02,  5.4529e+00  5.5408e+00  5.4947e+00
   5, 1.0000e-01,  5.6391e+00  5.6892e+00  5.6152e+00
   6, 1.2500e-01,  5.8246e+00  5.8263e+00  5.7226e+00
   7, 1.5000e-01,  6.0050e+00  5.9536e+00  5.8196e+00
   8, 1.7500e-01,  6.1779e+00  6.0721e+00  5.9083e+00
   9, 2.0000e-01,  6.3420e+00  6.1824e+00  5.9900e+00
  10, 2.2500e-01,  6.4971e+00  6.2853e+00  6.0655e+00
  . . .
  76, 1.8750e+00,  8.7241e+00  7.7332e+00  7.1129e+00
  77, 1.9000e+00,  8.7258e+00  7.7343e+00  7.1137e+00
  78, 1.9250e+00,  8.7274e+00  7.7353e+00  7.1144e+00
  79, 1.9500e+00,  8.7289e+00  7.7363e+00  7.1151e+00
  80, 1.9750e+00,  8.7303e+00  7.7372e+00  7.1158e+00
NOTE: steady state 8.7500      7.7500      7.1250

Time history reaction results at 'Fixed' DOF
Step, Time,          Reactions at DOF 4   5   6
   1, 0.0000e+00,  0.0000e+00  0.0000e+00  0.0000e+00
   2, 2.5000e-02, -4.8037e+00 -1.3560e+01 -4.0000e+00
   3, 5.0000e-02, -5.5165e+00 -1.4854e+01 -4.0000e+00
   4, 7.5000e-02, -6.1631e+00 -1.5958e+01 -4.0000e+00
   5, 1.0000e-01, -6.7567e+00 -1.6922e+01 -4.0000e+00
   6, 1.2500e-01, -7.3053e+00 -1.7781e+01 -4.0000e+00
   7, 1.5000e-01, -7.8145e+00 -1.8557e+01 -4.0000e+00
   8, 1.7500e-01, -8.2882e+00 -1.9267e+01 -4.0000e+00
   9, 2.0000e-01, -8.7296e+00 -1.9920e+01 -4.0000e+00
  10, 2.2500e-01, -9.1414e+00 -2.0524e+01 -4.0000e+00
  . . .
  76, 1.8750e+00, -1.4933e+01 -2.8903e+01 -4.0000e+00
  77, 1.9000e+00, -1.4937e+01 -2.8909e+01 -4.0000e+00
  78, 1.9250e+00, -1.4941e+01 -2.8915e+01 -4.0000e+00
  79, 1.9500e+00, -1.4945e+01 -2.8921e+01 -4.0000e+00
  80, 1.9750e+00, -1.4949e+01 -2.8926e+01 -4.0000e+00
Steady state      -15.000     -29.000     -4.0000
```

Fig. 15.4-3: Nodal and reaction time histories for square with heat generation.

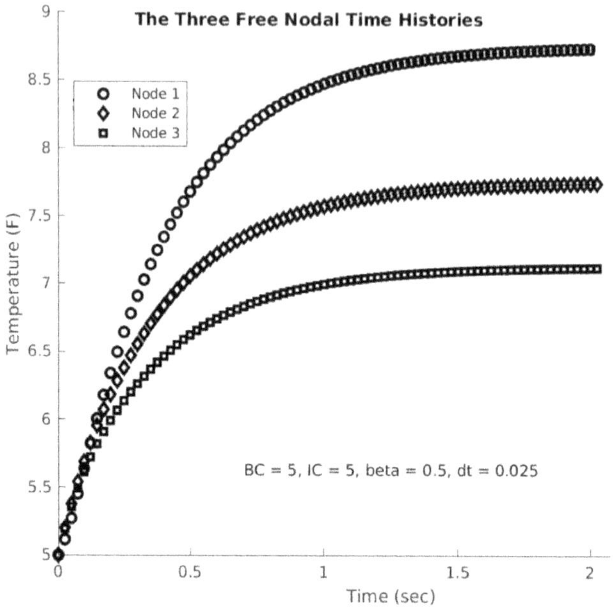

Fig. 15.4-4: Transient history of a square with heat generation.

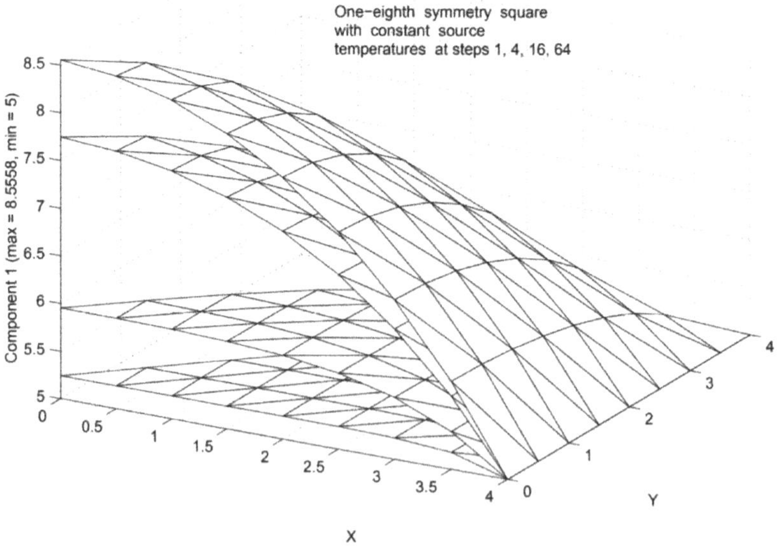

Fig. 15.4-5: Temperature surfaces at specified time steps.

15.5 Accuracy and Control

The much older finite difference method for spatial approximations leads to the capacitance, $[\boldsymbol{M}]$, being diagonal while the consistent finite element spatial form of $[\boldsymbol{M}]$ is a full element matrix. The finite element system matrix is still sparse and diagonally dominant, but not diagonal. More recent studies recommend using the average of $[\boldsymbol{M}]$ and its scaled diagonal.

For a given time step, the temperature response depends on the system non-dimensional Fourier number, $Fo \equiv k\,\Delta t/\rho\, c\, L^2$, which represents the ratio of heat transfer by conduction through a distance of L, in a volume of L^3, to the rate of energy storage in the same volume. The larger the Fourier number, the larger the distance of penetration of a temperature change into a solid in a given time due to a surface thermal shock (sudden change in surface temperature). A large value of the Fourier number indicates a faster propagation of heat through a body.

Transient finite element solutions are often validated by comparing the time history to analytical solutions where a surface temperature changes instantly from its IC value to a different value set by an EBC, or where a sudden heat flow into the surface occurs. There are physical problems of that sort, like a surface hit with a powerful laser beam, but if the solution at $t = 0^+$ is very important, the problem should be formulated with non-Fourier heat transfer which includes the second time derivative of the temperature.

Improper meshing and/or improper time step selection can lead to impossible physical temperatures in the first few time steps at locations just inside a surface subject to a thermal shock. Some authors say such a response is due to the consistent formulation of the capacitance matrix and the diagonal (finite difference) form should be used instead. If those early near-surface temperatures are important, then build the proper model and solve it in a consistent way. The diagonal matrix results always look physically possible and most analysts use it. Consider a thermal shock where a temperature is suddenly raised on the surface of a body. The temperature along a line normal to that surface is sketched in Fig. 15.5-1. There are analytical solutions for the transient temperature along a line normal to the surface. They start with a very sharp temperature gradient that decreases as time proceeds. In any element, the element temperature

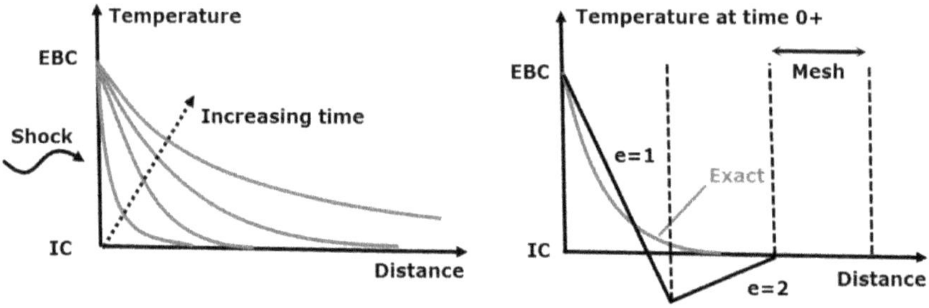

Fig. 15.5-1: Thermal shock requires both mesh and time step control.

value is like a least-square fit over the element domain to the exact value. In the direction normal to the surface there is a very narrow region of changed temperature. If the finite element lengths at and near the boundary are too large in comparison to the temperature change region, then the calculation likely will give a physically impossible temperature decrease when heat is added to the surface. This response is caused by the time step being too small in relation to the mesh size and the material properties. The non-dimensional Fourier number for the system is too small and the remedy is to decrease the size of the elements in the direction normal to the shocked surface and or to increase the time step size. In other words, the user has not built a consistent mesh and/or time step for the physical problem being modeled. Diagonal capacitance matrices are in part popular because they can hide poor and/or inexperienced modeling skills and assure what always looks like a physically correct solution.

Choosing the time step size affects the stability of the time history and the presence of oscillations in the solution. The Crank–Nicolson method is unconditionally stable (the solution will not blow up), but it still can oscillate wildly about the true solution. There are mathematical limits on the time step size needed to be stable and to avoid oscillations. When the parameter $\beta < 0.5$, the time step must be less than the critical value of $\Delta t_{\text{critical}} = 2/[(1-2\beta)\,\lambda_{\max}]$ in order to obtain a stable time history. There the eigenvalue is the maximum found from $|[\boldsymbol{S}] - \lambda\,[\boldsymbol{M}]| = 0$, which can be bounded by the maximum of the element eigenvalues $|[\boldsymbol{S}]^e - \lambda^e\,[\boldsymbol{M}]^e| = 0$ since it has been shown by Iron's theorem that

$$\lambda^e_{\min} \le \lambda_{\min} \le \lambda_{\max} \le \lambda^e_{\max}.$$

Example 15.5-1 Given: A transient heat transfer analysis is to be conducted using linear two-noded line elements in a uniform mesh. Estimate the critical time step using the eigenvalue from a single element.

Solution: The consistent element matrices give

$$|[\boldsymbol{S}]^e - \lambda^e [\boldsymbol{M}]^e| = 0, \text{ or}$$

$$\left| \frac{k^e}{L^e} \begin{bmatrix} 1 & -1 \\ -1 & 1 \end{bmatrix} - \lambda^e \frac{\rho^e c^e L^e}{6} \begin{bmatrix} 2 & 1 \\ 1 & 2 \end{bmatrix} \right| = 0.$$

The capacitance matrix, $[\boldsymbol{M}]^e$, can be diagonalized by scaling its original diagonal sum (4/6) up to match the total sum (6/6):

$$\frac{\rho^e c^e L^e}{6} \begin{bmatrix} 2 & 1 \\ 1 & 2 \end{bmatrix} \Longrightarrow \frac{\rho^e c^e L^e}{6} \begin{bmatrix} 3 & 0 \\ 0 & 3 \end{bmatrix} = \frac{\rho^e c^e L^e}{2} \begin{bmatrix} 1 & 0 \\ 0 & 1 \end{bmatrix}.$$

This form prevents physically impossible answers due to poor element sizes and an inconsistent time step size. Solving this small eigenvalue problem gives $\lambda_1^e = 0$ and the second value for the consistent form is $\lambda_2^e = 12\, k^e / \rho^e c^e L^{e^2}$ while the diagonal form is one-third smaller. For the Euler ($\beta = 0$), algorithm of time marching using the diagonal capacitance is

$$\Delta t \leq \Delta t_{\text{critical}} = \frac{\rho^e c^e L^{e^2}}{2\, k^e}.$$

That same time step size will avoid the onset of oscillations in the Crank–Nicolson method's diagonal form while the consistent form requires a third smaller time step to avoid oscillations.

15.6 Introduction to Dynamic Solutions

In the sections on elasticity and stress analysis in Chapter 13, it was shown that the element stiffness and consistent mass matrices

$$\boldsymbol{K}^e = \int_\Omega^e \boldsymbol{B}^{e^T} \boldsymbol{E}^e \boldsymbol{B}^e \, d\Omega\,, \quad \boldsymbol{M}^e = \int_\Omega^e \boldsymbol{N}^{e^T} \rho^e \boldsymbol{N}^e \, d\Omega$$

are assembled in exactly the same way to define the system stiffness and mass matrices, $[\boldsymbol{K}]$ and $[\boldsymbol{M}]$. Dynamic structures and wave propagation problems solved by finite elements usually lead to a matrix ordinary hyperbolic differential equation in time of the form

$$[\boldsymbol{K}]\{\boldsymbol{\delta}(t)\} + [\boldsymbol{D}]\{\dot{\boldsymbol{\delta}}(t)\} + [\boldsymbol{M}]\{\ddot{\boldsymbol{\delta}}(t)\} = \{\boldsymbol{f}(t)\},\ \dot{\{\}} = \partial\{\ \}/\partial t, \tag{15.6-1}$$

where $[\boldsymbol{D}]$ is the system damping matrix. The new term is the displacement acceleration

$$\frac{\partial^2\{\boldsymbol{\delta}(t)\}}{\partial t^2} \equiv \boldsymbol{N}(x,\,y,\,z)\,\frac{\partial^2\{\boldsymbol{\delta}(t)^e\}}{\partial t^2} \equiv \boldsymbol{N}(x,\,y,\,z)\,\{\ddot{\boldsymbol{\delta}}(t)^e\}.$$

These equations of motion for the system are subject to EBCs and the ICs, on the displacements $\boldsymbol{\delta}(0) = \boldsymbol{\delta}_{IC}$, and the velocities $\dot{\delta}(0) = \dot{\delta}_{IC}$. Many engineering applications involve sharp transients or nonlinear stiffness responses, $[\boldsymbol{K}] = [\boldsymbol{K}(\{\boldsymbol{\delta}(t)\})]$. Such applications require a direct time integration to obtain the solution time history. Some direct methods require an estimate of the initial acceleration of the solution. It is often approximated as zero, but it can be found from the initial condition as

$$\{\ddot{\boldsymbol{\delta}}(0)\} = [\boldsymbol{M}]^{-1}\left(\{\boldsymbol{f}(0)\} - [\boldsymbol{K}]\{\boldsymbol{\delta}_{IC}\} - [\boldsymbol{D}]\{\dot{\boldsymbol{\delta}}_{\mathrm{IC}}\}\right), \tag{15.6-2}$$

where the mass matrix, $[\boldsymbol{M}]$, can be approximated by its scaled diagonal $[\boldsymbol{M}] \approx [\boldsymbol{M}]_{\mathrm{Diagonal}}$.

The damping matrix, $[\boldsymbol{D}]$, definition varies with the application, but by far the most common form is a combination of structural damping and mass damping:

$$[\boldsymbol{D}] = \alpha\,[\boldsymbol{K}] + \beta\,[\boldsymbol{M}], \tag{15.6-3}$$

where the two proportions are usually related to the critical dampening, ξ, and a frequency range, $\omega_1 < \omega_2$, of interest:

$$\begin{aligned} \alpha &= \ 2\,(\xi_2\omega_2 - \xi_1\omega_1)/\left(\omega_2^2 - \omega_1^2\right), \\ \beta &= 2\omega_1\omega_2\,(\xi_1\omega_2 - \xi_2\omega_1)/\left(\omega_2^2 - \omega_1^2\right). \end{aligned} \tag{15.6-4}$$

After any EBCs are applied, the original system will be reduced in size to, say,

$$[\boldsymbol{K}]\{\boldsymbol{\delta}(t)\} + [\boldsymbol{D}\,]\{\dot{\boldsymbol{\delta}}(t)\} + [\boldsymbol{M}]\{\ddot{\boldsymbol{\delta}}(t)\} = \{\boldsymbol{p}(t)\}, \tag{15.6-5}$$

where $\{\boldsymbol{p}(t)\}$ includes the original time-dependent loads, $\boldsymbol{f}(t)$, plus the effects of the (constant or) time-dependent EBCs.

At this point, there are many algorithms for integrating this system in time. Most temporal integration schemes use finite differences in time or finite elements in time to derive the algorithm using constant increments of time, say Δt, to define time as $t_n = (t_0 + n\,\Delta t)$ at time step number n. Most of the algorithms form a linear system to be solved at each time step as

$$[\boldsymbol{S}(\Delta t, a_j, \boldsymbol{K}, \boldsymbol{D}, \boldsymbol{M})]\{\boldsymbol{\delta}\}_n = \{\boldsymbol{f}_n(a_j, t_n, t_{n-1}, \boldsymbol{K}, \boldsymbol{D}, \boldsymbol{M}, \boldsymbol{p}, \{\boldsymbol{\delta}\}_{n-1})\}, \tag{15.6-6}$$

where the a_j are a set of algorithm constants (usually $1 \leq j \leq 8$). In this form, the left square matrix is constant if the time step, Δt, is constant. Assembling $[\boldsymbol{K}]$ is computationally expensive and obtaining its inverse or factorization is very expensive. Thus, it is desirable to do those operations only once or twice. The right-hand column changes with every time step and the result at time step n is

$$\{\boldsymbol{\delta}\}_n = [\boldsymbol{S}(\Delta t, a_j, \boldsymbol{K}, \boldsymbol{D}, \boldsymbol{M})]^{-1}\,\{\boldsymbol{f}\}_n\,.$$

For example, the popular Newmark Beta method has two constants, β and γ, that combine with the time step to define six other constants

$$a_1 = \frac{1}{\beta\,\Delta t^2},\ a_2 = \frac{1}{\beta\,\Delta t},\ a_3 = \frac{1}{2\beta} - 1,$$
$$a_4 = \frac{\gamma}{\beta\,\Delta t},\ a_5 = \frac{\gamma}{\beta} - 1,\ a_6 = \left(\frac{\gamma}{2\beta} - 1\right)\Delta t,$$
$$[\boldsymbol{S}] = ([\boldsymbol{M}] + a_4[\boldsymbol{D}] + a_1\,[\boldsymbol{K}])\,,$$
$$\{\boldsymbol{f}\}_n = \{\boldsymbol{f}\}_{n-1} + [\boldsymbol{K}]\left(a_1\,\{\boldsymbol{\delta}\}_{n-1} + a_2\left\{\dot{\delta}\right\}_{n-1} + a_3\left\{\ddot{\delta}\right\}_{n-1}\right)$$
$$+\,[\boldsymbol{D}]\left(a_4\,\{\boldsymbol{\delta}\}_{n-1} + a_5\left\{\dot{\delta}\right\}_{n-1} + a_6\left\{\ddot{\delta}\right\}_{n-1}\right),$$

then the velocity and acceleration are updated as

$$\left\{\dot{\delta}\right\}_{n+1} = a_4\left(\{\boldsymbol{\delta}\}_{n+1} - \{\boldsymbol{\delta}\}_n\right) - a_5\left\{\dot{\delta}\right\}_n - a_6\left\{\ddot{\delta}\right\}_n,$$
$$\left\{\ddot{\delta}\right\}_{n+1} = a_1\left(\{\boldsymbol{\delta}\}_{n+1} - \{\boldsymbol{\delta}\}_n - \Delta t\left\{\dot{\delta}\right\}_n\right) - a_3\left\{\ddot{\delta}\right\}_n.$$

Four most common choices for β and γ are as follows:

(1) The Newmark average acceleration method, $\beta = 1/4$, $\gamma = 1/2$, is unconditionally stable. The accuracy is $O(\Delta t^2)$.
(2) The linear acceleration method, $\beta = 1/6$, $\gamma = 1/2$, is conditionally stable. $O(\Delta t^2)$ accurate.
(3) The Fox–Goodwin method, $\beta = 1/12$, $\gamma = 1/2$, is conditionally stable. $O(\Delta t^4)$ accurate.
(4) The Hilber–Hughes–Taylor α-method, $\beta = (1-\alpha)^2/4$, $\gamma = (1-2\alpha)/2$, with the main constant range $-1/3 \le \alpha \le 0$, is unconditionally stable. The accuracy is $O(\Delta t^2)$.

15.7 Wilson Method*

Another direct time history integration algorithm (used here) is the Wilson method. The Wilson method is an extension of the linear acceleration method with $\gamma = 1/2$, as illustrated in Fig. 15.7-1, in a manner that makes it stable. It assumes that the acceleration is linear from time t to $(t + \theta\Delta t)$ with $\theta \ge 1$, and calculates the displacement, velocity, and acceleration there. Then the method interpolates back to find those values at $(t + \Delta t)$. Theoretical studies show it to be unconditionally stable for $\theta \ge 1.37$, and that the optimal value is $\theta = 1.4208$ so $\theta = 1.42$ is the commonly used value.

Integrating the linear acceleration assumption gives the predicted velocity and displacement:

$$\dot{\delta}\,(t+\theta\Delta t) = \dot{\delta}\,(t) + \left[\ddot{\delta}\,(t+\theta\Delta t) + \ddot{\delta}\,(t)\right]\Big/\,2,$$

$$\boldsymbol{\delta}\,(t+\theta\Delta t) = \boldsymbol{\delta}\,(t) + \,\theta\Delta t\,\dot{\delta}\,(t) + (\theta\Delta t)^2\left[\ddot{\delta}\,(t+\theta\Delta t) + 2\ddot{\delta}\,(t)\right]\Big/\,6,$$

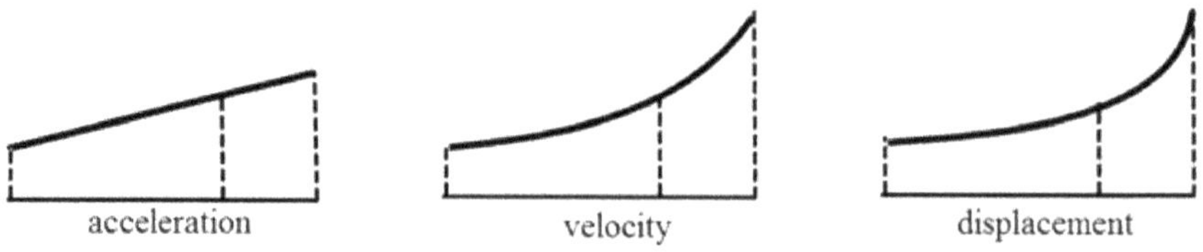

Fig. 15.7-1: The Wilson method extends the linear acceleration step.

and these are re-written in terms of the displacement at the extended time:

$$\ddot{\delta}(t+\theta\Delta t) = 6\left[\boldsymbol{\delta}\,(t+\theta\Delta t) - \boldsymbol{\delta}\,(t)\right] / \left(\theta\Delta t\right)^2 - \dot{\delta}\,(t)\,/\theta\Delta t - 2\ddot{\delta}(t),$$
$$\dot{\delta}\,(t+\theta\Delta t) = 3\left[\boldsymbol{\delta}\,(t+\theta\Delta t) - \boldsymbol{\delta}\,(t)\right]/\theta\Delta t\ - \theta\Delta t\,\ddot{\delta}\,(t)/2. \quad (15.7\text{-}1)$$

These estimates are substituted into the equation of motion (15.6-6) to define the matrix equations for solving one time step. In other words, during one step the Wilson method calculates the solution at $(t+\theta\Delta t)$ using the linear system

$$\boldsymbol{S}\,(t+\theta\Delta t)\ \boldsymbol{\delta}\,(t+\theta\Delta t) = \boldsymbol{c}\,(t+\theta\Delta t)\,, \quad (15.7\text{-}2)$$

where the effective matrices are

$$\boldsymbol{S}\,(t+\theta\Delta t) = 3\boldsymbol{G}/\theta\Delta t + \boldsymbol{K}, \text{with}\, \boldsymbol{G} \equiv 2\boldsymbol{M}/\theta\Delta t + \boldsymbol{D},$$
$$\boldsymbol{c}\,(t+\theta\Delta t) = \boldsymbol{p}\,(t+\theta\Delta t) + \boldsymbol{G}\left\{3\,\boldsymbol{\delta}\,(t)/\theta\Delta t + 3\,\dot{\delta}\,(t) + \theta\Delta t\ \ddot{\delta}(t)\right\}$$
$$-\,\boldsymbol{D}\left\{\dot{\delta}\,(t) + \theta\Delta t\,\ddot{\delta}\,(t)/2\right\}. \quad (15.7\text{-}3)$$

Equation (15.7-2) is solved once per time step for the new displacement, $\boldsymbol{\delta}\,(t+\theta\Delta t)$, and then the method interpolates backward to find the values at $(t+\Delta t)$ as

$$\ddot{\delta}(t+\Delta t) = \ddot{\delta}(t) + \left\{\ddot{\delta}(t+\theta\Delta t) - \ddot{\delta}(t)\right\}/\theta,$$
$$\dot{\delta}(t+\Delta t) = \dot{\delta}(t) + \theta\Delta t\ddot{\delta}(t) + \theta\Delta t\frac{\left\{\ddot{\delta}(t+\theta\Delta t) - \ddot{\delta}(t)\right\}}{2\theta},$$
$$\boldsymbol{\delta}(t+\Delta t) = \boldsymbol{\delta}(t) + \theta\Delta t\dot{\delta}(t), \quad (15.7\text{-}4)$$

which are then used to start the next integration step. The Wilson algorithm is implemented in the Matlab script *Wilson_time_history.m*.

The above algorithms are all single-step methods since they only require storing the results from the last time step. They minimize the memory requirements and were developed when computers had extremely small memories, but their main asset is that they deal well with sudden changes in the solution such as earthquakes imposing rapid changes in the displacements, or external impact forces. There are many other algorithms that lead to a linear system being solved at each time step.

It is difficult to debug and gain experience with these, and other, direct time history integration methods. Exact solutions are rare, except for single DOF models. Biggs, in *Introduction to Structural Dynamics*, gave the exact analytic time history for a three DOF spring-mass system with time-varying loads shown in Fig. 15.7-2. The exact time history solution given by Biggs consists of two segments. The first segment covers the time when each load is decreasing to zero. The values of the displacement and velocities at the end of that time are used as initial conditions to continue the solution as a free vibration response. That example solution for the displacements, velocities, and accelerations was also computed by the Wilson method included in the provided script. Using a smaller time step leads to a more accurate solution, but requires a proportionally longer execution time.

For example, using the Wilson method to solve the Biggs model with a time step of 0.00125 s. gives the displacement and velocity curves compared to the exact results (dashed) in Fig. 15.7-3. Those results are fairly accurate, but doubling the time step, in Fig. 15.7-4, to cut the run time in half significantly increases the errors in the results.

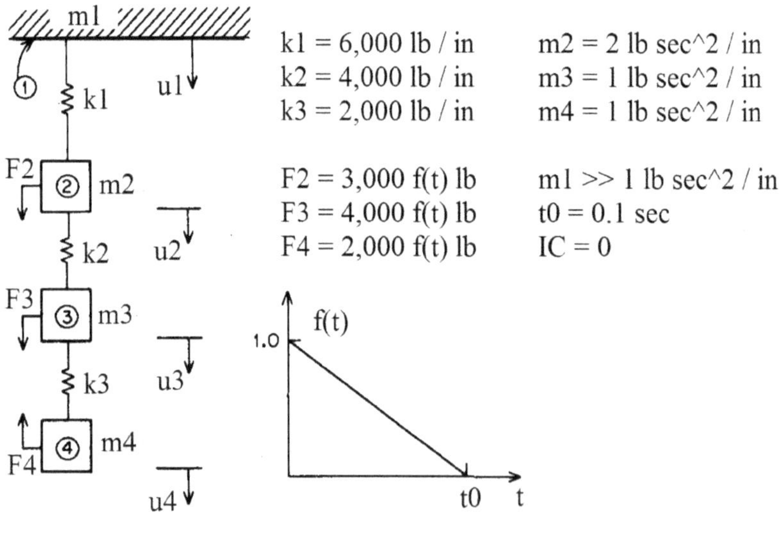

Fig. 15.7-2: The Biggs analytic time history spring-mass system.

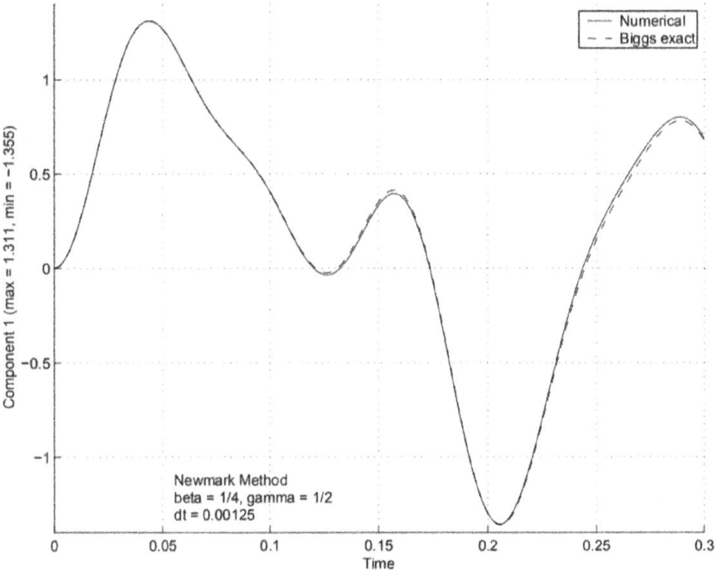

Fig. 15.7-3(a): Biggs's node 3 displacement for $\Delta t = 000125$s.

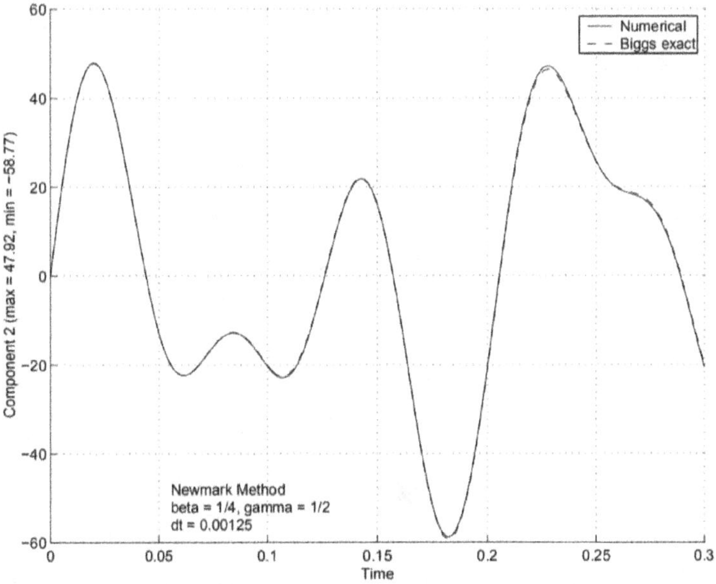

Fig. 15.7-3(b): Biggs's node 3 velocity for $\Delta t = 000125$ s.

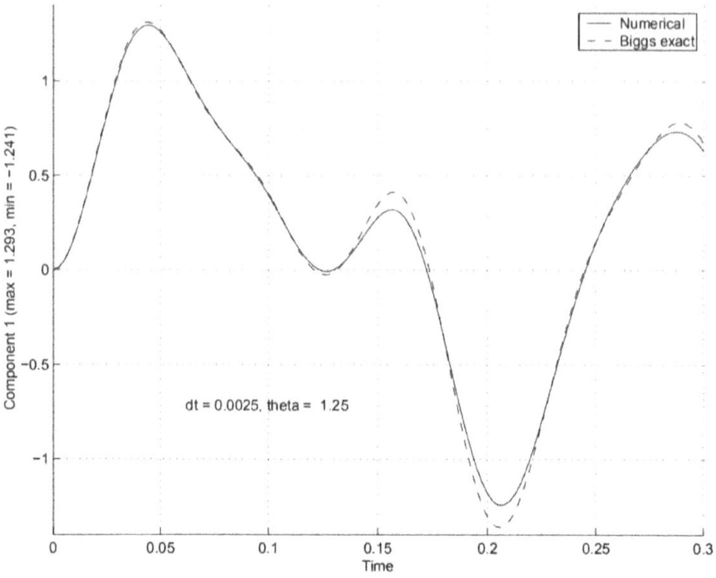

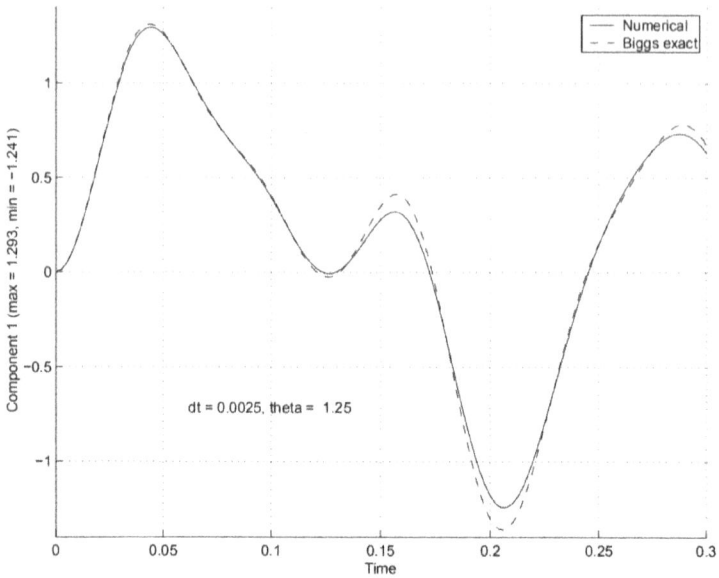

Fig. 15.7-4(a): Biggs's node 3 displacement form $\Delta t = 00025$ s.

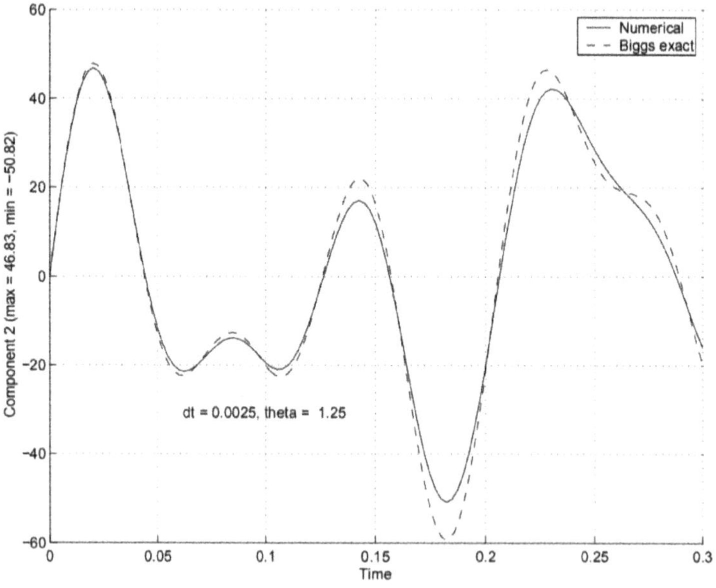

Fig. 15.7-4(b): Biggs's node 3 velocity for $\Delta t = 00025$ s.

15.8 Summaries

15.8.1 Transient summary

Scalar field model ordinary differential equation:

$$\frac{\partial}{\partial x}\left(k_x\frac{\partial u}{\partial x}\right)+\frac{\partial}{\partial y}\left(k_y\frac{\partial u}{\partial y}\right)+T\,u+Q\,(x,\,y)=\rho c_p\frac{\partial u}{\partial \tau}.$$

Equivalent integral form:

$$\int_\Gamma^b u\left(k_{nn}\frac{\partial u}{\partial n}\right)d\Gamma-\int_\Omega\left(\frac{\partial u}{\partial x}\left(k_x\frac{\partial u}{\partial x}\right)+\frac{\partial u}{\partial y}\left(k_y\frac{\partial u}{\partial y}\right)\right)d\Omega$$

$$-\int_\Omega u\,T\,u\,d\Omega-\int_\Omega u\,Q\,d\Omega-\int_\Omega u\,\rho c_p\,u\,d\Omega=0.$$

Conduction, convection, advection, and source matrices:

$$\boldsymbol{S}_\kappa^e=\int_\Omega^e \vec{\nabla}\boldsymbol{H}^{\boldsymbol{T}}\boldsymbol{\kappa}\,\vec{\nabla}\boldsymbol{H}d\Omega,\qquad \boldsymbol{A}_v^e=\int_\Omega^e \boldsymbol{H}^{\boldsymbol{e}^T}m^e v^e\boldsymbol{B}^{\boldsymbol{e}}\,d\Omega,$$

$$\boldsymbol{M}_h^e=\int_\Omega^e \boldsymbol{H}^{\boldsymbol{e}^T}h^e\boldsymbol{H}^{\boldsymbol{e}}\,d\Omega,\quad \boldsymbol{M}_\rho^e=\int_\Omega^e \boldsymbol{H}^{\boldsymbol{e}^T}\rho^e c_p^e\boldsymbol{H}^{\boldsymbol{e}}\,d\Omega,$$

$$\boldsymbol{c}_Q^e=\int_\Omega^e \boldsymbol{H}^{\boldsymbol{e}^T}Q^e\,d\Omega,\ \boldsymbol{c}_{NBC}^b=\int_\Gamma^b \boldsymbol{H}^{\boldsymbol{b}^T}\left(k_{nn}\frac{\partial u}{\partial n}\right)^b d\Gamma,$$

$$\boldsymbol{c}_q^b=\int_\Gamma^b \boldsymbol{H}^{\boldsymbol{b}^T q_n}d\Gamma.$$

Transient matrix system: $[\boldsymbol{S_k}+\boldsymbol{A_v}+\boldsymbol{M_h}]\,\boldsymbol{u}\,(\tau)+[\boldsymbol{M_\rho}]\,\dot{u}\,(\tau)=\boldsymbol{c}\,(\tau)$.
Steady-state matrix system: $\dot{u}\,(\tau)=\boldsymbol{0}$: $[\boldsymbol{S_k}+\boldsymbol{A_v}+\boldsymbol{M_h}]\,\boldsymbol{u}=\boldsymbol{c}$.

Linear triangle conduction and volumetric source matrices:

$$\boldsymbol{S}_\kappa^e=\frac{t^e}{4\,A^e}\left[k_x^e\begin{bmatrix}b_1b_1 & b_1b_2 & b_1b_3\\ b_2b_1 & b_2b_2 & b_3b_3\\ b_3b_1 & b_3b_2 & b_3b_3\end{bmatrix}+k_y^e\begin{bmatrix}c_1c_1 & c_1c_2 & c_1c_3\\ c_2c_1 & c_2c_2 & c_2c_3\\ c_3c_1 & c_3c_2 & c_3c_3\end{bmatrix}\right],$$

$$\boldsymbol{c}_Q^e=\frac{Q^eA^et^e}{3}\begin{Bmatrix}1\\1\\1\end{Bmatrix}.$$

Linear triangle face and edge convection matrices (and normal flux matrices, $h^e \to q_n^e$):

$$\boldsymbol{M}_h^e = \frac{h^e A^e}{12}\begin{bmatrix} 2 & 1 & 1 \\ 1 & 2 & 1 \\ 1 & 1 & 2 \end{bmatrix}, \quad \boldsymbol{c}_h^b = \frac{h^b\, t^b\, L^b}{2}\begin{Bmatrix} 1 \\ 1 \end{Bmatrix}.$$

Linear rectangle conduction and volumetric source matrices:

$$\boldsymbol{S}_\kappa^e = \frac{k_x^e\, t^e L_y^e}{6\, L_x^e}\begin{bmatrix} 2 & -2 & -1 & 1 \\ -2 & 2 & 1 & -1 \\ -1 & 1 & 2 & -2 \\ 1 & -1 & -2 & 2 \end{bmatrix} + \frac{k_y^e\, t^e L_x^e}{6\, L_y^e}\begin{bmatrix} 2 & 1 & -1 & -2 \\ 1 & 2 & -2 & -1 \\ -1 & -2 & 2 & 1 \\ -2 & -1 & 1 & 2 \end{bmatrix},$$

$$\boldsymbol{c}_Q^e = \frac{Q^e A^e t^e}{4}\begin{Bmatrix} 1 \\ 1 \\ 1 \\ 1 \end{Bmatrix}.$$

Linear rectangle face and edge convection matrices (and normal flux matrices, $h^e \to q_n^e$):

$$\boldsymbol{M}_h^e = \frac{h^e L_x^e\, L_y^e}{36}\begin{bmatrix} 4 & 2 & 1 & 2 \\ 2 & 4 & 2 & 1 \\ 1 & 2 & 4 & 2 \\ 2 & 1 & 2 & 4 \end{bmatrix}, \quad \boldsymbol{c}_h^b = \frac{h^b\, t^b\, L^b}{2}\begin{Bmatrix} 1 \\ 1 \end{Bmatrix}.$$

15.8.2 Dynamic summary

System equation of motion:

$$[\boldsymbol{K}]\,\{\boldsymbol{\delta}(t)\} + [\boldsymbol{D}]\,\{\dot{\boldsymbol{\delta}(t)}\} + [\boldsymbol{M}]\,\{\ddot{\boldsymbol{\delta}(t)}\} = \{\boldsymbol{f}(t)\},\ \dot{\{\}} = \partial\{\,\}/\partial t$$

$[\boldsymbol{K}]$ = stiffness matrix, $[\boldsymbol{M}]$ = mass matrix (consistent, diagonal, or averaged)

$[\boldsymbol{D}] = \alpha\,[\boldsymbol{K}] + \beta\,[\boldsymbol{M}]$ = damping matrix for two critical dampenings, ξ,

At two frequency ranges, $\omega_1 < \omega_2$ with

$$\alpha = 2(\xi_2\omega_2 - \xi_1\omega_1)/(\omega_2^2 - \omega_1^2), \quad \beta = 2\omega_1\omega_2(\xi_1\omega_2 - \xi_2\omega_1)/(\omega_2^2 - \omega_1^2).$$

Element stiffness matrix: $\boldsymbol{K}^e = \int_\Omega^e \boldsymbol{B}^{e^T}\boldsymbol{E}^e\boldsymbol{B}^e\, d\Omega$.

Element consistent mass matrix: $\boldsymbol{M}^e = \int_{\Omega}^{e} \boldsymbol{N}^{e^T} \rho^e \boldsymbol{N}^e \, d\Omega$.

Displacement interpolation: $\boldsymbol{u}(\boldsymbol{x}) = \boldsymbol{N}(r,s)\, \boldsymbol{\delta}^{\boldsymbol{e}}$.

Linear system solved at each time step: with algorithm constants a_j

$$[\boldsymbol{S}(\Delta t, a_j, \boldsymbol{K}, \boldsymbol{D}, \boldsymbol{M})]\, \{\boldsymbol{\delta}\}_n = \left\{\boldsymbol{f}_n(a_j, t_n, t_{n-1,}\ \boldsymbol{K},\ \boldsymbol{D},\ \boldsymbol{M}, \boldsymbol{p}, \{\boldsymbol{\delta}\}_{n-1})\right\}.$$

$$\{\boldsymbol{\delta}\}_n = [\boldsymbol{S}(\Delta t, a_j, \boldsymbol{K}, \boldsymbol{D}, \boldsymbol{M})]^{-1}\, \{\boldsymbol{f}\}_n\,.$$

Commonly

$$[\boldsymbol{S}] = ([\boldsymbol{M}] + a_4[\boldsymbol{D}] + a_1\,[\boldsymbol{K}]),$$

$$\{\boldsymbol{f}\}_n = \{\boldsymbol{f}\}_{n-1} + [\boldsymbol{K}]\left(a_1\,\{\boldsymbol{\delta}\}_{n-1} + a_2\left\{\dot{\delta}\right\}_{n-1} + a_3\left\{\ddot{\delta}\right\}_{n-1}\right)$$

$$+[\boldsymbol{D}]\left(a_4\,\{\boldsymbol{\delta}\}_{n-1} + a_5\left\{\dot{\delta}\right\}_{n-1} + a_6\left\{\ddot{\delta}\right\}_{n-1}\right),$$

$$\left\{\dot{\delta}\right\}_{n+1} = a_4\left(\{\boldsymbol{\delta}\}_{n+1} - \{\boldsymbol{\delta}\}_n\right) - a_5\left\{\dot{\delta}\right\}_n - a_6\left\{\ddot{\delta}\right\}_n,$$

$$\left\{\ddot{\delta}\right\}_{n+1} = a_1\left(\{\boldsymbol{\delta}\}_{n+1} - \{\boldsymbol{\delta}\}_n - \Delta t\left\{\dot{\delta}\right\}_n\right) - a_3\left\{\ddot{\delta}\right\}_n.$$

Linear bar stiffness and mass (or convection) matrices:

$$\boldsymbol{K^e} = \frac{E^e A^e}{L^e}\begin{bmatrix} 1 & -1 \\ -1 & 1 \end{bmatrix}, \quad \boldsymbol{m^e} = \frac{\rho^e A^e L^e}{6}\begin{bmatrix} 2 & 1 \\ 1 & 2 \end{bmatrix},$$

$$\boldsymbol{m^e_d} = \frac{\rho^e A^e L^e}{2}\begin{bmatrix} 1 & 0 \\ 0 & 1 \end{bmatrix}, \quad \boldsymbol{m^e_a} = \frac{\rho^e A^e L^e}{12}\begin{bmatrix} 5 & 1 \\ 1 & 5 \end{bmatrix}.$$

Linear bar linear line load resultant: $\boldsymbol{c^e_f} = \frac{1}{6L^e}\begin{bmatrix} 2 & 1 \\ 1 & 2 \end{bmatrix}\begin{Bmatrix} f_1 \\ f_2 \end{Bmatrix}$.

Quadratic bar stiffness, and mass (or convection) matrices:

$$\boldsymbol{K^e} = \frac{E^e A^e}{3L^e}\begin{bmatrix} 7 & -8 & 1 \\ -8 & 16 & -8 \\ 1 & -8 & 7 \end{bmatrix}, \quad \boldsymbol{m^e} = \frac{\rho^e A^e L^e}{30}\begin{bmatrix} 4 & 2 & -1 \\ 2 & 16 & 2 \\ -1 & 2 & 4 \end{bmatrix},$$

$$\boldsymbol{m_d^e} = \frac{\rho^e A^e L^e}{6}\begin{bmatrix} 1 & 0 & 0 \\ 0 & 4 & 0 \\ 0 & 0 & 1 \end{bmatrix}, \quad \boldsymbol{m_a^e} = \frac{\rho^e A^e L^e}{60}\begin{bmatrix} 9 & 2 & -1 \\ 2 & 36 & 2 \\ -1 & 2 & 9 \end{bmatrix}.$$

Quadratic bar quadratic line load resultant:

$$\boldsymbol{c_f^e} = \frac{L^e}{30}\begin{bmatrix} 4 & 2 & -1 \\ 2 & 16 & 2 \\ -1 & 2 & 4 \end{bmatrix}\begin{Bmatrix} f_1 \\ f_2 \\ f_3 \end{Bmatrix}^e.$$

Cubic bar stiffness and mass matrices:

$$\boldsymbol{K}^e = \frac{E^e A^e}{40L^e}\begin{bmatrix} 148 & -189 & 54 & -13 \\ -189 & 432 & -297 & 54 \\ 54 & -297 & 432 & -189 \\ -13 & 54 & -189 & 148 \end{bmatrix},$$

$$\boldsymbol{m}^e = \frac{\rho^e A^e L^e}{1{,}680}\begin{bmatrix} 128 & 99 & -36 & 19 \\ 99 & 648 & -81 & -36 \\ -36 & -81 & 648 & 99 \\ 19 & -36 & 99 & 128 \end{bmatrix}$$

$$\boldsymbol{m_d^e} = \frac{\rho^e A^e L^e}{194}\begin{bmatrix} 16 & 0 & 0 & 0 \\ 0 & 81 & 0 & 0 \\ 0 & 0 & 81 & 0 \\ 0 & 0 & 0 & 16 \end{bmatrix},$$

$$\boldsymbol{m_a^e} = \frac{\rho^e A^e L^e}{325{,}920}\begin{bmatrix} 25{,}856 & 9{,}603 & -3{,}492 & 1{,}843 \\ 9{,}603 & 130{,}896 & -7{,}857 & -3{,}492 \\ -3{,}492 & -7{,}857 & 130{,}896 & 9{,}603 \\ 1{,}843 & -3{,}492 & 9{,}603 & 25{,}856 \end{bmatrix}.$$

Cubic bar quadratic line load resultant:

$$\boldsymbol{c_f^e} = \frac{L^e}{1{,}680}\begin{bmatrix} 128 & 99 & -36 & 19 \\ 99 & 648 & -81 & -36 \\ -36 & -81 & 648 & 99 \\ 19 & -36 & 99 & 128 \end{bmatrix}\begin{Bmatrix} f_1 \\ f_2 \\ f_3 \\ f_4 \end{Bmatrix}^e.$$

Cubic beam stiffness, and mass matrices:

$$\boldsymbol{K^e} = \frac{EI^e}{L^3}\begin{bmatrix} 12 & 6L & -12 & 6L \\ 6L & 4L^2 & -6L & 2L^2 \\ -12 & -6L & 12 & -6L \\ 6L & 2L^2 & -6L & 4L^2 \end{bmatrix},$$

$$\boldsymbol{m^e} = \frac{\rho^e A^e L}{420}\begin{bmatrix} 156 & 22L & 54 & -13L \\ 22L & 4L^2 & 13L & -3L^2 \\ 54 & 13L & 156 & -22L \\ -13L & -3L^2 & -22L & 4L^2 \end{bmatrix},$$

$$\boldsymbol{m_d^e} = \frac{\rho^e A^e L}{420}\begin{bmatrix} 210 & 0 & 0 & 0 \\ 0 & L^2 & 0 & 0 \\ 0 & 0 & 210 & 0 \\ 0 & 0 & 0 & L^2 \end{bmatrix},$$

$$\boldsymbol{m_a^e} = \frac{\rho^e A^e L}{70{,}560}\begin{bmatrix} 30{,}744 & 1{,}848L & 4{,}536 & -1{,}092L \\ 1{,}848L & 420L^2 & 1{,}092L & -252L^2 \\ 4{,}536 & 1{,}092L & 30{,}744 & -1{,}848L \\ -1{,}092L & -252L^2 & -1{,}848L & 420L^2 \end{bmatrix}.$$

Cubic beam linear line load resultant: $\boldsymbol{c_f^e} = \frac{L}{60}\begin{bmatrix} 21 & 9 \\ 3L & 2L \\ 9 & 21 \\ -2L & -3L \end{bmatrix}\begin{Bmatrix} f_1 \\ f_2 \end{Bmatrix}.$

Cubic beam geometric stiffness matrix, for axial tension load N:

$$\boldsymbol{K_G^e} = \frac{N}{30\,L}\begin{bmatrix} 36 & 3L & -36 & 3L \\ 3L & 4L^2 & -3L & -L^2 \\ -36 & -3L & 36 & -3L \\ 3L & -L^2 & -3L & 4L^2 \end{bmatrix}.$$

Quintic beam stiffness, and mass matrices:

$$\boldsymbol{K^e} = \frac{EI}{35L^3} \times \begin{bmatrix} 5{,}092 & 1{,}138L & -3{,}584 & 1{,}920L & -1{,}508 & 242L \\ 1{,}138L & 332L^2 & -896L & 320L^2 & -242L & 38L^2 \\ -3{,}584 & -896L & 7{,}168 & 0 & -3{,}584 & 896L \\ 1{,}920L & 320L^2 & 0 & 1{,}280L^2 & -1{,}920L & 320L^2 \\ -1{,}508 & -242L & -3{,}584 & -1{,}920L & 5{,}092 & -1{,}138L \\ 242L & 38L^2 & 896L & 320L^2 & -1{,}138L & 332L^2 \end{bmatrix},$$

$$\boldsymbol{m}^e = \frac{\rho^e A^e L}{13{,}860}\begin{bmatrix} 2{,}092 & 114L & 880 & -160L & 262 & -29L \\ 114L & 8L^2 & 88L & -12L^2 & 29L & -3L^2 \\ 880 & 88L & 5{,}632 & 0 & 880 & -88L \\ -160L & -12L^2 & 0 & 128L^2 & 160L & -12L^2 \\ 262 & 29L & 880 & 160L & 2{,}092 & -114L \\ -29L & -3L^2 & -88L & -12L^2 & -114L & 8L^2 \end{bmatrix},$$

$$\boldsymbol{m}_d^e = \frac{\rho^e A^e L}{1{,}133{,}748} \times \begin{bmatrix} 241{,}626 & 0 & 0 & 0 & 0 & 0 \\ 0 & 409\,L^2 & 0 & 0 & 0 & 0 \\ 0 & 0 & 650{,}496 & 0 & 0 & 0 \\ 0 & 0 & 0 & 6{,}544\,L^2 & 0 & 0 \\ 0 & 0 & 0 & 0 & 241{,}626 & 0 \\ 0 & 0 & 0 & 0 & 0 & 409\,L^2 \end{bmatrix}$$

$$\boldsymbol{m}_a^e = \frac{\rho^e A^e L}{113{,}37{,}480} \times \begin{bmatrix} 2{,}063{,}758 & 46{,}626L & 359{,}920 & -65{,}440L & 107{,}158 & -11{,}861L \\ 46{,}626L & 5{,}317L^2 & 35{,}992L & -4{,}908L^2 & 11{,}861L & -1{,}227L^2 \\ 359{,}920 & 35{,}992L & 5{,}555{,}968 & 0 & 359{,}920 & -35{,}992L \\ -65{,}440L & -4{,}908L^2 & 0 & 85{,}072L^2 & 65{,}440L & -4{,}908L^2 \\ 107{,}158 & 11{,}861L & 359{,}920 & 65{,}440L & 2{,}063,758 & -46{,}626L \\ -11{,}861L & -1{,}227L^2 & -35{,}992L & -4{,}908L^2 & -46{,}626L & 5{,}317L^2 \end{bmatrix}.$$

Quintic beam quadratic line load resultant:

$$\boldsymbol{c}_f^e = \frac{L}{420}\begin{bmatrix} 57 & 44 & -3 \\ 3L & 4L & 0 \\ 16 & 192 & 16 \\ -8L & 0 & 8L \\ -3 & 44 & 57 \\ 0 & -4L & -3L \end{bmatrix}\begin{Bmatrix} f_1 \\ f_2 \\ f_3 \end{Bmatrix}.$$

Quintic beam geometric stiffness matrix, for axial tension load N:

$$\boldsymbol{K}_G^e = \frac{N}{630\,L}\begin{bmatrix} 1{,}668 & 39L & -1{,}536 & 240L & -132 & -9L \\ 39L & 28L^2 & -48L & -8L^2 & 9L & -5L^2 \\ -1{,}536 & -48L & 3{,}072 & 0 & -1{,}536 & 48L \\ 240L & -8L^2 & 0 & 256L^2 & -240L & -8L^2 \\ -132 & 9L & -1{,}536 & -240L & 1{,}668 & -39L \\ -9L & -5L^2 & 48L & -8L^2 & -39L & 28L^2 \end{bmatrix}.$$

Index

C

R

S

www.ingramcontent.com/pod-product-compliance
Lightning Source LLC
Chambersburg PA
CBHW052115230326
41598CB00079B/3687